2nd International
Conference on
River Flood Hydraulics

2nd International Conference on River Flood Hydraulics

Edited by

Dr W. R. White

and

Jacqueline Watts

HR Wallingford Ltd
Wallingford, Oxon OX10 8BA, UK

Published on behalf of
HR WALLINGFORD LTD, WALLINGFORD
by
JOHN WILEY & SONS
Chichester · New York · Brisbane · Toronto · Singapore

Copyright © HR Wallingford Ltd, 1994

Published by John Wiley & Sons Ltd,
        Baffins Lane, Chichester,
        West Sussex PO19 1UD, England

Telephone National Chichester 0243 779777
        International +44 243 779777

Other Wiley Editorial Offices

John Wiley & Sons, Inc., 605 Third Avenue,
New York, NY 10158-0012, USA

Jacaranda Wiley Ltd, 33 Park Road, Milton,
Queensland 4064, Australia

John Wiley & Sons (Canada) Ltd, 22 Worcester Road,
Rexdale, Ontario M9W 1L1, Canada

John Wiley & Sons (SEA) Pte Ltd, 37 Jalan Pemimpin #05-04,
Block B, Union Industrial Building, Singapore 2057

Library of Congress Cataloging-in-Publication Data

International Conference on River Flood Hydraulics (2nd : 1994 : York,
    England)
    2nd International Conference on River Flood Hydraulics / edited by
W. R. White and Jacqueline Watts.
        p.   cm.
    ISBN 0-471-95019-X
    1. Floods—Congresses.   I. White, W. R., Dr.   II. Watts,
Jacqueline.   III. HR Wallingford (Firm)   IV. Title.
GB1399.I574   1994
627'.4—dc20   93-48864
                                                               CIP

British Library Cataloguing in Publicataion Data

A catalogue record for this book is available from the British Library

ISBN 0-471-95019-X

Produced from authors' camera-ready copy
Printed and bound in Great Britain by Bookcraft (Bath) Ltd.

Papers presented at the 2nd International Conference on RIVER FLOOD HYDRAULICS held at York, England: 22–25 March 1994. Organised and sponsored by HR Wallingford Ltd and co-sponsored by: International Association for Hydraulic Research, UK Overseas Development Administration, National Rivers Authority (Northumbria and Yorkshire Region).

Acknowledgements

The valuable assistance of the UK Organising Committee, the International Organising Committee and Panel of Referees is gratefully acknowledged.

UK Organising Committee

Dr W. R. White (Chairman)	HR Wallingford Ltd
Dr D. A. Ervine	University of Glasgow
Mr B. Marsden	Bullen & Partners
Prof. P. Novak	Consultant
Mr T. D. Pike	Overseas Development Administration
Mr K. D. Riddell	Babtie Dobbie Ltd
Mr D. Rooke	NRA, Northumbria & Yorkshire Region
Dr P. G. Samuels	HR Wallingford Ltd

Conference Organiser

Jacqueline Watts	HR Wallingford Ltd

International Organising Committee

Dr P. Bakonyi	Vituki, Hungary
Prof. J. A. Cunge	Laboratoire d'Hydraulique de France, France
Prof. F. M. Holly	The University of Iowa, USA
Dr J. Jordaan	Department of Water Affairs, South Africa
Prof. A. Nishat	Bangladesh University of Engineering and Technology, Bangladesh
Prof. K. G. Ranga Raju	University of Roorkee, India
Dr Wang Shiqiang	Tsinghua University, P R China
Prof. M. S. Yalin	Queen's University, Kingston, Canada

2nd International Conference on
RIVER FLOOD HYDRAULICS
22–25 March 1994: York, England

CONTENTS

List of Contributors

Professor W. J. R. Alexander, *Department of Civil Engineering, University of Pretoria, Pretoria 0002, South Africa*

Professor M. F. Bari, *University of Engineering & Technology, Department of Water Resources Engineering, Dhaka-1000, Bangladesh*

Dr P. Belleudy, *Laboratoire d'Hydraulique de France, 6 Rue de Lorraine, F 38130 Echirolles, France*

Mr H. N. C. Breusers, *Delft Hydraulics, Postbus 177, 2600 mh Delft, The Netherlands*

Mr Cliff Dobson, *NRA Severn Trent Region, Sentinel House, Wellington Crescent, Fradley Park, Lichfield, Staffs WS13 8RR, UK*

Mr H. G. Enggrob, *Danish Hydraulic Institute, Agern Alle 5, DK-2970 Horsholm, Denmark*

Mr M. Erlich, *Laboratoire d'Hydraulique de France, 6 rue de Lorraine, E-38130 Echirolles, France*

Dr D. A. Ervine, *University of Glasgow, Department of Civil Engineering, Glasgow G12 8LT, UK*

Dr T. Estrela, *Center for Hydrographic Studies, Paseo bajo Vigen del Puerto, 3, 28005 Madrid, Spain*

Professor P. C. Fernandez, *Incyth-Centro Regional Andino, Casilla de Correo No 6, (5500) Mendoza, Argentina*

Mr M. G. I. Gilbert, *Tractebel, Ariane Avenue 5, B-1200 Brussels, Belgium*

Dr Ing S. Hartmann, *Hydromechanik und Hydrologie, Universitat der Bundeswehr Munchen, Werner-Heisenberg-Weg 39, D-8014 Neubiberg, Germany*

Dr N. N. J. Higginson, *Department of Agriculture, R462 Hydebank, 4 Hospital Road, Belfast BT8, Northern Ireland, UK*

Mr Hugh Clear Hill, *RPS Clouston, The Old Barn, Deanes Close, Steventon, Abingdon, Oxon OX13 6SY, UK*

Professor A. A. Hoque, *Bangladesh University of Engineering & Technology, Institute of Flood Control & Drainage Research, BUET, Dhaka-1000, Bangladesh*

Md Abdul Momin Khondaker, *Institute of Flood Control & Drainage Research, Buet, Dhaka-1000, Bangladesh*

Mr R. Kohane, *Institute fur Wasserbau, Universitat Stuttgart, Pfaffenwaldring 61, D-7000 Stuttgart 80, Germany*

Dr J. F. Lyness, *Department of Civil Engineering and Transport, University of Ulster, Shore Road, Newtownabbey BT37 0QB, Northern Ireland, UK*

Mr Bruno Matticchio, *Ipros Ingegneria Amientale, Corso del Popolo, 8-35100 Padova, Italy*

Dr J. Morris, *Silsoe College, Silsoe, Bedfordshire, MK45 4DT, UK*

Professor A Nishat, *Department of Water Resources Engineering, Buet, Dhaka-1000, Bangladesh*

Dr.-Ing. Anton Nuding, *c/o Lahmeyer International, Ref. RH 1, Lyoner Str. 22, 6000 Frankfurt/M 71, Germany*

Dr Ing H. Patt, *Institut fur Wasserwesen, Universitat der Bundeswehr Munchen, Werner-Heisenberg-Weg 39, D-8014 Neubiberg, Germany*

Dr Guna N. Paudyal, *Danish Hydraulic Institute, House 33, Road 24/30, Gulshan, Dhaka, Bangladesh*

Mr D. Pelleymounter, *NRA Yorkshire Region, Rivers House, 21 Park Square South, Leeds LS1 2QC, UK*

Dr G. Pender, *Department of Civil Engineering, Rankine Building, University of Glasgow, Glasgow, G12 8LT, UK*

Mr David Ramsbottom, *HR Wallingford Ltd, Wallingford, Oxon, OX10 8BA, UK*

Dr Charles Reeve, *HR Wallingford Ltd, Wallingford, Oxon, OX10 8BA, UK*

Professor A. Rooseboom, *Department of Civil Engineering, Private Bag X5018, Stellenbosch 7599, South Africa*

Ms S. R. Runham, *ADAS, ADAS Arthur Rickwood, Mepal, Ely, Cambridgeshire CB6 2BA, UK*

Mr A. P. G. Russell, *Sir William Halcrow & Partners, Swindon, Wiltshire SN4 0QD, UK*

Mr Paul Samuels, *HR Wallingford Ltd, Wallingford, Oxon, OX10 8BA, UK*

Dr A. S. Shakir, *Department of Civil Engineering, University of Engineering & Technology, Lahore-31, Pakistan*

Mr Abdolali Sharghi, *Catholic University of Leuven, Park van Arenberg, de Croylaan 2, 3001 Heverlee, Belgium*

Dr B. H. Schmid, *Technische Universitat Wien, Karlsplatz 13, A-1040 Vienna, Austria*

Professor F Schoberl, *University of Innsbruck, A-6020 Innsbruck, Technikerstrasse 13, Austria*

Miss C. P. Skeels, *Department of Mathematical Sciences, Frenchay Campus, Coldharbour Lane, Bristol, B16 1QY, UK*

Dr Nuray Tokyay, *Middle East Technical University, Civil Engineering Department, 06531 Ankara, Turkey*

Mr Sandor Toth, *Ministry of Transport, Communication and Water Management, 75-81 Dob u, H-1077 Budapest, Hungary*

Dr Haizhou Tu, *University of Tokyo, Department of Civil Engineering, University of Tokyo, Tokyo 113, Japan*

Professor Osman Uguncu, *Black Sea Technical University, Karadeniz Teknik Universites, 61080 Trabzon, Turkey*

Mr F. C. M. van der Knapp, *Delft Hydraulics, PO Box 152, 8300 ad Emmeloord, The Netherlands*

Dr S. Wang, *Tsinghua University, P.R. China, Sediment Laboratory, Department of Hydraulic Engineering, Beijing, China*

Mr J. B. Wark, *HR Wallingford Ltd, Wallingford, Oxon, OX10 8BA, UK*

Mr B. Westrich, *Institut fur Wasserbau, Universitat Stuttgart, Stuttgart, Germany*

Mr J. H. A. Wijibenga, *Delft Hydraulics, PO Box 152, 8300 ad Emmeloord, The Netherlands*

Dr X. L. Yang, *KTH, Hydraulics Laboratory, Royal Institute of Technology, S-100 44 Stockholm, Sweden*

Professor P. C. Young, *Centre for Research on Engineering Systems, I.E.B.S., University of Lancaster, Lancaster LA1 4YQ, UK*

Preface

Recent major flood events, such as the 1987 and 1988 monsoon floods in Bangladesh and the 1993 floods in the Mississippi basin, have highlighted once again the economic and social cost of flooding. Such events as these also show the effects which Man's intervention in the natural environment can have on flood magnitude and propagation. These materialise in terms of (i) increased flows due to urbanisation, (ii) reduced flow capacity due to the encroachment of man-made structures on the floodplain and (iii) changes in sediment loads and river morphology brought about by changes in land use practices.

Effective mitigation of the adverse effects of flooding requires an increased understanding of the mechanisms by which floods are generated and the processes which are involved in their propagation through the catchment. We also need a better understanding of the ways in which water courses develop with time and the effect that this development has on the ability of the system to evacuate flood events.

Our understanding of river flooding is increasing rapidly thanks to worldwide research efforts into the numerous hydrological, hydraulic and morphological processes which occur during flood events. There is a continual improvement in modelling technologies to predict and simulate these important processes, aided by advances in computer power and speed. It is the purpose of this, the Second International Conference on River Flood Hydraulics, to promulgate these new ideas and to pool the knowledge of international experts in the field.

The major topics covered by the conference are:

- flood analysis and prediction
- field data
- hydraulics of flood flow
- sediment transport and morphological effects
- physical and numerical modelling
- environmental, social and economic aspects of flood control

It gives me great pleasure to acknowledge the contribution made by the members of the National and International Organising Committees, particularly for the conscientious way in which they reviewed the submitted abstracts and papers. My gratitude goes to Dr Paul Samuels and other colleagues at HR Wallingford who have worked so hard for the success of the conference. Finally, I thank Jacqueline Watts, our Conference Organiser, for the efficient and enthusiastic way in which she has carried out her numerous and varied tasks.

Opening Keynote Address

RIVER FLOOD HYDRAULICS
22–25 March 1994: York, England

PRACTICAL EXPERIENCE IN DEALING WITH MAJOR FLOOD INCIDENTS

IN SOUTH AFRICA

J.M. Jordaan
Department of Water Affairs, Private Bag X313,
Pretoria, South Africa

INTRODUCTION

South Africa has a long history of severe floods, particularly in Natal in the north-eastern quadrant of the country. The following is an extract from one of the earlier documents.

> *Government Notice No. 86, 1869*
>
> *His Excellency the Lieutenant Governor directs the publication for general information the subjoined report of the Commission appointed to enquire into the causes of the destruction of certain Bridges in this Colony during the Flood of August, 1868. This report has been laid on the table of the Legislative Council.*
>
> > *By His Excellency's command,*
> >
> > *D. ERSKINE,*
> >
> > *Colonial Secretary,*
> >
> > *Colonial Office, July 14, 1869*

The report mentions "the great flood of 1856", which occurred twelve years earlier and remains the highest recorded flood along the coastal area of Natal.

Floods continued to cause damage over the years. More floods in 1959 in Natal initiated the establishment of the Hydrological Research Unit at the University of the Witwatersrand in Johannesburg, funded by the South African Institution of Civil Engineers. The research culminated in the publication of the manual *Design Flood Determination in South Africa* in 1969, one hundred years after the Colonial Office report (Midgley, 1969). The emphasis was on the unit hydrograph method and included a method for determining the probable maximum flood. Solution methods were based on graphical analyses.

Four severe, widespread flood events occurred in 1981, 1984, 1987, and 1988. There was widespread loss of life and destruction of structures, and once again the validity of current analytical methods was questioned. One irate reader wrote a letter to the editor of a local newspaper:

> *"I don't care a damn whether or not a degree in accountancy, engineering, medicine or anything else is recognised in foreign nations to the north of us. All I want is an accountant who can keep the Receiver off my back and look after my investments. All I want is a civil engineer who can build better bridges than the ones that are always washed away when there are floods in Natal."*

2nd International Conference on River Flood Hydraulics. Edited by W. R. White and J. Watts
© 1994 HR Wallingford Ltd. Published by John Wiley & Sons Ltd

In 1988 the South African National Committee on Large Dams commissioned the publication of the handbook *Flood hydrology for southern Africa* which was published in 1990 (Alexander, 1990). A deliberate decision was made NOT to specify a particular method. The following message appeared prominently on the first page of the publication:

> *The first and most important lesson to be learnt from this handbook is that there is no single calculation method that is better than all other methods under all the wide variety of flood magnitude determination problems that will be encountered in practice. Consequently you will have to apply your own experience and knowledge to your particular problem. The rest of this handbook will assist you in developing or expanding your knowledge; the case studies will help you develop your experience; and the computer programs will provide a tool for rapidly exploring a wide range of solutions - something that is seldom possible with the more laborious, time consuming and consequently more costly hand calculation methods.*

The computer programs distributed on disk with the handbook were also applied in subsequent research which concentrated on a re-appraisal of all methods for determining the flood magnitude-frequency relationship, and the development of methods for specific applications. The emphasis has since moved from flood hydrology to the broader fields of flood risk analysis, flood warning systems and the development of a national flood management policy. Some highlights of general interest are given below.

RECENT SEVERE FLOODS

Details of recent widespread, severe floods in South Africa are given in a separate paper by Alexander at this conference. Some features of general interest are given below. There is growing concern that global climate changes may result in an increase in the occurrence of severe floods in future. The data base is far too short for a conclusive analysis, but there are nevertheless some indications that weather phenomena are becoming more extreme. Some of these are indicated (*) in the following comment.

Laingsburg floods of January,1981.

Laingsburg is located in the arid Karoo region 250 km north-east of Cape Town on the main road and rail routes to the interior. The river overtopped its banks at 10:00 on Sunday morning and reached its peak eight hours later, during which time it traversed five street blocks. This would normally have been more than enough time to warn and evacuate most of the people in this small community, but nevertheless 104 persons were drowned. The Floriskraal Dam 20km downstream of Laingsburg did not fail despite the water level which was well above the non-overspill crest of the dam. A search for evidence of palaeoflood levels downstream of the dam was successful but these were LOWER than the 1981 flood (*). Elsewhere in South Africa palaeoflood levels are appreciably higher than recent flood levels.

Floods caused by the tropical cyclone Domoina in January, 1984.

The cyclone crossed the mainland coast near Maputo in Mozambique, followed a curved path, and exited out to sea in northern Natal three days later. The path of the cyclone in Natal was in a downstream direction which increased the magnitude of the floods. The loss of life and damage to structures would have been even more severe if the path had been across the more densely populated area further to the south. This is the first recorded tropical cyclone to have crossed into South Africa (*), although a number of previous tropical cyclones approached close enough to cause widespread rainfall and floods.

Natal floods of September, 1987

In many catchments these floods were the highest on record, exceeded only by the 1856 floods where this information was available (*). Not only did these floods cause severe damage and loss of life, they also destroyed the main water pipelines to Durban where water had to be rationed until repairs were completed.

An encouraging feature was the accuracy of the forecasts issued four days in advance of the rainfall, and five days before the occurrence of the floods.

The forecasting section of the South African Weather Bureau routinely receives a selection of prognostic fields from the European Centre for Medium-Range Weather Forecasts as well as from the British Meteorological Office's Bracknell numerical weather prediction centre. These prognostic fields are an important input in the preparation of medium term forecasts.

The first warning of the possibility of unusual rainfall over the south-eastern region of South Africa was the Bracknell forecast issued on Wednesday 23rd September in which it predicted widespread rainfall for the forthcoming Saturday. On Thursday the Weather Bureau issued special warnings of heavy rainfall which were repeated in the days that followed. The heavy rainfall commenced at midday on Saturday as forecast. A subsequent analysis by Triegaart *et al* (1988) showed that the forecast positions of the 850-hPa level low-pressure over the interior and the Indian Ocean high-pressure were remarkably good. The actual rainfall was much higher than the predicted rainfall, however. Tennant and van Heerden (1993) ascribe this to an underestimate of the role that the steep topography plays. This rises from sea level to an elevation of more than 3 000 m over a distance of less than 200 km.

Floods over the interior in February, 1988

The floods in many catchments were the highest on record (*). Two large dams failed but there were no lives lost from this cause. This was because by the time the dams breached the downstream areas and bridges were already under water. These floods occurred five months after the earlier floods in Natal, and were followed a month later with further floods. Prolonged seasonal rainfall is a characteristic of severe flood events.

Floods in urban areas

Smaller scale severe storms have also occurred in urban areas. Details of three of these are given below.

September, 1962	Port Elizabeth	552 mm in four hours
August, 1970	East London	447 mm in six hours
January, 1978	Pretoria	245 mm in four hours

Damage and loss of life were not on the same scale as the large area floods detailed above, but since then there has been an appreciable increase in residential occupation of flood plains in the major urban areas in South Africa, and a repetition of storms of this magnitude in any major urban area in future could result in a large loss of life.

Droughts over southern Africa from January to March, 1992

In October, 1991 minor floods occurred over much the same area of the interior as the February, 1988 floods. In some rainfall districts this was the highest rainfall for the month since records commenced in 1921 (*). Within three months the rainfall was the LOWEST on record for the month. The drought over the interior of southern Africa for the period January to March, 1992 was the worst since the availability of district rainfall records in 1921 (*).

CLIMATE CHANGE

Alexander and van Heerden (1991a) provided evidence to support the possibility of increase in frequency of flood producing rainfall in recent years (*). This is shown in Fig. 1. This information taken together with the severe drought over the past three years, reinforces the view that weather systems are becoming more extreme but it cannot be determined whether or not these are part of the natural climate variability.

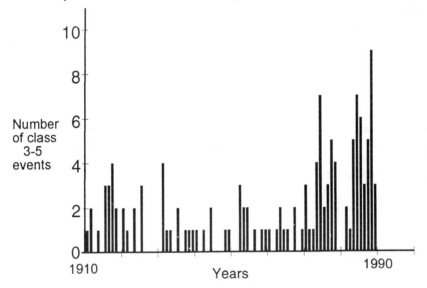

Figure 1. Number of severe rainfall events per year in South Africa from 1910 to 1990.

ANALYTICAL METHODS

The recent floods destroyed many major structures including two large dams, many bridges and hundreds of minor structures. Hundreds of lives were lost, and there was widescale interruption of communications and services. This led to a critical review of the analytical methods used in hydrological analyses.

All current analytical methods were reviewed, and computer implementations were provided in the handbook *Flood Hydrology for southern Africa* (Alexander, 1990). Algorithms were included in the direct statistical analysis methods to allow regionalisation of the distribution parameters, and conditional probability and retrofitting adjustments to accommodate zero flows, gaps in the record, as well as to accommodate historical and palaeoflood maxima.

Rainfall - runoff models

By the onset of the 1990's the average length of observed records of annual flood maxima was more than thirty years, with some reliable records having eighty years of data. There was little doubt that direct statistical analysis methods using regionally weighted parameters were more reliable than the deterministic unit hydrograph and rational methods when applied to gauged sites. Studies by Alexander and van Heerden (1991a, 1991b) identified shortcomings in the deterministic methods, particularly in the results for return periods exceeding 20 years. The main reason for the underestimation was the underlying assumption in these methods that the return period of the design flood peak was the same as that for the rainfall. This assumes that the catchment has an undefined average moisture status prior to the rainfall. However, severe rainfall events usually have durations well in excess of the catchment response times with the result that antecedent catchment moisture status also increases with increase in storm severity. In semiarid and arid climates the antecedent moisture status varies over a much wider range than in more humid climates, and plays a much greater role in the rainfall-runoff process.

The century-old rational method is alive and well in South Africa. The South African version which has been in use for the past two decades has the formulation:

$$Q_T = C_T \ I_T \ A$$

where the coefficient C is also dependent on the return period T.

The South African version of the unit hydrograph method has been in use since its development in 1969 (Midgley, 1969). Each method has its group of adherents. The unit hydrograph method becomes unstable for small catchments, whereas the rational method is used for catchments of any size.

Computer applications for both methods have been developed and comparisons can be made with the results of direct statistical analyses at sites where long records are available. Algorithms have been incorporated in the deterministic models which allow them to be calibrated against direct statistical analysis methods applied to sites with long records in the vicinity.

Direct statistical analysis methods

The severe floods of the 1980's produced many peaks that were the highest on record and appreciably higher than previous maxima. They appear as single outliers when plotted, but cannot be considered as being anomalous results. From a design point of view it would be most unwise to ignore them or to assume that they are chance occurrences with long return periods. On the contrary there is mounting evidence that the widespread rainfall events that cause severe floods are more frequent than previously assumed.

Four direct statistical analysis methods are currently in use in South Africa. These are:

Log normal distribution using conventional moment estimators	LN/MM
Log Pearson Type III distribution using conventional moment estimators	LP3/MM
General Extreme Value distribution using probability weighted moments	GEV/PWM
Wakeby distribution using probability weighted moments	WAK/PWM

The LN distribution has two parameters, the LP3 and GEV distributions each have three parameters, and the WAK distribution has five parameters. There is no meaningful difference between the results obtained when using the three and five parameter distributions at sites where there are no anomalies in the records. In particular, the GEV and WAK distributions produce very similar results in most cases.

All distributions including those using probability weighted moment estimators are sensitive to anomalous high and low values in the data set. Low values introduce negative skewness which may not be characteristic of the distribution and result in an underestimation of the flood peak. One of the reasons for low values is the effect of upstream storage and abstractions which significantly reduce river flow during dry years. This effect is hidden in the conventional linear-EV1 plots but is clearly discernable in graphs with logarithmic scale plots. If the interest is in flood magnitude estimation these anomalous low values have to be removed or corrected.

The same reasoning does not apply to anomalously high values which are of direct interest in flood magnitude estimation.

APPLICATIONS

Research and practice

Possibly because of the wide range of flood related problems, design specifications are less rigorous in South Africa than in some other countries. One fortunate consequence is that research is not inhibited by the knowledge that improved analytical methods may not be favourably received by practitioners. Indeed, the reverse is the case, and research in the field of flood hydrology has always been strongly user-oriented.

The following are some comments on research and practice in South Africa. A distinction is made between structural failure where the structure is damaged to the extent that the structure no longer serves its purpose, and functional failure where the structure fails to serve its purpose without necessarily suffering structural damage.

Minor structures

Examples of minor structures are those used in urban drainage works. The total cost of structures in this catagory is well in excess of the costs of structures in all other categories. Design practice is largely policy based rather than based on risk analysis or economic optimisation. Because of the high total costs, these structures are usually designed for low return period events wit. the consequence of a relatively high frequency of functional failure. Structural failure is relatively infrequent and the repair costs are generally a low percentage of the total annual costs. Functional failure results in inconvenience of the public rather than serious financial or life-threatening consequences.

Research
Most urban drainage design methods are essentially hydraulic models with hydrological components. The hydrological process assumptions in these models lead to the conclusion that urbanisation increases flood peaks and consequently structures have to have increased capacities. However, this increase has not been detected in recorded data sets where appreciable urbanisation has taken place during the period of record.

Moderately large structures

Bridges across major rivers are examples of structures in this category. While dams have a much higher potential for causing loss of life and damage, more lives have been lost in South Africa due to the structural and functional failure of bridges than due to the failure of dams. This is largely because of the more stringent safety requirements for dam construction.

Bridge location is determined more by optimum route location than by optimum foundation conditions. Bridges are built higher above the river beds to reduce the risk of functional failure but the higher elevations make them more vulnerable to structural failure when unusually severe floods occur.

There have been an unacceptably high number of failures of bridges due to floods in recent years, particularly in Natal, but also in the southern Orange Free State - Northern Cape region, and in the southern Karoo. In addition to the direct repair costs, the indirect costs to users have also been severe.

An even more tragic occurrence was the influence of the bridge over the Buffels River at Laingsburg during the January, 1981 floods when 104 lives were lost in the town. The combination of topography and the location and design of the bridge resulted in an appreciably higher loss of life and damage to buildings in the town than would otherwise have been the case. Sixteen persons were trapped on the bridge itself and lost their lives.

In most cases the bridges are designed for a high degree of safety as far as the traffic imposed loads are concerned. However, most designs have until recently made no provision for flood associated loads other than requiring a specified clearance above the water level reached by a flood of the specified return period. No additional allowance is required for wave action or floating debris. The consequence is that there have been many structural failures due to flood related loads and very few, if any, failures due to traffic imposed loads.

The risk of failure of a structure due to floods is a function of the flood magnitude-frequency relationship and the probable strength (resistance to failure) of the elements of the structure for a range of applied loads.

The determination of the flood imposed loads on a structure is difficult as it requires a knowledge of the velocity fields for a range of flood magnitudes, and the corresponding loads on the bridge elements. A knowledge of the failure probability of each structural element for a range of loads is also required for risk analysis.

Physical laboratory models may be useful in difficult situations, particularly for crossings of large alluvial floodplains. Computer models are less expensive and can be used to explore a wide range of alternative options, particularly where cost optimisation is an important consideration.

While a full risk analysis is analytically intractible, simplifying assumptions can be made and Monte Carlo methods used as an exploratory tool. These include the generation of synthetic flood and strength sequences for the principal structural elements for the assumed probability distributions. The method is described by Alexander (1993).

Research

The extensive damage to bridges caused by recent floods gave rise to a coordinated multi-disciplinary research programme which is approaching completion.

Large structures

The most important structures in this category are large dams whose failure could cause serious downstream damage and loss of life.

In South Africa as in most countries, a very high degree of safety is required and there are statutory requirements that have to be met for existing as well as new dams. South African guidelines allow designers to use either the South African version of the probable maximum flood (Midgley, 1969) or the regional maximum flood as described in Kovacs (1988). Cost optimisation procedures and flood magnitude - frequency analyses are not permitted for the determination of the design flood for high risk structures. There are some practitioners who question the use of these ultra-safe designs.

Research

The results of research on widespread, severe floods are given in a paper by Alexander at this conference.

Interruption of communications and essential services

Trunk roads are designed for high speed, all-weather transportation which includes heavy haulage vehicles, frequent passenger busses, and high densities of private vehicles. The direct and indirect costs of interruption of communication routes due to floods has increased in proportion to the increased usage.

Another recent development is the isolation of communities during floods. Large communities have been cut off from hospitals, health centres and places of work during floods. The present establishment of informal settlement areas in and near cities, and on the flood plains themselves in some instances, is a matter of considerable concern. The socio-political consequences of being unable to reach and assist these communities during severe floods due to the inundation and destruction of roads and bridges would be serious.

Residential occupation of floodplains

It is estimated that at least 50 000 persons, and possibly more than 100 000 persons are living along rivers and streams in South Africa below levels reached by previous floods. Most of these live in unplanned settlements within the jurisdiction of local or regional authorities.

As is the case in many developing countries, there has also been a general migration of the rural poor to urban areas and the surroundings. It is often the case that the only vacant land is in flood prone areas where planned development has been prohibited in the past. In South Africa this migration has been accelerated by the recent drought. This is in addition to the many thousands of persons living in planned development which is subject to flooding. The low-lying area of Ladysmith in Natal is one of many similar situations.

Operation of dams with gate controlled flood outlets

Owners of dams with gated spillways have to develop operating procedures based on a combination of knowledge of rainfall that has occurred and flows that have been measured in upstream rivers, and estimates based on forecasts of rainfall and resulting additional high flows that may occur in the immediate future. Consequently it is not possible to ensure that floods will be discharged optimally. Operating procedures have to take this into account.

FLOOD WARNING SYSTEMS

In most situations where lives are at risk, the only viable means for reducing the risk is through the operation of efficient flood warning systems. A computer-based National Flood Advisory Service has been developed and is now being tested operationally. In addition further methods are being developed for application by local authorities and small communities.

Three levels of warning are envisaged. At a national level the objective is to make flood related information available as soon as possible and as widely as possible. A computer-based system has been developed and can be interrogated by any authorised person who has access to a telephone, computer and modem. The information includes rainfall for the previous 24 hours recorded at some 500 sites, weather forecasts, the state of storage in selected reservoirs and the discharge in selected rivers. Provision has been made for relaying satellite imagery, and radar coverage when this becomes available. This is a flood advisory service and not a flood warning system.

The second level is action taken by local authorities on receipt of information that floods can be expected. The objective of local authorities is to issue warnings to all persons in threatened areas to watch the river. Because of legal implications they are not advised to evacuate their premises.

The third and most important level is the development of methods for ensuring that all persons at risk are fully aware of the danger, and action that they should take should floods occur.

These systems have been developed and are currently being evaluated operationally (Alexander, 1993).

NATIONAL FLOOD MANAGEMENT POLICY

Another consequence of the recent floods was the perceived need to develop a national flood management policy. Some of the policy issues that are being addressed are the equitable distribution of economic risks and an equitable basis for controlling development within flood prone regions.

ACKNOWLEDGMENTS

I express my appreciation to my colleagues Professors WJR Alexander and J van Heerden for their assistance in the preparation of this paper.

REFERENCES

Alexander WJR (1990) *Flood hydrology for southern Africa.* South African National Committee for Large Dams

Alexander WJR (1993). *Flood risk reduction measures.* Department of Civil Engineering, University of Pretoria

Alexander WJR and van Heerden J (1991a). *Determination of the risk of widespread interruption of communications due to floods.* Department of Transport Research Report Nr RDAC 90/16.

Alexander WJR and van Heerden J (1991b). *The destruction of bridges by floods during the past 120 years - what went wrong?* Proceedings of the Annual Transportation Convention, Pretoria.

Kovacs Z *(1988). Regional maximum flood peaks in southern Africa.* Department of Water Affairs Technical Report TR137.

Midgley DC (1969). *Design flood determination for South Africa.* Hydrological Research Unit. University of the Witwatersrand.

Tennant W and van Heerden J (1993) *The influence of orography and local sea surface temperature anomalies in the development of the 1987 Natal floods.* Accepted for publication in the South African Journal of Science.

Triegaardt DO, Terblanche DE, van Heerden J and Laing MV (1988). *The Natal floods of 1987.* South African Weather Bureau technical publication Nr 19.

Chapter One

Flood Analysis
and Prediction

EVALUATING DESIGN CHARACTERISTICS FOR FLOODS IN BANGLADESH

M Mozzammel Hoque, Ph. D.

Professor

Institute of Flood Control and Drainage Research
Bangladesh University of Engineering and Technology, Dhaka

ABSTRACT

Following the two successive catastrophic flood events of 1987 and 1988 which caused untold sufferings and losses to the people it has been felt necessary to improve the accuracy of current flood prediction practices and extension of prediction beyond the major rivers in Bangladesh. This needs establishment of a relationship between the depth and areal extent of floods at different levels of cross border inflows in the major rivers and their flood plains. This can be achieved by application of a computer based hydrodynamic model. This study is an attempt in determining the most appropriate statistical distribution that can be used in the analysis of the results of historical simulation of water level and discharge by a hydrodynamic model. Four different statistical distributions, namely, (1) Normal, (2) Log-Normal, (3) Gamma, and (4) Gumbel's Extremal Value Distributions have been used. A comparison among the results obtained by the four distributions has been made with Kolmogorov-Smirnov test to identify the best distribution. The Gumbel's Extremal Value distribution was found to be as the best distribution for analyzing the output of the hydrodynamic model for design and planning of water resources projects.

INTRODUCTION

Bangladesh is the biggest delta in the world formed at the confluence of the three large rivers: the Ganges, the Brahmaputra, and the Meghna. The total drainage area of these river systems is more than 1.55 million sq km, of which about 0.12 million sq km (7.5 percent) lies within Bangladesh. The average flood peak discharge of the combined Ganges-Brahmaputra system is 110,000

2nd International Conference on River Flood Hydraulics. Edited by W. R. White and J. Watts
© 1994 HR Wallingford Ltd. Published by John Wiley & Sons Ltd

m^3/sec(MPO, 1987a). The average rainfall within Bangladesh varies
from 1,100 mm in the east to 5,700 mm in the north-east. About 75
percent of the rainfall is concentrated in the period from June to
September.

The topography, rainfall pattern, and the river regime are
ideal for agriculture. But, due to its location Bangladesh is
subject to frequent floods which seriously affect the agriculture
and infrastructure development and cause immense sufferings to the
people. The flooding in the country is the result of a complex
series of factors. These include the huge inflows of water into the
country from upstream catchment of the major rivers coinciding with
heavy internal rainfall, low flood plain gradient, drainage
congestion in older flood plain areas, effect of the confluence of
the major rivers, and the influence of the sea level rise due to
tides and storm surges(MPO, 1987b).

On average, about 18 percent of the entire country or about
26,000 sq km of area is inundated by normal floods. During more
severe floods, the inundation area may go upto 52,000 sq km or
about 36 percent of the entire country. During the floods of 1988,
about 67 percent of the land was flooded which is the highest of
the ever recorded figures.

Following the two successive catastrophic flood events of 1987
and 1988 which caused untold sufferings and losses to the people,
it has been recognized necessary to (1) examine the effectiveness
of flood control options and (2) evaluate a sound flood action
policy(World Bank, 1989). Consequently, prediction of depth and
areal extent of flood at different levels of flooding in the major
rivers and their flood plains became necessary. As a result,
several studies were carried out. Sometimes the situation is
aggravated by adding the effects of high tides in the Bay of
Bengal. To analyze the complex interactions among the causes of
floods in Bangladesh in terms of magnitudes and phases, combined
probability analysis has been found impractical (Kruger Consult and
BCEOM, 1992). An approach adopted in the Flood Hydrology Study of
Bangladesh Flood Action Plan carried out the historical simulations
of recorded inflow and rainfall data to overcome the complex
probability analysis. In the present study, an evaluation has been
made to identify the best distribution which can be used to analyze
the results of a hydrodynamic model from historical simulation. For
this purpose, the historical discharge and water level data from
seven stations used as upstream boundary of the General Model (DHI
and BUET, 1990) have been used as test cases. For flood analysis,
Bangladesh National Water Plan(MPO, 1987b) used the Log Pearson
Type III which is the logarithmic form of Gamma (Pearson Type III)
distribution for discharge analysis, and the Gamma distribution for
water level analysis. However, the use of Log Pearson Type III
distribution and the Gamma distribution were not supported by any
technical justification. In flood hydrology study under FAP-25
(Kruger Consult and BCEOM,1992), it has been concluded that it is
appropriate to use the 3-parameter GEV or the 2-parameter Gumbel's

distribution for annual extreme discharge analysis, 2-parameter lognormal for annual maximum water level, and lognormal distribution for annual, seasonal, and subseasonal rainfall data analysis.

STATISTICAL DISTRIBUTIONS

The hydrologic variables are assumed to come from a continuous random process and therefore, the common continuous distributions can be used to fit the historical sequences of discharge. The four more common distributions, namely, Normal distribution, Log-Normal distribution, Gamma distribution, and Gumbel's Extremal Value distribution, applied in the hydrologic sequences have been considered.

The Normal distribution is a symmetrical bell-shaped function which describes many processes that are subject to random and independent variation. This is a two parameter (mean and standard deviation) distribution with the mean, mode, and median being the same. The Normal distribution is applicable, only when the variable is continuous, consecutive values are independent, and probabilities are stable.

Many hydrologic variables exhibit a marked right skewness, partly due to the influence of natural phenomena. In such cases, frequencies do not follow the Normal distribution but their logarithms follow a Normal distribution. The Log-normal distribution has the versatility of high parameter modes without the error and uncertainties which result from the use of higher order sample moments. It is a two-parameter distribution (mean and variance).

The Gamma or Pearson Type III distribution is extremely flexible in that a zero skew will reduce the Log Pearson III distribution to Log-normal and the Pearson Type III to normal. A very important property of Gamma variate as well as Normal variate is that the sum of the two variables retains the same distribution. This feature is important to generate synthetic hydrologic sequences. The Gamma distribution has wide range of applications and is being used increasingly in hydrologic studies.

The theory on which the extreme value distribution depends is not as strong as the central limit theorem for the Normal distribution. More assumptions concerning the underlying or parent distribution must be made and the rate of convergence to an asymptotic extreme value distribution may be rather slow. However, the extreme value distributions do provide a connection between observed extreme events and modes which may be used to evaluate the probabilities of future extreme events.

The accuracy of the fitted distributions used in the analysis of hydrodynamic modelling results is very important for planning and design of water resources projects. Therefore, it is very important to determine the most appropriate statistical distribution. To compare the performance in terms of accuracy of different distributions for a particular purpose, goodness of fit tests, for example, Chi-Square and Kolmogorov-Smirnov tests (Kite, 1977) may be employed. In the present study, the Kolmogorov-Smirnov test has been used to evaluate the performance of the four distributions by testing with the annual water level and discharge hydrographs for different return periods.

DATA COLLECTION AND ORGANIZATION

In order to determine the best distribution to analyze the results of historical simulations of hydrodynamic model, the historical water level and discharge time series data from the seven measuring stations on the cross boundary rivers of Bangladesh were used. These stations have been used as the upstream boundary of the so called General Model of Bangladesh (DHI and BUET, 1988, and 1990). The historical mean daily water level and discharge data of the cross boundary stations of the seven selected rivers were collected from the following secondary sources: (1) Bangladesh Water Development Board (BWDB) and (2) Water Resources Planning Organization (WaRPO). The detailed information on the data collected are given in Table 1. The locations of the selected cross boundary water level and discharge stations are shown in Figure 1.

The details of the data used for generating water level and discharge hydrographs are given elsewhere (Hoque, Ahmed, and Siddique, 1991).

Table 1: Cross Boundary Water Level Discharge Stations

Station	Years of Data	From-To	Source Data	River
Hardinge Bridge	35	1955-89	BWDB	Ganges
Mohadevpur	15	1974-88	WaRPO	Atrai
Dalia-Doani	16	1973-88	WaRPO	Teesta
Noonkhawa	34	1956-89	BWDB	Jamuna
Jariajhanjail	25	1965-89	WaRPO	Kangsa
Kanairghat	21	1969-89	BWDB	Surma
Sheola	26	1964-89	BWDB	Kushiyara

The historical water level and discharge data collected from the cross boundary stations of the major rivers flowing through Bangladesh has been processed for frequency analysis. Both the water level and discharge data of each hydrological year has been divided into 36 divisions, 3 for every month. In other words, at each return period, the 10-day average data has been arranged to get 36 points on the annual water level and 36 points on the annual discharge hydrographs. Therefore, for seven water level and discharge stations a total of 252 sets of data for each of water

level and discharge have been analyzed for generation of
hydrographs for using as test cases. The processed water level and
discharge data are reported elsewhere (Hoque, Ahmed and, Siddique,
1992).

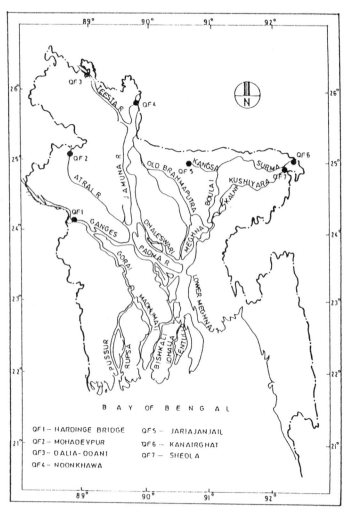

Figure 1: Major Rivers and the Cross Border Boundary
Water Level and Discharge Stations

RESULTS AND DISCUSSIONS

The algorithms of the Normal, Log Normal, Gamma, and Gumbel's Extremal distributions have been implemented by a computer based statistical model written in FORTRAN 77. The different points of the water level and the discharge hydrographs for 5, 10, 20, 50, 100, 200 500, and 1000 year of return periods have been generated independently. The results of the analysis have been reconstituted into water level and discharge hydrographs. These hydrographs may not represent the peak flow and the total seasonal flood. However, these hydrographs have been used as test cases to identify the best distributions in the analysis of the water levels and discharges. As an example, the reconstituted annual discharge hydrographs, starting with April 1, the beginning of the hydrological year in Bangladesh, for the river Ganges at return periods 20, 50, 100, and 200 year are plotted in Figures 2, 3, 4, and 5 respectively. Similarly, the reconstituted annual water level hydrographs are plotted in Figures 6, 7, 8, and 9 respectively. The difference between the generated values of water levels and discharges by different distributions at all return periods is significantly high during the peak season only and the Gumbel's Extremal Value distribution has produced higher water level and discharge than the other three distributions. The Normal distribution has produced the lowest water level and discharge. The difference in peaks becomes higher with higher return periods. The total generated data for annual water level and discharge hydrographs with given return periods have been reported elsewhere (Hoque, Ahmed, and Siddique, 1992).

To select an appropriate distribution in the analysis of water level and discharge hydrographs from the results of a hydrodynamic model for planning and design of water resources projects, it is necessary to evaluate the accuracy that can be achieved by different distributions and to make a comparison among the results obtained by different methods. An evaluation has been made using the generated water level and discharge hydrographs by employing the Kolmogorov-Smirnov statistics which concludes that the Gumbel's extreme value distribution is the preferred distribution for analysis of annual water level and discharge. An example of the results obtained at different points of 100 year return period water level and discharge hydrographs is shown in the Figure 10 which compares the Kolmogorov Smirnov test values for both water level and discharge at Hardinge Bridge of the river Ganges. The analysis shows that for all the 7 water level and discharge stations each with 36 sets of water level and discharge data, the Gumbel's distribution has produced the smallest Kolmogorov-Smirnov value, the Gamma distribution has produced the second smallest value and both the Lognormal and Normal distributions have produced the largest values.

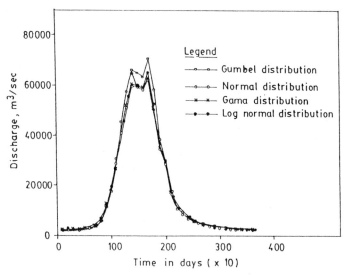

Figure 2: 20-year Return Period Discharge Hydrographs
of the River Ganges at Hardinge Bridge

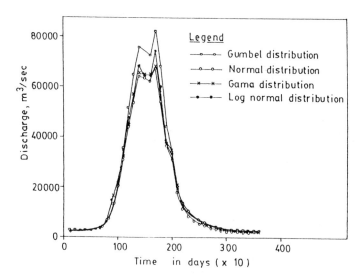

Figure 3: 50-year Return Period Discharge Hydrographs
of the River Ganges at Hardinge Bridge

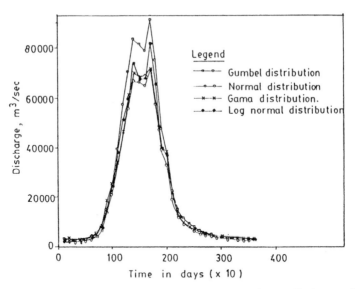

Figure 4: 100-year Return Period Discharge Hydrographs
of the River Ganges at Hardinge Bridge

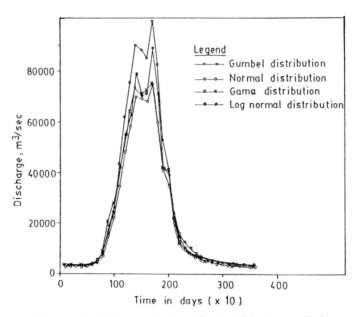

Figure 5: 200-year Return Period Discharge Hydrographs
of the River Ganges at Hardinge Bridge

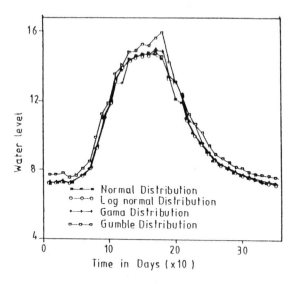

Figure 6: 20-year Return Period Water Level
Hydrographs of the River Ganges at
Hardinge Bridge

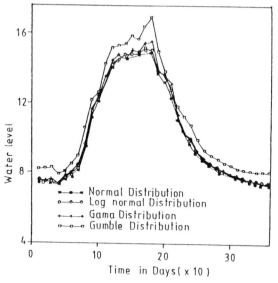

Figure 7: 50-year Return Period Water Level
Hydrographs of the River Ganges at
Hardinge Bridge

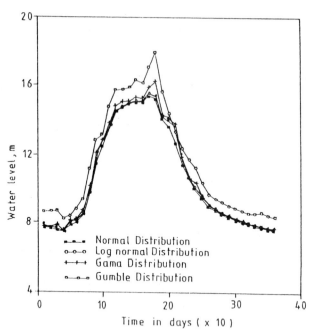

Figure 8: 100-year Return Period Water Level
Hydrographs of the River Ganges at
Hardinge Bridge

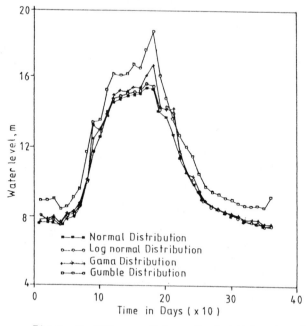

Figure 9: 200-year Return Period Water Level
Hydrographs of the River Ganges at
Hardinge Bridge

24

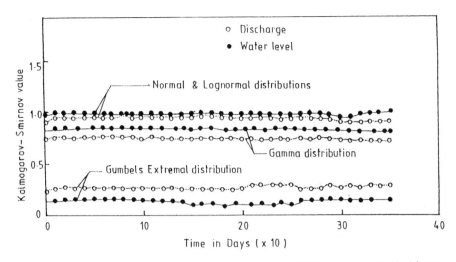

Figure 10: Kolmogorov-Smirnov Values for Different Distributions
at 100-year Return Period

CONCLUSIONS

The hydrographs generated by different distributions may be
conservative due to the facts that the period of analysis is very
small compared to the standard design life of a flood control
measures and the different parts of the hydrographs are generated
independently whereas in reality they are not independent. However,
the main objective of the analysis was to evaluate the most
appropriate distribution to minimize the error in analyzing the
results of a hydrodynamic model for planning and design purposes.
Since the Gumbel's distribution normally gives higher prediction
than the other selected methods and the error produced from the
analysis by the Gumbel's method is less than the other three
methods, the Gumbel's method may be confidently recommended.
    The results presented in this paper may be considered very
preliminary. Data used for some stations is doubtful and longer
period of data is needed for a better analysis. To use the results
for planning and design purposes further study is suggested.

ACKNOWLEDGEMENT

The work presented, is a part of the research entitled "Effects of
Different Planning Options on Floods in Bangladesh: A Numerical
Model Study", supported by the Institute of Flood Control and
Drainage Research, Bangladesh University of Engineering and
Technology, Dhaka. The assistance of Mr. Abdullah for data analysis
is fully acknowledged.

REFERENCES

1. DHI and BUET (1988), Surface Water Simulation Modeling Program, Final Report, Volume 1, Master Plan Organization, Ministry of Irrigation, Water Development, and Flood Control in Association with Bangladesh University of Engineering and Technology, Dhaka.

2. DHI and BUET (1990), Surface Water Simulation Modeling Program Phase II, Inception Report, Surface Water Modelling Center, Master Plan Organization, Ministry of Irrigation Water Development, and Flood Control, Government of Bangladesh in Cooperation with Danida.

3. Hoque, M. M., Ahmed, S. M. U., and Siddique, A. B. (1991), Effects of Different Planning Options on Floods in Bangladesh: A Numerical Model Study, Partial Completion Report, R04/91, 133pp.

4. Kruger Consult and BCEOM (1992), Flood Hydrology Study: Main Report, FAP-25: Flood Modelling and Management, Flood Plan Coordination Organization, Government of the People's Republic of Bangladesh, Dhaka.

5. Kite, G.W. (1977), Frequency and Risk Analysis in Hydrology, Water Resources Publication, Colorado State University, Fortcollins, Colorado, USA.

6. MPO (1987a), Surface Water Availability, Technical Report No.10 Master Plan Organization, Ministry of Irrigation, Water Development, and Flood Control, Governments of the People's Republic of Bangladesh, Dhaka.

7. MPO (1987b), Floods and Storms, Technical Report No.11, Master Plan Organization, Ministry of Irrigation, Water Development, and Flood Control, Government of the People's Republic of Bangladesh, Dhaka.

8. The World Bank (1989), Bangladesh Action Plan for Flood Control, Document of the World Bank Asian Region Country Department 1.

PREDICTION OF FLOODS FROM A MOUNTAIN RIVER WITH
GLACIERIZED AND SNOW COVERED AREAS

Pedro Fernández; Jorge Maza; Adrián Vargas Aranibar
Instituto Nacional de Ciencia y Técnica Hídricas
Centro Regional Andino, Mendoza-Argentina

ABSTRACT

The Mendoza river (Argentina-Figure 1) with a mean annual flow of 50 m^3/s is located in the Province of Mendoza at a South latitude of 33°. The watershed comprises a total area of 9,040 Km^2 with the upper basin leaning on the highest mountains of the Andes, the Aconcagua peak (7,000 masl) included. At elevations higher than 4,000 msal highly glacierized zones exist (Corte 1981). Most, or a large proportion of the total annual precipitation, falls as snow in late autumn and winter. Late spring and summer flows are a mixture of snow and glacier ice melting. These flows are essential for irrigation, water supply and industrial use for an area of more than 700,000 inhabitants. The river is not regulated so the problem of flood prediction and prevention is important.

Floods are mainly produced by a combination of snow and ice, with little incidence of some heavy rains in the lower basin area during summer thunderstorms. But in relation with flood prediction the real possibiblity of floods produced by the outburst of a glacier-dammed lake clearly appears. The analysis of these two kinds of floods, as well as a reference which deals with the definition of critical areas and inundation maps according to results of flood prediction, have been accomplished. A discussion related to these two different kinds of floods is presented.

INTRODUCTION

The Mendoza river upper watershed glacier inventory is based on photointerpretation and field verification over an area of 6,311 Km^2, 69% of the total basin area. (Corte 1981) 1,025 covered and uncovered ice bodies bigger than 0.02 Km^2 recognized and tabulated for their study and evaluation as a water resource; one of such glacier bodies is the "Glaciar Grande del Nevado del Plomo" (Figure 2) which cyclically produces surges and an ice dam 1,200 m long, 700 m wide and 90 m high, which blockades the Plomo river valley to form a glacier-dammed lake (Chow, 1964).

Snowfall in the high mountains and its subconsequent snowmelt produce an additional source of water supply for low valleys inhabitants. The abundance of water produced by snow and ice reservoirs in the Andean mountains area, as well as the arid conditions of low lands, highly dependent on melting glaciers and snow in the mountains, generates a remarkable confrontation.

The sudden melting of snowpacks in summer can result in important floods of a magnitude which is analyzed in the following paragraphs. Glaciers are usually not involved in these floods, but in case of glacier surges and formation of glacier-dammed lakes which can drain suddenly and produce catastrophic floods, prediction of location, timing and magnitude of such event is clearly necessary.

Fortunately, a good set of data related to the Mendoza river streamflow records and the ability to analyze such data rapidly with significant improvements in software technology, exists. Furthermore remote sensing by satellite is another specialized branch of technology which has grown very fast and studies have been undertaken to show the great potential of snow-cover and glacier mapping in order to estimate mass changes assisted by digital terrain models (Cazorzi, F. 1991). Figure 3 shows the Mendoza river upper watersheds in the Plomo and Tupungato subbasins (snow covered areas).

MATERIALS AND METHODS

The Mendoza river counts on a good set of data at Guido and Cacheuta stations (Figure 1). Data obtained since 1905 at Cacheuta and 1955 at Guido are available. From these data sets the discharges produced by the outburst of the ice dam lake were omitted, and with the rest of the data a statistical analysis related to the discharges produced by snow, glacier melting and rain was done.

Some information related to the floods produced by the outburst of the glacier-dammed lake are also handy for 1934 (King 1934, 1935; Razza, 1935; Prieto, 1985; Matson, 1934). A good information set of the 1985 floods (Fernández, 1985) and estimations of peak flows for 1900 and 1926 are also available.

For these floods,deterministic mathematical simulations were carried out (Fernández, 1985, 1990, 1991).

Statistical studies of snowmelt flows

From statistical studies of the Mendoza river (Fernández, 1976,1988) the following results were obtained:

Figure 4 shows,the characterization of mean flows and Figures 5 and 6 the maximum probable floods. The mean annual flow is 50 m^3/s,the monthly mean for January (summer) is 103.00 m^3/s and the monthly mean flow for June (winter) is 23 m^3/s.

With reference to the maximum probable flood (due to snowmelt and rain) the historical maximum at Guido is 450 m^3/s (January 1984) and the 100 years flood estimated as 580 m^3/s.

Floods produced by the outburst of a glacier-dammed lake

Historical floods

Historical floods with some information are the following: January 10-11, 1934 with a maximum discharge of 2,317 m^3/s at Guido (Fernández, 1991); 12-14 February 1985 with 380 m^3/s; 22-25 February 1985 with 361 m^3/s; 12-15 March 1985 with 263 m^3/s.

These last three successive floods are related to the same phenomenon, but the discharge of the lake is produced in three steps (Fernández, 1991).

There are also two references (King 1934) of outburst of floods in 1900 with an estimated peak of 2,000 m^3/s and 1926 with 1,000 m^3/s, plus some others during the 17th and 18th centuries with no reference to discharge values (Prieto 1985).

Flood of January 10-11, 1934

The maximum historical registered flood produced by the outburst of a glacier-dammed lake occurred in January 10-11, 1934 (Fernández 1991).

This flood produced many fatalities and seriously disrupted communications between Mendoza (Argentina) and Santiago (Chile). According to historical references (Matson, 1934) the maximum discharge at Punta de Vacas (See Figure 1), might have been of about 3,000 m^3/s. Comparison of the outburst floods between 1934 and 1985 is as follows (Fernández 1985, 1991):

TABLE 1 - COMPARATIVE VALUES OF THE 1934 AND 1985 OUTBURST FLOODS

	01/10-11/34	02/12-16/85	02/22-25/85	03/12-16/85
Breach area (m^2)	225	50	42	30
Discharge Volume (10^6 x m^3)	53	32	24	20
Breach developing time (hr)	5	30	2	4
Level difference(m)	75	26	21	33
Maximum discharge at Guido m^3/s	2,317	380	361	263

Maximum possible floods

Due to the fact that only few events of this kind occur it was only possible to carry out physically based deterministic calculations (Fernández, 1991) and no statistical analysis.

It is necessary to define maximum possible discharges from the ice-dammed lake in relation with their physical condition. The equation given by Krenke and Kotlyakov (1985) is solved for the values of the 1934 outburst

$$Q = K \, A^{4/3} \left(\sin \alpha + \frac{h}{1}\right)^{1/2} \quad \ldots \ldots \quad (1)$$

where Q = discharge in m^3/s at the glacier; A = cross section of the ice tunnel in square meters; α = inclination of the ice tunnel; h = depth of water in the lake in meters; 1 = length of the ice tunnel in meters. For the outburst of 1934 and the maximum discharge the values of such parameters (Fernández, 1985) are Q = 2,700 m^3/s; A = 225 m^2; α = 1,7726° sin α = 0.026; h = 75 m and 1 = 700 m. Solving equation 1 for K is obtain

$$K = \frac{2,700}{(225)^{4/3}\left(0.026 + \frac{75}{700}\right)^{1/2}} = 5.41$$

The Krenke and Kotlyakov (1985) values for K are in the range of 6.1 and 5.5.

Besides the similitude of the K-value and according to the studies of Young (1985), it was concluded that the most likely peak discharges would be in the range of 4,000 to 6,000 m^3/s and the maximum water surface elevation in the lake before the outburst should be about 0.9 of the ice dam altitude.

For the generation of a set of maximum possible floods the DAMBRK model was used (Fread 1984) for the following initial conditions: h = 75m and V = 54 x 10^6 m^3 (similar to the historical of 1934) and h = 82m, V = 67 x 10^6 which is the value correspondent to size of the river valley.

TABLE 2 - MAXIMUM POSSIBLE FLOODS IN m^3/s FOR 54 x 10^6 m^3 AND 75m IN THE ICE-DAMMED LAKE

Time of development of Breach (hours)	Breach Area (m^2)		
	225	375	750
2	3,077	4,760	8,340
3	2,940	4,438	7,309
5	2,700 (01/10/34)	3,897	5,340
7	2,490	3,409	4,007

TALBE 3 - MAXIMUM POSSIBLE FLOODS IN m^3/s FOR 67 x 10^6 m^3 AND 82m IN THE ICE-DAMMED LAKE

Time of development of the Breach (hours)	Breach Area (m^2)		
	225	375	750
2	3,570	5,521	9,500
3	3,413	5,107	8,300
5	3,104	4,432	6,371
7	2,843	3,902	4,780

Ref: ——— limit of physical conditions.

RESULTS

As a consequence of the previous analysis there are two different sorts of floods in this river: the snowmelt + rainfall floods and the ice-dam outburst floods.

TABLE 4 - MAXIMUM PROBABLE AND MAXIMUM POSSIBLE FLOODS OF THE MENDOZA RIVER

Time of Return (years)	Maximum Probable Floods m^3/s	Maximum Possible Floods m^3/s	
1	72		
2	140		
5	205		
10	260	263	
20	330	361	
30	390	380	
50	460		
100	580	1,000	Maximum possible historical floods
There are no reference as to time of return for M. Possible Floods		2,000	
		2,317	
		3,000	Maximum possible
		4,000	generated floods
		6,000	

30

We called "Maximum Possible Floods" the dam outburst floods which differ from the snowmelt+rain floods called "Maximum Probable Floods" (MPF). The Maximum Possible Floods are different not only in relation with the maximum values of peak discharges (which could be much greater than the MPF) but also because of their nature (dambreak floods) where significant inertial effects occur. These effects produce important impacts on bridges, diversion dams and other hydraulic works along the river, due to erosion and transport of sediments. Because of these studies a real time system of flood forecasting was installed (Fernández, 1990) and, with the aid of the HEC-2 Model (U.S.Corps of Engineers, 1990), inundation maps of the valley and Flood hazard tables (Fernández, 1990) were determined (Figure 7).

DISCUSSION

The flood analysis and prediction is an important task in hydrologic engineering for any kind of studies and design of hydraulic works in a river. In mountain rivers with glacier areas, it is possible to find glacier surges which determine the production of ice-dammed lakes (subjected to outbursts) or englacial water reservoirs also subjected to catastrophic discharges. Today with the aid of satellite imagery it is possible to detect the formation of lakes but, as to englacial reservoirs, the method of water balance and analysis of river discharges in relation with historical trends could be important.

The "Maximum Possible Floods" determined with the aid of hydraulic dambreak models in an important analysis to be added to the traditional calculations of "Maximum Probable Floods" for this kind of rivers.

From tables 2 and 3 the historical simulation of the 1934 and 1985 outbursts, it is possible to infer that the mode of dam failure is important in the determination of the characteristics of the flood wave (Fernández, 1991). The physical analysis of the ice-dammed lake is also important in order to define the possible maximum discharge in relation with the lake and ice dam conditions as well as the prediction of location, timing and magnitude of such events.

ACKNOWLEGMENTS

The writers wish to thank Hugo Yañez for the final revision of the English version of the paper.

REFERENCES

"Banco de Datos Hidrometeorológicos de la Región Andina" (1985). Instituto Nacional de Ciencia y Técnica Hídricas-Centro Regional Andino. Mendoza, Argentina.

Cazorzi, F. (1991). "WODITEM-Watershed oriented digital terrain model". University of Padova, Italy.

Corte, A. and Espizua, L. (1981). "Inventario de glaciares de la Cuenca del Río Mendoza". Instituto Argentino de Nivología y Glaciología. Argentina.

Chow, V.T., Editor (1964). "Handbook of Applied Hydrology". pp 16-30, 16-31. Mc Graw Hill.

Estadística Hidrológica hasta 1980. (1981) Agua y Energía Eléctrica de la Nación. Buenos Aires, Argentina.

Fernández, P., Segerer, C. and Caridad, R. (1976). "Estudio Hidrológico de los Ríos de Cuyo - Análisis Regional de Frecuencia y Magnitud de Crecientes". Instituto Nacional de Ciencia y Técnica Hídricas. Argentina.

Fernández, P., Fornero, L., Maza, J., Rollán, R. and Yañez, H. (1985). "Hidrología del Río Mendoza. Simulación Matemática de las Hipótesis de Rotura del Dique Natural Formado por el Glaciar Grande del Nevado del Plomo y del traslado de las Crecientes desde el Glaciar hasta 200m Aguas Abajo de Alvarez Condarco". Instituto Nacional de Ciencia y Técnica Hídricas. Argentina.

Fernández, P., Maza, J. and Vargas Aranibar, A. (1988). "Delimitación de Líneas de Ribera y Zonas de Inundación en el Río Mendoza". Jornadas de Seguridad de Presas y Aspectos de la Defensa Civil en Mendoza. Universidad Nacional de Cuyo. Argentina.

Fernández, P., O.Roby, J.Maza, H.Yañez, A.Vargas Aranibar. (1990). "A Real time system for flood forecasting of an ice dam outburst". International Conference on river flood hydraulics. Wallingford, England. pp 85-91.

Fernández, P., Fornero, L., Maza, J. and Yañez, H. (1991). "Simulation of Flood Waves From the Outburst of a Glacier Dammed Lake". Journal of Hydraulic Engineering Vol.117 $n^{\underline{o}}1$ pp.42-53.

Fread, D.L. (1984). "DAMBRK" The National Weather Service Dam-Break Flood Forecasting Model, National Weather Service, Silver Spring, Maryland.

HEC-2 Water Surface Profiles (1990). U.S. Army Corps of Engineers. Davis, California, USA.

King, W.D.V. (1934). "El aluvión del río Mendoza en enero de 1934". Conferencia ofrecida en el Centro Nacional de Ingeniería. Buenos Aires, Argentina.

King, W.D.V. (1935). "Observaciones Adicionales sobre la Obstrucción en el Valle del río Plomo, recogida en febrero de 1935". Conferencia en el Centro Nacional de Ingeniería. Buenos Aires, Argentina.

Krenke, A.N. and Kotliakov, V.M. (1985). "USSR case study Catastrophic floods". IAHS pub $n^{\underline{o}}$ 149 Wallingford,England, 115-124.

Matson, David H. (1934). "Causas que han motivado el aluvión del río Mendoza y Medidas preventivas". Expedición de abril de 1934. Compañía de Electricidad de los Andes. Mendoza, Argentina.

Prieto, M. (1985). "¿Un Fenómeno Cíclico? ¿Hubo otros Endicamientos en el Río del Plomo?". Diario Los Andes. Mendoza, Argentina.

Razza, L. (1935). "El Glaciar del Nevado del Plomo". Revista Geográfica Americana, Año 3(25). Buenos Aires, Argentina.

Young, G.J. (1985). "Canada case Study": "Catastrophic floods". IAHS Publ. n° 149, Wallingford, England 137-143.

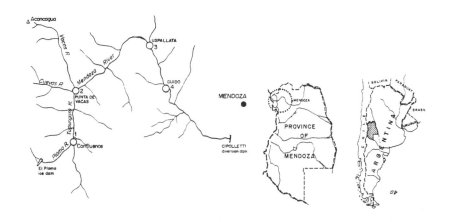

Figure 1 - Mendoza River and Location Maps

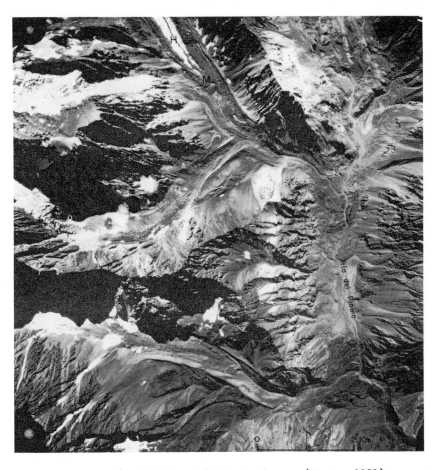

Figure 2 - Río del Plomo Glacierized zone (Corte, 1981)

33

Tupungato River Basin
Snow

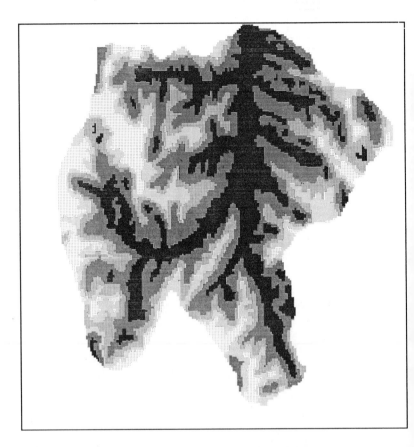

Soil
21/09/81
14/11/81
02/12/81
20/12/81

Figure 3 - Mendoza River upper watershed snow covered zones

Figure 4 - Mendoza River flow
duration curves

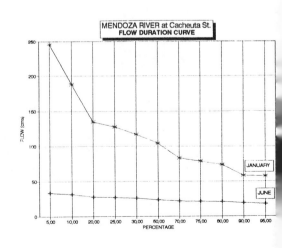

34

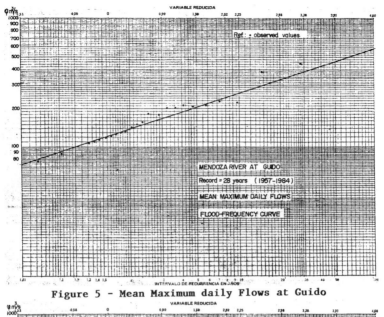

Figure 5 - Mean Maximum daily Flows at Guido

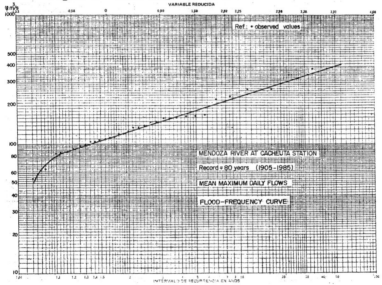

Figure 6 - Mean Maximum daily Flows at Cacheuta

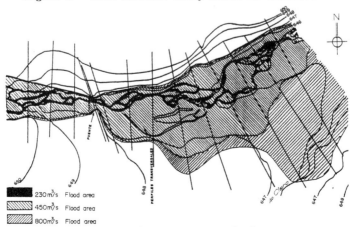

Figure 7 - Mendoza River inundation map

PROPERTIES OF WIDESPREAD, SEVERE FLOODS

W.J.R. Alexander

Department of Civil Engineering, University of Pretoria,

Pretoria 002, South Africa

RECENT WIDESPREAD FLOODS

South Africa experienced four severe, widespread flood events in 1981, 1984, 1987 and 1988, all of which produced the highest floods on record in some catchments. These floods were followed by the most severe nation-wide drought on record which was at its worst during the summer of 1991-92 and continued into 1993 in parts of the country. There is some concern that the floods and the subsequent drought are the result of global climate changes that are introducing larger swings in weather extremes, although the evidence for this is still inconclusive.

The meteorological and hydrological characteristics of these floods are well documented. The loss of life and wide scale damage caused by the floods resulted in a number of investigations, research projects, and a review of the national flood management policy, several of which are still in progress. A summary of some of the results of the studies is presented in this paper.

TOPOGRAPHY AND CLIMATE

The main feature of South Africa is the 1 000 m high interior plateau which is drained by the westward flowing Orange-Vaal river system to the mouth of the Orange River on the Atlantic coast. The rivers on the plateau are separated from the southerly and easterly flowing coastal rivers by the high escarpment which has a maximum elevation of 3 800 m north-west of Durban.

The northern region of the country receives 90% of the annual rainfall in summer compared with 10% in the areas in the south-west. The mean annual rainfall is highest in the eastern and southern escarpments where it exceeds 3 000 mm, and lowest in the arid western regions where it is less than 100 mm. River flow regimes vary from perennial, through seasonal, to episodic. In the arid areas there may be no flow at all for a number of years. The flood producing weather systems also vary over a wide range from tropical cyclones in the north-east, to cut-off low pressure systems east and south of the escarpment, and tropical/temperate wave interaction systems (Botswana Lows) over the interior.

The rainfall patterns produced by three quite different weather systems which occurred in 1981, 1984 and 1988 are shown in Fig. 1. The region affected by the 1987 floods overlapped the 1984 region and is not shown for clarity.

2nd International Conference on River Flood Hydraulics. Edited by W. R. White and J. Watts
© 1994 HR Wallingford Ltd. Published by John Wiley & Sons Ltd

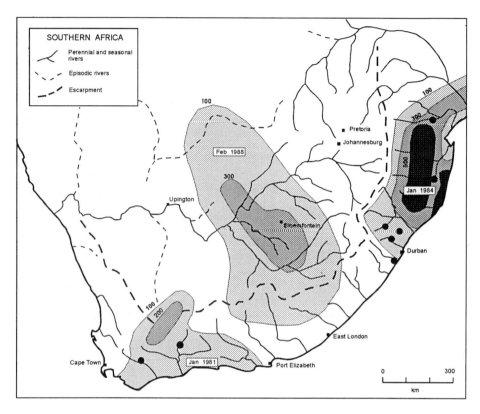

Figure 1. Main river systems and areas affected by recent floods

Some details of the rain produced by these weather systems are given in Table 1. Note the diverse geographic locations of the weather systems in Fig. 1, and the similarity of the rainfall properties of the 1984 and 1987 events in Table 1 despite altogether different weather systems.

Table 1 Rainfall produced by recent severe weather systems				
	Jan 1981	Jan 1984	Sep 1987	Feb 1988
Weather system	Cut-off low	Tropical cyclone	Cut-off low	Botswana low
Point rainfall (mm)				
one-day maximum	230	615	577	167
storm maximum (days)	288 (3)	906 (3)	902 (3)	425 (5)
Areal rainfall (km²)				
area receiving > 200 mm	N/A	94 000	69 000	131 500
area receiving > 500 mm	none	18 500	14 400	310
area receiving > 700 mm	none	1 750	1 600	none

The probability plots of data from eight selected widely dispersed sites with a combined record length of 288 station years are shown in Fig. 2. The locations of the stations are indicated in Fig. 1 above. The flood magnitude-frequency relationships are remarkably similar despite topographical and climatological differences. The anomalous high values are each the result of sound methods of measurement and were supported by other information. The weather systems that caused these high values have been identified in most cases. While it is clear that these values cannot be ignored in statistical analyses, an extrapolation of the flood magnitude - frequency relationships to long return periods gives unrealistic results. Methods for overcoming this difficulty have not yet been developed.

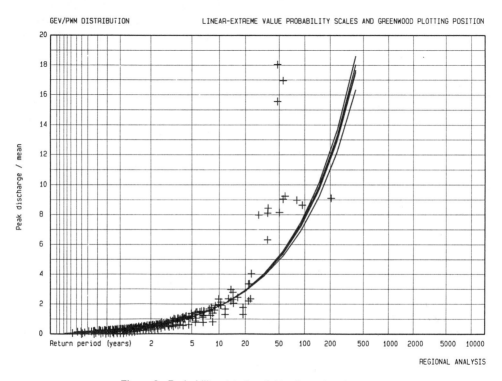

Figure 2. Probability plots for eight selected stations

SEVERE FLOOD PRODUCING WEATHER SYSTEMS

Tropical cyclones

The properties and regions of occurrence of tropical cyclones (called hurricanes and typhoons elsewhere) are well known. Most of those that affect southern Africa are generated in the Indian Ocean east of Madagascar, although some develop in the Mozambique channel between Madagascar and the mainland. They only rarely cross the continental coast. The tropical cyclone Domoina of January, 1984 was an exception and is the only recorded cyclone to penetrate the interior of South Africa and exit again further south.

Of the seventeen cyclones that entered the Mozambique channel during the period 1950 to 1988, ten produced heavy rainfall over parts of South Africa, and only one traversed over the mainland. The meteorological and hydrological aspects of the tropical cyclone Domoina in 1984 are described in Kovacs *et al* 1985.

Reliable numerical prediction models are in operation. The track and development of tropical cyclones can be forecast with sufficient accuracy for flood warning purposes. The efficiency of prediction models was demonstrated in the USA in August, 1992 when the hurricane Andrew caused widespread devastation, and became the costliest natural disaster to have occurred in the USA. Due to early warnings and efficient evacuation procedures the loss of life was minimal.

Cold fronts and cut-off low pressure systems

Cut-off low pressure systems are the major flood producing weather systems in South Africa. An anticyclonic disruption develops when a strong upper ridge advances south-eastwards south of the continent isolating a cold upper pool over the western parts of South Africa. This high advects large amounts of humid maritime air over the southern and eastern seaboard. At the same time a low pressure system develops over the central interior in conjunction with the upper cut-off low. This results in the southward and upward advection of moist tropical air over the inland areas. The presence of all of these factors results in widespread rainfall over the interior (Taljaard, 1985).

The meteorological aspects of the 1981 floods are described by Estie (1981), and the hydrological aspects by Kovacs (1982).

The September, 1987 floods in Natal were another example of severe floods produced by this weather system. Meteorological aspects are described in Triegaardt *et al* (1988) and the hydrological aspects in van Bladeren and Burger (1989). Tennant and van Heerden (1993) demonstrated that the orography of the high Drakensberg escarpment played an important role in the development of the system and the production of high intensity rainfall.

These systems are all associated with large amplitude mid-latitudinal pressure systems. Numerical weather prediction models are able to model these with considerable success for up to five days ahead. These models are improving rapidly and a new generation of regional models will probably be able to provide better prognosis of the area and duration of heavy rainfall. A recent example was the successful prediction of the heavy rainfall which resulted in the September, 1987 floods in Natal four days in advance of its occurrence (Triegaardt *et al* 1988).

Tropical / temperate wave interaction

The February, 1988 floods over the central interior of South Africa were caused by a near stationary hemispheric four-wave pattern in the upper atmosphere which maintained a steady southward advection of moist, tropical air. A stationary zone of heavy rainfall was sustained for four days over a 250 km wide band stretching south-eastwards from Botswana to the south-east coast. This caused severe damage, particularly to internal road and rail communication routes The meteorological aspects are described in Triegaardt *et al* (1991), and the hydrological aspects in du Plessis *et al* (1989).

These systems represent the interaction between tropical and temperate weather systems, but are also dependent on mesoscale cloud systems to initiate and anchor the weather systems in one place. They only develop where surface conditions and tropical air movement over South Africa have been maintained for a long period. Because of the importance of small scale processes, numerical methods have been less successful in predicting the possibility of heavy rainfall. New regional models hold promise for accurate 24-hour prognosis.

OTHER OBSERVATIONS

The number of weather systems that caused widespread rainfall events during the past 34 years are shown in Table 2.

Table 2. The occurrence of widespread rainfall events in the past 34 years.	
Cold fronts	22
Cut-off low pressure systems	29
Botswana low pressure systems	3
Tropical cyclones	8
Total	**61**

The country-wide frequency of these widespread rainfall events is about two events per year, but not all of these events caused serious floods. In any one catchment the frequency is one event in a number of years. The combination of severity and rarity results in the anomalous high outliers in the frequency plots seen in Fig. 2 above.

The following are some general observations based on wider studies of floods in South Africa.

- Floods that cause severe damage are typically the result of storm rainfall covering a much larger area than that of the individual catchments, and durations much longer than the catchment response times.
- These widespread, severe rainfall events typically occur within seasons of above average rainfall, and are often preceded by moderate rainfall over the previous days, weeks, or months.
- There is some evidence of global synchronous occurrence of seasons of extreme floods and droughts.
- There is an apparent non-random grouping of years of above and below average rainfall on a sub-continental scale.

SHORTCOMINGS IN SINGLE SITE ANALYTICAL METHODS

Widespread, severe floods are caused by weather systems that are not annual events in any one catchment, and the magnitudes of the floods caused by these events are often appreciably higher than the next highest values. As can be seen in Fig. 2 above, the resulting floods are not part of the same population as the rest of the annual maxima. This poses analytical problems in the determination of the flood magnitude - frequency relationship.

Direct statistical analyses using the methods and computer programs in Alexander (1990a) show that the mixed population analytical method using the five parameter Wakeby distribution does not solve the problem posed by these high outliers. There is no evidence to suggest that the four parameter two-component extreme value distribution will be successful either. These difficulties may seem to reinforce the views of those who have more faith in rainfall-runoff models than methods based on direct statistical analyses. However, the depth-area-duration-frequency relationship of the rainfall used in the rainfall-runoff models is equally suspect.

South African practice for determining long return period design floods is moving towards empirical envelope methods rather than away from them, despite (or possibly because of !) the increase in knowledge and increase in the lengths of rainfall and river flow records (Kovacs, 1988).

There has been some criticism of these empirical methods as shown in the following comment: *"....... the failure of flood envelope methods to take explicit account of catchment factors (other than AREA) is seen by some as a sign of scientific bankruptcy"* (Beran 1981 in Reed and Field 1992).

Two of the analytical methods that have been in use in South Africa and elsewhere for many decades have a similar form:-

$$Q_{max} = C \, A^x \qquad\qquad\qquad (1)$$

where A is the area of the catchment and C and x are derived empirically, and the well-known rational method:-

$$Q_T = C_T \, I_T \, A \qquad\qquad\qquad (2)$$

The two factors that determine the magnitude of a flood at a site are the size of the catchment and the intensity of the rainfall on the catchment. The intensity is a depth/time relationship where the time component is determined from the length and slope of the main channel. For the calculated catchment response time the rainfall depth is determined from the rainfall depth-area-duration-frequency relationship. Thereafter the effective rainfall is determined by subtracting rainfall losses which are assumed to be due to infiltration, evaporation, pondage and channel storage.

Only the trunks of the major rivers in South Africa have catchment response times greater than two days and catchment areas greater than 20 000 km^2. Weather systems that produce severe, widespread floods have durations that are well in excess of the response times for most catchments. With soil cover approaching saturation and rivers already full, the infiltration and storage losses are minimal and the effective rainfall equals the actual rainfall. In this situation the only remaining variable which controls flood magnitude is the size of the catchment.

Consequently, there are theoretically sound reasons for using the simple relationships in these two equations when estimating long return period floods.

Another variable in the unit hydrograph method is the shape of the unit hydrograph which is assumed to be a characteristic of the catchment being studied. However, hydrograph shape is a function of rainfall duration. As mentioned above the duration of rainfall generated by the severe weather systems is typically much longer than the catchment response times, which results in a larger volume/peak ratio than that used in the design procedures.

Our analyses have shown conclusively that the more complex unit hydrograph method is no better than the simpler rational method, and that both of them are less reliable than direct statistical analysis methods at gauged sites (Alexander 1990b).

MULTIPLE SITE ANALYTICAL METHODS

The probability that widespread damage, loss of life and interruption of communications will be caused by floods generated by a single rainfall event cannot be determined with confidence from statistical analyses of river flows within a region. This is largely because of the uneven geographical distribution of gauging stations, different catchment sizes and different lengths of record. The only alternative is to base the analyses on rainfall records. The rainfall properties of interest are the three variables depth, duration and area. An important additional property is the direction and rate of movement (or stationarity) of the weather system. For example movement is essential for sustaining tropical cyclones (1984 example), whereas stationarity is essential for sustaining rainfall caused by tropical / temperate wave interaction systems (1988 example).

A multivariate extreme value analysis of the large rainfall data set posed insurmountable problems as shown by the difficulties that hydrologists have in developing much simpler bivariate extreme value relationships between flood peaks and flood volumes. This relationship is required for routing the design flood through a reservoir to determine the flood peak attenuation. This should be a simple analytical exercise, but there is very little information in the literature on procedures which involve direct statistical analysis methods. I believe that this is because of the inappropriateness of the annual exceedance probability as a criterion for determining realistic combinations of flood peaks and volumes for a specified design flood.

The analysis based on rainfall data can be made more tractable by ignoring storm movement and using fixed geographical regions and fixed durations. Rainfall depth is the only remaining variable. Two data sets were prepared and analysed. These were four-day rainfalls within fifteen geographic regions, and monthly rainfalls within 93 standard rainfall districts. The essence of the analysis of the first data set was a classification algorithm where five wide area rainfall classes of increasing severity were specified. The criteria used in the two sets of analyses are summarised in Table 4.

Each combination has its advantages and disadvantages. The four-day rainfalls can be directly associated with the causative weather systems but statistical analysis is difficult because the dependent variable is the number of occurrences of each of five classes of rainfall events in each region. The dependent variable in the second set of analyses is monthly rainfall which is amenable to conventional statistical analysis as well as areal and serial correlation studies.

Table 4. Data sets used in widespread rainfall analyses			
Set number	Space resolution	Time resolution	Dependent variable
1	15 regions	4 consecutive days	number of occurrences
2	93 districts	1 calendar month	monthly rainfall

The results of the studies are detailed in Alexander, 1993. They include the preparation of monthly rainfall maps and catalogues for the period 1921 to date which are useful reference material for estimating vulnerability to widespread interruption of road and rail communications, and flood management policy development. The methods were also used for the estimation of the severity of the 1991-92 drought.

The results of the first set of analyses provided answers to many of the questions that we had asked regarding the severity and areas of occurrence of large area, severe rainfall events, and why bridges failed with greater frequency in Natal than in the interior despite the use of the same design standards (Alexander and van Heerden, 1991a).

The correlation analyses using the second data set produced surprising results that will be useful for future applications. In most correlation analyses the full data sets are used as statisticians usually frown on the use of censored or stratified data. The basis for this objection is the assumption that the data are from a single population. We had already demonstrated that this is not so (Fig. 2 above).

The interest was in the likelihood that if severe rain occurred in a specific district in a specific month, severe rain would occur in each of the 92 remaining districts in the same month. The period of record was 840 months. Obviously, if the whole record was used there would be a high degree of correlation because half of the record consisted of winter months when there was little or no rainfall in all of the summer rainfall region. The monthly rainfall depths in each district were converted to the equivalent exceedance probabilities for the specific month and district assuming that the data were LP3/MM distributed. This data set was progressively stratified by increasing the exceedance probability, and selecting those months of the record where the rainfall exceeded this value. The rainfall in all other districts during that particular month was used in a conventional correlation analysis.

The number of data pairs decreased with increased stratification, so care had to be exercised in interpreting the results. At first the correlation decreased with increased stratification, but thereafter it increased to the point that there was a consistent, meaningful correlation between districts in the arid western region of South Africa and the more humid regions to the east. The simple conclusion was that it only rains in the arid regions during periods of widespread rainfall over the rest of the country!

The analyses showed that the degree of regional correlation is a function of rainfall severity. This was analytical confirmation of our observations that severe floods are the consequence of large area, long duration rainfall events, and has important applications in the determination of the risk of large scale interruption of road and rail communication systems (Alexander and van Heerden, 1991b).

44

CONCLUSIONS

The occurrence of four recent, well documented, widespread flood events caused by diverse weather systems in different parts of South Africa, provided valuable information on the deficiencies of analytical methods on the one hand, and a greater understanding of the properties of severe, widespread floods and the weather systems that cause them on the other.

The studies continue, with emphasis on the development of flood warning systems, flood risk analysis, and policy formulation.

REFERENCES

Alexander WJR (1990a) *Flood hydrology for southern Africa.* South African National Committee for Large Dams, Pretoria

Alexander WJR (1990b). Determination of the design flood for dams. *Proceedings of the Symposium on Dam Safety*, South African Institution of Civil Engineers, Pretoria.

Alexander WJR (1993). *Flood risk reduction measures.* Department of Civil Engineering, University of Pretoria

Alexander WJR and van Heerden J (1991a). The destruction of bridges by floods during the past 120 years - what went wrong? *Proceedings of the Annual Transportation Convention*, Pretoria.

Alexander WJR and van Heerden J (1991b). *Determination of the risk of widespread interruption of communications due to floods.* Department of Transport Research Report Nr RDAC 90/16.

du Plessis DB, Burger CE, Dunsmore SJ and Randall LA (1989). *Documentation of the February - March floods in the Orange River basin.* Department of Water Affairs Technical Report TR 142.

Estie KE (1981). The flood disaster of 25 January, 1981 *Weather Bureau Newsletter, February, 1981.*

Kovacs ZP (1982). *Documentation of the January, 1981 floods in the south-western Cape.* Department of Water Affairs Technical report TR 116.

Kovacs ZP (1988) *Regional maximum flood peaks in southern Africa.* Department of Water Affairs Technical Report TR 137.

Kovacs ZP, du Plessis DB, Bracher PR, Dunn P and Mallory GCL (1985). *Documentation of the 1984 Domoina floods.* Department of Water Affairs Technical Report TR122

Reed DW and Field EK (1992). *Reservoir flood estimation: another look.* Institute of Hydrology Report No. 114

Taljaard JJ (1985) *Cut-off lows in the southern African region.* Weather Bureau Technical Paper No 14.

Tennant W and van Heerden J (1993) The influence of orography and local sea surface temperature anomalies in the development of the 1987 Natal floods. Accepted for publication in the *South African Journal of Science.*

Triegaardt DO, Terblanche DE, van Heerden J and Laing MV (1988). *The Natal floods of 1987.* South African Weather Bureau Technical Paper No 19.

Triegaardt DO, van Heerden J and Steyn PC (1991). *Anomalous precipitation and floods during February, 1988.* South African Weather Bureau Technical Publication No 23.

van Bladeren D and Burger CE (1989) *Documentation of the September 1987 Natal floods.* Department of Water Affairs Technical Report TR139.

Chapter Two

Flood Forecasting

2nd International Conference on
RIVER FLOOD HYDRAULICS
22–25 March 1994: York, England

Optimising a Conceptual Catchment Model in Real Time

Cliff Dobson   B.Sc. M.Sc. MIWEM
Richard C Cross B.Sc. M.Sc.

National Rivers Authority - Severn-Trent Region
Solihull, UK

1) Introduction - The Severn-Trent flood forecasting system

Real time flow forecasting, primarily for flood warning, was developed for the Severn and Trent basins in the 1980s (Bailey and Dobson (1981)). Two conceptual hydrological models are employed, one for rainfall runoff modelling of tributary catchments, and a second for flow routing in the larger river network.

Figure 1 shows the combination of rainfall runoff catchment models and flow routing reaches for part of the Trent basin.

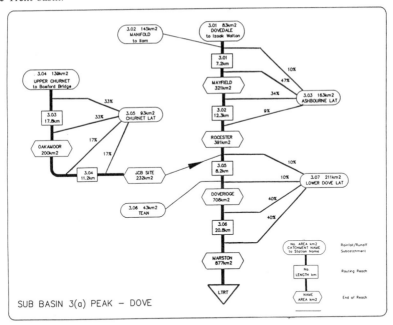

Figure 1   Combination of catchment and reach models

The models are combined together, and errors between observed and simulated flows in both models are analysed as a statistical time series, to refine model performance in the forecast period. The use of error predictors allows the hydrological models to employ a fixed parameter set during model runs, and this allows for rapid, direct mathematical solution.

2nd International Conference on River Flood Hydraulics. Edited by W. R. White and J. Watts
© 1994 HR Wallingford Ltd. Published by John Wiley & Sons Ltd

An example hydrograph from the system is shown on Figure 2. The two traces on the left (hindcast) of the hydrograph represent the **observed** and model **simulated** flows as solid and dotted lines respectively. To the right (forecast) of the hydrograph, the model simulation continues as a **forecast** shown by the dotted line. This is refined by the error prediction model, to give the **expected** trace as the solid line in the forecast period.

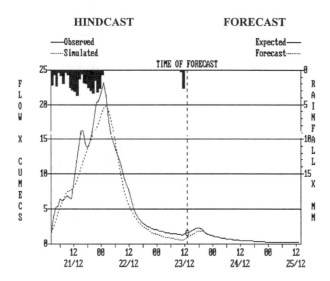

Figure 2   Example hydrograph from the catchment model

The inability of the error prediction model adequately to correct model errors prompted this research, which examined the structure of the rainfall runoff catchment model to find ways to make it more adaptive, without recourse to a fully variable parameter model.

2) Sources of forecasting error

The catchment model is a lumped conceptual rainfall runoff model, originally developed as a general hydrological simulation model (Dickinson & Douglas (1972)). It requires mean catchment rainfall, and meterological data for snowpack modelling as inputs, and the product is hourly flows. The model employs 26 parameters grouped to act individually, or in combination, on the input data via various conceptual storages within the model. Because the model is designed as a general purpose tool, there are several parameters whose value is not critical to successful use of the model for flood forecasting. The most dynamic response in the model is controlled by about 10 parameters, mainly affecting the estimation of rapid runoff from soil surfaces, and the timing and shape of the hydrograph.

The model parameters were calibrated using the Rosenbrock optimisation algorithm to find optimum values for groups of parameters for each of about six historic events (Rosenbrock, 1960). All events' optimum sets were then combined by trial and error to define a set of parameter values to be used in a given catchment for all future events. The defined set was validated on further events, and inevitable fine tuning employed to produce the operational parameters.

Optimising a conceptual catchment model in real time

Because the models were calibrated, and have to be used in a wide range of meterological and ground conditions, in winter and summer, it is not surprising that there is often a degree of error between the observed and simulated river flow. The degree of error cannot easily be predicted, because it is the product of a wide range of factors. Some well calibrated catchments, where the range of hydrological response is small, may have a tolerable error for most events. Less well calibrated catchments, where the response is very dependent on the rainfall or ground conditions may be very much poorer. The problem for the forecaster has always been to recognise and understand the significance of apparent model errors, and to make allowances for them in real time.

Errors in the tributary catchment models are fed on into the river routing models, and there they can significantly reduce the accuracy of an otherwise more dependable model, especially in the early stages of a flood event. Improving the performance of the catchment model will therefore have a beneficial effect in the flow routing models.

Sources of model error can be simplified into three categories:

> **Input data errors**, principally rainfall network or sampling inadequacies, or failure to detect snowfall. These errors are difficult to detect and correct in real time, because each raingauge's data is used in several catchments for computation of areal rainfall. Efforts to minimise these errors concentrate on quality controlling and discarding quality failed data on reception.

> **Model formulation errors**, which exist because lumped conceptual models are a simplification of a complex and variable process.

> **Parameter calibration inadequacy**, caused by poor or limited choice of calibration events, or by the constraint of having to choose a single parameter set to suit all conditions, and which is therefore a compromise.

3) Approach to the problem

The catchment model uses a number of storages to control the simulation of runoff from rainfall. These include an interception store, a snowpack, a single soil store, and a groundwater store, each holding a proportion of the rainfall inputs. These storages are modified dynamically, and increase or decrease their value in response to inputs and outflows. Water is lost to evaporation from the surface storages, and the groundwater store is replenished by excess water from a saturated soil store, and depleted by outflow estimated as baseflow.

The net or effective runoff from the soil store, plus estimated baseflow is lagged, and then routed through two conceptual reservoirs to simulate attenuation by river channels and floodplains, and the outflow from these modifying storages becomes the catchment hydrograph. Figure 3 shows the major storages in the catchment model. Each of these storages is updated hourly, the model timestep.

The content of each of these storages is maintained by the model at all times. The values are a byproduct of the application of the model parameters to the input data. As such these storage **state variables** are a transient link between model inputs, processes and outputs. They therefore reflect all three possible sources of error defined in section 2 above. If the values of the most significant state variables can be adjusted in order to achieve a better match between observed and simulated flows up to the time of the forecast, then much of the error might be addressed in a single operation, irrespective of its source.

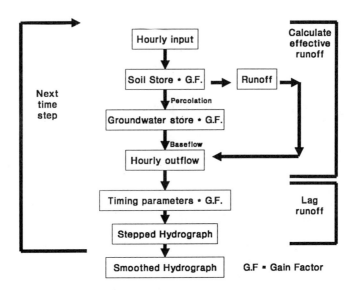

Figure 3   **Principal storages and time lags in the model**

Errors in hydrograph timing and shape are controlled by both parameters and by storages in the channel and floodplain reservoirs. To correct such errors it was decided to allow variation of two model parameters controlling timing, rather than adjust the reservoir storages. This was far simpler, and would be quicker to execute.

Because storages must respect the basic principal of continuity in the models, the mechanism for adjusting the model was to apply **gain factors** to the chosen state variables and timing parameters. The gain factors are optimised within limits, and thus apply a temporary modification to the model's response without either adding to or subtracting from quantities in the storages to which they relate.

Early investigation demonstrated that most errors in the volume of runoff could be related to the soil store and groundwater store. Errors in the interception store were less significant, and snowpack errors are complex, and were considered outside the scope of this pragmatic approach.

Hydrograph timing errors were related to poorly defined lag time, and duration of response parameters in the model.

Four gain factors were therefore designed to be optimised using the same Rosenbrock algorithm employed for model calibration. The advantage of Rosenbrock is it's flexibility and proven value for use with this type of model. By using only four gain factors, the optimisation of each catchment model could be achieved in a single operation, using up to five iteration cycles, for speed of execution.

4) Gain factors for model storages

Soil moisture is represented by an index (SMI) based on the UK Met. Office MORECS soil moisture deficit. SMIs below zero indicate saturated soil conditions. When the soil is considered to be supersaturated, (SMI about -10 mm) a supplementary rapid drainage function enhances runoff rates. SMI controls runoff proportion (ROP) for rainfall inputs using the relationship shown in equation 1. The remaining proportion of the rainfall input which does not form runoff is added to the soil store, so modifying SMI for the next time step in the model calculations.

$$ROP = RC \ e^{(-RE*SMI)} \qquad\qquad Eqn \ 1$$

Where: *ROP = Runoff Proportion*
                 SMI = Soil Moisture Index
                 RC,RE are model parameters

Application of a multiplying gain factor to SMI modifies the estimate of ROP, and therefore alters the behaviour of the soil store, and consequent runoff estimation. Because SMI can be negative, the gain factor is transformed when SMI is below zero, to preserve the desired effect. The transformed gain factor and the modified ROP relationship are shown in equations 2 and 3a and 3b.

$$TGF = (1 - GF) + 1 \qquad\qquad Eqn \ 2$$

Where: *TGF = Transformed gain factor for SMI < 0*
                     GF   = Standard value for gain factor

$$ROP = RC \ e^{(-RE*SMI*GF)} \qquad for \ SMI > 0 \qquad Eqn \ 3a$$

$$ROP = RC \ e^{(-RE*SMI*TGF)} \qquad for \ SMI < 0 \qquad Eqn \ 3b$$

Figure 4 shows the ROP vs. SMI relationship, and the scope for modification of the response by introduction of the gain factor. Practical upper and lower limits for the soil store gain factor are 1.99 and 0.1 respectively. The ROP relationship is such that the modification by the gain factor is most effective in extreme wet or dry catchments, which are the conditions least well calibrated in the models. At zero SMI the gain factor can have no effect.

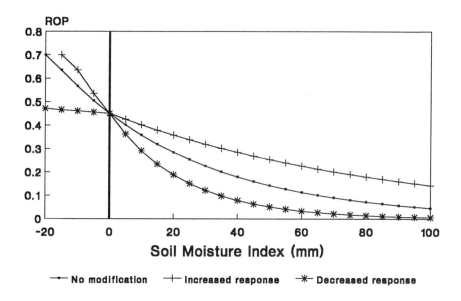

Figure 4   Gain factor applied to the soil store relationship

The second important contributor to runoff is baseflow from the groundwater store. Recharge of the groundwater store occurs when SMI is negative. Outflow as baseflow is controlled by the relationship in equation 4.

$$Baseflow \; = \; BC * GWS^{1.5}$$ *Eqn 4*

Where: GWS = Groundwater storage
             BC is a model parameter

The groundwater gain factor was used to modify the relationship as show in equation 5, and so the assessed outflow can be altered, without affecting the inputs to the store, and at the same time preserving continuity, (see figure 5).

$$Baseflow \; = \; BC * GWS^{1.5} * GF$$ *Eqn 5*

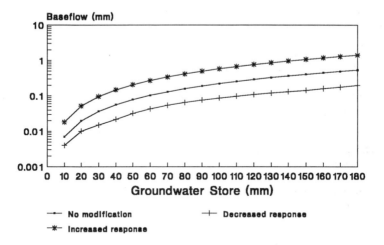

Figure 5   Gain factor applied to groundwater store

5) Gain factors for timing parameters

Hourly runoff volumes are subjected to a lag time, and then apportioned over a number of hours, controlled by the lag time, and duration parameters in the model. Each parameter was multiplied by a separate gain factor, to modify the timing of the hydrograph.

The model calculates runoff and adjusts the timing as described above, for each hourly timestep. This produces a stepped hydrograph of effective runoff. The application of the four gain factors modifies both the magnitude, and the timing of this stepped hydrograph. The hydrograph is smoothed using a cascade of two non-linear reservoirs, for inbank and floodplain flows. These two smoothing reservoirs are controlled by parameters, but gain factors are not considered to be applicable here.

6) Practical use and limitations for gain factors

The four gain factors, each having a neutral value of 1.0, are calibrated by the Rosenbrock algorithm, using a simple sum of squares objective function. When the algorithm is used for parameter calibration the modeller uses the data for the full event. In real time the calibration has to be performed with the data available up to the time the forecast is required. To simulate this feature in the archive event data, an **optimisation window** was defined. Data before and within this window were considered as hindcast data, and the gain factors were calibrated from the data within the time window, with no knowledge of the future flows contained in the data set. This allowed several pseudo-forecasts to be performed, simply by moving the optimisation window forwards through the dataset for each optimisation run.

The limits for the soil store gain factor are conditioned by the form of the ROP function. All other gain factors' limits were chosen to constrain the degree of modification allowed in the optimisation, to avoid inconsistency between successive model runs caused by wildly differing gain factor values. The use of modest ranges also limits the time taken for the Rosenbrock algorithm to achieve convergence.

Several combinations of gain factors, optimised in different orders were evaluated, and a preferred order chosen. Experimentation with different lengths of optimisation window showed that there was little benefit in extending this beyond the latest 24 hours of hindcast data. The shortest optimisation window (6 hours) was too short, and this caused model instability. This may present a practical constraint in very flashy events, where the time to peak is not much more than 6 hours.

The technique ideally requires a complete, unbroken set of observed and simulated flows to allow the gain factors to be calibrated. In real time this cannot be guaranteed, as even the most reliable outstation equipment will fail from time to time. Experiments with events containing missing or unreliable observed flows showed that the technique was tolerant of some data loss, but that the performance was obviously degraded.

7) **Preliminary results**

The preferred order for gain factor optimisation applied to several events, with differing characteristics, demonstrated that practically all of the available improvement from the technique is achieved after 3 Rosenbrock iteration cycles. With an optimisation window of 24 hours (the maximum length), the computation time for the rainfall runoff model with optimisation is not a significant issue.

Data from a winter event, with a peak discharge representing the 1 in 30 year flood, from a Pennine river were tested with varying optimisation window durations. All runs showed a worthwhile improvement in the simulation up to the time of the forecast, and therefore an improved forecast, see figures 6a and 6b. The degree of improvement clearly improves as the peak is approached, but this is to be expected of any modelling system, since the full rainfall input for the event is not available in the earlier forecasts. For these events, where time to peak exceeded 24 hours, the optimisation window of 24 hours proved to be the most successful.

Data from a summer event on the upper reaches of the Trent, below the mean annual flood, were tested with a similar 24 hour optimisation window, see figure 7. In this case the event followed a short convective rainstorm, and the time to peak was significantly less than the optimisation window. This means that the information available to the optimisation within the window is insufficient to allow the required improvements, until after the peak has been passed. Despite this failure, the technique did not degrade the standard simulation, and experiments with shorter optimisation windows are expected to yield more encouraging results.

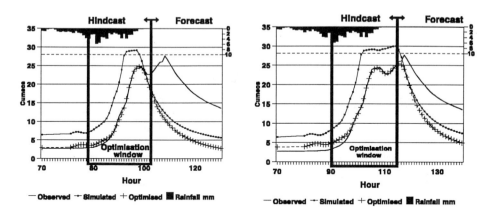

Figure 6 a & b   Winter event performance

Data from an event where the observed data are not reliable were tested. If the optimisation detects unreliable or missing observed data within the optimisation window, the affected hours are excluded from the optimisation calculations, and the remaining data used to provide a degraded service. Figure 8 shows an optimisation where 50% of the observed data are unreliable, from a winter event which exceeded the capacity of the measurement structure. A worthwhile improvement in the model response in the earlier part of the event is possible when the observed data are reliable, but once the observed data are excluded from the calculation, no improvement is seen.

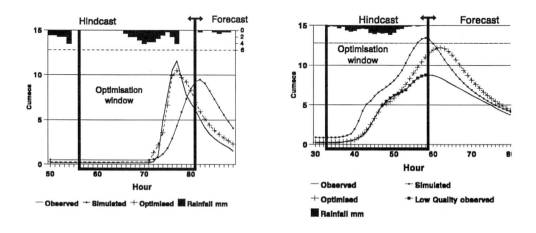

Figures 7 & 8 Summer event and missing data performance

8) Summary and conclusions

This research has identified two storage state variables, and two model parameters in a conceptual rainfall runoff model, which together control a significant part of the response of the model. Application of gain factors to these elements, and automatic optimisation of these gain factors in real time, using the Rosenbrock algorithm, enables worthwhile improvements in model performance up to the time each successive forecast is made.

By improving the matching of the observed and simulated hydrographs up to the time of the forecast, the forecast itself is invariably improved. The degree of improvement is dependant on the type of event. Events with a rapid time to peak are improved only slightly by the optimisation. Events with a slower response, typically winter frontal rainfall in medium to large catchments, are significantly improved by the technique.

The technique is quick to execute, and produces stable results. The optimised values of the gain factors generally follow through from one forecast to another in the same event, indicating that the gain factors are correcting model errors in a broadly consistent manner.

Improvements to the match between observed and simulated data up to the time of the forecast mean that the forecast refinement (error prediction) model has a simpler task to perform, and this normally leads to a further improvement in the refined model forecast. The combination of gain factor optimisation and further refinement by error prediction is complementary. Improvements in the performance of the rainfall runoff model are valuable in themselves, but there is a secondary improvement in the performance of the flow routing models which receive inputs from the rainfall runoff model applied to tributaries. The degree of improvement will be most apparent in upstream river reaches, where the dependence on accurate rainfall runoff modelling in the tributaries is greatest.

Further work is required to evaluate the technique in a true real-time situation, where many events can be tested on many catchments. Work to improve the utility of the technique for rapid response events is particularly needed. Trends in gain factor values in individual catchments may point to the need for review of the raingauge allocation, or model parameters in the catchment.

Acknowledgements

The authors wish to thank Doug Raindow, Regional General Manager, National Rivers Authority, Severn Trent region, for permission to publish this paper. The views expressed in the paper are those of the authors and not necessarily those of the NRA.

References

Bailey, R.A. & Dobson, C.   (1981) **"Forecasting for floods in the Severn catchment",**
J. Inst Water Engrs. Sci. **Vol 35(2),** pp 168-178

Dickinson, W.T & Douglas, J.R   (1972) **"A conceptual runoff model for the Cam catchment"**   Inst. Hydrology report No. 17

Rosenbrock, H.H.   (1960) **"An automatic method of finding the greatest or least value of a function",**
Computer J. , **Vol 3,** pp. 175-184

FLOOD FORECASTING FOR BEIJIANG RIVER
(People's Republic of China)

Authors : M. Gilbert and J. De Meyer, TRACTEBEL, Brussels, BELGIUM

Summary

In 1986, the European Communities entrusted TRACTEBEL Engineering with a support assignment to the Water Resources and Electric Power Bureau at Guangdong (WREPB), in the People's Republic of China, to assist Chinese engineers in the scope of the design and implementation of a flood gauging and forecasting system for the river Beijiang. The project was aimed at installing in the river Beijiang basin a network for the automatic gauging of rainfall and water levels, a telecommunications network and a computer centre at Guangzhu, where the data will be centralised and processed. The system will enable hourly forecasts to be established regarding water levels in the river Beijiang, the knowledge of which becomes essential in periods of extreme floods. The forecasts are based on various simulations that check via which existing flood basins and diversion channels the extreme floods can be controlled. Together with substantial reinforcements to dykes and diversion channels carried out by the WREPB, the flood forecasting system will contribute to preventing or lessening the risks and damage caused by flooding. The support assignment comprised the development of a mathematical model for the simulation of flood propagation in the river BEIJIANG. This paper summarises the development of this model.

### 1.	General description of the modelled river

The Pearl River consists of three tributaries (Beijiang, Dongjiang and Xijiang) with a total catchment area of 452.600 km^2, of which 46.700 km^2 is accounted for by the Beijiang. Fig. 1. shows the Beijiang catchment area, as well as the portion of the Beijiang and tributaries that has been modelled.

The model allows simulation of dyke overflooding and breaching. In total, about 50 nodes are included for the locations where dyke overflooding and breaching are considered. Dyke overflooding is simulated automatically by the model, while the data for breaches such as breach length, bottom level, time when the breaching starts, ... must be entered manually.

The model includes :

1°)	the Beijiang from SHAOGUAN to SANSHUI, with 15 lateral storage areas ;
2°)	the tributary Wengjiang, from CHANHU to the Beijiang ;
	the tributary Liangjiang from GAODAO to the Beijiang ;
	the tributary Binjiang, from ZHUKENG to the Beijiang, with 5 lateral storage areas ;

2nd International Conference on River Flood Hydraulics. Edited by W. R. White and J. Watts
© 1994 HR Wallingford Ltd. Published by John Wiley & Sons Ltd

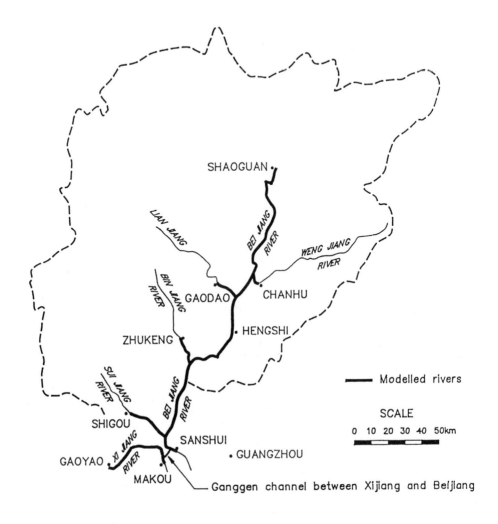

Fig.1.   :   Beijiang catchment area ; modelled portions of Beijiang, tributaries and Xijiang.

the tributary Suijiang, from SHIGOU to the Beijiang, with 7 lateral storage areas ;

3°)   the Xijiang, from GAOYAO to MAKOU ;
4°)   the Ganggen channel, interconnecting the Xijiang and the Beijiang.

Interconnections between lateral storage areas are taken into account. Small tributaries as well as local run-off is simulated by a nodal input point. The total length of the modelled part of the Beijiang, the tributaries and the Xijiang is about 400 km. The average slope of the Beijiang is 0,19 ^{0}/00, the maximal historical discharge is 18.000 m^3/sec.

2.   Modelling principles

The model for the Beijiang and tributaries is based upon the Saint-Venant relations. After examination and interpretation of the available cross sections, the model was based upon a total number of about 250 nodes.

The lateral storage areas are seen as horizontal cells characterised by an area-water level relation, a hydraulic link between cells, and the above-mentioned connections with the river through dyke overflooding or dyke breaching.

Lateral inflow (small tributaries and local run-off) is simulated by nodel discharge points (about 15 in total).

At the upstream limits of the model, discharge versus time is given. At the two downstream limits, a level versus discharge relation is implemented.
These downstream level-discharge relations are not single valued. Discharges may vary up to 5000 m^3/s for the same water level, and levels may vary up to 1 m for a typical discharge. An acceptable simulation of the relationship was based upon a relation of the type Q (H, H^2, dH/dt)

The time step for the calculations is 1 hour as a standard, but it is reduced automatically in case of dyke overflooding or dyke breaching, to meet the dynamical characteristics of these situations.

3.   Overview of the model calibration

The calibration was achieved in 3 steps :
Step 1   :   calibration of the river bed for steady flow conditions
Step 2   :   peak propagation calibration under unsteady flow conditions
Step 3   :   further calibration under unsteady flow conditions.

The step 1 calibration has only a preliminary purpose, namely to obtain best estimate values for the Strickler coefficients in order to proceed afterwards to the calibration under unsteady flow conditions, i.e. steps 2 and 3. Table 1 gives the calibration results for the HENGSHI station, situated in the lower portion of the river.

HENGSHI			
Discharge m^3/s	Target water level m	Steady flow waterlevel m	Difference m
1500	13.60	13.80	- 0.20
3000	15.63	15.60	0.03
4000	16.59	16.56	0.13
5000	17.55	17.43	0.08
6000	18.19	18.24	- 0.05
7000	18.96	18.99	- 0.03
8000	19.60	19.70	- 0.10

Table 1 : Step 1 calibration, HENGSHI station

The preliminary runs for the step 2 calibration indicate that there was a shift for the peak propagation in the upstream part of the BEIJIANG river.
It was recognised that the number of cross sections had to be increased, in order to better take into account local river enlargements. After correction and recalibration of Strickler coefficients, the computed peak propagation matches much better in time with the observations.

The step 3 calibration had to deal with the complex situation of important local lateral inflow, dyke overflooding and dyke breaching, as these phenomena occurred during the important historical floods for which water level data are available.
Local lateral inflow may in certain cases influence the river discharge by up to 30 %, and while dyke breaching and overtopping, in some cases, may influence the river level by 1 to 2 meters. As fully reliable historical data are not available for local lateral inflow, dyke breaching and overtopping, it was decided to study the historical floods through test runs in order to decide upon an acceptable modelling approach (see above), while the final calibration was highly concentrated on the 1982 flood, for which the most accurate, detailed and updated information is available. Fig. 2 and 3 show a typical calibration result for HENGSHI station.

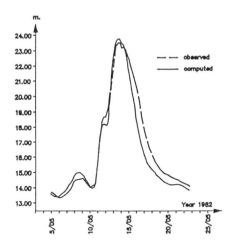 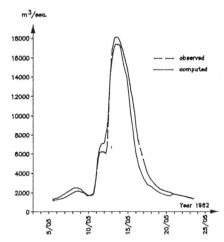

Fig.2. : Flood 1982, HENGSHI station Fig.3. : Flood 1982, HENGSHI station
Step 2 and 3 calibration, waterlevel   Step 2 and 3 calibration, discharge

4.   Conclusion

A mathematical model has been developed to simulate flood propagation through the Beijiang River.
The model comprises the Beijiang River, tributaries and overflooding areas, and allows one to simulate dyke overflooding and dyke breaching.
The model, which is destined to be used as a management model for design purposes, has been integrated in a real time flood forecasting application.
The model accuracy shows that an adequate river simulation has been achieved.

5.   References

(1)   Cunge J A Holly F M and Verwey A, (1980), *Practical aspects of computational river hydraulics,* Pitman, London.
(2)   J. De Meyer, *Gauging and flood forecasting system for the river Beijiang,* People's Republic of China, Tractebel Engineering Information 1990, Brussels.
(3)   J. De Meyer, *Forecasting system for the Beijiang River,* Water March/April 1991, Wel V.Z.W. Antwerp.

AN ADAPTIVE FLOOD WARNING SCHEME FOR THE RIVER NITH AT DUMFRIES

Matthew Lees, Peter Young, Scott Ferguson[*], Keith Beven and John Burns[*]

Centre for Research on Environmental Systems and Statistics (CRES),
Lancaster University,
Lancaster, LA1 4YQ, UK.

Abstract. The paper describes a low cost but advanced automatic flood warning system developed by CRES for the Solway River Purification Board. The River Nith causes regular flooding in the Dumfries town centre, resulting in considerable damage and inconvenience to residents. The system provides a totally automated, five hour ahead, level forecast at the Whitesands site in Dumfries and then automatically informs the authorities if there is any strong likelihood of inundation. The flood warning system exploits a data-based, adaptive forecasting model which is continuously updated on-line during a flood event using a recursive least squares procedure. The five hour ahead, probabilistic, level forecast is achieved by a novel technique incorporating artificial time delays into the model during identification. The PC based system, with attractive graphical user interface has been in operation since 1990 and the forecasting results for all subsequent major events are presented in the paper.

Introduction

During the last decade, many sophisticated real-time flood warning systems utilising improved communications and computing technology, such as the National River Authority (NRA) Yorkshire Region's River Flow Forecasting System (RFFS; see Moore et al, 1990), have been commissioned in the UK. The Solway River Purification Board (SRPB), which has responsibility for flood forecasting in the River Nith catchment, is a much smaller organisation than the Regional NRA and, as such, has limited manpower and financial resources available for advanced computer systems development. In order to satisfy the SRPB's need for a more cost and labour efficient system, therefore, CRES was commissioned in 1990 to design and implement a real-time adaptive flood warning system for the Scottish town of Dumfries.

The design specification for the warning scheme is to provide five hour forecasts of Nith level in Dumfries. These requirements are similar to flood warning systems operated in England and Wales by the NRA with one important exception: the Dumfries system must be fully automatic, since duty officers are only available during normal working hours. Consequently, once initiated by outstation alarms, the system produces a five hour ahead level forecast, decides on necessary action, and issues warnings to police via a speech generator. As duty officers are not available, on-line adjustments to the model are made automatically using a sophisticated but fairly simple adaptive parameter estimation technique which updates the model in real time, so producing improved forecasts.

The Flooding Problem

As shown in Fig.1, the River Nith drains a catchment area of 1275 km^2 and flows into the Solway Firth estuary thought the town of Dumfries, the low lying areas of which suffer from regular flooding. The Nith catchment has two main contributing tributaries: Cluden Water and Scar Water, which drain sub-catchments of 247 km^2 and 157 km^2 respectively. The average annual rainfall for the catchment is 1400 mm (Meteorological Office, Average Annual Rainfall, international standard period 1941-1970), with a large proportion of this total arising from frontal rainfall events. Flooding usually follows a 10 to 12 hour period of

---

[*] Solway River Purification Board

2nd International Conference on River Flood Hydraulics. Edited by W. R. White and J. Watts
© 1994 HR Wallingford Ltd. Published by John Wiley & Sons Ltd

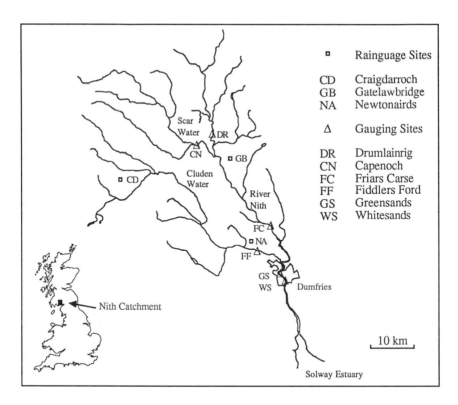

Fig. 1. Map of the Nith Catchment and outstation locations

rainfall in excess of 4 to 5 mm/hour intensity, although flooding can occur from much longer, lower intensity, rainfall events.

The problem of flooding in Dumfries is not trivial, nor is it a recent one. There have been 33 serious floods this century (i.e. peak discharge of over 500 cumecs; Ferguson, 1993), which have caused significant damage though inundation of property in the town. The largest flood this century occurred in January 1962 when peak flow was estimated at 1270 cumecs. The return period, based on a 33 year period from 1958 to 1991, for a serious flood (> 500 cumecs) is 3.5 years and the mean annual flood based on these data has been calculated at 470 cumecs. The problem of flooding may have been exacerbated in more recent years by land drainage improvements and the extensive flood plain protection works carried out in 1946. Extensive embankments were built along the main corridor of the Nith, resulting in a loss of flood plain storage and larger magnitude flood events affecting Dumfries.

The cost of flood damage is not easily quantifiable (Collinge and Kirby, 1987), making cost benefit studies difficult. Reported losses of £280,000 followed a 750 cumec flood in 1977 and consultants Babtie, Shaw & Morton estimated the cost of a 700 cumec flood in 1982 to be in the region of £500,000. In 1984 the responsibility for the provision of flood warning was transferred to the SRPB who considered a number of flood alleviation schemes. These included flood defences, an upstream flood storage basin, a diversion channel to the nearby River Locar, re-development of the flood-prone areas of Dumfries and the implementation of a flood warning scheme. The flood warning system described in this paper was commissioned in 1990 and became fully operational in October 1991 with a total cost, including computer hardware, of £30,000.

Forecast Modelling

The mathematical model which provides the basis of the flood warning system consists of interconnected sub-catchment rainfall-runoff and flood routing transfer function (TF) models (see Young, 1984, 1986, 1992, 1993a,b). The Nith catchment has 9 outstations connected via the telephone network to the SRPB's headquarters in Dumfries. There are 6 river stage recording stations and 3 tipping bucket rain gauges, the positions of which are shown in Fig. 1. The four river gauging sites upstream of Dumfries are long established stilling well installations with reliable stage-discharge rating curves available. Arcon bubbler level gauges are positioned at the Greensands and Whitesands sites in Dumfries and are unrated. The lack of rating curves at the sites in Dumfries restricts the nature of the predictive modelling system, since the model has to deal directly in terms of level rather than flows.

Each sub-catchment flood routing model is described by single input, single output (SISO) transfer function model of the following form,

$$y(k) = \frac{B(z^{-1})}{A(z^{-1})} u(k - \delta) + \xi(k) \tag{1}$$

where $y(k)$ is the downstream level; $u(k - \delta)$ is the upstream level δ sampling intervals (hours) previously; $\xi(k)$ is a general noise term included to account for all stochastic disturbances or unmeasured inputs to the reach; and the polynomials $A(z^{-1})$ and $B(z^{-1})$ are defined as,

$$A(z^{-1}) = 1 + a_1 z^{-1} + \cdots + a_n z^{-n} \qquad B(z^{-1}) = b_0 + b_1 z^{-1} + \cdots + b_m z^{-m} \tag{2}$$

where z^{-i} is the backward shift operator, i.e., $z^{-i} y(k) = y(k - i)$ and $a_1, a_2, \ldots, a_n$; $b_0, b_1, \ldots, b_m$ are the model parameters. Except for the stochastic term, this model is similar to the conventional hydrological lag and route model (e.g. Young, 1986). As we shall see, the presence of the advective time delay in this model (hereafter termed an $[n, m, \delta]$ model) is particularly important in forecasting terms, since it relates the upstream level at time $k - \delta$ to the downstream level at time k, giving a lead time of δ sampling intervals which can be exploited for forecasting purposes.

During model development based on historical level records, prior off-line identification and estimation of the TF model (1) for each reach was carried out using the Simplified Refined Instrumental Variable algorithm (SRIV) algorithm (see refs. in Young and Beven, 1991) in the microCAPTAIN computer program package (Young and Benner, 1991). Here, inputs to the lower catchment TF models are calculated by simple linear addition of the pre-confluence levels, weighted according to the catchment size and gauging channel dimensions. The philosophy of this approach is to maximise the simplicity of the predictive model, while still achieving the required predictive performance. Although multiple input models could have been derived and used, adequate performance was found possible when using this kind of lumped input, single output modelling strategy: in effect, it is a rational simplification which avoids possible problems of collinearity (i.e. multiple correlated inputs, leading to poorly estimated parameters) and increases the potential reliability of the model in practical application.

SRIV identification and estimation produced TF models describing the Nith/Scar confluence to Friars Carse reach and Nith/Cluden confluence to Greensands reach. In both cases, the best identified models were first order with unity time delay (i.e. [1,1,1]), providing an overall forecasting lead time for the whole catchment of only 2 hours. Nominally, forecasts greater than 2 hours require associated forecasts of the input variables (i.e. upstream levels predicted from rainfall inputs), something which is particularly difficult in this area due to the lack of quantitative weather radar coverage. To avoid this, we introduce artificial 5 hour time delays into the model identification, which results in a

67

somewhat reduced level of model fit to the data but significantly improved forecasts at the 5 hour lead time.

With the artificial hour 5 delay present, the inherent recursive nature of the TF model (1) enables the current output data to be used in the production of the next 5 hour forecast. At each forecasting step, past forecasts are updated using the current actual value of the output *not* a previous forecast of output. This updated model output is then used to produce the next forecast. The implementation of the model in this manner prevents the forecast drifting off due to the build up of past forecasting errors. One minor complication of this 5 hour lead time is the need for a three hour forecast of level at the Fiddlers Ford site, which is an input to the lower catchment routing model. However, since there is no river gauging site upstream of Fiddlers Ford, a rainfall-runoff model is required.

Many hydrological methods are available for the modelling of rainfall-runoff, ranging from the simple Unit Hydrograph (UH) techniques to large distributed catchment models such as the Stanford Watershed Model (see e.g. Kraijenhoff and Moll, 1986), the Système Hydrologique Européen (SHE), and the TOPMODEL (Beven and Kirby, 1979). However, a simpler approach, more suited to the present application, is to use an alternative nonlinear transfer function modelling approach.

Rainfall-Runoff Modelling

Although the relationship between measured rainfall and runoff is inherently non-linear due to antecedent soil moisture conditions and seasonal evapotranspiration rates, it is well known that the relationship between effective rainfall (i.e. the rainfall that contributes to runoff) and the resultant runoff is approximately linear, provided the effective rainfall computation is adequate. Thus the combination of an effective rainfall nonlinearity in series with a linear TF model provides a simple approach to modelling the rainfall-runoff processes. Here, we utilise a bilinear model of this type proposed by Young and Beven (1991; see also Young, 1992, 1993a,b), where the effective rainfall, $u(k)$ is defined as the product of the observed rainfall $r(k)$ and the delayed river flow $y(k - \tau)$ where, in this case, $\tau = 0$. The overall relationship between $u(k)$ and $y(k)$ is then given by,

$$u(k) = r(k)y(k - \tau) \tag{3}$$

$$y(k) = \frac{B(z^{-1})}{A(z^{-1})}u(k - \delta) + \xi(k) \tag{4}$$

Where $A(z^{-1})$ and $B(z^{-1})$ are defined by equation (2) and δ is the artificial time delay.

It is, perhaps, instructive to note that the TF model can be related to the simple unit hydrograph method if we note that the infinite dimensional impulse response of equation (4) is the underlying unit hydrograph of the system, as obtained indirectly from the finite dimensional and parametrically much more efficient (parsimonious) TF model parameterisation. Considered in this unit hydrograph context, we see that the result of introducing the artificial time delay into the TF model is that the first δ elements of the impulse unit hydrograph are zero. This unit hydrograph representation could be used on-line to forecast stage level in the normal discrete convolution integral method where the model output $y(k)$ is defined as,

$$y(k) = \sum_{i=0}^{k-1} UH(i)u(i)$$

and $UH(i)$, $i=0,1,...k-1$ are the first k numerically significant ordinates of the unit hydrograph and $u(i)$ is the effective rainfall.

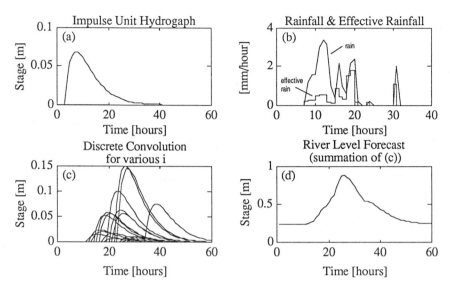

Fig. 2. Discrete convolution implementation of a transfer function rainfall-runoff model

Figure 2 shows an example of the discrete convolution integral method of TF model implementation for a real flood event where the effective rainfall (b) is calculated using the bilinear model with τ =0. This example serves to illustrate the inherent relationship between the TF model and the unit hydrograph approach. In practice, however, the TF model is implemented as a real-time recursive filter based directly on the TF model (4). This has two obvious advantages: (i) it is less computationally demanding; and (ii) actual output data are used to correct past forecasts, which are then used in the calculation of the new forecast.

In the present case, a three hour forecast of the Cluden Water catchment runoff is required as an input to the lower flood routing TF model. This is achieved using a bilinear rainfall-runoff model with an artificial time delay of 3 hours. The rainfall input to this model is a single spatially averaged value calculated using the Craigdarroch and Newtonairds rain gauges. Inspection of historical flood events suggests there is little baseflow contribution to the runoff hydrographs over the period of forecasting interest, caused by the event rainfall. This observation is confirmed by model identification analysis which results in a first order TF model, rather than a second order parallel structure TF model which tends to apply when baseflow effects are important (see Young, 1992, 1993a,b).

Table 1. Rainfall-runoff, 3 hour lead time forecasting results

Date	Peak Error [m]	R.M.S.E. [m]
25/12/90	0.0185	0.0938
01/01/91	0.1433	0.0874
31/10/91	0.0923	0.1129
04/11/91	0.0347	0.1122
12/11/91	0.2782	0.0941
21/12/91	0.0896	0.0739
23/12/91	0.0420	0.0772
09/01/93	0.0964	0.0960
15/01/93	0.0404	0.0598
Mean	0.0928	0.0897

The first order model performs very well in operation as can be seen from Table 1 and Fig. 3 which gives the operational forecasting results of four recent important flood events. Table 1 shows the Peak forecast Error (error between forecast and actual, peak stage) and Root Mean Squared forecast Error (RMSE) for the 3 hour ahead forecast time series of stage at Fiddlers Ford. The mean peak error is only 9 cm with the largest error of 28 cm occurring during the 12/11/91 event. However, this much larger than average over estimation error was, in fact, caused by recorded rainfall falling as snow at levels over 150 metres, and hence not contributing to river flow (Ferguson, 1993). At present, there is no facility to incorporate such snow effects in the system since no telemetered measures of snowfall are available. Also the SRPB specification did not call for such effects to be incorporated in the first version of the warning system, since they do not appear to significantly affect flooding at Dumfries.

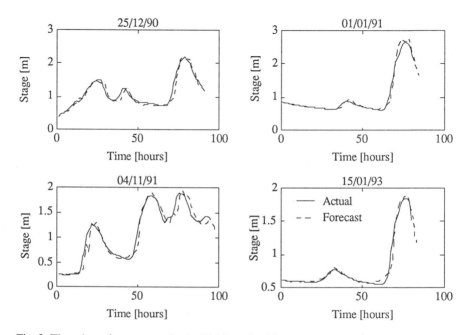

Fig. 3. Three hour forecast results for Fiddlers Ford level

Estimation of the time varying adaptive gain parameter

The model identification and estimation studies based on a wide range of historical flood events revealed a wide range of different models with similar *transient* dynamics but varying steady state gains (SSG; see Young, 1984). These SSG values were also found to vary significantly within flood events as a non-linear function of level, caused by non-rectangular gauging channel sections and bank full flow conditions. In order to allow for these variations in a simple and reliable fashion, we have employed a method of real time parameter adaption based on the following modified form of equation 1,

$$y(k) = g(k)\frac{B(z^{-1})}{A(z^{-1})}u(k - \delta)$$
(5)

where $g(k)$ is a time variable model scaling factor introduced to allow for the variable SSG, while δ is the artificial time delay. This approach has some similarities with the simpler technique suggested by Cluckie (1993) in his work on real time flood forecasting using weather radar.

The adaptive gain $g(k)$ is recursively estimated in real time using a stochastic time variable parameter (TVP) estimation algorithm (e.g. Young, 1984). This on-line estimation technique, which has a similar algorithmic form to *Kalman filtering*, results in an adaptive gain parameter which effectively estimates the changing river system dynamics. If a stochastic random walk model is used to describe the non-stationary in $g(k)$, then the 'prediction-correction' form of the adaptive algorithm is defined as,

Prediction:

$$\hat{g}(k/k-1) = \hat{g}(k-1)$$
$$P(k/k-1) = P(k-1) + Q \tag{6}$$

Correction:

$$\hat{g}(k) = \hat{g}(k/k-1) + \frac{P(k/k-1)x(k)\{y(k) - \hat{g}(k/k-1)x(k)\}}{1 + P(k/k-1)x^2(k)}$$

$$P(k) = P(k/k-1) - \frac{(P(k/k-1)x(k))^2}{1 + P(k/k-1)x^2(k)} \tag{7}$$

in these equations $x(k)$ is the model forecast, $y(k)$ is the actual river level and $\hat{g}(k)$ is the estimate of the adaptive gain parameter $g(k)$. The rate at which the gain parameter value is allowed to change is governed by a parameter termed the Noise Variance Ratio (NVR), which effectively sets the length of an exponentially decaying 'memory' into the past (Young, 1984, 1993a). In this manner, a large NVR results in a short memory which allows the gain to change rapidly if a prediction error has occurred. At first sight, it appears desirable to have a high value of NVR to allow for fast adaption. In practice, however, the gain parameter estimated at time k is applied to the forecast at $k + 5$, which may have a considerably different system gain: for example, the system gain will tend to change at the point of overbank flow.

In the present application, we have found that the best method of setting NVR is to relate the memory of the estimator to the adaptive prediction error: if the adapted forecast error is large, then the NVR is increased proportionally, resulting in rapid correction of the gain error. Analysis of historic flood events for the Nith shows that changing system gains between events are caused by seasonal variations in the catchment characteristics, differing areal rainfall events and changing river dynamics. The adaptive gain approach enables these fairly slow changes in the system gain to be incorporated into the model on-line, resulting in considerably improved model forecasting performance when compared with an equivalent non-adaptive model forecast, as shown in Fig 4.

One additional advantage of the adaptive gain estimation is that large deviations of the gain parameter can be used to alert hydrometric officers to river gauging problems, such as change in gauging site dimensions or, in the case of bubbler gauges, a leakage. For instance, a previously undetected leak in an Arcon bubbler gauge at the Greensands site was discovered in this manner during the early months of the system operation.

Probabilistic Forecasts

One important advantage of using a stochastic approach to modelling used in this paper is the ability to obtain forecasts directly in probabilistic terms and so associate confidence bounds with the mean forecast at every sampling interval. For example, the recursive nature of the algorithm allows us to calculate the five step ahead forecast error using the following expression,

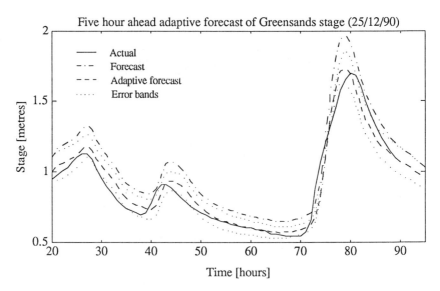

Fig. 4. Adaptive and non-adaptive Greensands level forecasts

$$\text{var}\{\tilde{y}(k+5)\} = \hat{\sigma}^2(k)[1+\hat{y}^2(k+5)p(k+5)]$$
$$\text{sd}(k+5) = \sqrt{\text{var}\{\tilde{y}(k+5)\}} \tag{8}$$

where $\tilde{y}(k+5)$ is the five hour forecast error, i.e.,

$$\tilde{y}(k+5) = \hat{y}(k+5) - y(k+5) \tag{9}$$

and $\hat{\sigma}^2(k)$ is a recursive estimate of the forecast error variance obtained from the following recursion,

$$\hat{\sigma}^2(k) = \hat{\sigma}^2(k-1) + p(k)\{e^2(k) - \hat{\sigma}^2(k-1)\}$$
$$e(k) = \frac{y(k) - \hat{y}(k)}{\sqrt{1 + p(k)\hat{y}^2(k)}} \tag{10}$$

where $e(k)$ is the normalised innovations sequence (recursive residuals) and $p(k)$ is a recursively computed scalar gain (see Young, 1984). Fig 4 shows a specific example of a five hour forecast and its associated upper and lower standard error bounds. These are useful in providing the authorities with some idea of the possible range of levels that might be expected and are helpful in decision making.

System operation and forecasting results

The complete adaptive model described above is incorporated into a flood warning computer package with an advanced Graphical User Interface (GUI), a screendump of which is shown in Fig. 5. This makes the system particularly easy to use by the hydrologists at the SRPB. The operation of the program is initiated by an incoming outstation alarm or by a request from the operator; the nine telemetered outstations are then polled in order to recover the past three days of recorded hourly data. These data are processed for errors and missing samples, prior to the calculation of a five hour forecast of

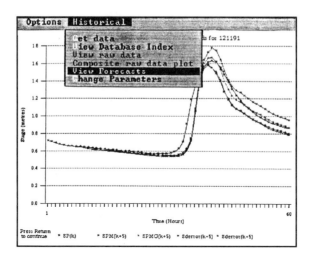

Fig 5. Screendump of the system GUI

level (together with the associated standard errors) at the Whitesands site in Dumfries. The computer package running on a 486 DX Personal Computer (PC) takes less than one second to produce the forecast. A simple expert system then uses this forecast to determine what action is necessary: for example, if there is a strong likelihood of flooding, the police are informed using pre-recorded messages via a speech modem card contained in the PC. The package has been fully operational since October 1991 and has performed well for every significant event since then. Table 2. provides a list of the peak error and RMSE for every significant event since November 1990: it is clear that the adaptive forecasts are superior to the standard (off-line estimated) model forecasts, with a mean peak error of only 6 cm. The two largest events (approximately 450 cumec peak flow) during this period occurred on the 21st of December 1991 and the 15th of January 1993, both causing flooding in the centre of Dumfries. These flood events were forecast to within 5 cm of the actual peak level, with only small timing error, as illustrated in Fig. 6. Note that the adaptive gain parameter, as shown on the plots, updates the model using the available telemetered data, and results in considerably more accurate peak flood forecasts.

Table 2. Operational forecasting results of all significant events since November 1990

Event Date	Peak Level [m]	Timing Error [hr]	Peak Error [m]	Adaptive Peak Error [m]	R.M.S.E [m].	Adaptive R.M.S.E [m]
25/12/90	1.6980	0	0.2721	0.1068	0.1482	0.0766
01/01/91	1.8700	0	0.3156	0.2168	0.1058	0.0845
31/10/91	1.7350	-3*	0.0225	0.0201	0.0967	0.0951
04/11/91	1.2870	2	0.0901	0.0295	0.0979	0.0857
12/11/91	1.6310	1	0.0490	0.0623	0.0954	0.0795
21/12/91	1.9970	0	0.1381	0.0446	0.0567	0.0541
23/12/91	1.7610	1	0.1204	0.0114	0.1479	0.0864
09/01/93	1.7350	1	0.0415	0.0083	0.0696	0.0710
15/01/93	1.9740	1	0.0811	0.0121	0.0690	0.0652
Mean	1.7431		0.1256	0.0569	0.0986	0.0776

*Caused by a shallow peak.

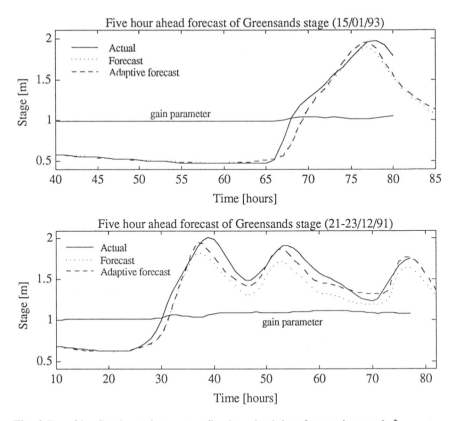

Fig. 6. Dumfries flood warning system five hour lead time forecasting results[*]

Conclusions

This paper has described the design and implementation of a real-time adaptive flood warning system for the Scottish town of Dumfries. This PC based system has been in operation since 1990 and has produced accurate and reliable results since this time. Based on these results, certain enhancements to the system are being considered.

The main source of error in the present system is the rainfall-runoff model which uses a spatially averaged rainfall input calculated from only 2 point sources. The areal distribution of rainfall is highly heterogeneous in the Nith catchment, particularly from convective storms, which could cause significant errors in the present model in certain circumstances (although this has not occurred so far). There are two methods that could be employed in the future to lessen this potential problem: the deployment of more rain gauges; and the use of radar data when this becomes available. Another improvement to the system would be to include the rating of Greensands and Whitesands sites, so enabling flow-flow flood routing as opposed to the stage-stage routing used at present, and so further reducing nonlinearity in the system.

This paper has concentrated on the forecasting the level of the river Nith stage in Dumfries. However, the river at this point is tidal with large tides sometimes contributing to flooding. A rudimentary tidal forecasting model is used at present, based on tide tables produced by the Proudman Oceanographic Laboratory, Bidston; this component of the

---

[*] Error bands omitted for clarity

74

model could be significantly improved by the use of real-time tidal data as an input to a tidal forecasting model, so introducing tidal surge information into the forecast.

Finally, it should be noted that the techniques described in this paper are applicable not only to flood forecasting but to many other hydrological and environmental problems, including solute transport modelling and low flow forecasting. For example, adaptive flow forecasting has been used in the development of a real-time water resource management package for Severn Trent NRA (Young et al, 1993). This Derwent Water Resources Model (DWRM) combines river flow measurements with real-time abstraction/release data supplied by Severn Trent Water PLC to forecast river flow and levels at all important locations in the Derwent catchment down to Derby. Management of the River Derwent is complicated by the industrial operation of weirs, which can impound the river at various points. Once again, an adaptive gain parameter is used to cope with the changing dynamics caused by such operations.

Acknowledgements

The adaptive flood warning system described in this paper was developed by the Centre for Research on Environmental Systems and Statistics at Lancaster in association with the Solway River Purification Board. The authors are most grateful to the Board for commissioning the work and for continuing to supply event data after delivery of the system.

References

Cluckie, D. (1993) Real-Time Flood Forecasting Using Weather Radar. In P. C. Young (ed.) *Concise Encyclopaedia of Environmental Systems*. Pergamon Press: Oxford

Collinge, V. K., and Kirby, C. (1987) *Weather Radar and Flood Forecasting*. John Wiley & Sons, Chichester.

Ferguson, S. (1993) M. Phil. Thesis, CRES: Lancaster University.

Kraijenhoff, D.A. and Moll, J.R. (eds.) (1986) *River Flow Modelling and Forecasting* (Water Science and Technology Library). D. Reidel: Dordrecht.

Moore, R. J., Jones, D. A., Bird, P. B., and Cottingham, M. C. (1990) A basin-wide flood forecasting system for real-time flood warning, river control and water management. In W. R. White (ed.), *International Conference on River Flood Hydraulics*. John Wiley: Chichester.

Young, P. C. (1984) *Recursive Estimation and Time Series Analysis*. Springer-Verlag: Berlin.

Young, P. C. (1986) Time series methods and recursive estimation in hydrological systems analysis. In Kraijenhoff, D.A. and Moll, J.R. (eds.) *River Flow Modelling and Forecasting* (Water Science and Technology Library). D. Reidel: Dordrecht.

Young, P. C. (1992) Parallel processes in hydrology and water quality: a unified time-series approach, *Inst. Water and Environ. Management (IWEM) Jnl.*, **6**, 598-612.

Young, P.C. (1993a) Time variable and state dependent modelling of nonstationary and nonlinear systems. Chapter 26 in T Subba Rao (ed.) *Developments in Time Series*, volume in honour of Maurice Priestley. Chapman and Hall: London.

Young, P.C. (1993b) Systems Models of Rainfall-Flow Processes. In P. C. Young (ed.), *Concise Encyclopaedia of Environmental Systems*. Pergamon Press: Oxford.

Young, P.C. and S. Benner (1990) *microCAPTAIN 2 User Handbook*, CRES: Lancaster University.

Young, P.C. and K.J. Beven (1991) Computation of the Instantaneous Unit Hydrograph and Identifiable Component flows with application to two small catchments - Comment. *Journal of Hydrology*, **129**, 389-396.

Young, P.C., Beven, K.J., Holland, M., Lane, K. and Lees, M.J. (1993) Derwent Water Resources Model, *Technical Report TR/94*. CRES: Lancaster University.

TOWARDS SCENARIO-BASED REAL-TIME FORECASTING FOR FLOOD-AFFECTED BASINS USING A MULTIMODEL INTEGRATED SYSTEM

by

J.A. Cunge, M. Erlich, J.-L. Rahuel
Laboratoire d'Hydraulique de France - LHF
Grenoble-Echirolles, France

Introduction

Real-time flood forecasting based on mathematical modelling has been until recent years deeply influenced by a hydrological approach which focussed all efforts on the methods. Hydrologists naturally are interested in the methods: deterministic, stochastic or statistical methods of transformation of rainfall (and other hydro-meteorological input variables) into surface runoff and river flow discharge. The argument as to which method is best (incidentally leading to a number of "comparison with observed data" exercises which cannot, of course, indicate an official "winner") obscured the fact that the "scientifically best" method does not exist. This is simply because of complexity of catchment topography and physics as well as the purpose of modelling. Distinct models should be used for distinct engineering purposes (design master plan for water resources, design flood protections, encapsulate a model into a real-time flood forecasting-warning system etc.) and as a function of available funding.

Uncertainty of forecast and simulation results is of course studied and, for example, there are many methods allowing for statistical estimation of errors. But the very concept allowing that one method can be intrinsicly better than an other, added to relatively limited informatic means, made it difficult for the engineering approach which consists in giving an engineer the *choice* of the tool as a function of his *engineering judgement* and, incidentally, a possibility to *compare* the solutions furnished by several tools and make his mind us as to the validity of results.

This engineering approach seems to be especially important for real-time forecasting because of the variety of situations which can occur for the same catchment. E.g. seasonal changes can prove wrong the idea of applying over a whole year one particular method of rainfall-runoff transformation. Even for the same season slow floods/flash floods forecasting is another example and possible reason for surprisingly wide differences between various methods

2nd International Conference on River Flood Hydraulics. Edited by W. R. White and J. Watts
© 1994 HR Wallingford Ltd. Published by John Wiley & Sons Ltd

observed during the above-mentioned exercises in "comparisons with observed data".

In what follows the authors describe applications of an information system conceived in order to give a possibility to the forecaster to build various *scenarios of modelling* and *scenarios of forecast* for a basin, and to use the results which they furnish *for the same event*. The basic idea consists of the possibility of dividing a catchment into a number of sub-catchments (cells) and to model each subcatchment in several different ways, these ways being distinct either by methods or, for the same method, by calibration parameters. Then it is possible to build a number of scenarios of flood genesis and propagations, each scenario based on a different combination of models. Simulation of the forecast applied to past events using various scenarios allows for estimate of errors, for assessment of scenarios and situations and, last but not least, for calibration of filters (e.g. Kalman filter) for improvement of real-time forecast. Thus the forecaster, during the flood event, can use several scenarios and compare their forecasts. This scenario-based forecasting is qualitatively different (and, hopefully, more efficient) than previous practice.

Such a concept requires the abandonment of "method patriotism" and also imposes a requirement for a facility for a hydrologist to introduce into the system his own method, which he may think to be the best. This concept is considered by the authors as essential because it allows for a comparison and leads towards the idea of an "open informatics platform" with a *library of methods* integrated into it. Applications of scenario-based real-time forecasting are conditioned by availability of such open information system and in what follows the shaping of the system over the last several years is described before giving examples of applications.

Historical background

Before describing applications of scenario-based forecasting it could be of some interest to follow historical developments of the ideas, systems and applications which culminated in LHF developing **MISTERE** (**M**ultimethod **I**ntegrated **S**ystem for **T**ime **E**volving **R**isks in **E**nvironment).

The general idea of the LHF multimethod-multimodel system goes back to 1983-84 when SOGREAH developed software for the WMO HYDRONIGER Project, a real-time discharge forecasting system for the Niger and Benoué rivers between Kouroussa (Guinea) and the Republic of Niger/Nigeria border (Erlich, 1986; Erlich and Sauvaget, 1986).

The HYDRONIGER software was difficult to adapt for other applications - essentially because of the rapid development of informatics tools. It was based on a new concept in the sense that it is a multimethod integrated system, but hardware and software support became both obsolete very quickly and offered no possibilities for real portability or repetitive use.

The second step, historically speaking, was the Fuchun Project. This project was a cooperation project between the CEC/DG XIII and China. LHF developed for the project management, databases and forecasting software. While working on the project LHF developed multi-method, multi-model software (called Système de Prévisions Hydrologiques/Hydrological Forecasting System - SPH/HFS) allowing for construction and calibration of models and for building scenarios (Cunge et al., 1990; EC-China Cooperation, 1992).

This software was implemented in Hangzhou Flood Forecasting Center and connected to a VHF radio network of real-time data acquisition system and is currently used there (EC-China Cooperation, 1992).

The third stage of progress is linked to another CEC cooperation project with China called Data Transmission System Concept for Decision Suport System for Shanghai. The project, for which LHF is CEC's main contractor, started 1st January 1992 and lasts 4 years (including a last year of test-guarantee operations). It is described below. The Shanghai Project made LHF understand the limitations of the SPH/HFS developed for Fuchun River and the total impossibility to transform it into a complex information system which integrates modern communication networks. Thus, while concepts invented for SPH/HFS were innovative and valid, the architecture of the system was limited to the application of Fuchun type, i.e. forecast of floods. This system could not be applied to the management of basin risks in a large sense, including low discharge problems, water pollution propagation forecast, warning function and other extensions such as communications with civil protection and remote decision centres.

Consequently the "usual" decision was taken: SPH/HFS will not be maintained by LHF except as far as it is required by Fuchun project. A new system, of different architecture has been developed, and all system management software was programmed anew (with the exception of LHF modelling methods), with a view much larger than before and using the latest software and interface generating tools.

Application to Shanghai area DSS

The Shanghai area is located on the banks of Huangpu River, a Yangtze tributary.The city is inhabited by population of 13.5 millions and its industrial output in 1989 was more that 14% of national Chinese production.

The urban area is surrounded by a rural, agricultural fertile province. The elevation of the whole Province, rural areas as well as the city, is low. Shanghai province is similar to the Netherlands and lives under permanent threat of inundation. A disaster can come from two sides (see Fig.1):

- Huangpu floods coming from Taihu Lake area in conjunction with monsoon rains falling on the area are the threat coming from inland direction;
- A conjunction of a typhoon propagating from the sea along Yangtze axis with a high tide is the sea-born storm-surge threat.

The natural situation of risk (there are, on average, two typhoons hitting Shanghai area every year, fortunately of varying strength and not necessarily creating storm surge, plus annual monsoon flood) is aggravated by disastrous exploitation of underground water resources. Starting with the beginning of the century and for 50 years underground water was pumped unrestrictively causing subsidence of the urban area of some 2 metres (the Netherlands situation is combined here with Venice problem!). The average tide amplitude is of the order of 5 metres and, because of subsidence, the ground elevation of the area is lower than the average sea level (viz. Fig 1).

Structural protection of the area attained its engineering limits: the urban area is protected against catastrophic events which can occur with probability of once every thousand years and rural area is dyked against events which can statistically occur once in a hundred years. It is financially unsound to pursue the race between the hazard and the structural defences. Nevertheless the risk of major disaster is still there.

In case of major disaster, but also for every year inundations, there is a need for state-of-the-art management aids. The municipality has to organise flood defence, to evacuate water from the area by pumping (some 60 MW of installed power activating 150 pumping stations) or by complex manoevering of sluices.

From all these problems stemmed the decision that a DSS (Decision Support-System) is needed for the management purposes of Shanghai Municipality. A cooperation project between the CEC/DG XIII and Shanghai Municipality was implemented with the aim to build one, essential part of such DSS. This part would show European capabilities in the area of ICT (Information and Communication

Technologies) put into the service of real life application.

The Project consists of three main parts (see Figs.2 & 3):

1) Telecommunication microwave (frequency of 1.5 GHz) network allowing at each of its 15 nodes for connection of telephone-telefax-telex, and computer terminals for data transmission. The network will be the backbone not only of the future DSS *and* of the management of flood-protection organization, but also of the future water resources management system in the Shanghai area. The network is point-multipoint, Time - Division - Multi - Access (TDMA) system allowing up to 320 subscribers, comprising a PABX at the management centre and connected to the general telephone network.

2) Real-time telemetry system consisting of a number of "clusters" of intelligent outstations measuring and transmitting in real-time observations. Two such clusters are provided by the European side. One is for hydrometeorological purposes and is concerned with rainfall, water levels, wind speed, atmospheric pressures etc. Another is for pumping station management purposes and collects in real-time data concerning the pumping station network. Each "cluster" has its frontal microcomputer PC concentrator and dedicated UHF radio network linking all outstations of the cluster with the front-end micro. The latter is connected to the TDMA network described above.

3) Computerised management centre including network of graphical workstations and, more important, *management software* comprising: user interface, communication software, off-line and real-time simulation software, real-time and historical databases.

The project makes full use of MISTERE software allowing for management of such systems, including communication components and interfaces. Simulation software used for the forecast and off-line studies includes sub-systems for simulation of typhoon trajectories and of 2-D storm-surge propagation (developed by the Chinese side), as well as the usual MISTERE library of methods such as unsteady tidal and flood flow propagation in looped networks of rivers including regulated structures (dams, sluices, weirs, gates) and several methods for hydrological rainfall-runoff transformation. Thus a multimethod-multimodel and scenario-comparison approach is fully preserved.

Real-time forecasting of flow in the large sewer network

This is a straightforward application of MISTERE software which was made possible because of its multimethod-multimodel capabilities. The principle of a cascade of Multiple Input - Single Output models has been applied to the representation of flow in the large sewer network of Seine-Saint Denis district (near Paris, France). Using MISTERE software a simplified approach to the modelling was defined for real-time supervision of the overall sewer network with the aid of typical, ready-to-apply scenarios. The scenarios, which include various strategies of management corresponding to a range of typical referenced rainfall situations, are prepared and tested off-line.

The detailed analysis of average to high intensity rainfall events occurring 2-3 times every year resulted in the preparation of a limited number of scenarios which are characterized by three elements: rainfall intensity, topology of the network (drainage system, nodes, hydraulic structures) and control strategies (opening/closing of gates, management of retention reservoirs etc.).

To simulate off-line the behaviour of the network exposed to the rainfall perturbation the Seine Saint Denis County uses CAREDAS modelling software which accounts for the hydrodynamic unsteady character of the flow in the storm sewer systems. Due to the size of the network, the CAREDAS full De Saint-Venant equations solver cannot be used in the real-time decision making process. Therefore the feasibility study (Cunge et al., 1992a) was oriented towards the identification of transfer functions between different subbasins of the urban catchment.

A northern part of the Seine Saint Denis County sewer network (covering only about 1/3 of the total existing network) was selected for the study. According to the principles of the MISTERE forecasting cell identification, the area was subdivided into a number of topological entities having multiple inputs (rainfall, net rainfall, levels and/or discharges) and a single output (level or discharge). Each cell is in fact a black-box model, which represents the mechanism of the transfer of time dependent information between upstream points and the downstream end of the subbasin. These simplifications eliminates the possibility to take into account a looped network topology. The cascade of forecasting cells which covers the area under study will furnish the information required by the operator at the limited number of locations of the network (particularly upstream of the retention reservoirs). The catchment being the object of the feasibility study has been divided into 11 sub-basins and for each sub-basin a simplified model (or a family of models) were identified. Every input and output point corresponds to the node of the CAREDAS hydrodynamical model and the cascade is represented on the Fig.4.

Lack of complete real-time measured data and the need to study future configurations of the network oriented the sampling strategy towards the approach based on CAREDAS simulations of the flow in the network.Thus hydrodynamical model simulation results of 20 artificial and 5 historical rainfall events were considered as a representative sample of historical data.

As a result the data corresponding to time dependant variables at 60 points (CAREDAS nodes) were extracted, sampled using a constant time step equal to 5 minutes and inserted into the MISTERE Historical Data Base.

Four methods among those implemented in the MISTERE library were used in order to identify the transfer functions:

- Constrained Linear System (CLS), which furnishes the estimates of transfer function parameters (Natale & Todini, 1976);
- Multiple Regression model MULCOR, which allows for an identification of the best (in the statistical sense) linear (or linearized) relation between a dependent variable and a set of independent variables.
- AutoRegressive Integrated Moving Average (ARIMA), the classic method based on the Box and Jenkins (1976) approach of one-dimensional time series.
- RESERVOIR describes the physical behaviour of a retention storage reservoir having a number of inputs and a number of outputs.

For every computation point of the network the sample of 1920 data (corresponding to the 20 rainfall events * 96 time steps per event) was split into 2 samples of 960 observations each and the transfer function calibration was performed separately for the events considered as having low risk (rainfall intensity < 15 mm/h) and those falling to the category of average to high intensity rainfall.

Three different types of transfer functions resulting from the above-mentioned methods have been calibrated:

- the responses of 11 sub-basins calculated as a generalized hydrograph by CLS;
- 19 ARIMA based models for the extrapolation of boundary conditions of each sub-basin (stations being the points of injection of net rainfall);
- 4 multiple regression based models

The validation procedure of simplified models consisted in simulation of the sewer network flow for 5 observed historical rainfall events, which were not used during the calibration phase. The referenced values of discharges and levels in the nodes have been obtained by CAREDAS simulations. Standard quality tests for the forecasting scenarios have been used in order to define the reliable configuration of forecasting cells, which can be applied for real-time operation (Cunge et al., 1992b).

In general for all simulations of forecasts performed in the frame of the study the reaction of the zones MS4-MS10 were considered as satisfactory (see Figs. 4, 5 & 6). The quality of forecasts depends on the quality of the extrapolation of the upstream boundary conditions by ARIMA based models. The latter furnish a reliable forecast for a range of 5 to 10 time steps ahead. For this reason it is planned to replace in the final version of the simulator the ARIMA models by rainfall-runoff models.

The application shows that simplified modelling of sewer network by a cascade of transfer functions can be used as an operational tool in the frame of DSS for reservoir management of an urbanized catchment. MISTERE software makes it possible to identify typical rainfall and rainfall-runoff transformations.

Innovative side of the project and MISTERE system

Technological innovation consists in creating a multi-method, multi-model *integrated* and *active* system for risk management based on the latest ICT developments including a *dedicated communication network*. Here, communication network is defined as a technological jump as compared to traditional passive one-way UHF or VHF hydrological measuring networks. The central management software is an integrated ensemble which manages *actively* the whole system, including communication networks, and permits the decision maker, to that end, the use of various media allowing the management of administrative sub-centres through telephone, fax, telex. It permits as well the forecast and warning dissemination. It allows for active control of hydraulic structures and also for retrieval by outstations the information from real-time and historical databases. The Shanghai application illustrates well these characteristics. On the other hand the system allows for off-line studies leading to the real-time scenario approach as shown for the Seine-St.-Denis example.

Acknowledgments

The authors thank Direction de l'Eau et de l'Assainissement du Departement Seine-St.Denis and CEC/DGXIII, International Cooperation, for permission to refer to studies commissioned to LHF.

References

Box, E.P. and Jenkis E.M. (1976), "Time series analysis, forecasting and control", Holden-Day.

Cunge, J.A., Rahuel, J. L., Todini, E. and Vignoli, R. (1990), "The Hydrological Forecasting System (HFS)", NATO Advanced Res. Workshop on CASS for Watr Resources Res. & Management, September 22-28, Ericeira.

Cunge, J.A., Erlich M., Bassot C.,Delattre J-M. and Auriaux G., (1992a) "Faisabilité de nouveaux outils pour la supervision globale de la conduite dans un réseau d'assainissement", NOVATECH 92, Lyon, 3-5 Novembre 1992, pp. 385-399.(in French).

Cunge, J.A., Erlich M, Negre J-L and Rahuel J-L., (1992b) "Construction and Assessment of Flood Forecasting Scenarios in the Hydrological Forecasting System HFS/SPH″ , in : A.J. Saul (Editor), "Floods & Flood Management", Kluwer Academic Publishers, BHR Group 3rd Intern. Conf. on Floods and Flood Management, Florence, Italy, 24-26 November 1992, pp. 291-312.

EC - China Cooperation (1992), "The Fuchun River Project, A Computer Based Real time System", Synthesis Final report prepared by E. TODINI & PARTNERS for CEC/DGXIII, International Cooperation.

Erlich M. (1986) , "Computerised forecasting system (CFS): a study of hydrological prediction using mixed deterministic-stochastic methods for Niger river basin", in : Tavares and da Silva (Eds): "Systems analysis applied to water and related land resources", Proc. of IFAC Conference, Lisbon (Portugal), 2-4 Oct. 1985, IFAC Series n° 4, Pergamon Press, pp. 7-11.

Erlich M. and Sauvaget P (1986), "Computerised forecasting system", HYDROSOFT'86, Proc. of International Conf. on Hydraulic Engineering Software, Southampton (U.K.), Sept. 9-12, 1986, Springer-Verlag, Computational Mechanics Publ., pp 333-355.

Natale, L. and Todini E. (1976) "A stable estimator for linear models - 1.Theoretical development and Monte Carlo experiments", Water Resources Research, vol.12, n° 4, p.667-671.

Figure 1 : J. CUNGE et al.

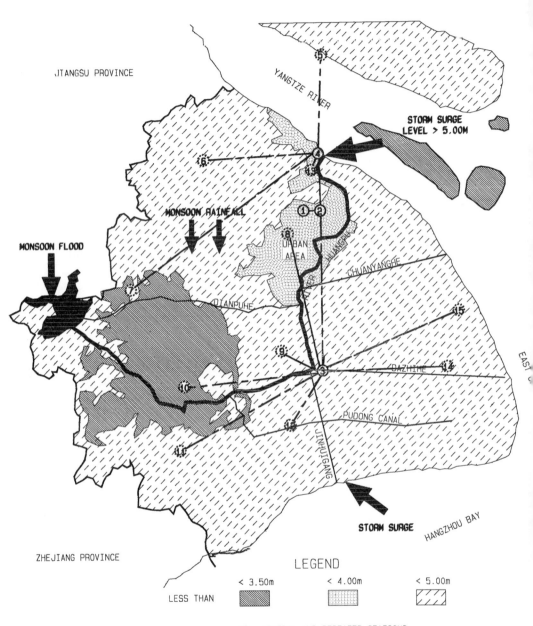

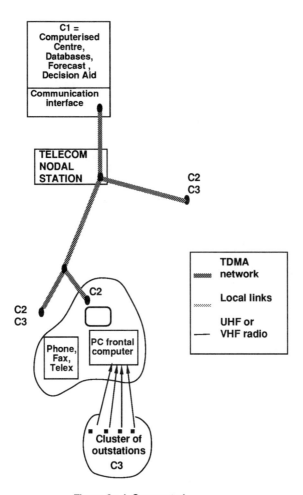

Figure 2 : J. Cunge et al.

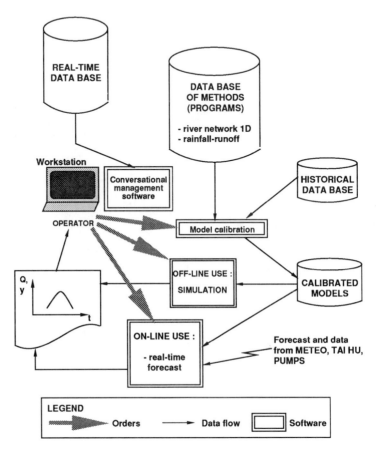

Figure 3 : J. Cunge et al.

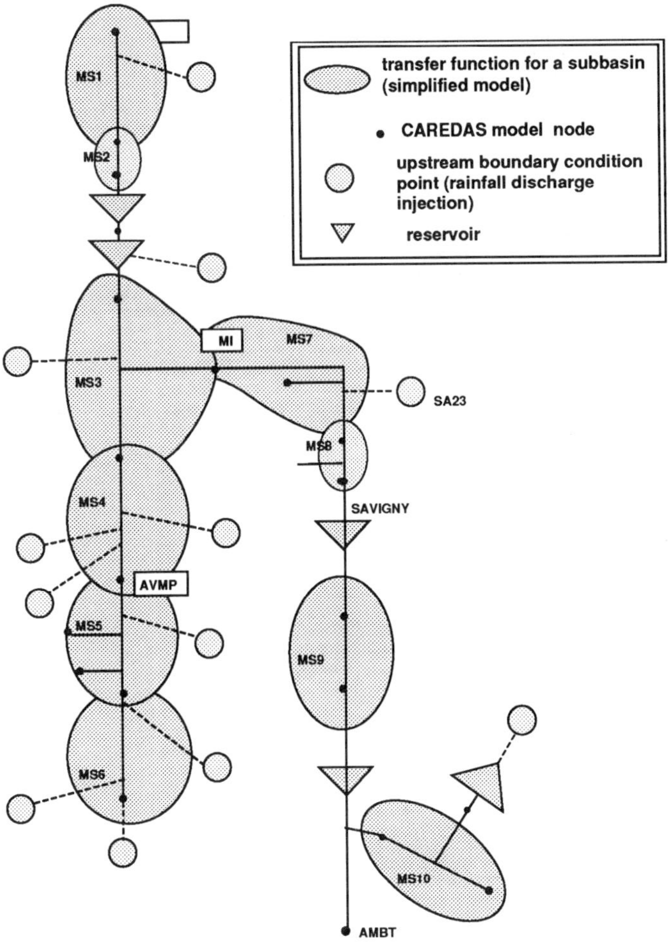
transfer function for a subbasin (simplified model)
CAREDAS model node
upstream boundary condition point (rainfall discharge injection)
reservoir
MS1
MS2
MI
MS7
MS3
SA23
MS8
SAVIGNY
MS4
AVMP
MS5
MS9
MS6
MS10
AMBT

Figure 4 : J. Cunge et al.

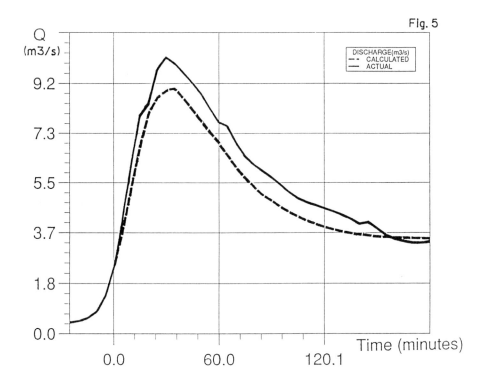

Fig. 5

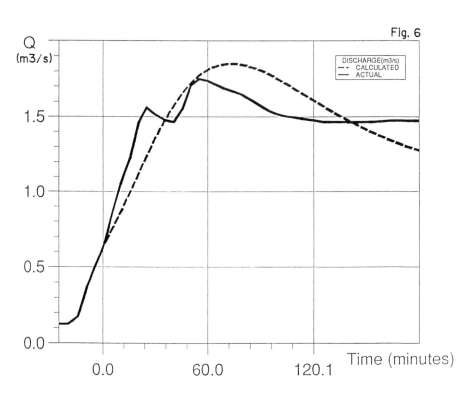

Fig. 6

Fig. 1: Data Transmission System Concept for DSS for Shanghai area: ground altitudes, menace of flooding, microwave TDMA telecommunications network.

Fig. 2: Data Transmission System Concept for DSS for Shanghai: conceptual scheme of data and control communication-transmission network.

Fig. 3: Data Transmission System Concept for DSS for Shanghai: general scheme for central software.

Fig. 4: Seine-St. Denis storm sewer network: topology for simplified modelling.

Fig. 5: Seine-St. Denis storm sewer network: CLS model results with MISTERE software, station **MI**.

Fig. 6: Seine-St. Denis storm sewer network: CLS model results with MISTERE software, station **AVMP**.

Chapter Three

Computational Modelling— Bangladesh

2nd International Conference on
RIVER FLOOD HYDRAULICS
22–25 March 1994: York, England

NORTH WEST REGIONAL STUDY OF BANGLADESH
- EXPERIENCE OF MODEL CALIBRATION

Dr P G Samuels MICE MIWEM FIMA & Dr N Walmsley
HR Wallingford, Howbery Park, WALLINGFORD, OXON OX10 8BA, UK

Summary
The North West Regional Study is part of the Flood Action Plan (FAP) in Bangladesh. In common with all the other regional studies, computational hydraulic modelling was a key component of the project, providing information on river flow conditions, both currently and after the implementation of possible flood control and drainage measures. The model results were used in the agricultural, fisheries, economic and social analyses. In the NW region the modelling covered approximately 2000 km of river channel in a catchment area of about 35000 km². The scale of the model led to some complex problems in the model calibration which could not be solved purely by adjustment of roughness. The paper describes some of the challenges faced in the initial development of the flow models in the NW region, giving examples of how various discrepancies between the simulations and observation were interpreted. During the calibration phase it became clear that there are no generally accepted criteria to determine the quality of calibration of a model. The paper concludes with a discussion of some possible criteria.

1   Introduction
More than three quarters of the land area of Bangladesh is at risk of flooding from rivers or the sea. Signs of adaptation to flood risk are evident in rural areas with villages situated on elevated ground, including road and river embankments, which lies the level of the surrounding fields; in severe floods this is the only dry land available. However, some parts of the rural economy, especially fishing, depend upon the annual monsoonal rise and fall of water level. The extreme floods of August and September 1988 drew international attention to vulnerability of the population to flooding when 57% of the land area was inundated including, in Dhaka, foreign embassies and the Zia international airport. That flooding was caused by the monsoon peaks on the Ganges and Brahmaputra being nearly coincident rather than separated by about a month. Following this event the major international aid agencies decided to promote a coordinated Flood Action Plan (FAP) to identify and implement sustainable development options which mitigate the effects of flooding on the population of Bangladesh. In all the FAP has 26 components including some projects which commenced prior to the launch of the FAP in late 1990. The country was divided into 5 regions and a study leading to a regional development plan was commissioned in each region; the publication from FPCO (1992) describes progress in the first two years of the FAP. The North West Regional Study (NWRS) was amongst the first to start with the study team led by Mott MacDonald International

2nd International Conference on River Flood Hydraulics. Edited by W. R. White and J. Watts
© 1994 HR Wallingford Ltd. Published by John Wiley & Sons Ltd

and Nippon Koei being mobilised in Dhaka during the Gulf War in early 1991.

In the mid 1980s, the Surface Water Modelling Centre (SWMC) was set up with assistance from the Danish Hydraulics Institute (DHI) initially with funding from UNDP and later from DANIDA and is under the ultimate control of the Ministry of Irrigation Water Development and Flood Control in Dhaka. DHI has provided software, training and expatriate staffing at SWMC under these contracts. The SWMC has set up models of the water movement in each region based on the MIKE11 hydrodynamic model and the NAM hydrological model. SWMC employs local engineers to work on each regional model with overall direction and support from the expatriate staff. SWMC started assembling the North West Regional Model (NWRM) as a series of sub-models in early 1990 with a planned work programme lasting over two years before the completion of the verified model of the region. The development of all the regional models followed a programme in which a *pilot model* first is set up using readily available data. For the NWRM this included an earlier model of the southern part of the region which had been constructed with the HR Wallingford LORIS software (Samuels et al, 1991). The pilot models may be somewhat coarse in many areas pending the collection of further topographic and hydrometric data under the direction of the SWMC. Once this information is available the *full model* is established and finally following the successful application to at least two flood seasons data the full model achieves the status of the *verified model*. HR Wallingford provided modelling specialists to the main consultants team and the modellers worked closely with the SWMC throughout the project. This paper describes the calibration of the pilot model of the NW region.

2   The rivers of the NW region and the calibration events

The NWRM includes the major river channels in an area bounded by the River Ganges to the south, the Brahmaputra (Jamuna) to the east, the River Teesta to the north and the international border with India to the west, see Fig 1. The full NWRM comprises several of the sub-models initially prepared by SWMC. The hydrodynamic model assumes that, unless there are specific connections to flood plain cells, the river flow is contained within the river channel described by the cross sections. There is a facility to add extra storage width to any continuity cell without this contributing to the dynamics of the flow. This facility was used at certain sites to represent areas of flood plain storage which are isolated from the main flow paths but which appear to have a freely draining connection to the river channel.

The flows in the rivers in the NW regional model were determined from observations at gauging sites located at the model boundaries and the hydrological model for ungauged inflows. SWMC divided the river basins in the NW region into hydrological sub-catchments and calibrated the pilot hydrological models, the pilot NWRM used these without further adjustment. The hydrological model calibration was achieved through the simulation of flow conditions in four water years. Although good agreement was obtained for the annual hydrographs as a whole, some of the flood peaks were substantially greater than the gauged peaks. This problem was particularly noticeable for the catchments to the north of the lower Atrai and was addressed by SWMC in the later development of the full model of the NW region.

The hydrodynamic model was calibrated against observations made during two water years: April 1987 to March 1988 and April 1990 to September 1990. The 1990 flood season data were more comprehensive than those available for any previous year as the gauging network in the NW region had been enhanced to collect information for the NWRM. The 1990 wet season was of average severity and the river flows were not unduly high. Whilst this data was particularly suitable for calibrating the capacity of the river channels, it provided little information about the behaviour of the river system in severe flood conditions. During 1987 the river flood peaks were much higher than average with a return period of 10 years or more. The substantial flooding of the region in 1987 was caused by the high river flows rather than exceptional backwater from the Brahmaputra such as occurred in the following year.

3   Phases of the calibration

The calibration of the model had three phases:

1   the building of the pilot level sub-models at the SWMC and their *preliminary calibration* as separate units;

2   the amalgamation of the sub-models into a single model of the NW region south of the River Teesta and the *initial calibration* of that model including all the runoff generated by the hydrological model; and

3   a review and modification of the initial calibration in light of the modelling needs of the interim phase of the NW regional study.

The principal difference between the initial calibration of the NWRM and the preliminary calibration of the sub-models by SWMC was that in the preliminary calibration the outflow from the downstream end of one sub-model was not fed in as the inflow to the next sub-model downstream. Instead the gauged flows were used as the inflow to the upstream ends of all the sub-models.

Some of the calibration coefficients of the model were adjusted from the values set during the preliminary calibration on the 1990 data. The preliminary calibration had used a variable roughness with depth of flow in the river channels. The roughness values sometimes showed large variation with depth and it was by no means clear that such variation could be explained on hydraulic grounds and not be the consequence of unrepresentative or erroneous survey. The initial and modified calibration used only a single value of roughness at each section because the depth variation of roughness suggested by the SWMC preliminary calibration for 1990 did not give good results for the 1987 flood.

4   Problems identified during calibration

4.1   Cross border flows

Over 90% of the water which flows into the Bay of Bengal from Bangladesh enters the country through its borders with India and thus cross-border flows are an important issue. Within the NW region the rivers are gauged regularly near the border and these flow records made appropriate boundary conditions. The River Atrai passes out of Bangladesh near Shamjiaghat to re-enter the country 30 km upstream of Mohadevpur; with a 40 km reach of the river being in India. In the sub-models developed at SWMC the two portions of the Atrai in Bangladesh were modelled separately using observed boundary data closest to the international border. For some of the engineering options being investigated this treatment was inappropriate as they influenced the flow in the upper reach of the Atrai. The two portions of the Atrai were joined using estimated dimensions for the river through India; it was not possible to obtain information on this reach. Thus any errors arising from estimation of the inflows or attenuation through the middle Atrai in India accumulated downstream unlike the case for the separate sub-models. This initially degraded the quality of the overall model calibration in the lower Atrai for the 1987 flood. Fig 2 shows the discharge predictions from the initial calibration in which there was no allowance for flood plain storage along the Atrai in India. The peak flow predicted in mid-August was more than twice the observed flow and the hydrograph was too "flashy" in appearance. The calibration was improved by adding a significant volume of flood plain storage to the middle reach of the Atrai, see Fig 3; Fig 4 shows the water levels for the same event which agree well with observations for the flood peak in mid-August. A corollary of this sensitivity of the flow at Mohadevpur to upstream storage is that it shows that, should extensive flood control works be undertaken in India which eliminated flooding for events like the 1987 flood, then the consequences downstream in Bangladesh could be substantial.

4.2   Rating equations

The Bangladesh Water Development Board (BWDB) is responsible for collecting river flow and water level observations throughout the country. BWDB has a regular programme of measurement at key sites including survey of the river cross-section, fortnightly gauging of the flow and daily level measurement (at some sites 3 hourly measurement of level during daylight). Thus there is a substantial body of data for model building and calibration. The gauged discharge measurements are processed into annual average rating curves for each site and these used with the water level measurements to generate daily flow sequences. In some areas of the lower Atrai basin the water levels are dominated by backwater from the Brahmaputra which leads to a non-unique stage-discharge rating curve, (Samuels (1989) estimates the backwater length as about 90 km on the Atrai). In the backwater zone the final calibration of the NWRM was based on the fortnightly measured flows rather than the derived sequence of daily flows since an annual average rating curve will under-estimate flood flows and over-estimate dry season flows.

4.3   Survey and gauge board uncertainties

As is the case with many river engineering studies, the NWRM used data collected over a considerable period of time by many individuals leading to the possibility of human error and natural uncertainty in the data. The successful application of a hydrodynamic model is a good test of the consistency of the data used in its construction and many of the problems identified in the calibration of the NWRM were resolved through correction of the model data set. Typical of these were adjustments made to the recorded water levels to take account of differences in the datum of the staff gauge during the flood. It is common practice for the staff gauges to be moved up and down the river banks as the flood rises and falls since the range of water levels exceeds the length of the gauge and there are insufficient resources to supply several staff gauges at a site. The datum of the gauge must be reset after each movement and any error in the new datum can be identified from comparison with the simulated water level or, if flow is measured at the site, from a plot of the stage-discharge relationship with the date of observation indicated. Further difficulties arose from uncertainties in the relative levels of benchmarks used in topographic survey. A component of the FAP has been established to provide a network of accurate benchmarks over the whole country and modern large scale topographic maps.

Since within the NWRM the river channel was represented by cross-sections every 5 to 10 km, several places were identified where the dry season water level was being controlled by some feature not included within the surveyed sections. This could either be a natural variation in the topography or from the practice of constructing low level bunds across the rivers in the dry season to retain water for agricultural or domestic use. The simulation shown in Fig 4 indicates the effect of this type of uncertainty in the representation of the river channels with a good reproduction of the annual maximum level but a discrepancy of about 1 m in the dry season.

4.4   Inter-catchment transfers

The pilot sub-models were developed using readily available data and for the river system to the north of the lower Atrai the information on the flood plain topography was sparse. Although the combined model gave a reasonable calibration for the moderate 1990 flood, its performance initially for the larger 1987 flood in this area was poor. From an inspection of the hydrographs it was evident that once the river flows exceeded a threshold (approx bankfull) water passed overland from one channel network to another. This was confirmed from flow gauging made during the course of the flood, with flow in one river being limited to a little above bankfull capacity and another river receiving an "unaccounted" inflow between two gauging stations. This type of calibration problem for the hydrodynamic model can easily be resolved by a local reschematisation of the hydraulic network. However, the use of such gauging station records to calibrate a hydrological runoff model must be questionable in extreme flood conditions.

4.5   Spilling from the Brahmaputra

The Brahmaputra forms the eastern boundary of the NW region. The design condition is that the Brahmaputra Right Embankment (BRE) should prevent all spilling into the region from the Brahmaputra. However, the integrity of the BRE cannot be guaranteed since the river is actively eroding its banks and breaches have formed most years on some part of the BRE. Flow through these breaches was evident in the lower reaches of the Karatoya-Bangali river system on the northern bank of the Atrai, where it appeared as an unidentified inflow. The water levels in these rivers were seen to respond to the water level in the Brahmaputra with sustained periods of high flood flows much larger than could derive solely from the catchment upstream. The flow gauging on these rivers were checked to see whether the anomalies were caused by backwater on the rating curves (see 4.2) but these were found to be correct and the flow was found to be associated with a significant change in water surface gradient along these reaches. Breaches in the BRE for the 1990 flood were identified from aerial inspection of the river and for the 1987 flood these were shown by satellite imagery. The flows and levels in the Karatoya-Bangali river system were reproduced successfully by treating breaches in the BRE as weirs diverting flow into abandoned river courses. Fig 5 shows the simulated flows in the lower reach of the Bangali for the 1987 flood and the flow derived from the annual rating curve for the site.

4.6   Flood plain storage

Downstream of Mohadevpur, several polders have been constructed to protect the flood plain of the Atrai. However, in most years one or more breaches have formed in the embankments and the polders have tended to act as flood storage reservoirs. One of the options in the regional planning studies was to examine the rehabilitation of these polders and possibly constructing new polders along most of the remainder of the river course. Thus it was important to include the influence of the flood storage on the existing river system and the polders were represented as isolated storage cells which did not contribute to the conveyance of the flood flows. During the initial calibration, realistic simulation of water levels in the lower Atrai was only possible with the addition of a substantial volume of storage on the floodplains behind the polder embankments. In all cases the flood cells were allowed to communicate with a single river stage point only and there was no interconnection of flow between contiguous flood plain cells. Eleven flood cells were included in the pilot model; those on the left bank of the lower Atrai were open on their northern boundary whereas those on the right bank of the lower Atrai were fully enclosed. The connection of the flood cells to the main river channels was achieved mostly through structure equations representing breaches and cuts in the embankments as weirs. During the calibration, the hydrodynamic model proved to sensitive to the representation and numerical treatment of the flows through the breaches, this is a well known area of difficulty in computational modelling of rivers, see for example, Cunge et al (1980) and Pender (1992).

5   Calibration criteria for river models

Currently there are no objective means of assessing the quality of the calibration of a computational river model, parameters which are important in one application may not be so in another with the calibration being achieved by matching important features of observed hydrographs. Usually the point is reached where adjustments which improve the calibration in one area, result in a worsenment elsewhere. The situation at the end of the 1970's is summed up by Cunge et al (1980) who, when discussing this topic, state (p222) "..no such quantitative criteria can really be objectively applied to all models because each has its own set of particular problems which must be treated subjectively."

However, over the past decade computational models have become much more widespread in their use for the design of flood defence schemes and the decision on which scheme to adopt is based on the changes in the predicted flow conditions and their impact on economic and environmental factors. Obviously, a subjective element must remain in the selection of the calibration parameters but it would be helpful to estimate the range of uncertainty in modelling to be passed through when considering the appropriate freeboard in the design stage and the sensitivity of the cost-benefit ratio to the model results. Ideally, the uncertainties in the model calibration will be sufficiently small so that they do not affect the engineering decisions on the project. Also, there is increasing interest in the validation and benchmarking of standard hydraulic modelling packages (MAFF, 1992). The development of consistent calibration criteria for models against standard datasets will be an important step in achieving objective benchmarking of commercial codes.

Several factors will influence the overall perceived quality of hydrodynamic simulations including:

the accuracy of the hydrological model used;

the accuracy of the flow and level records used for comparison;

the influence of backwater at discharge comparison sites;

the schematisation of the flow network in the model;

the accuracy of the cross section survey for the event being modelled;

the importance of processes excluded from the model; and

the internal accuracy of the hydraulic model calculations.

Obviously a good model which has small errors in the last four categories above may still show up poorly in comparison with the observations because of errors in the first three categories. Hence it is appropriate to separate out the uncertainties in the data, hydrological modelling and the hydrodynamic modelling. One of the best methods for estimating the accuracy of observations is to repeat the measurement but this is not always practical. Repeat river sections can show up errors in survey and the extent of accretion and erosion at the site. Ultimately it is likely that the assessment of the quality of the survey data will remain a subjective opinion of those who have been closely involved in using it. The assessment of the accuracy of hydrological models is more developed than that of hydrodynamic models. Typical measures are the reproduction of the observed volume of runoff in definable events, the peak values of discharge, the number of flood peaks and the flow duration curve. Most of these measures concentrate on runoff volume rather than its timing and are appropriate for the design of flood defence schemes. Obviously this assessment may be qualified by the accuracy of the rainfall, river flow and other data used in the model calibration.

The remaining issue is the assessment of the accuracy of the hydrodynamic model from comparing observed and simulated conditions at gauged sites in the interior of the catchment. The observations should be screened to remove obvious errors such as changes to the benchmarks or movement of gauge boards. The modeller may compare the simulations and observations of flow and level for an event or a long time series by:

checking the conservation of volume;

comparing the range, absolute values and timing of hydrographs;

comparing the curvature and skewness of the hydrographs;

examining flow and level duration or exceedance curves;

examining peaks-over-thresholds statistics for the flood season;

counting maxima, minima and inflexions on the hydrographs; and

examining event (annual) mean flow and water level.

When calculating the standard deviation of the difference between the model and the observations, time shifts of otherwise good predictions will show up as high values of variance. When looking at such measures of fit and their use, criteria should be sought which have a unique root on a match between the observed and simulated conditions. It will be important to assess the sensitivity of the calibration criteria to uncertainties in the calibration parameters. The application of consistent calibration criteria to water level records will prove more challenging than to river discharge since water level is sensitive to the local river geometry and how representative this is of the prototype conditions. Research is underway at HR Wallingford to address these issues.

6   Conclusions

There is a computing cliche - GIGO - garbage in garbage out and during the calibration of a computational model of a new area it is the modellers' task to throw out the garbage.   Much has been written on the merits of different numerical techniques and particular packages but when modelling large complex systems it is the interpretative and diagnostic skills of the modellers that are crucial.   Model calibration involves detective work and requires a good grasp of the fundamentals hydraulics and hydrology and a healthy scepticism about anything which cannot be verified.   The successful calibration of the NWRM required a proper identification of difficulties caused by the discretisation of the hydraulic network, survey data, the hydrological estimates of runoff and the calibration parameters of the main hydrodynamic modelling. The development of objective criteria for model calibration should assist both inexperienced and experienced modellers to determine when adjustment of the model parameters should cease.   Such criteria should also be of benefit to other professionals who use the results of hydraulic modelling to assess the environmental impact or economic viability of a proposed design condition.

7   Acknowledgements

The development of the NW regional model was only possible through the hard work of S I Khoshru and Dr Afzal Hossain on the consultants project team and the staff of SWMC.   The NW regional study was funded by the Overseas Development Administration and the Japanese International Cooperation Agency

8   References

Cunge J A, Holly F M and Verwey A, (1980), *Practical aspects of computational river hydraulics*, Pitman, London.

FPCO (1992), *Bangladesh action plan for flood control - achievements and outlook - an update*, Flood Plan Coordination Organisation, Ministry of Irrigation Water Development and Flood Control, Dhaka, (November 1992)

MAFF (1992), *Report of the research consultative committee*, Ministry of Agriculture Fisheries and Food, London, published by HMSO.

Pender G (1992), *Maintaining numerical stability of flood plain calculations by time increment splitting*, Proc Instn Civ Engrs, Wat Marit & Energy, Vol 96, Mar, pp35-42

Samuels P G (1989), *Backwater lengths in rivers*, Proc Instn Civ Engrs, Pt 2, Vol 87, Dec, pp 571-582.

Samuels P G, Reeve C E & Dent J E, (1991), *River flooding and morphology in Bangladesh*, Int Symp. on Environmental Hydraulics, Hong Kong, 16-18 Dec, Proceedings Ed J W H Lee & Y K Cheung, Published by A A Balkema, Rotterdam, pp 1377-1382.

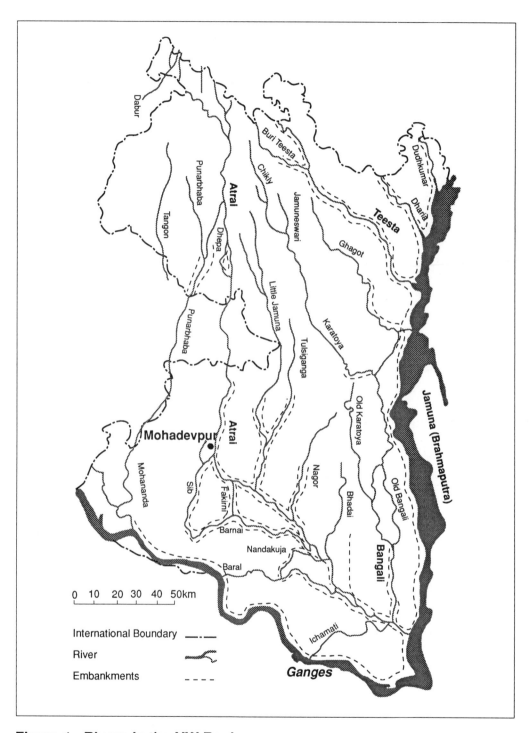

Figure 1   Rivers in the NW Region

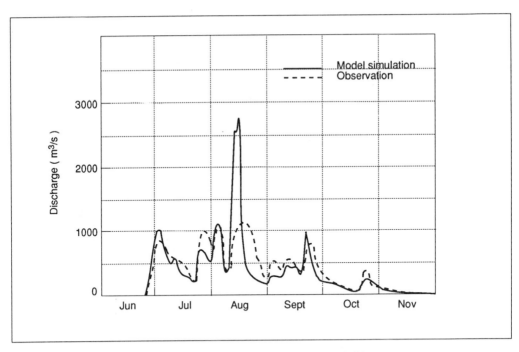

Figure 2   Discharge at Mohadevpur (initial model)

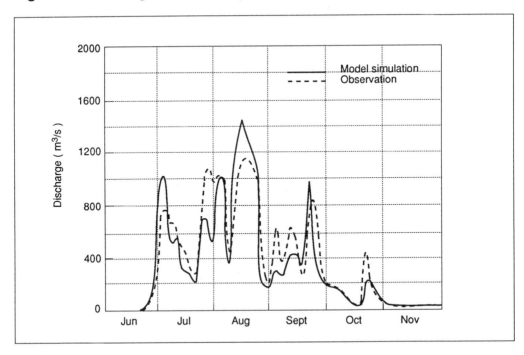

Figure 3   Discharge at Mohadevpur (modified model)

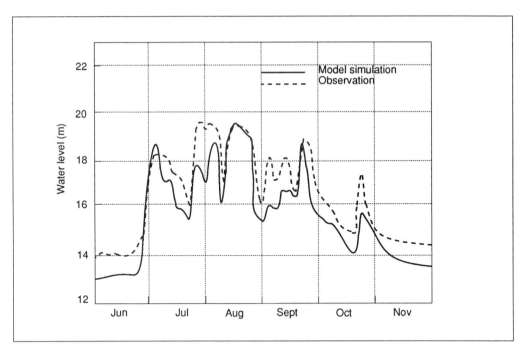

Figure 4   Level at Mohadevpur (modified model)

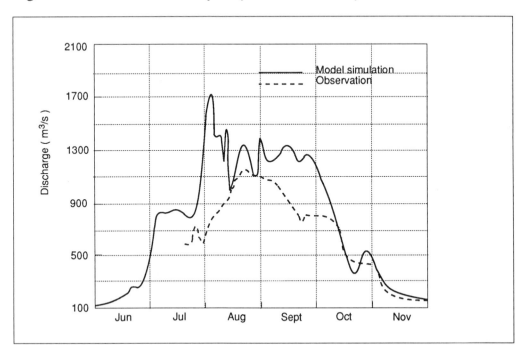

Figure 5   Discharge in Lower Bangali

RIVER FLOOD HYDRAULICS

22–25 March 1994: York, England

Application of computational models in defining flood/depth phases and cropping patterns on floodplains

Dr Charles Reeve
HR Wallingford, Wallingford, Oxon, UK

Dr Nigel Walmsley
HR Wallingford, Wallingford, Oxon, UK

ABSTRACT : Surface water flow models are specifically orientated to provide water level and discharge time series at nodes within the modelled river system. This information is used extensively to assist in the engineering design of flood control measures. When considering flood control measures it is vitally important to be able to assess the impacts away from the main river courses on the floodplains. A suite of post-processing programs were developed to provide additional data and information relating to floodplains. In particular these were to assess the impact flood control measures would have on :

- the timing, duration and depth of floodplain inundation
- the change this may make to future cropping patterns
- the change this would introduce on potential fisheries areas.

This paper describes the methodology of the approach taken and illustrates the application of the techniques by examples from the North West Regional Study in Bangladesh. The techniques developed are a useful tool to provide additional primary and secondary data for experts in disciplines such as agriculture, fisheries, environmental impact assessment, sociology and economics. The analysis is also of considerable benefit to modellers since it serves as an additional verification of the model's ability to predict flooding regimes in areas away from the river system, that is, on the active floodplains.

1 INTRODUCTION

Surface water flow models are specifically orientated to provide water level and discharge time series at nodes within the modelled river system. This information is used extensively to assist in the design of river engineering and flood control measures.

In river basins which experience regular inundation over their floodplains floods impose an important, often dominant, constraint on the development of the floodplains. Flood control measures in these areas relies on achieving a fine balance between engineering based solutions and the impacts these may have on the development of the floodplains, most notably agricultural, together with the dis-benefits which may be introduced through loss of fisheries potential and other possible negative impacts on the environment.

Typical of these types of flooded areas is the Bangladeshi delta. Upto 60% of the country is inundated annually by riverine flooding. These floods not only cause severe hardship to the Bangladeshi population but also restrict the agricultural development of the country, which is trying to remain self-sufficient in rice despite an ever increasing population.

2nd International Conference on River Flood Hydraulics. Edited by W. R. White and J. Watts
© 1994 HR Wallingford Ltd. Published by John Wiley & Sons Ltd

Post-processing of the surface water flow model results can lead to additional data and information related to the floodplains. This can be used to assist in the evaluation and interpretation of non-engineering aspects such as, agricultural potential and changes in cropping patterns, fisheries potential, environmental impacts, and socio-economic evaluations.

The post-processing relies on using the model results together with topographic data relating to the ground elevation. These enable flood depths and durations to be calculated and together with simplified agronomic principles, for example, can be used to predict potential cropping patterns under pre- and post scheme conditions.

2 METHODOLOGY

2.1 Long term simulations

Many flood studies undertaken using computational models use design events (input discharges and tailwater levels) of a specified return period for design purposes. However, in very complex hydraulic regimes where rainfall, upland discharges and tailwater level all play an important role the specification of design events may not be possible.

Where data is available, long time series simulations can provide sufficient information from which to estimate the return period levels and discharges at specified points within the model system, thereby avoiding the need for complex joint probability calculations.

Due to the complexity of the Bangladeshi Delta and the interaction of the various flood causing factors, the definition of design events of a given return period in terms of standardised boundary conditions is impossible. In an attempt to overcome these problems a rationale was used which involved long term simulations of hydraulic models over a period of 25 years. In detail the rationale required,

- the preparation of boundary conditions required to run models for the period 1965-89.

- running the models for the full 25 year period, at least once for the present (baseline) conditions and once for the ultimately adopted scheme(s).

- combinations of various options to reach the final plan may be studies on the basis of simulations for a reduced number of selected seasons, the selections being based on the analysis of the 25 year baseline run.

- sensitivity analysis of ultimately adopted scheme considering changed boundary conditions in the major rivers due to proposed schemes outside the region.

- statistical analysis of the results, aimed at assigning return periods to historic peak, seasonal or sub-seasonal values of selected design variables.

2.2 Topographic data

The primary objective of the post-processing is to predict the depth and duration of flooding over the floodplain. This requires water level predictions from the computational model and also details of the ground elevations.

The floodplain areas are sub-divided into a series of cells in which the flood level is represented by a water level node within the computational model set-up. In each cell, the area/elevation characteristics of the ground elevation are obtained from spot heights from suitable topographic maps. The finer the resolution of the spot heights the greater the accuracy of the area/elevation curve. The water levels together with the area/elevation curves for the floodplains allows the flood depths and durations to be calculated for the floodplain area.

2.3 Flood / depth phases

In Bangladesh, the land is often categorised by reference to its flood phase. The flood phase is a measure of the maximum depth of flooding in a flood of a given return period, say 1:5 year flood event. Whilst this is a useful measure of categorising the land it does not include a time dependent element; the computational model results give a time history of flood levels throughout the flood season. A better measure of the characteristics of a flood event is therefore the 'depth phase' which gives the percentage of land flooded to different depths throughout the flood season. It is the depth phase which is most useful in determining other factors such as potential cropping patterns or fisheries areas.

3 POST-PROCESSING ANALYSIS

3.1 General

The 25 year simulations generate 25 years of daily water levels and discharges at the model nodes. This is a vast amount of information which in its raw form is of limited use, hence there is a need for post-processing. The output required from this post-processing will depend on the use to which it is to be put. The simulation results were used for three forms of analysis; engineering, agriculture and fisheries/environment. Figure 1 is a flow diagram illustrating the procedure used.

The post-processing involved the following analyses to be undertaken for the different disciplines:

Engineering : Hydrological analysis to give minimum, mean and maximum values for each decad. In addition, return period values of stage and water level for 2, 5, 10, 20, 50 and 100 year return periods for different durations (1 day, 3 day, etc.) and on a decad basis.

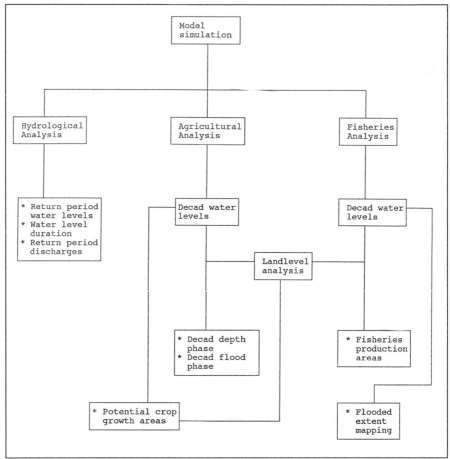

Figure 1 : Post-processing analysis

Agriculture : Decad, ten day, analysis of water levels in terms of four-day exceedances. Depth phase analysis which define depth categories for flooding analysis. Flood phase figures were derived from the depth phase analysis. Cropping analysis was based on agronomic principles of water depth limitations for each stage of growth in a crop's growth cycle. The potential cultivable land for each crop, at any required return period, was derived from the depth phase analysis and these tolerances.

Fisheries/Environment : Decad analysis of water levels based on the minimum water level over the decad and return period analysis of flooded areas throughout a hydrological year.

3.2 Engineering analysis

The engineering analysis is relatively standard and is not discussed in great detail here. The analysis involves the hydrological analysis of water level and discharge time series to give design data for different return periods.

3.3 Agricultural analysis

In each decad (with three decads per calendar month), crop failure occurs on the fourth day on which the level exceeds the critical value. Hence each decad should be represented as the maximum of a running four day minimum level, starting by looking three days backwards into the previous decad.

Following agronomic principles water depth limitations can be defined for each stage of the growth cycle of a crop. This can be done for each crop of interest; Figure 2 illustrates the depth limitations for HYV Aman, Boro and HYV aus.

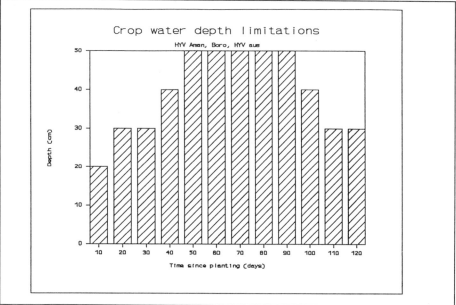

Figure 2 : Crop water depth limitations

Using the decad water levels together with the cropping water depth limitations, the lowest land level on which the crop can grow in each year can be determined. Having determined the lowest land level, the land area associated with that level can be determined by using the land-level database.

From the information on the lowest land level on which each crop can survive in each year water level statistics can be produced and the levels for various return periods established. The cultivable land for each crop at any required return period can be derived from the land-level database.

3.4 Fisheries analysis

For the purposes of the analysis areas which were flooded to a depth greater than 30 cm are potentially suitable for fisheries. The areas flooded to depths greater than 30 cm can be mapped. This can be done for different return period water levels and different decads by considering the representative water level in the model and the variation in topographic level.

3.5 Other analysis

Model results can be used to assess the social impacts of proposed engineering measures. The effect floods will have on infrastructure and dwellings can be estimated from model results. In many countries the most significant risks to public health are those from water-related diseases. The model can be used to predict the extent, depth and duration of flooding; this information can be used in turn to assess the likelihood of disease.

4 CALIBRATION AND VERIFICATION

It is crucial in studies in which long time series are used that the model is suitably calibrated for a large range of events ranging from relatively low flow events to the most severest of floods; as this will be the range that is likely to occur within a representative 25 year period.

A minimum of 3 flood seasons should be used for the calibration of the model with a further 2 or 3 flood seasons for the verification of the models performance.

It must be stressed that the use of the long time series simulations is not to reproduce the historic results but merely to provide a representative series of events on which to base the hydrological analysis. They are a measure of the performance of the hydraulic system under the present conditions and under different developments. In the actual prototype system the topology and topography are likely to be changing with time, as intermediate developments take place, and therefore the response of the system is constantly changing also. The long time series runs are undertaken with a fixed topology and topography and would not therefore reflect these changes.

In general, the most widely available data for calibrating the models is water levels, and discharges, within the modelled river system itself. Little or no data is available relating to flood levels on the floodplains. However, where this data is available it should be used in the calibration and verification of the model.

Other sources of information, non hydraulic, can be used as a verification of a computational models performance. For example, farmers cropping patterns are often dependent on the depth and duration of flooding with different crops being suitable for different hydraulic regimes. By relating model predicted flood depths and durations to potential cropping patterns, the correlation between the model predicted cropping patterns and those obtained from field surveys can serve as a useful further source of verification of the models performance. Indeed, these not only give confidence in the prediction of peak flood levels but also in the rise and fall of the floods throughout the flooding season.

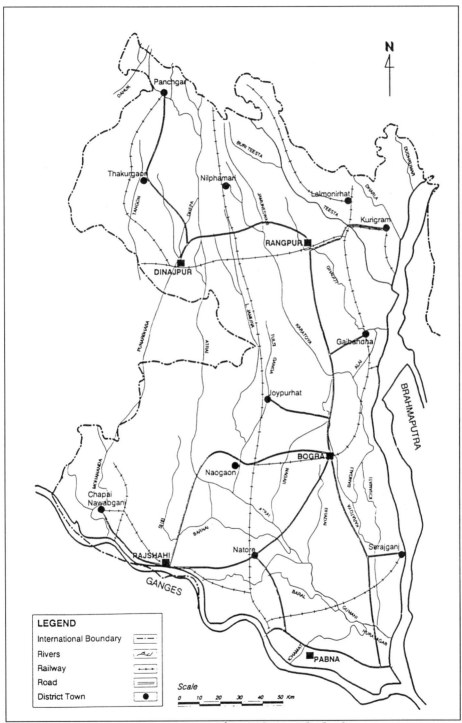

Figure 3 : The North West region of Bangladesh

5 CASE STUDIES FROM THE NORTH WEST REGION OF BANGLADESH

5.1 Flood phase analysis

The North West region of Bangladesh is bounded by the Ganges river to the south, the Brahmaputra river to the east, and the Indian border to the north and west, see Figure 3.

In Bangladesh the flooding situation is commonly classified in flood phases according to depth of flooding as follows:

F0	0 - 0.3 m
F1	0.3 - 0.9 m
F2	0.9 - 1.8 m
F3	1.8 - 3.6 m
F4	> 3.6 m

Construction of an embankment along the right bank of the Brahmaputra (BRE) was started in the 1960's to prevent spilling from the Brahmaputra in to the area. Since its completion, the BRE has suffered continual breaching due to the erosive nature and shifting coarse of the Brahmaputra. These breaches cause damage to crops and homesteads as they result in rapid rises in water levels on the floodplain beyond those which the rice varieties grown in the area can withstand.

In 1991 six main breach sites were in evidence along the BRE. An investigation was undertaken to ascertain the impact of sealing these breaches and the effect this would have on the flood phase categories of the land behind the BRE.

The investigations showed that peak flood levels would be reduced by over 1 m along a majority of the area behind the BRE. In an average flood year (1985) the area of land flooded to a depth of less than 0.9 m, F0 + F1, increased from less than 60% to over 90% if the breaches were sealed, Figure 4. In a much more severe flood year (1988) the effect is still large with the percentage figures changing from less than 20% to over 60%. These results indicated that the sealing of the breaches would effectively remove the constraint that flooding imposes on agricultural development in the area by allowing a much greater area of land to be planted with high yielding varieties of rice. In addition, the losses due to the sudden breaching of the embankment would be reduced and farmers would be able to plant their crops under a much more predictable flooding regime.

5.2 Cropping analysis

Agricultural benefits in the North-West Region mainly come from increasing the area of transplanted rice at the expense of monsoon fallow or broadcast rice. Boro crops can only be substantially increased by additional irrigation facilities and in general the restriction to boro due to flooding is minimal. Thus, from an agricultural viewpoint, the issue is how can the areas of transplanted aman, HYV or local, be increased and how accurately can the post-processing procedures predict this increase.

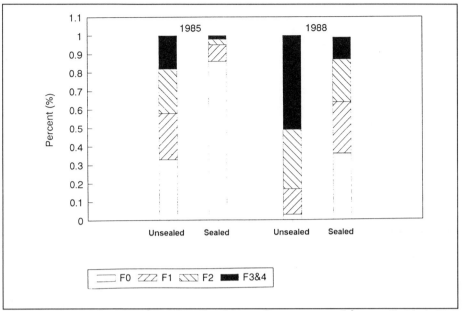

Figure 4 : Change in Flood Phase due to sealing of the BRE breaches

In order to confirm that the procedures developed were applicable to a large range of different areas, calculated cropping patterns were compared with cropping statistics from the Bangladesh Bureau of Statistics (BBS). The project areas were in the Lower Atrai basin of the region, the area which suffers the most severe flooding, and the results of this analysis are shown in Table 1.

Table 1

Comparison of model predicted areas (ha) of HYV and t aman and BBS statistics

Project area	Calculated	BBS	Total
Naogaon	20061	19813	42982
Chalan Beel A	20550	17236	72955
Chalan Beel B	11618	11583	30214
Chalan Beel D	16502	16627	57460
Bogra Polder 2	26940	26692	56395
Total	108303	101079	295568
(%)	(37%)	(34%)	(100%)

Table 1 illustrates a reasonable agreement between the model predicted areas and those presented in the BBS statistics. The results indicate that the post-processing procedures form an acceptable basis of primary, or secondary, data on which to assess the agricultural impacts of different development options.

6 CONCLUSIONS AND RECOMMENDATIONS

The use of computational models can be expanded by linking the model results to further post-processing software thereby allowing useful information to be available for the many disciplines which are involved in water resources planning.

Linking the model results to area/elevation data allows flood depth profiles to be established on the floodplains. Further analysis through the application of cropping rules or fisheries principles enables potential development scenarios to be established. Together with the pre-project conditions, these can be used to establish the differential benefits and dis-benefits associated with a particular development scenario.

Under pre-project, or present, conditions the post-processing analysis serves as an additional verification of the computational models performance and can give greater confidence in the models ability to predict post-project conditions.

The work described in this paper was developed for use in the Flood Action Plan in Bangladesh. The methods employed and cropping rules applied, etc., would benefit by further research in order to refine the methods.

Additional work is also required to investigate the applicability of the methods in other flood prone areas in which the flooding regime forms a major restriction to development in the country.

7 ACKNOWLEDGEMENTS

The work described in this paper was carried out by the authors during assignments in Bangladesh. The authors were part of the teams working on the North-West and South-East regional studies. The collaboration and assistance of the other members of the project teams is gratefully acknowledged. The projects were funded by the UK Overseas Development Administration and the World Bank.

2nd International Conference on
RIVER FLOOD HYDRAULICS
22–25 March 1994: York, England

AN APPLICATION OF 2-D MATHEMATICAL MODELLING
ON THE BRAHMAPUTRA RIVER

H.G. Enggrob, Hydraulic Engineer
Danish Hydraulic Institute

P.H. von Lany, Principal Engineer
Sir William Halcrow & Partners Ltd.

1.   INTRODUCTION

The River Brahmaputra is one of the largest braided rivers
in the world. The last lower 240 km of its course runs
through Bangladesh where it is called the Brahmaputra-
Jamuna. It then joins the River Ganges to become the river
Padma, see Figure 1.1, which is then joined by the river
Meghna before flowing into the Bay of Bengal. The geomorphological characteristics of the river have been well described in papers by Coleman (1969), Bristow (1988), Ullah
(1989), Goswami (1985), Klaassen and Vermeer (1988). These
publicatiuons are supplemented by a contemporary description by Thorne et al (1993). Little has however been published to date on mathematical modelling of the Brahmaputra-Jamuna.

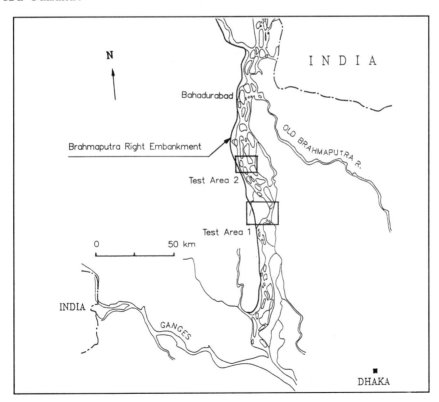

Figure 1.1   The Brahmaputra-Jamuna River system in Bangladesh

2nd International Conference on River Flood Hydraulics. Edited by W. R. White and J. Watts
© 1994 HR Wallingford Ltd. Published by John Wiley & Sons Ltd

The principal characteristics of the Brahmaputra-Jamuna are summarised below. Peak monsoon flows down the river can exceed 100,000 m³/s at Bahadurabad (with a return period of 100 years or more) whilst during the dry season flows can drop as low as 3,000 m³/s. Bankfull discharge is about 40,000 m³/s and the river carries a total annual sediment load of the order of 400 million tonnes (Halcrow/DHI/EPC/-DIG,1993). The width of the braid belt of the Jamuna varies between 4 and 15 km with a variable braiding intensity. The channel is anastomosed in places (Bristow, 1988) where meta-stable *chars* or islands (with a life span of over 20 years) have formed. Elsewhere the *chars* are transient, sometimes appearing or disappearing during the course of a single flood season. Near-bank flow velocities can exceed 3 m/s and scour depths in excess of 25 m below bank top level are not uncommon. Bank erosion can be aggressive; lateral erosion rates of 800 m per year have been recorded, and an average erosion rate of 50 to 100 m per year can be sustained over several years.

This paper describes an application of a two-dimensional (2-D) curvilinear mathematical modelling system on the Brahmaputra-Jamuna in Bangladesh. This was one of a set of mathematical models set-up during the course of the Brahmaputra River Training (BRT) Studies. The BRT Studies commenced in 1990 and were completed in 1993 forming one of the constituent projects of the Flood Action Plan for Bangladesh. One of the principal objectives of the BRT Studies was to devise a long term master plan for the protection of the Brahmaputra Right (flood) Embankment (BRE) which, despite succesive retirements since its construction in the 1960's, still suffers frequent failures from progressive river bank erosion along reaches of the river.

1.1 Modelling Strategy

The strategy devised for the BRT Studies , illustrated in Figure 1.2, was based on the interactive use of mathematical and physical modelling integrated with specialist studies covering the geomorphology, sedimentology, and hydrology of the Brahmaputra-Jamuna and its flood plain.

The roles of the various modelling techniques within the overall strategy of the study are as follows (Halcrow/ DHI/EPC/DIG,1993).

a)   A one dimensional (1-D) hydrodynamic model of the Bra-
     hmaputra-Jamuna from the border with India to down-
     stream its confluence with the Ganges was used to
     establish design levels for flood embankments under
     various schemes to confine flood discharges to within
     the braid belt of the river. A 1-D sediment transport

model of the same length of river was used to determine its overall sediment transport characteristics and to establish general trends in bed aggradation/degradation following implementation of prospective flood alleviation schemes.

b) A series of 2-D hydrodynamic sediment transport models were set up to represent areas of interest within the channel network of the river in order to:

  - improve the understanding of the behaviour of the river,

  - determine parameters for the design of river training and bank protection works, particularly with respect to scour depths and near-bank flow velocities,

  - establish the sensitivity of the above results to variations in the hydrodynamic and sediment transport processes, as well as the time scales over which such variations can occur,

  - indicate some of the hydrodynamic effects of engineering schemes at specific sites along the river.

c) A series of physical model tests of particular river bank geometries and river training layouts on basis of information on the likely performance of bank revetment and river training works under various flow conditions such as flow velocity and angle of attack (Halcrow/DHI/EPC/DIG, 1993).

The modelling programme was designed to interface with the geomorphological studies, in particular. These are described in Thorne et al (1993) and were directed at providing an understanding of the processes involved in river bank erosion, bank line changes, and *char* evolution.

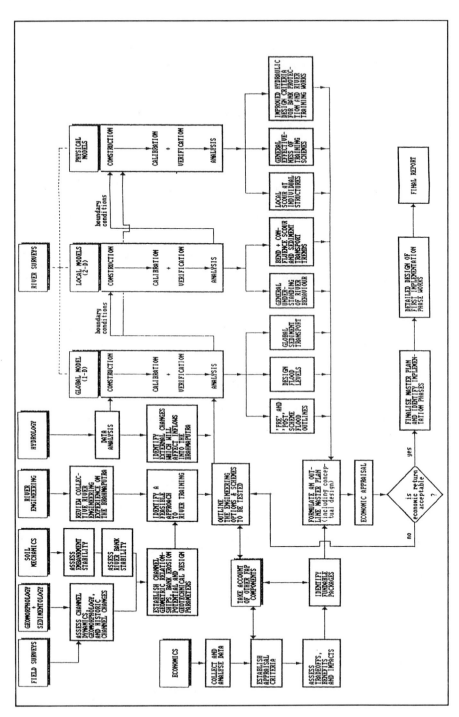

Figure 1.2   Illustration of Overall Approach to the BRTS Master Plan

2.   MODEL SET-UP

The 2-D models were set-up using the curvilinear grid version of System 21, a general purpose suite of models for simulating the hydrodynamics of flow and sediment transport in vertically homogeneous flow. System 21 has been developed by the Danish Hydraulic Institute and comprises computational modules to describe:

-       flow hydrodynamics, i.e. the simulation of water levels and flows over a curvilinear or rectangular computational grid covering the area of interest by solving vertically integrated (de St Venant) equations of continuity and conservation of momentum

-       the hydraulic resistance due to bed material and bedforms using a model developed by Fredsøe (1979) for the dynamic development of bed form size combined with a calculation of skin friction due to shear at the bed

-       sediment transport, based on the Engelund and Fredsøe transport model (1976) and the van Rijn (1984) model; the effect of helical flow (secondary current) in places with curving stream lines and the effect of gravity on a sloping river bed is taken into account

-       the large-scale movement of bed material due to scour or deposition resulting in changes to the bed topography; this is obtained by integrating the net inflow of bed material to or outflow of material from each grid cell; the time and space lag of the suspended load is included by using an advection-dispersion model.

The modules can be run interactively, incorporating feedback from variations in the hydraulic resistance and bed topography to the flow hydrodynamics and the calculation of sediment movement.

Modelling of bend scour requires an accurate resolution of the boundaries in the numerical model, which is possible with a curvilinear model. It has the advantage, that the grid lines can follow the bank lines and/or the main stream lines. Moreover, areas which require a more accurate discretization , eg. areas with extensive bed scour, can be resolved with a more dense computational grid mesh.

2.1 Calibration and verification

The resources available to the BRT Study did not permit an extensive pre- and post flood survey of the Brahmaputra-Jamuna. They were however sufficient to carry out detailed surveys at two sites on the river, see Figure 1.1.

The sites for detailed survey were selected because they contained features of particular relevance for the objectives of the BRT studies. Both sites had features which are known to be associated with the occurence of deep bed scour. The first site (known as Test Area 1) covered the entire width of the river at the confluence of two major anabranches. Intermittent historic cross section surveys and bathymetric measurements are available since 1967 (Coleman, 1969). The second site (Test Area 2) was located about 20 km further upstream in an area where the river is anastomosed around a large meta-stable *char*. It covered part of the right hand anabranch system centering on an actively eroding bend on the edge of the braid belt with deep near bank scour. Test area 1 did not contain a strongly curved flow pattern, usually associated with river bends and Test Area 2 was selected specifically to provide insight into this.

Test Area 1 was surveyed during the rising stage of the monsoon in June/July 1990 and again during the recession of flood flows in November 1990. Test Area 2 was surveyed in December 1990, during the dry season, and then again in August 1991 during the monsoon season. Measurements at each site included the velocity distribution, the sediment load, and the depth at verticals arranged over a grid of approximately 1000m by 500m. In addition, the *char* topography at both sites and the bank line retreat at Test Area 2 from December 1990 to November 1991 were also surveyed.

The sub-models based on System 21 were calibrated and verified using data of velocities, water levels, suspended sediment concentrations, erosion and deposition rates as described in Halcrow/DHI/EPC/DIG, 1993. An example of the hydrodynamic model calibration is shown in Figure 2.1 which shows the velocity pattern in Test Area 1. The simulated velocities agreed very well with the measured velocities. In Figure 2.2, the observed erosion pattern from July 1990 to November 1990 in Test Area 2 is shown together with the simulated erosion pattern. The alternating erosion/deposition pattern along the thalweg from the uppr right corner to the lower left corner was reproduced with a good degree of similarity.

3. MODEL EXPLOITATION

Models were set up to explore the following processes: additional bed scour after protection from bank erosion; river bend development; confluence of anabranches; bifurcation of anabranches; river training by using strategically located revetments; and flow around groynes. Only river bend scour and confluence scour will be dealt with in detail in this paper. The purpose of the modelling described below was to analyse under which conditions critical scour holes could develop. This was necessary as part of the information leading to the writing of guidelines for design of protective works. The calibrated 2-D model offered a powerfull tool for investigation of various schemes.

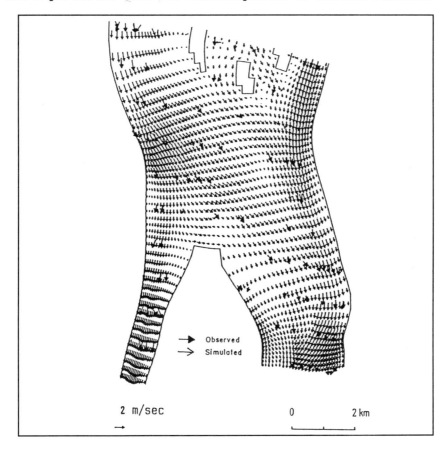

Figure 2.1 Observed and Simulated Velocities in Test Area 1, July 1990

123

3.1 Bend Scour

Many sites of severe bank erosion along the BRE are on channel bends. Thus, in order to provide a good basis for the design of bank protection measures, it was necessary to carry out a thorough analysis of the processes associated with river bend evolution and scour.

The 2-D model was applied to establish the dominant parameters in river bend development and to derive relationsships between maximum velocities and maximum depths in river bends in order to design scour protection measures.

The bathymetry at the start of the simulation corresponded to the monsoon conditions at the surveyed channel bend in Test Area 2 with a mean depth of 7 m below bank top. The model simulated the dynamic change of the bathymetry until an equilibrium in bed geometry was reached.

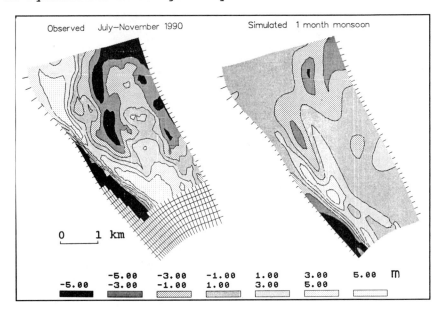

Figure 2.2   Observed and Simulated Erosion and Deposition Patterns in Test Area 2.

The erosion and deposition patterns for different ratios between width and radius of curvature were simulated in order to find the most critical channel width-radius of curvature ratio with respect to scour, see Figure 3.1.

124

Maximum erosion was found a little downstream of the middle
of the channel bend because the curvature of the banklines
does not quite coincide with the curvature of the stream-
lines. This space lag is a characteristica for a channel
bend that is moving downstream.

The simulated maximum scour depth was 15 m below bank level
and occurred at the outer bank for a channel radius-width
ratio of 3. Figure 3.1 shows the tendency of the bend migration: outwards and downstream. This pattern was in
agreement with observation of aerial and satelite images
from a series of years from 1973 to 1992, which also
revealed a critical radius-width relationship of 3 associated with a maximum erosion rate during the life cycle of a
bend (Halcrow/DHI/EPC/DIG ,1993).

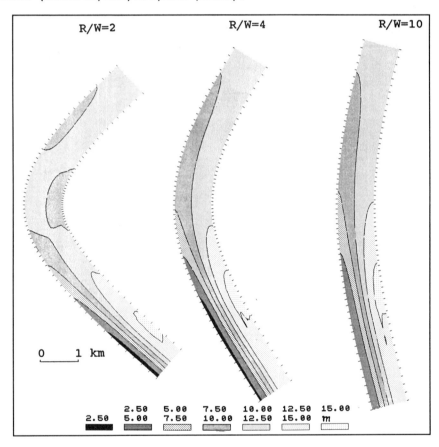

Figure 3.1   Simulated Bed Levels in River Bends with Different Ratios
             of Radius of Curvature (R) to Channel Width (W).
             Bank Level = 17 m.

Figure 3.2 depicts the development of the bend scour with time. The time required for reaching the equilibrium scour depth was about 170 days. This was on the assumption of a fixed bank-line and constant boundary conditions. The time before equilibrium was reached was small compared to the life cycle (5-10 years) of a typical bend in the Brahmaputra-Jamuna. The simulations showed that the time scale associated with bed scour in connection with bend evolution was much smaller than the time scale for sidewards and downstream movements of the river bend through lateral (bank) erosion.

Data from field surveys along the Brahmaputra-Jamuna (RPT et al. 1989) showed considerable scatter in the scour depths in river bends owing to the migration of dunes and *chars* which add to the mean scour depth. Only the mean scour depth was simulated in the 2-D model, and this corresponded closely to the mean value of the field measurements of maximum bend scour.

Sensitivity analysis with the 2-D model revealed significant sensitivity to changes in the grain size of the bed material, the degree of turbulence (eddy viscosity), bank erosion rate, and upstream boundary conditions. As these parameters vary extensively in the river, the sensitivity analysis added to an explanation of the scatter in field data.

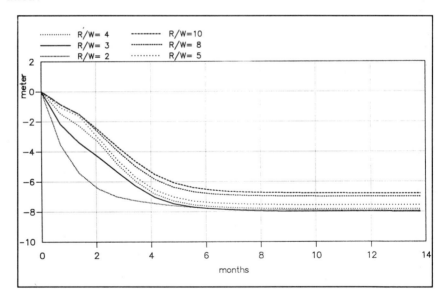

Figure 3.2   Simulated Evolution in Maximum Scour Depth in River Bends with Different R/W ratios.

3.2 Confluence Scour

One of the alternatives considered in the BRTS masterplan (Halcrow/DHI/EPC/DIG,1993) was to reinforce the bank lines by so called hard points at different places along the river. At these hard-points the flow was confined to a narrow pass where braiding of the river was suppressed. Upstream, confluence points and belonging bed scour would occur due to the convergence of parallel anabranches into one channel. Thus, it was necessary to investigate the possible maximum scour depths under these circumstances.

The principal hydraulic parameters: velocity, depth, width and gradient were based on monsoon field data from the two test areas. At the upstream boundary of the model, see Figure 3.3, a partly submerged *char* divided the two incident anabranches each of which was assumed to carry an equal discharge (case a in Figure 3.3). At the beginning of the simulation, the mean depth was 7 m below bank top over the whole area. The model then simulated the dynamical morphological changes until equilibrium was reached.

The maximum scour depth at the confluence point was 27 m which was much deeper than simulated with the river bend model. The bathymetry was in equilibrium after simulation of approximately 600 days. The reason for the time scale being 3-4 times the time scale for bend erosion is explained by a larger extent and depth of the bed scour in the confluence simulation. The simulated maximum depth corresponded well to observed maximum depths at confluence points (RPT/Nedeco/BCL, 1989).

To analyse the sensitivity of the morphology to the distribution of discharge between the two upstream anabranches, the simulation was repeated with a division of flow between the anabranches changed from 50:50 % to 45:55 %. The simulated bathymetry, Figure 3.3 , was found to be very sensitive to changes in the distribution in discharge. The main flow line went from the anabranch carrying the largest portion of the flow to the opposite river bank downstream the confluence point where maximum water depth of 33 m occurred. The position of the scour hole moved from the middle of the river to the bank and the maximum depth increased by 22 %. At Test Area 2 in the Brahmaputra, two anabranches have been seen forming a confluence point and a bend in combination. The large observed scour depth was therefore explained as a combination of confluence and bend scour depth.

An essential assumption on the simulated scour depth was that the bank lines were fixed over several flood seasons. If bank erosion was included, the scour depth would be reduced because an additional sediment source would be present. This is usually the case in the undisturbed river, eg. in Test Area 2. However, bank lines *can* be fixed by human intervention. Thus, the river training works should be designed for the maximum possible confluence scour as simulated by the 2-D model.

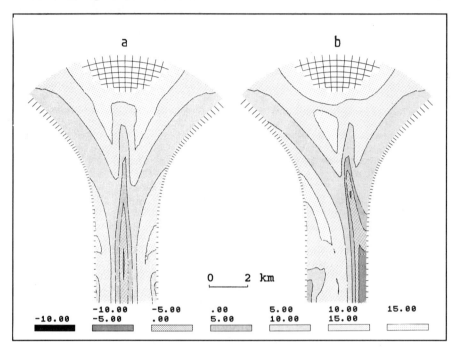

Figure 3.3   Simulated bed levels at a Confluence with 50:50 % Division of flow (a) and 55:45 % Division of flow (b). Bank level = 17 m.

4. CONCLUSION

The two-dimensional curvilinear morphological model was set-up for two sections of the Brahmaputra-Jamuna River, calibrated and verified against field data. It was then applied to calculate maximum possible scour depths and associated time scales in connection with design criteria for construction of river bank protection.

For typical monsoon conditions, scour depths of up to 15 m for bend scour alone and up to 33 m for combined bend and confluence scour were predicted. This agrees well with observations, where in one of the test areas, a scour depth close to the bank of nearly 30 m was observed during a normal year. The origin of this scour hole was found to be a combination of bend and confluence scour.

The model representation was based on the assumption of fixed bank lines, which would be the case with construction of protection works along the banks. Erosion of the banks was shown to limit the scour of the bed. Thus, the simulated maximum scour depths were considered as upper bound values for the scour in the existing conditions in the Brahmaputra-Jamuna.

By sensitivity analysis, it was shown that simulated scour depths were quite sensitive to a number of parameters such as lateral distribution of discharge, grain size distribution, and eddy viscosity (degree of turbulence). These parameters vary significantly in a braided river like the Bramaputra-Jamuna, and model simulations confirmed that scatter in field data from surveys of the river are to be expected. Small scale bed forms like dunes were not directly included in calculations of bed levels. These fluctuations in bed level will further add to the scatter.

Together with the results from the other mathematical and physical models built during the study as well as the accompanying specialist studies, the 2-D model contributed to an improved understanding of the natural physical processes of the Brahmaputra-Jamuna and added to the current knowledge and understanding of the complex hydraulics of the river.

ACKNOWLEDGEMENTS

The authors of this paper acknowledge with gratitude the contributions made by the Bangladesh Water Development Board, the Bangladesh University of Engineering and Technology and the members of the Brahmaputra River Training Studies Team to various aspects of this paper.

EFERENCES

alcrow/Danish Hydraulic Institute/Engineering & Planning onsultants Ltd./Design Innovation Group, River Training tudies of Brahmaputra River,Masterplan report, Bangladesh ater Development Board, Dhaka, 1993

oleman J.M, "Brahmaputra River:Channel Processes and edimentation", Sedimentary Geology,Vol.3,1969

ristow C.S,"Brahmaputra River Channel Migration and Deposi-ion",Dept. Earth Sciences, Univ.Leeds, UK, 1988

llah, "Channel Changes of the Brahmaputra",Proc. IAHR, ech.Sessn, B Ottawa, 1989

oswami D.C,Water Resources Research,21(7),959-978, 1985

laassen and Vermeer,"Channel Characteristics of the Braiding amuna River, Bangladesh", Intl.Conf. on River Regime, allingford,May 1988

horne C.R, Russell A.P.G and Alam M.K, "Planform pattern and hannel evolution of the Brahmaputra River in Bangladesh",-raided Rivers, editors: C.Bristow and J.Best, Geological ociety, UK (1993)

oward,Keetch and Vincent,"Topographical and Geometrical roperties of Braided Streams",Water Resources Research, ol.6, no.6, dec1970

endel Palmer & Tritton,Nedeco and Bangladesh Consultants td."Jamuna Bridge Project. Phase II Study, Feasibility eport",1989

redsøe J.,"Unsteady Flow in Straight Alluvial Streams: odification of Individual Dunes",J.Fluid Mech.,Vol.91,pp 97-512, 1979

ngelund F. and Fredsøe J.,"A Sediment Transport Model for traight Alluvial Channels",Nordic Hydrology 7:293-306, 1976

an Rijn L.C.,"Sediment Transport, Part I: Bed Load Trans-ort, Part II: Suspended Load Transport",ASCE J.Hyd.Eng.,Vol 10,no.10-11,1984

2nd International Conference on
RIVER FLOOD HYDRAULICS
22–25 March 1994: York, England

RIVER BED AGGRADATION THROUGH RECURRENT MEASURES

F.C.M. van der Knaap, DELFT HYDRAULICS, The Netherlands

Abstract

Simplified Models are presented for assessing the river bed aggradation through the application of recurrent measures in both a single channel system and a bifurcating channel system. The simplified Models have been calibrated and verified with computational results of the one dimensional model MIKE 11.

1.   Introduction

One of the projects of the Flood Action Plan (FAP) for Bangladesh is the River Training Pilot Project (FAP 22). The scope and objectives of this project have been focused on an "active" approach for stabilizing the planform of the Jamuna River. In this respect, the technical feasibility of recurrent measures (e.g. surface screens, bottom vanes, dredging, etc.) has been studied.

The floodplain of the Jamuna River actually consists of a system of channels with islands ("chars") in between. This implies, that the outer channels along the banks of the Jamuna River are frequently headed by a bifurcation point (see Figure 1.1). In case of heavily eroding outer channels with bank erosion as result, the presence of the bifurcations is of prime interest for preventing further outflanking or to promote closing of these outer channels. The application of the recurrent measures should be such that the natural sediment and/or water discharges will be redistributed at the bifurcation. The hydraulic and morphological response to such a redistribution has been estimated with "tailor made" simplified mathematical models. These models should give a good insight in the sensitivity of the result to variations in a number of parameters (such as: Chézy's roughness co-efficient, grain size D_{50}, water level slope i, sediment transport, etcetera) on the prediction of discharge and bed level changes.

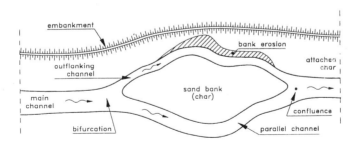

Figure 1.1   Layout of bifurcating channel system along the outer bank.

A simple mathematical description of this time dependant process should facilitate a sensitivity analysis resulting in preliminary guidelines for optimization of the effectivity (i.e. dimensions of the recurrent measure) with respect to the life time of channels in an highly dynamic river like the Jamuna. For achieving these objectives, the redistribution of flow through the recurrent measure is schematized by a constant sediment overloading ΔS and constant discharge withdrawal ΔQ. The aggradation in the outer channel will last until the original discharge has completely stopped. At that time a complete closure of the outer branch has been achieved. The required simplified mathematical model has been developed by schematizing the aggradation in a single channel (Chapter 2) in order to extend this to a bifurcating channel system (Chapter 3).

2.   Single channel system

2.1   Set up of Simplified Model

The hydraulic and morphological process in a single channel can generally be described with motion and continuity equations for both the water and sediment discharge (e.g. see Jansen et al., 1979). Such equations can be used to derive an equation with respect to the bottom level changes. Considering channel cross section averaged flow conditions, the resulting equation (see also List of Symbols) is as follows:

$$\frac{\partial z_b}{\partial t} + c\frac{\partial z_b}{\partial x} = R(x,t) \qquad (R = \text{damping parameter}) \qquad (2.1)$$

In case of a sonstant sediment overloading q_s to a single channel with initial flat bottom and water surface, the bottom level $z_b(x,t)$ will rise and the sedimentation front propagates with celerity c (see Figure 2.1)

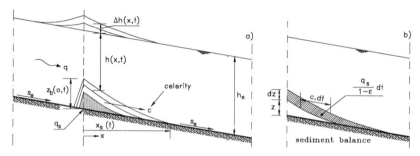

Figure 2.1   Sedimentation due to constant sediment overloading q_s

The propagation celerity c will not be constant due to the sediment balance for the bottom disturbance. As it has been observed from computations with the one-dimensional model MIKE 11, the most important sedimentation features are a negative sloping front, a time dependant propagation celerity c(t) and a time dependant aggradation height $z_b(0,t) = z(t)$. The sediment balance leads to the following relation (see Figure 2.1b):

$$z.c.dt = \frac{q_s}{1-\epsilon}.dt \qquad (\epsilon = \text{porosity of sediment}) \qquad (2.2)$$

From Equation (2.2) it becomes clear that the propagation celerity c decreases while the aggradation height z increases and the sediment overloading q_s remains constant, according to:

$$c = \frac{q_s}{1-\epsilon} \cdot \frac{1}{z} \qquad (2.3)$$

The validity of Equation (2.3) only holds during the phase, in which the aggradation height z is less than a value z_e. In this phase the celerity decreases to a constant value c_e which can be considered as the equilibrium celerity defined by the river characteristics. Assuming a fith power relation between sediment transport and water velocity in equilibrium conditions, e.g. $s_e = a_s(q/h_e)^5$ according to Engelund and Hansen (1967), the equilibrium celerity of a bottom disturbance is approximated by:

$$c_e = \frac{5s_e}{h_e} \cdot \frac{1}{(1-\epsilon)} \qquad (2.4)$$

which, according to Equation (2.3), also should meet to:

$$c_e = \frac{q_s}{1-\epsilon} \cdot \frac{1}{z_e} \qquad (2.5)$$

Reference is made to the List of Symbols and to Figure 2.1 with respect to the symbols used in Equations (2.4) and (2.5). As a consequence of these equations the equilibirium aggradation height z_e should meet to:

$$z_e = 0.2 \; n \; h_e \qquad (n = q_s/s_e) \qquad (2.6)$$

The following pragmatic assumptions (see Figure 2.2) have been made to solve the basic Equation (2.1):

(1) the general solution is:

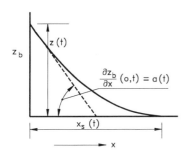

$$z_b(x,t) = z(t) \cdot (1 - \frac{x}{x_s})^\alpha \qquad (2.7)$$

(2) the initial slope of the front holds to:

$$\frac{\partial z_b}{\partial x}(0,t) = a(t) = \left(\frac{z_e}{z}\right)^\beta a_e \qquad (2.8)$$

Figure 2.2 Typical front of the sedimentation

The front of the sedimentation should be linear if the power $\alpha = 1$. However, MIKE 11 results and flume tests (see Ribberink and Van der Sande, 1984) do not show such linear fronts under the condition of a constant sediment overloading. Therefore a variable α has been taken. The gradient of the front on $x = 0$ has been assumed to behave according to Equation (2.8). In addition the gradient a_e is defined as the initial slope of the front corresponding to the equilibrium aggradation height z_e.

According to Equations (2.7) and (2.8) the following should hold:

$$\frac{\partial z_b}{\partial x}(0,t) = -\alpha \frac{z}{x_s} = a(t) = \left(\frac{z_e}{z}\right)^{\beta} a_e \tag{2.9}$$

while using Equation (2.7) for defining the gradients $\partial z_b/\partial t$ and $\partial z_b/\partial x$ and substituting them into the basic Equation (2.1), the following result has been obtained:

$$\frac{dz}{dt} - \alpha \frac{z}{x_s}.c = R\left(1 - \frac{x}{x_s}\right)^{1-\alpha} + \frac{x}{x_s}\left(\frac{dz}{dt} - \alpha \frac{z}{x_s}\frac{dx_s}{dt}\right) \tag{2.10}$$

Equation (2.10) shows clearly the significance of the damping parameter R. If this parameter would be neglected, the only solution could be a bottom sedimentation with constant slope (z/x_s) of the front and consequently $\alpha=1$. This is not in agreement with observations from the 1-D computations as well as from model tests. Therefore the following assumption has been made in order to achieve a more general solution for the differential Equation (2.10):

$$R\left(1 - \frac{x}{x_s}\right)^{1-\alpha} + \frac{x}{x_s}\left(\frac{dz}{dt} - \alpha \frac{z}{x_s}\frac{dx_s}{dt}\right) = (\lambda - 1)\,\alpha\,\frac{z}{x_s}\,c \tag{2.11}$$

Substitution of this result as well as the result of Equation (2.9) into Equation (2.10) leads to:

$$\frac{dz}{dt} + \lambda.c\left(\frac{z_e}{z}\right)^{\beta}.a_e = 0 \tag{2.12}$$

Using the celerity function according to Equation (2.3) the following solution has been obtained:

(i) $\qquad z = z_e\left(\frac{t}{T_e}\right)^{\frac{1}{2+\beta}}$ $\qquad\qquad$ (for t < T_e) $\qquad\qquad$ (2.13)

(ii) $\qquad z = z_e\left\{1 + \frac{1+\beta}{2+\beta}\,(\frac{t}{T_e} - 1)\right\}^{\frac{1}{1+\beta}}$ $\qquad$ (for t $\geq$ T_e) $\qquad\qquad$ (2.14)

(iii) $\qquad T_e = -\dfrac{z_e^2 \,.\, (1-\epsilon)}{(2+\beta).\lambda.a_e.n\ s_e}$ $\qquad\qquad\qquad\qquad$ (2.15)

with:

(iv) $\qquad z_e = 0.2\ n\ h_e$ $\qquad\qquad\qquad\qquad\qquad\qquad\qquad$ (2.16)

(v) $\qquad \dfrac{dz}{dt}(t=T_e) = \dfrac{z_e}{2+\beta}.\dfrac{1}{T_e}$ $\qquad\qquad\qquad\qquad$ (2.17)

(vi) $\qquad \alpha = -a_e\,.\,\dfrac{x_e}{z_e}$ $\qquad\qquad$ (see Eq. 2.9) $\qquad\qquad$ (2.18)

The symbols are explained in the List of Symbols. The unknown parameters are α, β, λ and a_e. These parameters have been fitted and calibrated with the use of 1-D computational results as described in the following Section.

2.2 Calibration of the Simplified Model

The parameters α, β, λ and a_e can be determined indirectly either from physical model tests or from computational results with a simulation model. The present Simplified Model has only been calibrated and verified with 1-D computational results. The most suitable output for calibration and verification consists of:
- plots giving the aggradation height z [= z_b (0,t)] as a function of time,
- plots giving longitudinal presentations of the aggradation after various time periods.

Four characteristic parameters can be collected very easily from such plots with the known boundary condition for the equilibrium aggradation height ($z_e = 0.2$ n h_e). These parameters are:

T_e	= a morphologic time (Eq. 2.15)	(years)
b_e	= dz/dt on t=T_e (Eq. 2.17)	(m/year)
a_e	= slope of the sedimentation front on t=T_e	(-)
x_e	= sedimentation length on t=T_e	(km)

Seven calibration runs have been made. The input data and results of these runs are summarized in Table 2.1. The parameters α, β and λ have been determined with Equations (2.18), (2.17) and (2.15), while the fourth parameter γ has been determined on the basis of the assumed relation:

$$a_e = \gamma \, n \, i \qquad\qquad (2.19)$$

Table 2.1   Calibration of Simplified Model

INPUT:C = 60 m$^{1/2}$/s, i = 7*10^{-5}, D$_{50}$= 2 mm						MIKE 11 OUTPUT				CALIBRATION			
Case	h$_e$(m)	q(m²/s)	s$_e$(m²/s)*)	n(-)	z$_e$(m)	T$_e$(yr)	a$_e$(10^{-5})	x$_e$(km)	b$_e$(m/yr)	α	β	λ	γ
1	5.1	5.8	2.7*10^{-4}	1.37	1.4	1.6	-3.7	41	0.32	1.08	0.73	0.62	-0.38
2	5.1	5.8	2.7*10^{-4}	4.11	4.2	2.1	-10.3	57	0.90	1.40	0.22	0.63	-0.36
3	3.0	2.6	0.68*10^{-4}	5.44	3.3	3.4	-13.0	40	0.45	1.58	0.16	0.58	-0.34
4	3.0	2.6	0.68*10^{-4}	7.35	4.41	3.45	-17.0	45	0.60	1.74	0.13	0.59	-0.33
5	4.0	4.0	1.40*10^{-4}	2.64	2.1	2.2	-6.3	42	0.40	1.26	0.39	0.69	-0.34
6	7.0	9.3	5.63*10^{-4}	0.66	0.92	1.45	-1.7°)	>50°)	0.18°)	- °)	1.5	0.51°)	-0.37
7	8.0	11.4	8.0*10^{-4}	0.46	0.74	1.25	-1.1°)	>50°)	0.14°)	- °)	2.2	0.50°)	-0.34

*) $s_e = \dfrac{0.05}{\Delta^2\sqrt{g}\; C^3\, D_{50}}\cdot\left(\dfrac{q}{h_e}\right)^5$ according to Engelund and Hansen (1967)

°) results probably influenced by boundary conditions in MIKE11 (x_e > boundary length of 50 km)

Results
$\alpha = 1 + 0.1$ n
$\beta = 1/n$
$\lambda = 0.6 (\approx 1\text{-}\epsilon)$
$\gamma = -0.35$

The calibration runs have been executed with a sediment porosity ϵ resulting in the relations as presented in Table 2.1 for the parameters to be determined. The impression exists that the porosity ϵ is only affecting the sedimentation shape in such a way that T_e, a_e and b_e remain unchanged while x_e will change with varying ϵ. The described influence of the porosity ϵ on the sedimentation process could be included in the Simplified Model by multiplying the fitted relation for α with 0.6/(1-ϵ) and assuming that $\lambda=1$-ϵ. This should be investigated and verified in more detail. The present Simplified Model holds for conditions with porosity

$\epsilon=0.4$. Any deviation from this condition should be done with care taking into account the recommended influence of ϵ on the parameters α and λ.

Figure 2.3 shows a calibaration run for the aggradation height z regarding case 3 of Table 2.1 as well as a verification run for a Jamuna flood condition ($q=34$ m²/s, $h_e = 15$ m, $C = 70$ m$^{1/2}$/s, $s_e = 5.14 * 10^{-3}$ m²/s and n = 2).

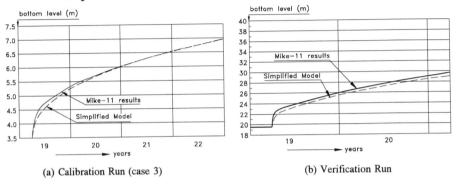

(a) Calibration Run (case 3)   (b) Verification Run

Figure 2.3   Calibration and Verification of Simplified Model

The set of Equations (2.9) and (2.13) through (2.18) including the calibration results of Table 2.1 provides the information on the aggradation to be expected, which is presented dimensionless in Figure 2.4. This figure presents design graphs for the aggradation height and length enabling a simple sensitivity analysis to a designer.

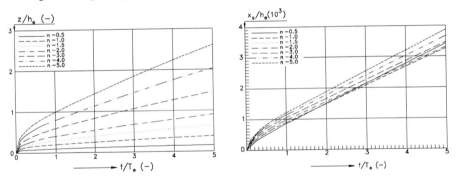

Figure 2.4   Aggradation dimensions depending on time and sediment overloading in a single river.

Once the morphological time scale T_e according to Equation (2.15) has been determined from the known river characteristics and the sediment transport ratio n, the aggradation height and length can be assessed easily from Figure 2.4.

3. Aggradation in outflanking channels

3.1 General

The Simplified Model as presented in Section 2 has been adapted for predicting the aggradation in an outflanking channel downstream of a bifurcation as result of the sediment transport and/or water discharge redistribution. This redistribution should be considered as the effect of a recurrent measure (e.g. surface screens) at the bifurction. Referring to Figure 3.1 the redistribution of sediment transport has been schematized as respectively a constant sediment supply $+\Delta S$ in the outflanking channel (1) and a constant sediment withdrawal $-\Delta S$ from the inner channel (2). Similar schematizations have been made regarding a constant water discharge withdrawal ΔQ from the outflanking channel into the inner channel.

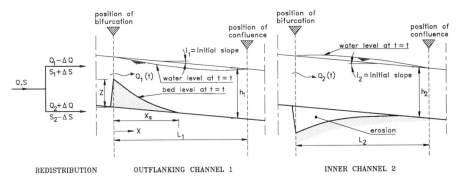

Figure 3.1   Morphological response due to flow and/or sediment transport redistribution

The induced aggradation and erosion as result of the flow and/or sediment transport redistribution is presented schematically in Figure 3.1 while the governing symbols are also indicated.

3.2 Adaptation of the Simplified Model

MIKE 11 runs, with separate flow and sediment transport redistributions as well as combined redistributions, have shown that any redistribution at the bifurcation might be reduced to a fictive sediment transport redistribution. Therefore, the following aspects have been considered for adapting the Simplified Model (see Section 2) to a bifurcating channel system:

(1) The aggradation process as derived for a single channel (see Section 2) holds only during a relatively short initial period $t < T_a$, in which the water level is supposed not to be affected.

(2) The water depth at the crest of the aggradation decreases from its initial equilibrium water depth h_1 to a water depth h_a, which enables a total sediment transport $S_1 + \Delta S$ on $t = T_a$. Applying the effectivity $n = \Delta S/S_1$ and the sediment transport equation according to Engelund and Hansen (1967), the aggradation height z_a satisfies to:

$$z_a = h_1 - h_a = \{1 - (n+1)^{-0.2}\}h_1 \tag{3.1}$$

(3) The time T_a is defined by substitution of Equation (3.1) in Equation (2.13), taking $z_e=0.2$ n h_1, $T_e=T_1$ and $\beta=1/n$. The result is as follows:

$$\frac{T_a}{T_1} = \left[\frac{5}{n}\{1 - (n+1)^{-0.2}\}\right]^{\frac{2n+1}{n}} \qquad (3.2)$$

with T_1 being the morphological time scale of the outflanking branch according to Equation (2.15):

$$T_1 = \frac{\lambda}{5.25} \frac{h_1^2 . B_1}{S_1 . i_1} . \frac{n}{2n+1} \qquad (3.3)$$

(4) The discharge in the outflanking channel is only time dependant and decreases approximately linearly. The discharge gradient on the location of the aggradation crest (x=0) should satify, according to the continuity requirement, to:

$$\frac{dQ}{dt} = B_1 (h_1 - z)\frac{du}{dt} - B_1 u \frac{dz}{dt} \qquad (3.4)$$

Neglecting the acceleration term and assuming that u remains contant after $t=T_a$ and that on $t=T_a$ the local water depth above the aggradation crest is equal to h_a (see Eq. 3.1), the following result has been obtained:

$$Q = Q_1 + \frac{dQ}{dt}.t = Q_1 + \dot{Q}_a.t = Q_1 - \frac{Q_1}{h_1} (n+1)^{0.2} . \dot{z}_a. t \qquad (3.5)$$

while the gradient $\dot{z}_a$ can be computed from Equation (2.13) with the result:

$$\dot{z}_a = \frac{n^2}{5(2n+1)} \left(\frac{T_a}{T_1}\right)^{-\frac{n+1}{2n+1}} . \frac{h_1}{T_1} \qquad (3.6)$$

A number of 1-D calibration runs has been made for determining the unknown parameter λ in the morphological time scale as defined with Equation (3.3) as well as the effectivity n. The discharge gradients as computed from the 1-D calibration runs have led to the following results:

$$\lambda = 0.6 + 0.0675 \frac{\sqrt{gh_1}}{C_2 i_1^{1.5} L_1} \qquad (3.7)$$

$$n = \frac{\Delta S}{S_1} + \frac{\Delta Q}{Q_1} \qquad (3.8)$$

To illustrate the agreement between MIKE 11 results and the results of the adapted Simplified Model two examples are given in Figure 3.2. This Figure presents the discharge as a function of time for both examples with input data according to Table 3.1.

Table 3.1   Input data

MAIN CHANNEL		$Q = 12{,}000 \ m^3/s$		$B = 2{,}000 \ m$				
OUTER/INNER CHANNEL		$Q_1 = Q_2 = 6{,}000 \ m^3/s$		$B_1 = B_2 = 1{,}000 \ m$				
CASES	MAIN / OUTER / INNER / CHANNEL							
	$L_1 = L_2$ (km)	$h_1 = h_2$ (m)	$C_1 = C_2$ $(m^{1/2}/s)$	$i_1 = i_2$ (-)	$\Delta Q^{*)}$ (m^3/s)	$\Delta Q / Q_1$ (-)	$\Delta S^{**)}$ (m^3/s)	$\Delta S / S_1$ (-)	$n = \dfrac{\Delta s}{S_1} + \dfrac{\Delta Q}{Q_1}$
1	24	5.23	60	$7*10^{-5}$	1,200	0.2	0.081	0.3	0.5
2	6	5.23	60	$7*10^{-5}$	-	-	0.135	0.5	0.5
*) positive ΔQ value means withdrawal from outer channel								
**) positive ΔS value means supply to outer channel								

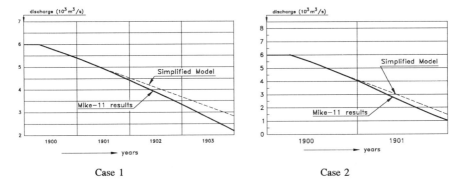

Case 1   Case 2

Figure 3.2   Decreasing discharges in outflanking channel

3.3   Closure of outflanking channels

The applicability of recurrent measures at bifurcations in the Jamuna River depends strongly on the time necessary for achieving a closure of the outflanking channel within the life time of such a channel. Some indications for the life time of the various Jamuna channels are roughly as follows:
- small channels   : life time 1 to 3 years, length 8 to 10 km
- medium channels   : life time 3 to 6 years, length 12 to 20 km

These indications can be considered as the boundary conditions for the type of recurrent measures to be applied. The time as required to achieve a closure of an outflanking channel can be derived from the Simplified Mathematical model as presented in Section 3.2. The substitution of the boundary condition that the discharge has completely stopped ($Q = 0$) in the outflanking channel, into the discharge equation (see Eq. 3.5) leads to the closure time ($= T_c$). The closure time depends on: (i) a variety of river characteristics with specific emphasis on the channel length and depth and (ii) the effectivity ($= n$) of the recurrent measures. Computations have shown that surface screens with an effectivity $n=0.2$ to 0.3

(see Van der Wal, 1993) seem to be a very attractive alternative for preventing bank erosion. Partial or complete closures seem possible within the life times of the various channels.

4.   Conclusions and Recommendations

The analysis of the river behaviour occuring as the morpholoigcal response to various measures (sediment overloading, water withdrawal and/or combinations) has led to the following conclusions and recommendations:

(i)   It has been shown that a Simplified Mathematical description of the hydraulic and morphological changes due to various (recurrent) measures is possible.

(ii)   Partial or complete closures of outflanking channels seem to be possible within time limits less than the life time of various Jamuna channels. Principles for selection of channel type and effectivity of recurrent measures are presented in Section 3.3.

(iii)   The calibration and verification of the various Simplified Models has been done with computation results of the one-dimensional model MIKE 11. Due to the schematization of the hydraulic and morphological process the validity of the developed Simplified Models should be checked and/or upgraded with physical model tests. Only such tests can produce experimental data for similar hydraulic and morphological schematizations. Once having a better insight in the validity of the Simplified Models, pilot tests in the Jamuna are recommended.

Acknowledgement

The study discussed here is carried out as a part of the Bank Protection and River Training (AFPM) Pilot Project (FAP21/22), which was funded by the Kreditanstalt für Wiederafbau (Kfw, Germany) and Caisse Francaise de Developpement (CFD, France). The study was carried out by the combination Rhein-Ruhr Ingenieur-Gesellschaft. MBH (RRI, Germany) as lead partner, Compagnie Nationale du Rhone (France), Prof. Dr. Lackner & Partners (Germany), DELFT HYDRAULICS (The Netherlands), Bangladesh Engineering and Technological Services Ltd. (Bangladesh) and Desh Upodesh Ltd. (Bangladesh). The client is the Flood Plan Coordination Organization (FPCO). The paper expresses the views of the author only, and not necessarily the views of the institutions and companies mentioned above.

References

Engelund, F. and Hansen, E., 1967: A monograph on Sediment Transport in Alluvial Streams, Teknisk Forlag, Copenhagen

Jansen, P. Ph. et al., 1979: Principles of River Engineering, Pitman, London.

Klaassen, G.J. and Vermeer, K., 1988: Channel characteristics of the Braiding Jamuna River, IHE, Delft, The Netherlands.

Klaassen, G.J., Mosselman, E. and Brühl, H., 1993: On the prediction of planform changes of braided sand-bed rivers, Int. Conf. on "Hydroscience and Engineering", Washington.

Ribberink, J.S. and Van der Sande, J.T.M., 1984: Aggradation in Rivers Due to Over-loading, Comm. on Hydr., Rep. No. 84-1, Dept. of Civil Engineering, Delft University of Technology.

Van der Wal, M., 1993: Traning of a braided river with surface screens, XXV congress IAHR, Tokyo.

List of Symbols

a_e	= aggradation slope on origin at $t = T_e$	(-)
a_s	= sediment transport paramter	(s^4/m^3)
$a(t)$	= aggradation slope on origin	(-)
B	= width of (main) channel	(m)
B_1	= width of outflanking channel	(m)
B_2	= width of inner channel	(m)
C	= Chezy's roughness parameter	$(m^{1/2}/s)$
C_1	= Chezy's roughness parameter of outflanking channel	$(m^{1/2}/s)$
C_2	= Chezy's roughness parameter of inner channel	$(m^{1/2}/s)$
c	= celerity	(m/s)
c_e	= equilibrium celerity	(m/s)
D_{50}	= specific grain size passing 50 % of weight	(mm)
g	= acceleration due to gravity (=9.81)	(m/s^2)
h	= local water depth	(m)
h_1	= initial water depth of outflanking channel	(m)
h_2	= initial water depth of inner channel	(m)
h_a	= water depth above aggradation crest at $t = T_a$	(m)
h_e	= initial equilibrium water depth	(m)
i	= water level slope	(-)
i_1	= water level slope of outflanking channel	(-)
i_2	= water level slope of inner channel	(-)
L_1	= length of outflanking channel	(m)
L_2	= length of inner channel	(m)
n	= q_s/s_e, $\Delta Q/Q_1 + \Delta S/S_1$ = effectivity	(-)
Q	= discharge in outflanking channel	(m^3/s)
Q_1	= initial discharge in outflanking channel	(m^3/s)
Q_2	= initial discharge in inner channel	(m^3/s)
$\dot{Q}_a$	= discharge gradient at $t = T_a$	(m^3/s^2)
q	= discharge per unit channel width	(m^2/s)
q_s	= sediment overloading per unit channel width	(m^2/s)
R	= damping parameter	(m/s)
S_1	= initial sediment transport in outflanking channel	(m^3/s)
S_2	= initial sediment transport in inner channel	(m^3/s)
s_e	= initial equilibrium sediment transport per unit channel width	(m^2/s)
T_a	= initial aggradation period	(s)
T_e	= morphological time scale	(s)
T_1	= morphological time scale of outflanking channel	(s)
t	= time	
u	= cross section averaged current velocity	(m/s)
x	= distance from origin	(m)
x_e	= aggradation length at $t = T_e$	(m)
x_s	= aggradation length	(m)
z	= aggradation heigth	(m)
z_a	= aggradation height at $t = T_a$	(m)
$\dot{z}_a$	= aggradation gradient at $t = T_a$	(m/s)
z_b	= local bottom level	(m)
z_e	= aggradation heigt at $t = T_e$	(m)
α	= power of bottom level function	(-)
β	= power of aggradation slope function	(-)
γ	= a co-efficient related to a_e	(-)
Δ	= specifice mass (= 1.65)	(-)
ϵ	= porosity	(-)
λ	= aggradation co-efficient	(-)

Chapter Four

GIS and Modelling

2nd International Conference on
RIVER FLOOD HYDRAULICS
22–25 March 1994: York, England

A COUPLED 2D MODEL FOR INTERACTING SURFACE WATER
AND GROUNDWATER FLOWS

A. Defina[*] - B. Matticchio[**]

[*]   Istituto di Idraulica "G. Poleni", Università degli studi, Padova, Italy

[**] IPROS Ingegneria Ambientale, Padova, Italy

ABSTRACT

The present paper describes a two dimensional model solving unsteady state coupled groundwater and surface water flow. Groundwater flow is based on the Darcy's law, while surface water flow is described by the Saint-Venant equation, assuming that convection terms are negligible. Coupling of the two system is achieved by mass balance conditions at the interface nodes. The model applies to shallow aquifers for which the Dupuit-Forchheimer assumption is valid. The numerical solution is based upon a standard finite element Galerkin approximation.

1. INTRODUCTION

Problems involving both surface water and groundwater flows are rather frequent in hydrology. The usual approach to solve such problems consists of uncoupling surface and subsurface hydrosystems, considering them separately. Boundary conditions for one system usually come from the solution of the other one.

This approach, however, is generally successful only when approximately steady state conditions exist for at least one of the two systems, that is when time scales for the groundwater and for the surface water flows are greatly different.

2nd International Conference on River Flood Hydraulics. Edited by W. R. White and J. Watts
© 1994 HR Wallingford Ltd. Published by John Wiley & Sons Ltd

Uncoupled analysis becomes difficult if time scales for the flow in the two systems are of the same order of magnitude. In such cases interactions and exchanged fluxes become very important, strongly depending on the dynamics of flow both in the free surface system and in the aquifer. A better approach to these problems is provided by a coupled surface-subsurface model, which considers interactions between the two hydrosystems as internal conditions.

2. MATHEMATICAL MODEL

The model solves simultaneously the vertically integrated momentum equations for free surface flow (the Saint-Venant equation), and for groundwater flow (Darcy's law):

$$\frac{\partial \mathbf{u}}{\partial t} + g \cdot \nabla h + g \frac{\mathbf{u}|\mathbf{u}|}{K_S^2 Y_S^{4/3}} = 0 \qquad [1]$$

$$\mathbf{u} + \mathbf{k} \cdot \nabla h = 0 \qquad [2]$$

where h is the piezometric head, $\mathbf{u}$ is the depth-averaged velocity, g is the gravitational acceleration, K_S is the Strickler friction coefficient, Y_S is the water depth, t is the time and $\mathbf{k}$ is the hydraulic conductivity. Convective terms for surface water flow were neglected in equation [1]. This approximation is justified in view of the relatively small values that velocity assumes in most problems involving interactions between surface and subsurface flows.

Volume conservation equations are:

surface water flow:

$$\frac{\partial h}{\partial t} + \nabla \cdot \mathbf{u} Y_S + w_{SD} = 0 \qquad [3]$$

groundwater flow:

$$S \frac{\partial h}{\partial t} + \nabla \cdot \mathbf{u} Y_P = 0 \qquad [4]$$

$$\nabla \cdot \mathbf{u} Y_D - w_{SD} = 0 \qquad [5]$$

where Y_D and Y_p are the thickness of the confined and of the unconfined part of the aquifer, respectively, S is the storage coefficient, neglected for confined flow, and w_{SD} is the exchanged flux between the surface stream and the underlying groundwater flow field.

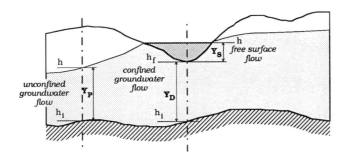

Fig. 1 - *Schematic vertical section of the flow domain*

Substituting $\mathbf{q}$ for $\mathbf{u}Y$ and q_w for $|\mathbf{u}|Y$ the set of momentum equations reduce to:

$$\frac{\partial q_S}{\partial t} + g\,Y_S \cdot \nabla h + g\,\frac{q_S\,q_{WS}}{K_S^2\,Y_S^{7/3}} = 0 \qquad [6]$$

$$q_D + Y_D\,\mathbf{k} \cdot \nabla h = 0 \qquad [7]$$

$$q_P + Y_P\,\mathbf{k} \cdot \nabla h = 0 \qquad [8]$$

In equation [6] the term q_S/Y_S was neglected assuming that the free surface flow takes place at low Froude numbers.

By introducing the following function $\alpha^*(x,y)$:

$$\alpha^* = \begin{cases} 1 & \text{if} \quad h > h_f \\ 0 & \text{if} \quad h \le h_f \end{cases}$$

where h_f is the ground surface level, the volume conservation equation for the whole flow system at a point can be written as:

$$\left[\alpha^* + (1-\alpha^*)S\right]\frac{\partial h}{\partial t} + \alpha^* \, \nabla\cdot(\mathbf{q}_S + \mathbf{q}_D) + (1-a^*)\nabla\mathbf{q}_P = p_Z \qquad [9]$$

where p_Z is the rate of net inflow at the point.

Equations [6] and [9] are discretized in time by using a centered finite difference approximation. Assuming:

$$G_S = g\,Y_S \,/\,(\frac{1}{\Delta t} + g\,q_{ws}\,/\,K_S^2\,Y_S^{7/3}) \qquad ; \qquad F_S = \dot{q}_S\,/\,(g\,Y_S\,\Delta t)$$
$$G_D = Y_D\,k \qquad\qquad\qquad\qquad ; \qquad G_P = Y_P\,k$$

equations [6], [7], [8] take the form:

$$\mathbf{q}_S = -\,G_S\,(\nabla h - F_S) \qquad [10]$$
$$\mathbf{q}_D = -\,G_D\,\nabla h \qquad\qquad [11]$$
$$\mathbf{q}_P = -\,G_P\,\nabla h \qquad\qquad [12]$$

where the apex ' indicates values at the previous time level.

The resulting system of equations is solved by the finite element method. The two dimensional domain is divided into triangular elements: water levels are considered linearly varying between element nodes, while depth-integrated velocities, G_S, G_D, G_P, F_S, are considered constant over the element.

In the numerical solution of equation [9] the function α^* is subsituted by $\alpha^e = \frac{1}{A_e}\int_{A_e}\alpha^* \, dA_e$ and the following dependence of α^e upon water depth Y_S is introduced:

$$\alpha^e = \begin{cases} e^{-(1-Y_S/Y_{lim})^2} & Y_S < Y_{lim} \\ 1 & Y_S \geq Y_{lim} \end{cases}$$

where Y_{lim} is choosen depending upon unevenness of the ground surface.

When approximating the main unknown h by a linear function $\hat{h} = \sum_{n=1}^{N} h_n \, \xi_n(x,y)$ and applying the Galerkin's method and the Green's first identity, equation [9] reduces to:

$$\sum_e \left[\alpha^e + (1-\alpha^e)\,S \right] \int_{A_e} \frac{h_n - h_n'}{\Delta t} \cdot \xi_n^e \cdot \xi_m^e \, dA_e + Q_m - P_m +$$

$$+ \sum_e \left\{ \left[\alpha^e \, (G_S + G_D) + (1-\alpha^e)\,G_P \right] \frac{h_n + h_n'}{2} \cdot \nabla \xi_n^e - \alpha^e G_S F_S \right\} \cdot \nabla \xi_m^e A_e = 0$$

where $G_S = G_S \cdot \mathbf{I}$ and Q_m and P_m are nodal fluxes. Depth-integrated velocities are then computed by backward substitution from equations [10], [11], [12].

3. APPLICATION

The model described above has been applied to a real case. The example serves to highlight the general modelling philosophy that is being followed and to indicate the problems for which the method represents a useful tool.

The study area is a part of a river basin located in Northern Italy. The aquifer consists of highly permeable alluvial deposits ($k \approx 10^{-2}$ m/s) about 15 m thick. The water table lies few metres below the ground surface.

A schematic view of the area is shown in Fig. 2, where the spatial discretization by finite triangular elements is also represented. Just before entering the domain, the R. Fibbio discharges are partially diverted by a spillway along a flood by-pass channel and driven into three large basins.

The applied boundary conditions are:

- specified water head along the upper and the lower sides of the domain
- no flow occurring across left and right sides of the domain
- specified relationship between water head and discharge at the downstream end of both the by-pass channel and R. Fibbio
- specified discharge at the upstream end of both the by-pass channel and R. Fibbio

The initial flow field is illustrated in Fig. 3. It was achieved by a transient simulation assuming steady boundary conditions.

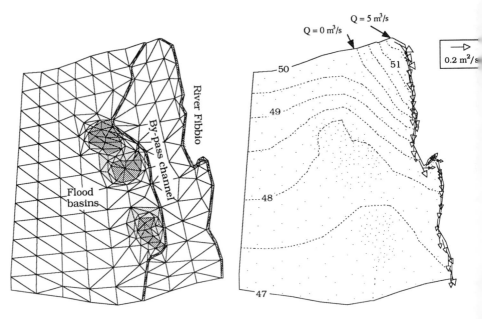

Fig. 2 - *Schematic view of the study area and finite element mesh*   Fig. 3 - *Initial flow field*

A set of flood hydrographs due to rainfalls of different duration were estimated by a rainfall-runoff model and the computed discharges were imposed as boundary conditions to the by-pass channel and to R. Fibbio.

Fig. 4 illustrates the results obtained when a flood due to a 36 hours rainfall is routed through the system (case A): both downstream hydrographs show a highly reduced volume mainly because of seepage. The velocity field and the contours of the water head at time t=12 hours and t=24 hours are illustrated in Fig. 5.

To highlight effects due to interaction with the groundwater flow, a simulation was run assuming a strongly reduced permeability (k = 10^{-4} m/s). The results of this simulation (case A') are shown in Fig. 6. Comparison between Fig. 4 and Fig. 6 clearly indicates the important effect of seepage. The discharge peak reduction for case A' is about 5%, and it is mainly due to the water storage in the basins. When seepage is allowed (case A) the peak reduction grows to about 24%, due to the high permeability introduced.

Computed hydrographs for a 8 hours rainfall flood routing through the system (cases B and B') are shown in Fig.7. Peak reductions for such a small volume flood are 48% and 31% respectively.

These results clearly show that storage and seepage effects are equally important for the selected example.

4. CONCLUSIONS

In the presented case study, floods and storage volumes were of the same order of magnitude and ground permeability was very high. Therefore the problem of evaluating flood routing through the system could not be correctly solved without taking into account both storage and seepage. For this reason a coupled surface water and groundwater flow model was developed.

Results of simulations confirmed that both phenomena play an important role in flood routing. On the other hand they demonstrate that the described model is an adequate and powerful tool to solve this kind of problems in a simple and effective way.

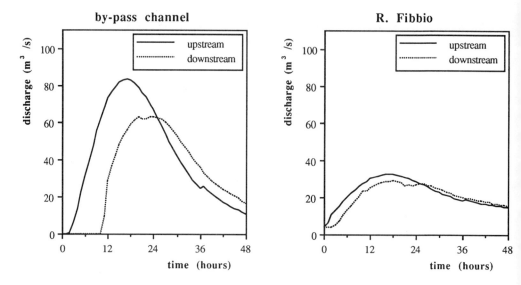

Fig. 4 - *Computed hydrographs for the by-pass channel and R. Fibbio*

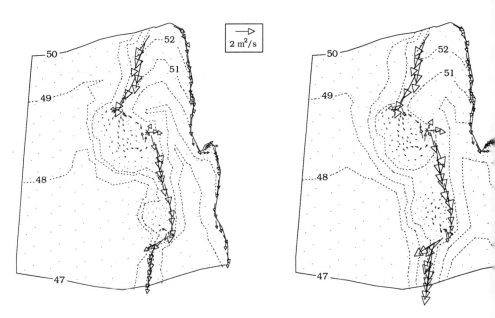

Fig. 5 - *Depth integrated velocities and water head contours at t=12 hours and t=24 hours*

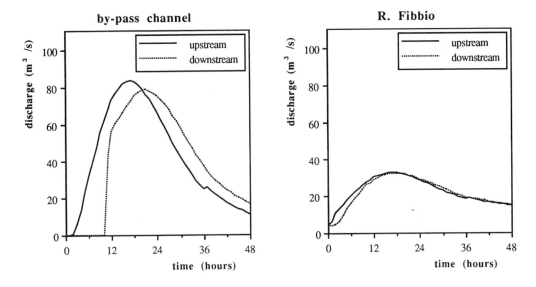

Fig. 6 - *Computed hydrographs for the by-pass channel and R. Fibbio*

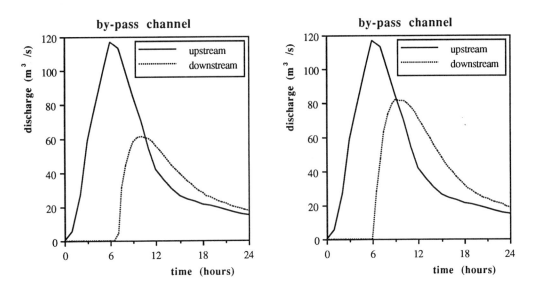

Fig. 7 - *Computed hydrographs for the by-pass channel ($k=10^{-2}$ m/s left and $k=10^{-4}$ m/s right)*

2nd International Conference on
RIVER FLOOD HYDRAULICS
22–25 March 1994: York, England

COUPLING OF 2D AND 1D MODELS AND INTEGRATION
INTO GEOGRAPHIC INFORMATION SYSTEMS (GIS)

Wilhelm Bechteler[1], Sven Hartmann[2], Alfred J. Otto[3]

ABSTRACT

For flood simulations geographic data and the presence of structures play an important role. Discretising the whole domain two-dimensionally mostly involves an undesireable increase of grid cells and computational time. A more efficient way is to treat some parts one-dimensionally and to embed them into the 2D model. It turned out that the coupling of 1D and 2D models can be done very efficiently and accurately by using the Poleni formula, especially for rivers or channels the dimensions of which are significantly smaller than the grid size of the 2D grid. This approach was successfully used for a terrain (4 km by 2.5 km) near the river Rhine, where a dam failure was assumed and for a flood event near Coburg. It also turned out that the application of GIS is undoubtedly useful for capturing, analysing and visualizing data to become familiar with the terrain and to model it in a proper way. A concept was developed which suggests the integration of the hydrodynamic models and a data base into GIS.

---

[1] Professor, Institute of Hydrosciences, Federal Armed Forces University Munich, Germany
[2] Dipl.-Ing., Institute of Hydrosciences at the same university
[3] Dipl.-Ing., Institute of Hydrosciences at the same university

---

2nd International Conference on River Flood Hydraulics. Edited by W. R. White and J. Watts
© 1994 HR Wallingford Ltd. Published by John Wiley & Sons Ltd

COUPLING OF 2D AND 1D MODELS

A flooded area usually contains rivers, channels, roads etc. that may have an essential influence on the process of flooding. All topological features have to be modeled properly to represent the domain in a realistic way. The terrain is mainly calculated two-dimensionally [3], some parts of it, however, can be described one-dimensionally in a more effective way. Mostly the flow in rivers can be determined one-dimensionally. In such cases the coupling of the 1D and 2D approaches can save a lot of computational time because the grid size just has to take into account the overall topographical situation of the terrain and is not restricted by the dimension size of small rivers or channels.

Fig. 1 shows the treatment of a river, embedded into the two-dimensional computational grid. The river is placed on the cell-faces of the 2D grid, so that the process of coupling is like an internal boundary condition for the 2D model and means lateral inflow or outflow for the 1D model. The quantity of mass and momentum transfer between both models is determined by using the weir formulae for free and drowned flow (Poleni).

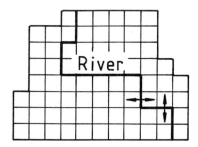

Fig. 1. 2D Domain with Embedded River

The quality of this kind of interface can be demonstrated best using a 1D model. The example is a channel with negative and positive slopes of 0.1 % and a reservoir at the top (Fig. 2).

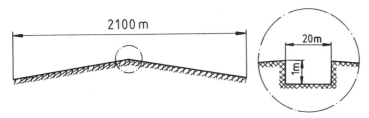

Fig. 2. Domain to Test the Coupling

The length of the reservoir is 40 % of the constant grid-spacing. In general such a grid composition causes numerical troubles and may destroy the whole solution. On the left side of the domain a constant discharge of $Q = 1$ m³/s is given, on the right side zero-gradient condition is used. The water fills up the left branch, overtops into the reservoir and finally into the right branch. Figure 3 shows the steady state solution (dotted line), which was reached after some time. In order to prove the reliability of the result, the reservoir was removed and the calculation done again without the coupling mechanism (solid line in Fig. 3). From a practical view the influence of the reservoir should be small at all, which was completely confirmed by the simulation.

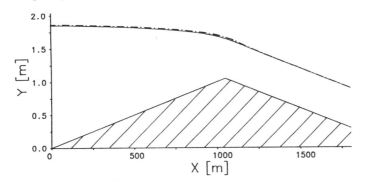

Fig. 3. Qualitative Behavior of the Coupling Mechanism. Water Elevation Y with Coupling (- - -) and without (—).

The possibility to calibrate the interface by adopting the coefficients of the Poleni formulae to the particular situation makes it suitable to many practical applications. Two of them are presented later.

PROGRAM PACKAGE FLOODSIM

The coupling mechanism described above is integrated in the program package FLOODSIM which is an interactively driven simulation tool with pull-down menues applicable for the numerical simulation of general flooding problems. Possible applications range from the calculation of overtopping river embankments to the simulation of floodwave propagation induced by a dam break.

The explicit algorithm is based on the semi-discrete approach, with the use of Finite Volumes for space discretisation and Forward Euler or Runge-Kutta Method for time discretisation. The scheme is stabilized by upwinding the convective fluxes. The advantage of the Runge-Kutta-scheme to be able to handle Courant numbers greater than 1 cannot be used in the calculation if the topographical situation includes steep gradients. This is because of stability problems. Using Courant numbers less than 1 can cure this problem but in this case the simpler Euler-scheme needs less computational time.

The shock-capturing capability, the keeping of some compatibility relations [3] guarantees robustness and reliability of the scheme even on a coarse grid.

THE USE OF GEOGRAPHIC INFORMATION SYSTEMS (GIS)

The numerical simulation of floodings requires geographic informations, data of different parameters of the terrain, and informations about structures within the domain. The result of the simulation has to be visualized in a proper way. This kind of application recommends the use of GIS which includes computer-aided procedures for the capture, analysis, and display of spatial features and their attributes. Especially the treatment of large domains needs powerful tools for data management and visualization.

GIS as a tool for visualizing spatial relationships include the physical computing capacity to merge, overlay, desegregate, and otherwise manipulate data and query the data by posing hypothesis for e.g. testing assumptions.

As a consequence a concept to integrate hydrodynamic models into GIS was built up (Fig. 4).

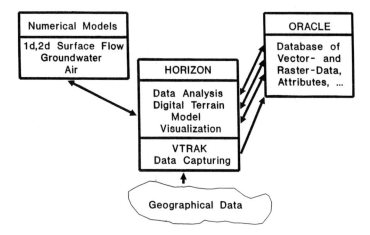

Fig. 4. Concept for Integration of Hydrodynamic Models in GIS

Basis for all simulations are the geographic data which are transformed into a Digital Terrain Model (DTM), a computer presentation of earth's surface. The terrain where the height z mostly is a function of the coordinates x and y, can be obtained by :

-   surveying of the terrain,
-   digitizing maps,
-   photogrammetry or satellite information.

Depending on the source, data are either regularly or irregularly distributed reference points or digitized contours. The generation of a DTM has to take into account additional features, like cliffs, lake edges, and rivers as well as single spots (hills) which cause breaks (discontinuities) in the terrain. As one of different methods we are using a Triangular Irregular Network (TIN) structure which is optimized by Delauney triangulation in the sense that it builds a set of nearly equal triangles to avoid problems possibly caused by strongly varying density of primary data. Further operations calculate the slope derivatives at each point and generate the resulting regular grid.

APPLICATIONS

As part of a study we investigated a domain at the river Rhine near the barrage Iffezheim (Fig. 5).

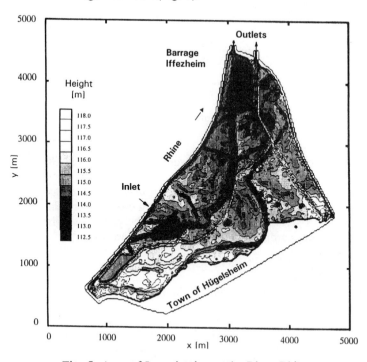

Fig. 5. Area of Investigation at the River Rhine

The extension of the domain is approximately 4 km by 2.5 km and is restricted by the river and two streets situated on dams. The primary data were gained from 8 topographic maps (scale 1 : 5000) which were scanned and digitized using VTRAK and HORIZON from LaserScan, UK. Resulting from the triangulation and matrix operations a DTM with a resolution of 10 m by 10 m in x- and y-direction and 0.5 m in z-direction was obtained.

An observation of the terrain was useful to assess structures within the terrain, like small dams, weirs, and small channels, which are essential for a high quality simulation. The roughness, which is essential for the calculation too, was estimated from photographs and maps. Values of the Manning coefficient range from 0.03 to 0.08.

As input for the flooding the inflow hydrograph calculated with DEICH [4] was used leading to a maximum discharge of 800 m³/s into the terrain. The propagation of the flood was investigated for 8 hours and showed reasonable results (Fig. 6).

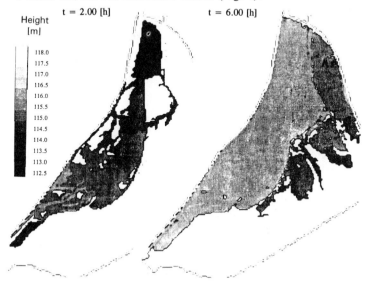

Fig. 6. Flooding Situation at Different Time Levels.

For a further verification of FLOODSIM including the coupling mechanism a numerical simulation was done for a river valley near Coburg in the northern part of Bavaria. Some years ago this river section was investigated at our institute by means of a physical model with the scale of 1 : 25/ 1 : 45 and documented very well [5]. The terrain is about 2000 m by 600 m in size with a maximum drop in height of 12 m. The situation of the meandering river and a flooding trench is shown in Fig. 7.

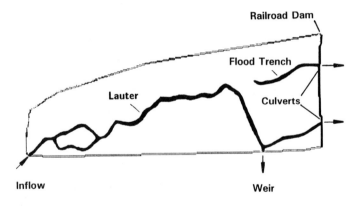

Fig. 7. Terrain and Boundary Conditions at River Lauter.

The terrain is limited by a railroad dam with a height of 3 m. The culverts through the dam and the weir characteristics provide the outflow hydrographs. The terrain is represented by using 8.300 2D grid cells (10 m by 10 m) and approx. 350 1D cells.

Figure 8 shows the flooding of the Lauter valley at different time levels for a flooding of a 100 year probability. The discharge was increased within one hour from 0.7 m^3/s to 36 m^3/s. After about two hours steady-state conditions were reached. The comparison of the numerical simulation with the investigations on the pyhsical model (Fig. 8, bottom) shows the high quality of the result.

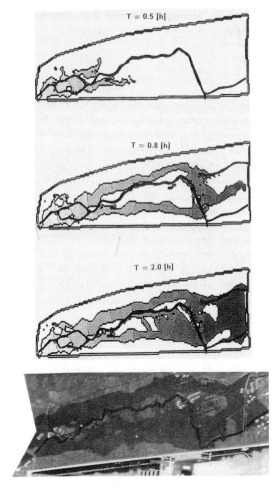

Fig. 8. Flooding Situation at Different Time Levels.

A second calculation was performed with a complete 2D-discreti-
sation, which was done with about 33.000 cells (constant spacing

5 m by 5 m) necessary in order to represent approximatly the quantities of the river, resulting in an increase of computational time of about factor 3.5.

CONCLUSIONS

In this article it is shown that a two-dimensional numerical simulation of flooding can be performed very well. Using a reliable and robust algorithm with shock-capturing capability and the ability of handling steep topographical gradients (compatibility relations) is one basic feature of a successful computation. On the other side the modelling of small structures like dams, channels and rivers contributes as well to the quality and effectivness of the simulation.

The coupling approach of 2D and 1D models used in FLOOD-SIM leads to a reduction of grid cells for the 2D calculation and therefore of the computational time without loosing the important influence of small structures smaller than the grid spacing.

The integration of hydrodynamic models into GIS is highly desirable because e.g. flooding simulations depend on the effective analysis of geographical information. Especially the calculation of large domains strongly depends on the access to accurate data and recommends an effective use of GIS

REFERENCES

[1] Abbott M. B. (1979), Computational Hydraulics, Elements of the Theory of Free- Surface-Flows, Pitman Advanced Publishing Program, London

[2] Bechteler W., Kulisch H., Nujić M. (1992), 2D Dam Break Flooding Waves - Comparison between Experimental and Calculated Results, 3rd Int. Conference on Flood and Flood Management, Florence, Italy

[3] Bechteler W., Nujić M., Otto A. J. (1993), Program Package "FLOODSIM" and its Application, 1st Int. Conference on Hydro-Science and -Engineering, Washington, edited by Sam S. Y. Wang

[4] Bechteler W., Broich K. (1993), Computational Analysis of the Dam-Erosion -Problem, 1st Int. Conference on Hydro-Science and -Engineering, Washington, edited by Sam S. Y. Wang

[5] Bechteler W., Patt H. Vollmers H.-J. (1990), Modellversuch Lauter, Gut-achtliche Stellungnahme, Institut für Wasserwesen, Universität der Bundes-wehr München, Germany

[6] Cunge J.A., Holly R.M., Verwey A. (1980), Practical Aspects of Computa-tional River Hydraulics, Pitman Advanced Publishing Program, London

[7] Jameson A., Schmidt W., Turkel E. (1981), Numerical Solution of the Euler Equations by Finite Volume Methods Using Runge-Kutta Time Stepping Scheme, AIAA Paper, 81-1259

[8] Miller S.R. (1989), DTMCREATE Operations and MATRIX Utilities, Laser-Scan Ltd., Cambridge, UK

[9] Reinhardt D.R. (1992), Geographic Information Systems (GIS) - A Global Perspective, Global Environmental Change Report, Arlington, USA

[10] Weiyan T. (1992), Shallow Water Hydrodynamics, Elsevier Science Publi shing Company Inc., New York

BANGLADESH FLOOD MANAGEMENT MODEL
Towards a Spatial Decision Support System

W.J. Syme and G.N. Paudyal
Danish Hydraulic Institute

Abstract

In Bangladesh, floods and flood management are a part of life. Farmers for centuries have been managing and controlling the passage of flood waters for rice and other crops. Major floods, however, can be devastating on human life, agriculture, industry and infrastructure. Total flood prevention is unrealistic and unwise, but schemes from flood preparedness to embankments are viable options. Schemes which reduce flood damage, optimize rural production and improve living standards are necessary for Bangladesh's development.

Calibrated computational flood models provide reliable data on flood hydraulics and are useful tools to study flood management problems. Geographically combining flood model data with agriculture, fisheries and socio-economic data opens new avenues for flood management. The Flood Management Model (FMM) interfaces a geographic information system (GIS) with computational flood models as the first step towards a spatial decision support system (SDSS). The paper presents a brief background to floods and flood modelling in Bangladesh, FMM GIS interface design and initial developments.

Introduction

Severe floods in Bangladesh cause loss of human life and widespread damage to crops, roads, railways, cities and towns. The floods of 1987 and 1988 were two of the most severe floods in its history. The Government of Bangladesh in cooperation with several bilateral and international agencies has undertaken a major study called the Flood Action Plan (FAP), mainly to identify and prepare structural and non-structural flood control and water management plans for the country.

In order to study and predict the hydraulic behaviour of the complex river systems of Bangladesh mathematical modelling tools are being used. The mathematical models are based on one dimensional (1-D) hydraulic modelling of flows in rivers and channels and a quasi 2-D modelling of floodplain flows. The MIKE11 modelling system developed by the Danish Hydraulic Institute (DHI, 1992) was selected as the standard.

The hydraulic modelling tools have proved to be most useful in assisting the planning, design and operation of flood control options and hence are being used as a basis for decision support tools to manage river hydraulics problems.

However, their limitation in terms of spatial display and analysis is becoming more apparent when there is a greater need of a spatial decision support system (SDSS) in floodplain management. Due to the flat topography and Bangladesh's very complex river network, SDSS tools will be vital in the future. The present study aims to guide the flood modelling activities toward the development of an integrated SDSS. The first step is the development of the Flood Management Model (FMM) which fully integrates the MIKE11 modelling system with the geographic information system, ARC/INFO.

2nd International Conference on River Flood Hydraulics. Edited by W. R. White and J. Watts
© 1994 HR Wallingford Ltd. Published by John Wiley & Sons Ltd

Flood Modelling in Bangladesh

Flood control and management of floodplains is a continuing challenge to policy makers and agencies. Computer based modelling techniques have successfully amplified management skills in the industrial realm owing to the abundance of mathematical models.

Large scale (basin wide) hydraulic problems cannot be solved by a direct procedure or by physical modelling. The hydraulic behaviour of any complex system, however, can be simulated using a computational - mathematical model.

Figure 1   Catchment Boundaries of Bangladesh's Rivers

Background

Bangladesh through its complex network of rivers drains an area of about 2 million square kilometres of which only 8% lies within its territorial boundaries (Figure 1). This physical setting severely limits the degree of control and management that can be applied to the inflow of water both in the monsoon season and during the dry period.

Owing to its geographical location, Bangladesh is exposed to a wide range of extreme natural phenomena; it is located on a fragile portion of land in the world's largest delta which comprises three of the world's most unstable rivers. The rivers flowing into Bangladesh drain some of the wettest catchment areas on earth with average yearly rainfalls as high as 11 m. In addition, Bangladesh is one of the most fertile and densely populated regions in the world. Life in Bangladesh is pervasively influenced by the rivers.

The rivers also cause vast damage when they sweep over the country during massive floods. Approximately 40 per cent of the country is subject to regular flooding causing death as well as extensive damage. Apart from river floods, Bangladesh suffers severely from storm surges generated in the Bay of Bengal. The surge waves are induced by tropical cyclones and can reach heights of 7m as they approach the coast. The consequences are often disastrous and have cost hundreds of thousands of human lives in the coastal regions.

The need for control of water varies within the country. In rural areas, floods provide a livelihood when not too extreme and the rural population has, over the centuries, perfected its ability to cope with the water. In many such regions it is desirable to maintain the beneficial aspects of floods, eg. for the water demanding rice and jute crops and for inland fisheries. Under these circumstances, control - rather than elimination - of floods is required.

Flood Action Plan (FAP) and Flood Management
The floods of 1987 and 1988 focused attention on the need to develop a long term strategy to cope with the complexity of flood impact. The extent and complexity of these floods underlined the fact that total elimination of flooding is neither feasible nor desirable from the agro-ecological perspective. However, the protection of peoples lives and their places of habitation is absolutely essential as are the commercial and industrial centres. With these thoughts in mind, the government prepared a National Flood Protection Program, and, with the assistance of UNDP specialists carried out a Flood Policy Study (GOB and WB, 1992).

FAP focuses on the identification, planning and possible construction of technically, economically, environmentally and socially acceptable projects. FAP follows a staged approach through which regional and supporting studies will provide input into the planning and design of the main components of this and subsequent Action Plans. This work will investigate the feasibility of embankments on both sides of the major rivers, river training, channel improvement and protective infrastructure for major towns and key installations. It will also develop improvements to flood forecasting and warning systems and study the issues of watershed management, coastal afforestation and sustainable development of agriculture and fisheries.

Flood Simulation Models
The Brahmaputra, the Ganges and the Meghna form the backbone of the water system in Bangladesh; with lesser rivers and 'khals', these form a complex drainage pattern. Through equations and data, the mathematical computer-based model represents this complex drainage pattern. The model can simulate the passage of floods through the rivers. They may then be altered to test the effect of design proposals, eg. embankments and barrages. Such a powerful tool is vital for flood control and drainage planning in Bangladesh.

The Surface Water Modelling Program was established because of the widespread recognition that the effective control and utilization of water resources in Bangladesh is vital to the economic and social development of the country. Mathematical models of the complex river system are in this respect indispensable tools for an integrated approach to planning and design.

The main modelling tool being used in Bangladesh is the MIKE11 package developed at the Danish Hydraulic Institute. MIKE11 is a professional engineering software platform for the simulation of flows, water quality and sediment transport in estuaries, rivers, irrigation systems, channels and other water bodies. It is a dynamic, user-friendly, one-dimensional modelling tool for the detailed design, management and operation of both simple and complex river and channel systems. Due to its flexibility and speed, MIKE11 provides a complete and effective design environment for engineering, water resources, water quality management and planning applications. It owes its power to advanced programming techniques and mathematical model formulations which have been tested, developed and proven in many applications since the 1960s.

The modelling strategy has been to develop detailed regional models of the six separate regions of Bangladesh (Figure 2). The General Model (GM) covers the main rivers of almost the entire country and can thus provide the hydraulic linkages among the regional models. It serves as a planning and design tool for large scale flood control, drainage and irrigation projects (WRPO, 1992).

The regional models provide a finer resolution of the regional river and drainage network than does the GM. They are used as planning and design tools within the particular region to describe effects of embankments along minor rivers, polders, regulators, pump stations, dredging etc; they may also be the basis for accurate flood forecasting at a regional scale and finally, they may provide boundary conditions for subregional models which may be required for detailed analysis of specific projects.

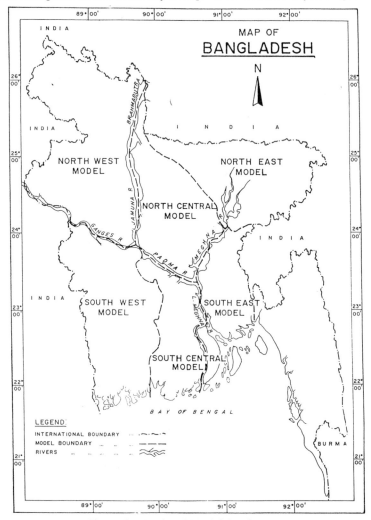

Figure 2   Regional Model Study Areas

GIS Interface - Step One Towards a SDSS

The first step towards a SDSS is interfacing existing flood management practices with a spatial or geographic information system (GIS). The development of the flood management model (FMM) encompasses this first step.

After a three month inception phase the FMM development commenced in March 1993 and is due for completion in September 1993. From October 1993 to October 1994 the FMM will be rigorously applied at national, regional and sub-regional scales.

Building of local expertise and technology transfer are key issues of the project. Carrying out the development are two Bengali professionals under the guidance of two expatriates. The FMM application will also be carried out by a group of local and expatriate engineers.

ARC/INFO (workstation) was selected as the GIS for interfacing with MIKE11. This decision has thus far proven sound, especially for prototyping methodologies. However, a less expensive and more portable platform (PC based) is being investigated for field installations. Such a platform is unlikely to facilitate all FMM functions, but would incorporate those necessary for on-site operation. The combination of ARC/INFO on workstations in a central office with PC based platforms in the field is a possible long-term solution.

The FMM GIS interface is based on a modular design. The major modules are:

System	Process control, file management, initialisation.
Database	Import of MIKE11 data into relational database. The database format facilitates easy data retrieval, comparison and management.
Edit	FMM coverage editors. Main coverages are the branch route system, storage cells, cross-section profile lines, water surface coverage for generating 3-D surfaces, catchment boundaries and rain gauges.
Topographic Data	Generates cross-section profiles and surface area-elevation (AE) curves from a DTM, and exports to a MIKE11 cross-section database. Profiles and AE curves can be interactively selected, displayed and exported (Figure 3).
Surface Generation	3-D surface generation of water levels, water depths, flood duration and water and ground levels combined, at instances in time or as a statistical measure (eg. maximum; monthly average).
Analysis and Display	Data viewing and impact assessment analysis. The viewing environment displays: flood inundation, depth and duration maps; water level and cross-section profiles; water level and discharge time-series and 3-D views. Impact assessments are aided by comparing MIKE11 simulations using time-series graphs and by mapping water level differences. Mapping agriculture and fisheries flood damage estimates based on water level changes and flood duration will be prototyped.

Two important FMM developments, the branch route system and generating a 3-D water surface from MIKE11 model output are discussed below.

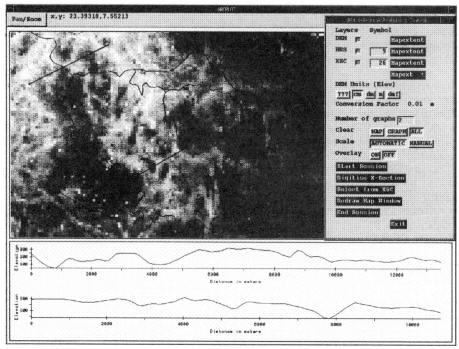

Figure 3   Extraction and Display of Cross-Section Profiles

Branch Route System (BRS)

GIS representation of MIKE11 model networks uses ARC/INFO's dynamic segmentation facility which models route systems (for example bus routes). The MIKE11 model network concept is similar to say, a bus route system. A network branch could be envisaged as a bus route; cross-sections and structures as bus stops.

The branch route system (BRS) is a single route system, representing all MIKE11 models for a study area. Its branch routes locate the models' branches using a measuring system. For example, a branch route named 'MAIN' is measured starting from 0.000 and ending at 60.000km. A MIKE11 model branch, 'MAIN' from 0.000 to 35.000km, will be located along branch route 'MAIN' according to its measures.

Branches from a model must not overlap or extend outside the branch route end measures. However, it is acceptable not to cover the entire branch route by branches. This is useful if a branch is modified, for example, by a diversion channel as illustrated below.

The user specifies and calibrates the route measures using imported branch measures from MIKE11. Initially the end measures of a route are specified and intermediate measures are linearly interpolated. Usually the linear interpolation is inaccurate and calibration of the measures is needed. Useful calibration points are branch route junctions (nodes). The branch routes' measures at the node are specified and the routes are re-measured (calibrated). A linear interpolation is used between calibration points.

172

Branch route measures control the location of features such as cross-sections and structures. For example, a structure at 'MAIN' 20.000 will be located on branch route 'MAIN' at measure 20.000. Re-measuring of branch routes will automatically re-locate all features. Figure 4 illustrates branch routes and cross-section locations for part of the North Central Region.

Two branch routes, 'Main' and 'Diversion', are shown. 'Main' measures from 0.000 to 60.000km and is calibrated at 15.000 and 40.000km. 'Diversion' measures from 0.000 to 5.000km.

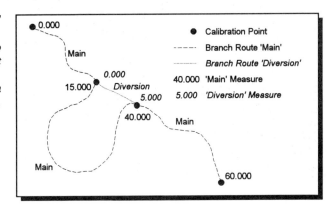

The MIKE11 model branches for the before diversion case are shown. No branch named 'Diversion' exists in the model therefore no 'Diversion' branches are shown along the 'Diversion' branch route.

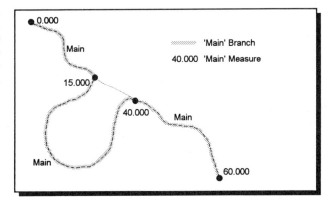

The MIKE11 model branches for the after diversion case are shown. The branches on 'Main' are 0.000 to 15.000km and 40.000 to 60.000km. As the branch 15.000 to 40.000km is not in the model, this section of branch route 'Main' is ignored.

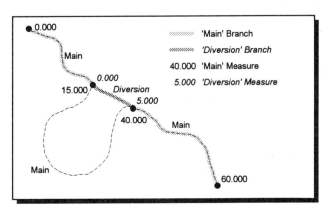

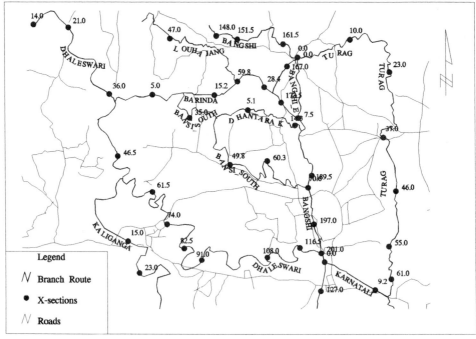

Figure 4   BRS for Part of the North Central Region, Bangladesh

Creating Water Surfaces from a 1-D Network Model

Creating a 3-D water surface from a 1-D network model such as MIKE11 is not a simple interpolation task. The water levels can be located in 3-D space, but a mathematical interpolation between levels produces a poor, badly represented surface as illustrated below.

Water levels are calculated at two h-points around a meander. The water level location halfway between them (Point A) is best estimated by measuring along a "centreline" (channel line), but without any knowledge of the meander shape (channel boundary) the best estimate, which is a poor one, would be at Point B.

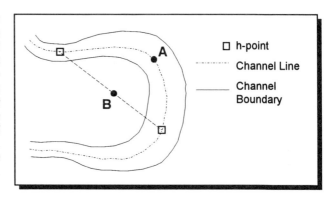

The simplest approach assumes each h-point represents a level pool. A polygon is digitised for each h-point and assigned a water level. Syme and McColm (1990) and FAP19 (1993) have applied this method successfully in Australia and Bangladesh respectively. The method's drawback is the water surface has a stair-step shape, ie. not a continuous surface which is more realistic.

Producing a continuous water surface requires knowledge of a branch's shape and width to create a water surface. Applying the 1-D assumption that the water level is horizontal across a cross-section, assign each h-point (water level calculation point) a line with a horizontal water level. This line is referred to as a water level line (WLL). Between these lines create intermediate lines (pseudo WLLs - PWLLs) which help define the branch's shape.

Pseudo water level lines (PWLLs) help define the branch's shape. The PWLL's water level is linearly interpolated using the water levels at the upstream and downstream WLLs.

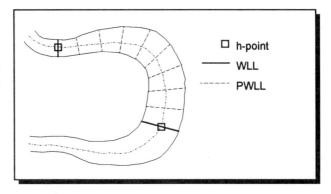

Using ARC/INFO edit and dynamic segmentation functions a robust methodology for automatically generating PWLLs for complex model networks was developed (Syme et al, 1992) and tested on the Hutt River, New Zealand.

PWLL water levels are interpolated from the adjacent WLL water levels which are imported from a MIKE11 simulation. A 3-D continuous water surface modelled as a TIN (triangular irregular network) is then created from the WLLs and PWLLs in the Surface Generation Module, along with other surfaces such as water depths and flood duration. Figure 5 shows the PWLLs and a water depth greyshade (the lighter the shading the shallower the depth) of the Hutt River.

A TIN is created from the WLLs and PWLLs to give a continuous 3-D water surface based on MIKE11 water levels.

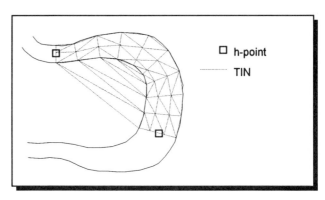

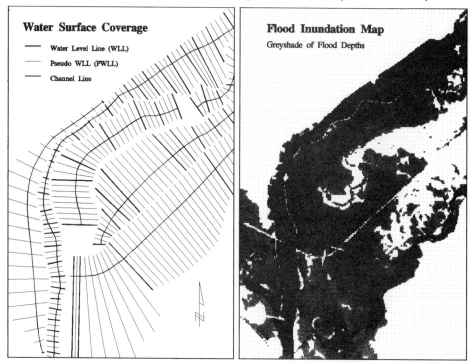

Figure 5   3-D Water Surface Generation - Hutt River, New Zealand

Conclusions

A Flood Management Model primarily based on an interface between MIKE11 river modelling software and the ARC/INFO GIS is being developed as a management tool for Bangladesh's rivers and floodplains. The interface will be used to analyze and display MIKE11 flood data combined with spatial data on agriculture, fisheries and socio-economics.

Two key developments thus far have been the branch route system concept which dynamically represents MIKE11 model networks, and creating 3-D water surfaces from MIKE11 output.

References

DHI (1992) Danish Hydraulic Institute *MIKE11 - A Micro-Computer Based Modelling System for Rivers and Channels*

FAP19 (1993) Geographic Information System (FAP19) *Draft Technical Report - Classification of Flood Depth and Extent using GIS and MIKE11* Flood Plan Coordination Organisation, Ministry of Irrigation Water Development and Flood Control, Bangladesh, February 1993

GOB and WB (1992) The Government of Bangladesh and the World Bank *Proceedings of the Second Flood Action Plan Conference* Dhaka, Bangladesh, March 1992

Syme W.J., McColm G.A. (1990) *Integration of Numerical Flood Modelling into Geographic Information Systems* Conference on Hydraulics in Civil Engineering, 1990, Sydney, Australia

Syme W.J., Barnett A.G., Turton G.B. (1992) *GIS Floodplain Management* ITMG Conference, New Zealand, October 1992

WRPO (1992) Water Resources Planning Organization *Surface Water Modelling Centre, SWSMP-II, Interim Report II* August 1992

2nd International Conference on
RIVER FLOOD HYDRAULICS
22–25 March 1994: York, England

USE OF A GIS IN THE MODELLING OF FLOWS ON FLOODPLAINS

Teodoro Estrela
Centro de Estudios Hidrográficos del CEDEX
Madrid, Spain
Luis Quintas
Centro de Estudios Hidrográficos del CEDEX
Madrid, Spain

ABSTRACT

This article presents an integrated model for a two-dimensional hydraulic flow module for floodplains and a raster-based geographical information system and its application in a real situation, the River Júcar floodplain, on the Spanish Mediterranean Coast.

1.- INTRODUCTION

Mathematical flow models in a non-stationary regime have often been used to simulate one-dimensional flows. When flood levels cover extensive areas of a plain, it is sometimes necessary to use two-dimensional models which simulate water levels and discharges. However, these models handle a great deal of spatial and temporal information, and using them becomes complex and laborious. To overcome these drawbacks, we have developed the link up between a two-dimesional hydraulic model and GRASS [1], a geographical information system (GIS) which was deviced by the U.S. Army Corps of Engineers, along the same lines [2] that the latter organization adopted to link the one-dimensional and stationary model, HEC-2 [3] and GRASS. With this GIS, we can easily handle, display and analyze different spatial and temporal data (terrain, depths, flows, etc.). This paper describes the integrated model GISPLANA and its application to a real case. The study site is the floodplain of the River Júcar, on the Spanish Mediterranean Coast. The Júcar floods considerable areas of land, along several kilometres on either side of the river, for flows with high recurrence intervals. The water is not only stored on the plain, but also flows with an important transverse velocity component. This work studies the 1987 flood, which had a peak flow of 5,000 m^3/sec. and a recurrence interval of 50 years.

2.- HYDRAULIC MODEL

2.1.- Zonification and Equations

The floodplain is envisaged as a series of cells interlinked by hydraulic circulation channels. This division into cells also applies to the river courses. Cell determination is not arbitrary, but responds to already existing boundaries such as drainage ditches, roads, railways, walls, etc. The water level in each cell is assumed to be horizontal and the same depth as the level at the centre. The other essential hypothesis on which the model is based is that the connecting flow between cells is a unique function of the cell levels themselves, which implies an exclusion of the inertia terms, as the velocities are assumed to be inconsequential. Once this hypothesis is admitted the type of formulation consists of an equation system which establishes the flow continuity in each cell as outlined below.

It is called:

Q_{ik}^n = Flow in the connection that links cell k to cell i at instant $n\Delta t$.
Z_i^n = Elevation in cell i at instant $n\Delta t$.
$A_i(Z_i)$ = Free surface of cell i corresponding to elevation Z_i.

2nd International Conference on River Flood Hydraulics. Edited by W. R. White and J. Watts
© 1994 HR Wallingford Ltd. Published by John Wiley & Sons Ltd

P_i^n =   Net rainfall intensity in cell i at instant nΔt. In fact it is a direct cell recharge or discharge term.

The continuity equation of a cell can be formulated as

$$A_i (Z_i) \, \Delta Z_i = P_i \, \Delta t + \sum_k \left[\int_{n\Delta t}^{(n+1)\,\Delta t} Q_{i,k} \, dt \right]$$

assuming that the surface does not vary between levels Z_i and $Z_i + \Delta Z_i$, it being understood that the sum total includes all of connections that have acces to cell i. Averaging the integrals in the time interval, the following expression can be obtained:

$$A_i (Z_i) \cdot \Delta Z_i = P_i \cdot \Delta t + \sum_k Q_{ik} \left\{ Z_i (\tau), Z_k (\tau) \right\} \cdot \Delta t$$

where $n\Delta t < \tau < (n+1)\Delta t$, there being as many equations as there are cells in the model. The solution to the system is unique once the initial conditions (water levels) and the boundary conditions (inflow hydrographs, known levels), have been fixed.

2.2.- Hydraulic Connections

The model envisages three types of connections: a) river-type, b) weir-type and c) pressure flow-type

a) River-type connection

In this case the hydraulic connection becomes equivalent to reaches of the channel and Manning's formula is the discharge interchange law considered:

$$Q = A.R.^{2/3}.S^{1/2}/n$$

where:
Q =   Discharge
n =   Manning's coefficient
A =   Wetted section
R =   Hydraulic radius
S =   Slope of free water surface
    A and R depend on the average level of the reach. If the elevations in the cells are Z_i and Z_j, the level in the connection will be $Z_{ij} = \alpha Z_i + (1 - \alpha) Z_j$, with α predetermined. For each reach, Z_{ij} is the average weighted value of the characteristic levels. The value of the slope is $S = (Z_j - Z_i)/L$, where L is the distance between cell centres i and j.

b) Weir-type connections

A width b and a threshold elevation ZU_{ij} are taken. The discharge interchanged is given by:

-    Free flow:

$$Q_{ij} = \phi_1 \, (Z_j - ZU_{ij})^{3/2}$$

-    Drowned flow:

$$Q_{ij} = \Phi_a \cdot (Z_i - ZU_{ij}) \sqrt{Z_j - Z_i}$$

Assuming for both cases that $Z_j > Z_i$, ϕ_l and ϕ_a are the discharge coefficients of the weir, generally expressed as:

$$\Phi_l = \mu_l \cdot b \cdot \sqrt{2g}$$
$$\Phi_a = \mu_a \cdot b \cdot \sqrt{2g}$$

Where b is the width, g the gravity and μ_l and μ_a are the coefficients of the weir flow. The criterion for distinguishing the two types of weir is:

When $Z_i - ZU_{ij} < 2/3 \ (Z_j - ZU_{ij})$ the weir is free and if it is not it is drowned

c)   Pressure flow-type

In this case, the formulae used are (for $Z_i < Z_j$): If $Z_i < ZEJE$, where ZEJE is the elevation of the drainage system axis.

$$Q_{ij} = K \sqrt{2g \ (Z_j - ZEJE \ )}$$

If $Z_i > ZEJE$

$$Q_{ij} = k \sqrt{2g \ (Z_j - Z_i)}$$

k is a coefficient that includes located and distributed losses throughout the connection and the area of the cross-section. Its value is:

$$k = \frac{S}{\sqrt{k_p}}$$

where S is the cross-section and k_p is the sum of the loss coefficients at the inlet, throughout the drainage system and the mouth.

2.3.- Numerical Formulation

Given the continuity equation in each cell:

$$A_i \cdot \Delta Z_i = P_i \cdot \Delta t + \sum_k Q_{i,k} \cdot \Delta t$$

where Q_{ik} lies between Q_{ik}^n and Q_{ik}^{n+1}, and n is the calculation period. A parameter θ can be fixed so that $0 < \theta < 1$, which defines the values of Q_{ik} in the following way:

$$Q_{ik} = \theta \cdot Q_{i,k}^{n+1} + (1-\theta) \ Q_{i,k}^n$$

By developing the term $Q_{i,k}^{n+1}$ in the Taylor series, ignoring higher terms and assuming that the level variations are slight for the interval considered, then:

$$Q_{i,k}^{n+1} = Q_{i,k}^n + \frac{\delta Q_{i,k}^n}{\delta Z_i} \Delta Z_i + \frac{\delta Q_{i,k}^n}{\delta Z_k} \Delta Z_k$$

Replacing in the continuity equation, making $\theta = 1$ to solve the equations implicitly:

$$\left[-\frac{A_i}{\Delta t} + \sum_k \frac{\delta Q_{i,k}^n}{\delta Z_i} \right] \Delta Z_i + \sum_k \frac{\delta Q_{i,k}^n}{\delta Z_k} \Delta Z_k = -P_i - \sum_k Q_{i,k}^n$$

and in simplified form:

$$CM_{ii} \Delta Z_i + \sum_j CM_{ij} \Delta Z_j = T_i$$

These equations, written for the n cells, form a system of linear equations where ΔZ_i are unknown, that can be solved from an initial state once the boundary conditions have been introduced. Such conditions can be of three types: a) level as a function of time, b) recharge and discharge as a time function and c) recharge or discharge as a water level function. The Gauss-Seydell's numerical solution is used.

3.- IMPLEMENTATION OF A GRAPHICAL USER INTERFACE

3.1.- Graphical User Interface and Linkage of the Hydraulic Model to a GIS

The hydraulic model is written in FORTRAN 77 and reads and generates information in ASCII files. A graphical user interface (GUI) with XGEN [4] generator from the U.S. Army Corps has been implemented, in order to analyze the information contained in these files. In this way the hydraulic model is connected to GRASS. The different routines of the model have been integrated into shell scripts that can be interpreted by XGEN and executed through MOTIF [5] widgets in X Window. The software developed has been implemented in a Hewlett-Packard HP9000/400 work station in the X Window environment and UNIX operating system. Some examples of information that can be analyzed with this GUI are: a) temporal discharge evolution in a given connection or frontier (set of connections), b) temporal water-level evolution in a cell, c) maximum levels on a profile formed by a set of cells, d) digital terrain model, e) spatial maps of depths or water levels throughout time, f) spatial maps of maximum depths or levels, g) spatial maps of level differences for diverse simulations, etc.

3.2.- General Characteristics of the Geographical Information System GRASS

The Geographical Resources Analysis and Support System (GRASS) is a general purpose GIS belonging to the Army Corps of Engineers (U.S.A.), originally developed as a tool for helping land planners in military installations. It can be regarded as software designed to display, analyze and manage geographical data. Initially, it was designed as a raster-based conception, although at the same time an image processing module was developed. Currently, it also has a vectorial approach that makes it possible to digitize, store and process data. GRASS has been developed to operate within the UNIX operating system and has been used in numerous hardware environments which support this operating system.

GRASS has several design characteristics which make it suitable for hydraulic modelling. Its ability to digitize, edit and store layers of vectorial data from maps, combined with the use of the analytical power of the raster technology, mean that this GIS constitutes a suitable basis for hydraulic modelling. Among the most interesting uses to which it can be put are: a) Defining river basins and plotting the drainage networks from a digital terrain model, b) Interpolation of a surface from rasterized specific values. Therefore, temporal evolution maps can be obtained for water levels, or for any other variable, using terrain values in the cells where the physical environment has previously been discretized, c) Image processing. It is possible to extract and interactively classify satellite images and aerial photography. The georeferenced images can be the subject of raster analysis. By way of example, the discretization of the model and information concerning rasterized variables can be superimposed onto an image of the physical environment being studied. d) Combination of the different information layers rasterized. This technique makes it feasible to assess relationships between the different information layers constituting the GIS, e.g. Manning's coefficient from vegetation data, land use (agricultural, urban) etc., and e) Integration of mathematical models that interact with the various information layers. Thus, the evolution of complex dynamic systems can be studied.

4.- CASE OF A REAL STUDY

4.1.- Context of the Study

In 1988, the Roads Administration of the present Department of Public Works and Transport commissioned the Public Works Studies and Research Centre (CEDEX) to conduct a study [6] whose aim was to determine the effect of roads upon water levels that were reached on the River Júcar floodplain during the November 1987 floods. The difficult nature of the task and the problematic case history involving the modelling of the 1982 flood in the same basin, justified a detailed analysis of the phenomenon and the use of a mathematical model to simulate the variable two-dimensional flow regime over extensive flooded areas together and the influence of the main communication networks. A first version of the GUI of the hydraulic model is beeing developed within the framework of the R+D Project conducted by the CEDEX called "Numerical Modelling of Hydrological Processes". The real case used for the development of these works was the floodplain of the River Júcar during the 1987 flood.

4.2.- Description of the Study Zone and Zonification of the Flood plain

The River Júcar runs over its own deposits, following a course that lies at a greater elevation than most of the surrounding plain. In times of floods, this layout is conducive to the flooding of extensive areas, several kilometers wide, where the water is not only stored on the plain but also flows with a considerable transversal component of its velocity leading away from the riverbed. The flood limits of the plain cover a surface area of about 250 km^2, which is regardless of the magnitude of the discharges when floods with a high return period (50 - 500 years) are concerned. The floodplain has been discretized into cells of variable surface. Generally, the cells which represent the rivers or channels are smaller (only a few thousand square metres) than the floodplain cells, without obstacles and gently sloping. As a rule, the largest cells are on the borders, those lying off the flow concentration lines. There are 403 cells and 959 hydraulic connections. Each of the latter connects two adjacent cells. The type of connection can vary (river, weir or pressure flow) on the basis of the water levels of the cells upstream.

4.3.- Model Parameters and Boundary Conditions

Among the information required for the working of the model, the physical data, such as cross-section profiles of the river bed representing a reach or the surface of the cells, is relatively easy to quantify, but there are other parameters about which only their magnitude is known. An accurate determining of these parameters depends on the concordance between the model and the physical reality.

The parameters of the model are: a) relative roughness coefficient, used for river-type connections, b) discharge coefficients of the weir and c) loss coefficients for the pressure flow connections. Therefore, for each type of connection there is a different adjustment parameter. The calibration parameter for the river-type connections, once the riverbed is defined, is the roughness coefficient, whose value on the model is inverse to Manning's. With the aid of aerial photography, various roughnesses were defined depending on the zone considered: a) River beds. Manning coefficients ranging between 0.025 and 0.035 were used. In the case of channelled sections the coefficients are smaller (between 0.014 and 0.017). b) Orange groves. The greater the density of orange trees, the larger the coefficient of Manning, above all when the trees are bigger (Coefficients of Manning ranging from 0.05 to 0.025) and d) Paddy fields. Bearing in mind that the flood studied occurred in November, after the rice harvest, the roughness was assumed to be slight (coefficients of Manning between 0.020 and 0.025) and d) Horticultural land. In this case, the roughness lies midway between that of the orange trees and the rice fields, and coefficients of Manning ranging from 0.025 to 0.040 were used.

The discharge coefficients of the weir for the model tries to simulate a complex discharge loss between two plots. The value of the free discharge coefficients ranges from 0.35 at the weir connections for railway lines, roads or highways, to 0.20 at the connections between cells on the plain and in riverbeds when the flow runs perpendicular to the connection. The drowned discharge coefficients range from 0.90 to 0.25. The losses are assumed to be equivalent to 0.5 $(V^2/2g)$ at the inlet and at the 1.0 $(V^2/2g)$ at the mouth. The distributed losses along the connections have been ignored because they are usually short and the diameter of the main connections is considerable, so losses due to friction are slight. Therefore the total losses are 1.5 $(V^2/2g)$.

Two types of boundary conditions exist: a) Discharges that vary with time. These correspond to the hydrographs of the rivers that flow onto the floodplain. The main rivers are, in order of importance, the Júcar, Magro and Verde and b) Water levels constant in time. These boundary conditions correspond to the water level in La Albufera (a fresh-water lake with outlet to the sea) and the Mediterranean. It was assumed that the sea level remained constant at 0.6 m. above its average level and that the elevation remained 0.8 m. in La Albufera.

4.4.- Calibration and Validation of the Model

The model described was calibrated [7] with the 1982 flood, the latter being greater than the 1987 one, 15,000 m³/sec, as opposed to 5,000 m³/sec. The information available for the calibration of the 1982 flood model was: a) Maximum levels reached and sometimes occurrence time, b) Levels observed as a function of time and c) Maximum flows calculated at particular sections: highway, railway connecting the towns of Sollana and Sueca, etc.

In the case of the 1987 flood, the model could be validated with information similar to that used during the calibration, by testing how it functioned with lower discharges and levels. Slight modifications were made to the parameters, which served to further improve the calibration carried out with the 1982 flood. The lower flood levels suggested that the flood evolution was more greatly affected by local phenomena and obstacles, which meant that in some zones the digital terrain model (Fig. 1), had to be re-examined more thoroughly.

4.5.- Simulation of Levels and Discharges

Regarding the temporal evolution of discharges, Fig. 2., shows the hydrograph where the highway crosses the river. The peak discharge at this point was 5,000 m³/sec. As regards the temporal evolution of the depths, Figs. 3 and 4, show the spatial distribution of the depths for t = 24 hours and t = 44 hours.

Among the many model simulations carried out to analyze the effect of different ways of dealing with the physical environment, the following serves as an example: a) the hypothetical situation for the 1987 without the highway. The effect of the presence of the highway on the maximum levels during the 1987 flood can be seen immediately upstream, the downstream water flowing away rapidly owing to the steep slope of the water level and the widening of the riverbed downstream from the confluence with the River Magro (Fig. 5) and b) the hypothetical situation with the highway drainage system in the real situation plus the supplementary one constructed close to the Algemesí junction and the widening of the bridge over the Júcar, after the 1987 flood (Fig. 6). These measures are clearly beneficial upstream from the highway, because the water level descends appreciably on the left bank, leaving some zones almost dry. On the other hand, the possible negative effect of a rise in downstream levels is negligible. As can be deduced from Figs. 5 and 6, these works tend to revert to the situation prior to the construction of the highway.

5. CONCLUSIONS

The use of two-dimensional hydraulic simulation models in a non-stationary regime to study flood effects on a floodplain involve the management of enormous amounts of spatial information. The creation of a graphical user interface that permits display and analysis of all such information can be of great help in using this type of model, especially if the physical environment is discretized into a high number of cells. In the work done, the implementation of a graphical user interface that includes linkage to the geographical information system GRASS, has permitted the display of the variable spatial and temporal information that generates the model, and this has meant considerable time-saving when interpreting the results and analyzing the coherence of the information; without doubt, such tasks would be very difficult to achieve without the use of a tool of this nature. In this way, it has been possible to assess the effects that different environmental activities, such as infrastructure construction and the corresponding transversal drainage, would have upon flood levels. Furthermore, these tools will make it possible to be able to generate new spatial layers with information concerning the hydraulic parameters of the model, using the existing layers of spatial information (vegetation, land use, nehworks, etc.), so most of the model's construction process would be practically automated.

BIBLIOGRAPHICAL REFERENCES

(1)   U.S. Army Corps of Engineers. "Manual for the Geographical Resources Analysis Support System GRASS. Version 4.0". CERL ADP Report N-87/22. July 1991.
(2)   Hydrologic Engineering Center, U.S.A. "F-Tools. Floodplain Analysis Tools. User's Documentation. Version 1.7" May 1992.
(3)   Hydrologic Engineering Center, U.S.A. "HEC-2 Surface Profiles. User's Manual". September 1982.
(4)   BUEHLER, K.A., "Xgen: An Application Interface Generator Program". U.S.A. CERL. U.S. Army Corps, 1991.
(5)   Open Software Foundation, "OSF/Motif. Release 1.1, Programmer's Reference". Prentice Hall, Englewood Cliffs, New Jersey 07632, 1991.
(6)   C.E.D.E.X. Spain. "Estudio Hidrológico e Hidraúlico de la Crecida de Noviembre de 1987 en la Ribera del Júcar". Final Report. Agreement C.E.D.E.X. and D.G.C. December 1988.
(7)   C.E.D.E.X. Spain. "Estudio en Modelo Matemático de las Inundaciones de Octubre 1982 en la Plana del Júcar". Final Report. Agreement C.E.D.E.X. and D.G.O.H. October 1988.

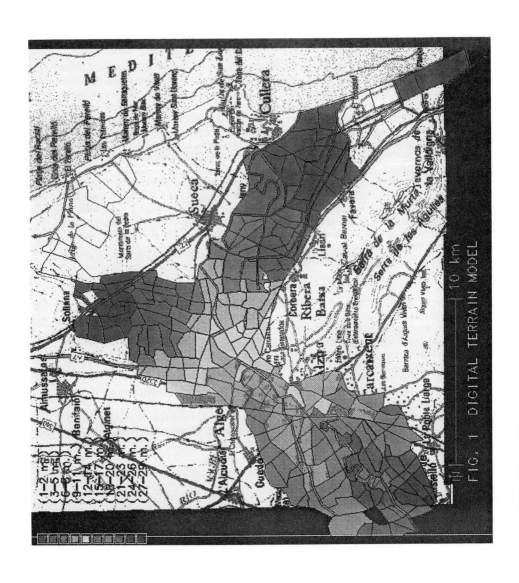

FIG. 1 DIGITAL TERRAIN MODEL

FIG.2 HYDROGRAPH (HIGHWAY)

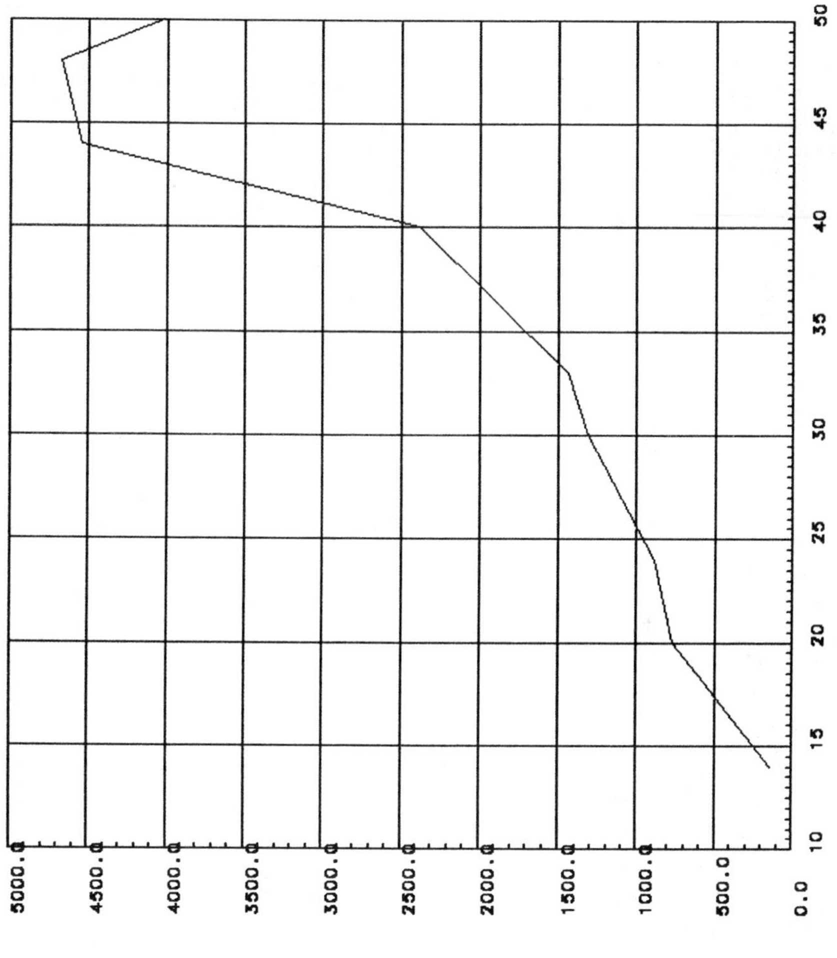

FIG. 3 WATER DEPTHS (TIME = 20 HOURS)

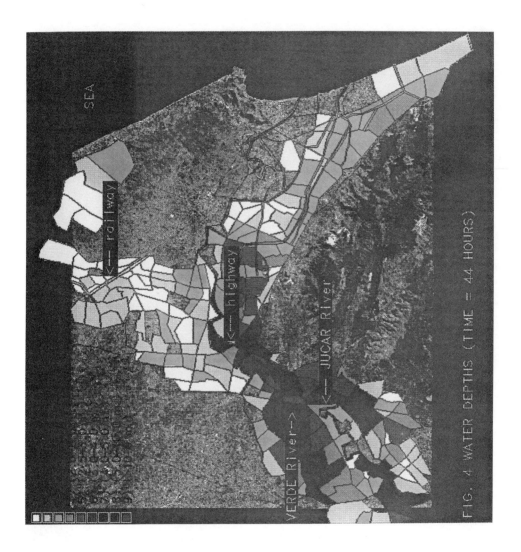

FIG. 4 WATER DEPTHS (TIME = 44 HOURS)

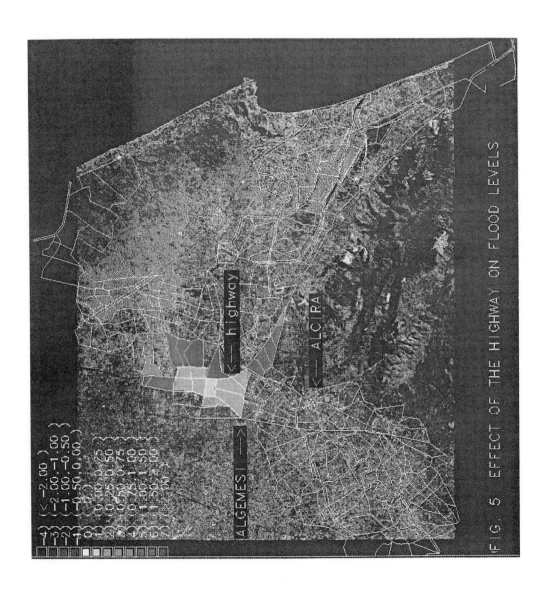

FIG. 5 EFFECT OF THE HIGHWAY ON FLOOD LEVELS

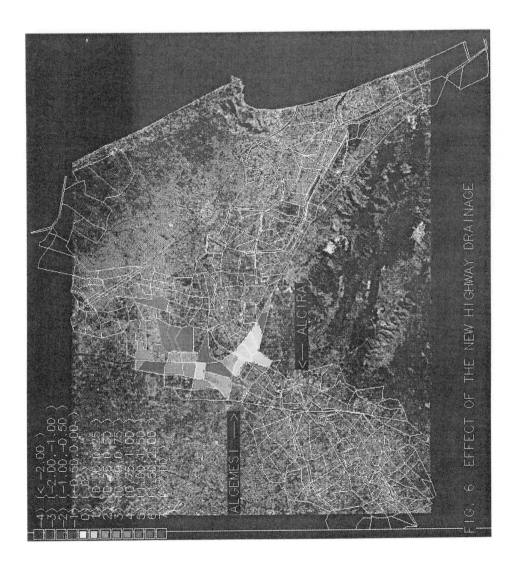

FIG. 6 EFFECT OF THE NEW HIGHWAY DRAINAGE

Chapter Five

Engineering, Design and Maintenance

2nd International Conference on
RIVER FLOOD HYDRAULICS
22–25 March 1994: York, England

Policy analysis of river-dike improvement in the Netherlands

by H.N.C. Breusers and M. Vis[2]

ABSTRACT

River-dike improvement along the rivers Rhine and Meuse has given rise to large-scale protests in the Netherlands due to its harmful impact on the river landscape and the natural and cultural values of the river dikes. A Government Commission was set up to assess the present basis for river-dike improvement such as the required safety level, the design methods and the procedures used to involve local and general interest groups in the design process.

To support the advice of the Commission, a study was commissioned by the Dutch government to DELFT HYDRAULICS and RAND's European-American Center for Policy Analysis (RAND/EAC) to analyse all design and institutional aspects related to river-dike improvement. The study has resulted in a set of recommendations and strategies to reduce the impact of dike improvement on other functions of the river dikes. Most recommendations were adopted by the Commission in their advice to the government and included in the Government Decision on the matter. The paper summarizes the way the problem was analysed and how strategies for dike improvement were derived.

1   INTRODUCTION

Flooding in the Dutch part of the rivers Rhine and Meuse regularly occurred in the past, the last major flooding was in 1926. The government decided in 1958, in the aftermath of the 1953 flood disaster in the delta area, to increase the safety against flooding from the river Rhine, by strengthening the existing river dikes to a safety standard of 1/3000 per year. Implementation of the strengthening however was very detrimental to the river landscape, to natural values and characteristic houses along the dikes, and generated intense protests from society. The Dutch river landscape is the result of a age-long natural and cultural development and is of great natural beauty.

In a review of the dike-improvement process, a River dikes Commission recommended in 1977 to mitigate the impact of dike strengthening by lowering the safety standard to 1/1250 per year and by improvements in the technical design. It was also recommended to improve the decision procedures to enable a better participation of the parties concerned and the general public in the decision process.

---

[2] DELFT HYDRAULICS, Delft, The Netherlands

2nd International Conference on River Flood Hydraulics. Edited by W. R. White and J. Watts
© 1994 HR Wallingford Ltd. Published by John Wiley & Sons Ltd

However, these recommendations had little effect on the actual process and did not improve social acceptance. Protests against river-dike improvement kept growing. In July 1992, the protests prompted the Minister of Public Works, Transport and Water Management to establish a new River dikes Commission (the Boertien Commission) and to assign a policy analysis study for the verification of the existing concepts to the combination DELFT HYDRAULICS/(RAND/EAC).

The policy analysis study on river-dike improvement had to focus on three main questions expressed by the Minister, viz:
- Do the considerations underlying the selection of the safety standard for river dikes contain any elements that have changed to such an extent that this might give rise to a different choice?
- Are there any new technological/scientific insights that may result in different calculation results?
- Have new elements emerged in recent commentaries (outside the scope of the previous questions) that might likewise result in a different choice or other calculation results?

The project area included the dikes along the non-tidal stretches of the river Rhine, its branches and the Meuse. The total length of river dikes in the project area amounts to 570 km of which 200 km had already been improved or was strong enough. The remaining 370 km required an estimated budget of 900 Mf. (1 Mf = 10^6 Dutch guilders) for improvement of the river dikes to a safety level of 1/1250 per year.

2   ORGANIZATION OF THE STUDY

For the execution of the project, DELFT HYDRAULICS/(RAND/EAC) associated with Delft Geotechnics, Bureau SME (institutional aspects) and Hamhuis+van Nieuwenhuijze+Sijmons (landscape architects).

The study had to be completed within a very short time period (5 months) in order not to lose momentum in the dike-improvement activities. In the first month, interviews were held with all agencies and groups involved, from which essential information on the pros and cons of the present decision-making and design process was obtained. The agencies involved are the waterboards, having the primary responsibility for flood protection, the provinces and Rijkswaterstaat, the national agency for water management and flood defence works.

Groups involved are action groups, environmental protection groups and nature conservation groups. Especially the water boards and the action groups held opposite views, the water boards putting emphasis on safety and the action groups on the preservation of the existing landscape, natural and cultural values of the dikes and the surrounding landscape.

It followed from the analysis that designs had improved in recent years, but were still insufficiently aimed at preserving the integral value of the river landscape. The system of subsidies provided by the central government did not stimulate creative design methods. The procedures for design and approval of dike improvement projects were inadequate for involvement and weighing of local interests and values, which limited the social acceptance of the projects.

The execution of the study was structured following a policy analysis approach as presented in figure 1. For various study aspects (safety standard, boundary conditions, design methods and the improvement of the tuning of function and values of the dikes) measures were generated to improve the process. Measures were, after screening, combined into (promising) strategies. Strategies were assessed using a number of decision criteria. Assessment of existing (and proposed) decision procedures led to the design of a new procedure.

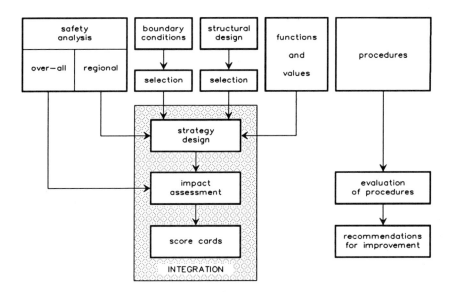

Figure 1 Policy analysis approach

3 RESULTS

3.1 Safety standard

The effects of a lower safety standard were assessed, using a number of criteria, such as the length of the dikes to be improved, the impact on landscape, nature and cultural values (the LNC-values), the present value (PV) of expected residual flood damage and construction costs. Personal risk could not be estimated with a reasonable accuracy as it depends on too many factors, such as failure probability of the dike system, rate and depth of flooding, possibilities for evacuation, etc.. Historical data on the number of victims could not be used, as conditions in the area (population density, infrastructure, communications) have greatly changed.

As can be seen from table 1, the effects of a lower safety standard on the preservation of LNC-values is limited, as most of the dikes, even those that are high enough, still need improvement. However, with a lower safety standard, personal risk and residual material flood damage increase. The optimum safety standard from a purely economic point of view is in the order of 10^{-4} per year. Taking all factors into account, the Boertien Commission recommended to maintain the present safety standard of 1/1250 per year. For areas with smaller flooding depths, the Commission suggested a lower safety standard.

As a lowering of the safety standard only has a minor effect on the preservation of existing values of the dikes and the river landscape, other measures will be necessary. Examples are a lowering of the design water levels for a given design discharge or improved design methods.

Criterion	Unit	Safety standard (per year)		
		1/1250	1/500	1/200
Length to be improved	km	370	320	270
Preservation of LNC values	%	75	79	84
Residual damage by flooding (PV)	Mf	1,400	3,300	7,600
Dike improvement costs	Mf	870	770	640

Table 1 Effects of the value of the safety standard against flooding

3.2 Boundary conditions

River Rhine discharge data were used to verify existing discharge extrapolation methods. Based on this verification, it was proposed to reduce the design discharge for the Rhine from 16,500 to 15,000 m³/s. The proposed discharge includes a correction for effects of changes in the German part of the river basin.

The corresponding decrease in the design water level of 0.25 to 0.45 m resulted in a reduction by 5% of the length of the dikes to be improved. The reduction in construction costs was estimated at 10%. Verification of the analysis of river Meuse discharges confirmed the current design discharge of 3,650 m³/s.

Numerous measures to lower the design water level for a given design discharge were evaluated with respect to their effectiveness and technical, financial and social feasibility. Some examples of measures:

- a partial diversion of the river discharge by means of overflow sections;
- flood storage in reservoirs or overflow basins;
- lowering of the minor riverbed and groynes; and
- lowering of the major riverbed by excavating the flood plain or by constructing secondary channels in the flood plains (in agreement with a plan for nature development in the flood plain proposed by the World Wildlife Fund).

None of the investigated measures or a combination of measures appeared to be feasible as an alternative for dike improvement. Excavation of the flood plain in combination with nature development can, however, contribute to the solution of local bottlenecks and the compensation for possible effects of climate changes.

3.3   Constructive design

The existing guidelines for river-dike design and present design practice were assessed, taking new technology and the state-of-the-art design practice into consideration. This led to recommendations for 'optimal' design methods by using more intensive soil-mechanical investigations and new computation methods. This will result in less massive dike cross-sections, thus allowing a better landscape design. At present, if there are valuable elements (natural or cultural values) on both sides of the dike, often only the element on one side of the dike is saved. To obtain a better solution in such a situation (a 'bottle-neck'), relatively expensive technical solutions are required to decrease the width of the new dikes. The application of these 'smart' structures like sheet piles, diaphragm walls and flap gates in solving these 'bottlenecks' was therefore also evaluated.

Based on this analysis, two design strategies for solving bottle-necks were developed and assessed. Solving half of the presently unsolved problems requires an increase of the construction costs with roughly one third. Solving almost all bottlenecks will double the costs.

3.4   Tuning of functions and values

Apart from the flood-protection function, other functions and values of a dike are of importance. Dikes often have a special vegetation, people live along them, many characteristics of the dikes have a cultural-historical value and dikes are an important element in the river landscape. Prior to dike improvement design, drawing up an extensive inventory of the present values is required. Also 'smart' designs should be more applied to create possibilities for the development of other values.

The quality of dike vegetation can be substantially improved by an environment-friendly management (no application of fertilizer, mowing once or twice a year). Recommendations were given for a change of the subsidy structure to stimulate creative designs and nature friendly management of the vegetation.

3.5   Procedures

The present practice in which technicians prepare their designs in a 'closed shop' situation while presenting them too late for review by the people concerned, was causing much discontent. Existing and proposed procedures for design and approval were therefore assessed and improvements recommended.

The recommendations included: (1) the development of provincial river-dike improvement plans that will give the boundary conditions for local designs and (2) the formation of steering groups at the local level that represent all interest groups involved. These groups can then express their ideas at an early stage of the design process, which will lead to a more open and creative design process. Verification of the quality of the design with respect to the preservation of existing values has to take place through a compulsory environmental impact assessment procedure.

4   POLICY OPTIONS

Measures to improve the present dike-strengthening practice were combined into strategies. The impact of these strategies, as well as the effect of a change in the safety standard, can be assessed using a number of criteria, like damage to the present functions and values, possible flood damage and the construction and maintenance costs. Policy options were formed by combining a choice for the safety standard and strategies for dike improvement, from which the decision makers can make their choice after weighing the effects of the policy options with respect to the decision criteria.

To illustrate the type of policy options presented to the decision makers, some options are presented in table 2. The effects of a change in the design discharge of the river Rhine and of various improvements of the present design methods is given. The strategy 'improved practice' refers to a 'sharper' design method, using the most up-to-date computation methods. The strategies 'selective saving' and 'saving all' refer to strategies in which part (50%) or almost all bottlenecks are solved by the application of alternative 'smart' constructions. The 'base case' refers to present design discharge and design practice.

Criterion	Unit	Base case	Strategy			
			present practice	improved practice	selective saving	safe all
Length to be improved	km	370	350	350	350	350
Preservation of LNC-values	%	75	79	79	89	98
Landscape quality	-	0	0	+	+	+
Quality of the vegetation	-	0	0	+	+	+
Dike improvement costs	Mf	870	780	800	1055	1655

Table 2 Effects of changed river Rhine design discharge and alternative design methods

5   IMPLEMENTATION

The Boertien Commission adopted almost all recommendations for improvement that resulted from the analysis and advised the Minister to adopt the 'selective saving' strategy. The Government Decision on dike improvement closely followed the Commission's advice. It is expected that the new government policy will promote major improvements in the dike-strengthening process and will widen the public support for its results.

OPTIMIZING OF THE DEVELOPMENT OF THE STANDARD OF FLOOD PROTECTION WITHIN FLOOD PLAIN BASINS

Sándor TÓTH M. Sc.
Counsellor
Ministry of Transport, Communication
and Water Management

75-81 Dob St.
H-1077 Budapest
Hungary

ABSTRACT. This paper - on the grounds of the results of Hungarian R + D activities, supervised by the author - is going to introduce briefly the determination of separate flood plain basins, the selection and determination of the significant components of possible damages caused by floods, the determination of flood damage reduction achieved by taking appropriate structural measures.

Introduction

For any kind of investment to be realized, economic efficiency - or in other words: does it worth or not - is a very important question for decision makers. The same question arises in the case of flood mitigation projects.

There are several types of flood mitigation measures [1] such as
- doing nothing but learning from the experience and adjusting life to the circumstances,
- non structural measures, mainly regulation, defence and insurance,
- structural measures
    = extensive - integrated catchment planning, land control etc.
    = intensive - flow control, incl. reservoirs, retention and release basins, levees, dikes and walls, flood plain polders, improvement of the conditions of flood routing
- combination of structural and non structural methods.
This paper is going to deal only with intensive structural measures, first of all, with the construction or reinforcement of embankments to avoid damages caused by floods.

2nd International Conference on River Flood Hydraulics. Edited by W. R. White and J. Watts

To make a well established decision on a flood protection project, including the development of existing flood protecting construction in order to raise the standard of protection of the flood prone area, detailed information on the extension of the affected flood plain basin as well as on the potential damages within that are required.

1. Determination of the extension of the separate flood plain Basins

A separate flood plain basin is understood as a particular part of the flood plains, which is bounded on the one side by natural higher terrain extending along the edge of the flood plains, on the other side - in case of protected flood plains - by the flood embankment,and which is inundated in the event of a breach in the defence without the inundation spreading into the adjacent flood plain basins.

The size of the flood plain basins was of interest in the early periods of flood protection already, to allocate the costs of flood defence to the various parties interested. In the past, at the contemporary level and possibilities of engineering, the extension of flood prone areas was determined simply by horizontal projection of the peak stages recorded so far, to the terrain.

The progress made in surveying and computation technology, further in hydrologic and hydraulic research have introduced the possibility of modelling of the actual physical phenomenon: the flow and storage on the terrain of the water pouring in through a breach in the embankment at different initial levels having different probability. Thus extension of possible inundation in the protected flood plain with different probabilities may be determined.

1.1. THE METHOD USED IN HUNGARY FOR THE DETERMINATION OF THE CONTOURS OF THE FLOOD PLAIN BASINS [2]

To determine the size and the contours of the separate flood plain basins, one or several breach points in the defence were assumed, depending on the size of the particular basin, which result in the largest inundation area there. The flood hydrographs of 1 % and 1 ‰ probability were then transformed to this breach point.

Flow in through the breach was computed using the general weir formula. The shape of the breach was assumed to be a hexatic parabola. The length of the breach was computed on the base of geotechnical and hydraulic considerations taking into account practical experience too.

W = f(H) capacity curves of the basin was calculated using valley sections taken from detailed topographic maps in each km-s.

The process of inundation was reproduced by assuming variable unsteady flow, solving the differential equation describing the process of inundation by the method of finite differences, by successive approximation.

Two basical version of inundation process was distinguished (see Fig. 1. and 2.). In case of a basin with a relatively small capacity equalization of the level of inundation with the level of the river is expected over the altitude of the terrain on the protected side.

In case of large basins the volume of water flowed in through the breach is not sufficient to fill the basin until the falling river level reaches the altitude of the terrain at the breach. Storage will be realized only in the deepest parts of the basin at a level corresponding to the volume of the water flowed in. The surface of the water flowing in the valley to the lowest "reservoir" was computed starting from the storage level of the lowest "reservoir" upwards section by section, as a variable unsteady flow in an open channel.

The intersection of the inundation, flow and storage profiles with the terrain contours have defined the boundaries of the flood plain sections and the elevated "islands" therein.

1.2. BRIEF INTRODUCTION TO THE HUNGARIAN SEPARATE FLOOD PLAIN BASINS

As a result of the above research the map scaled 1:50 000 and the records of the endangered areas for each flood plain basin likely to be inundated in case of a levee failure during floods with probabilities of 1 % and 1 ‰ have been completed.

As an example, the map of a smaller separate flood plain basin can be seen on Fig. 3. Characteristic technical data of the Hungarian flood plain basins are given in Table 1. [3,4].

It is of interest to note that no more than eight basins being larger than 1.000 km2 - of which are two along the Danube and six along the Tisza River - represent 45 % of the total flood plain area. At the same time there are 65 minor basins (29 along the Danube and 36 along the Tisza River), specific area of which is less than 1 km2/km of embankment. The total area of these small basins is 634 km2, only 3,1 % of the total flood plain area, while the length of the flood defence protecting these is 691 km, or 16,4 % of the total defence. Beyond these, each km of the 3 529 km long embankments protects a flood plain area of 5,65 km2 size on the average.

2. The economic effects of flooding

Flooding incurs adverse economic effects to a variety of individuals and activities. Generally these effects can be divided into three categories, as follows [5].

DIRECT ECONOMIC EFFECTS - impacts directly attributed to the occurrence of flooding, such as property damage (destruction or degradation of individual, business and public property due to contact with flood water), income losses (lost profits and wages resulting from business being flooded) and emergency costs (monetary costs of emergency measures like rescue, evacuation, flood fighting and cleanup).

INDIRECT ECONOMIC EFFECTS - losses of the interrelated economy (business not located in a flood prone area, but that purchases inputs from or sell outputs to directly affected business, may incur economic costs, reduction in production and employment, due to shortages in materials etc.)

INTANGIBLE EFFECTS - impacts that are real, but are difficult to assign a monetary value to (human health and safety effects incl. personal injury or death, directly attributable to flooding, or health effects due to decreased sanitation, emotional trauma, etc.).

In identifying the potential flood losses attention has been concentrated on the analysis of the direct economic impacts, taken as the most typical ones the following into consideration:

- Property losses including all damages to fixed and current assets identifiable in the particular flood plain basin and attributable to contact with water and/or to flood emergency operations (e.g. damages to the rescue or transport roads or to the flood defence themselves);

- Income losses including the lost profits on production discontinued or reduced due to
 * involving workforce or equipment in emergency operations,
 * traffic interruption or limitation as a consequence of
   flooding or emergency operations,
 * evacuation,
 * inundation of business;

- Emergency costs divided in two groups, such as
 = costs of flood defence operation (or flood fighting)
 = costs of evacuation and rescue. Costs of cleansing, disinfection and epidemic control
   are also included.

3. Determination of characteristic flood stages inducing typical economic impacts

The efficiency of a flood protection project can be determined as a ratio that equals the flood damage reduction related to the cost of investment. The occurrence of flood losses is closely related to the parameters, in particular the height and duration of the flood waves causing these. The analysis consists substantially of determining by flood plain basins the limit values of flood stages which are associated with losses of different types and magnitudes to economy. Since 97 % of the flood plains in Hungary are protected, the occurrence of the various loss types can be related to the flood stages affecting the stability or safety of the flood defence [6].

The characteristic flood stages are as follows:

h_a - the absolute safety stage, below which no flood defence activities are needed and no losses occur. Concerning the defence structure, the actual factor of safety pertaining to this stage equals that prescribed in the relevant standard specifications:

$$n_{act} = n_{spec}$$

h_b - the reliable safety stage, below which any necessary defence operations can be performed with a high degree of probability (relying mainly on the defence efforts of the local workforce). Practical experience has shown this value to be around the mid- and two-thirds points of the range between h_a and h_c

h_c - the critical safety stage, above which inundation is expected to occur, i.e., where

$$n_{act} = n_c = 1,0$$

These three stages subdivide the range of possible fluctuation into four zones with typical flood defence operation and economic impacts (see Fig 4.):

$h < h_a$ - no flood-related costs/losses occur;

$h_a < h < h_b$ - monitoring and guard service is operated on the flood embankments, minor defence activities within the capacity of local forces are needed, no loss or damage occurs in the flood plain basin;

$h_b < h < h_c$ - the unstable sections of embankments are to be strengthened by great emergency efforts involving public workforce and the military to avoid breaches. Production in the basin is reduced owing to mobilization of workforce and equipment. The basin is not inundated yet, but preparations for possible confinement works are going on, preventive evacuation of the most threatened houses or communities might be necessary;

$h > h_c$ - as before, also confinement of inundations, rescue of people and property, losses of assets in the inundated flood plain basin.

The stages pertaining to the different safety levels of the defence are thus determined for each flood plain basins and the frequency of occurrence of these stages is estimated. Occurrence of typical damages or activities will have the corresponding frequency.

4. The main components of possible damages in the separate flood plain basin [7]

The potential magnitude of the losses due to the four types of impacts defined in paragraph 2 are to be estimated and thus four loss functions are to be generated.

To assess the losses and costs, possible events and necessary emergency activities of flood with a probability of 1 % were assumed. In order to obtain more accurate results, on the hydrograph of the design flood wave not only the threshold values of flood stages defined in the previous paragraph but a finer h_i, τ_j grid of 0,2 m x 1 day were inserted.

Determination of property and income losses needs accurate survey at all the dominant economic units of the flood plain basin on the spot. Other general data, concerning for example residences or infrastructures are available in statistical handbooks, or in the office of the local authorities. (Data on potential depth and duration of inundation in the flood plain basin in case of breach in the defence are collected in the confinement plan of the basin.)

4.1. INCOME LOSSES

Annual income loss in the flood plain basin is equal with the subtotal of f1 values of each business in the basin

$$ f1 = \sum_s \sum_{ij} /T_s \cdot \alpha_{ij} \cdot q_{ij}/ $$

where

T_s - daily income of affected business

$q(h_i, \tau_j)$ - frequency of occurrence of flood of h_i stage and τ_j duration

$\alpha(h_i, \tau_j)$ - ratio of damage of individual business depending on the stage and duration of flood - to be deterpmined individually in each zone of the h_i, τ_j grid

Factors inducing losses are given in paragraph 2. Duration of inundation resulting from flood wave exceeding h_c should include the time demand of all the activities necessary before restarting businesses.

4.2. COSTS OF FLOOD FIGHTING

Flood fighting interventions are planned as required technical volume of work to avoid loss of stability of the flood defence of the basin. Volume of work is assessed on the base of the technical parameters of the embankment depending on the actual flood stage. Transformation of natural expenditures for costs were carried out on guiding price. '0 3 Annual costs of flood fighting in the flood plain basin were determined as

$$f_2 = \sum_{ij} /V_i \cdot q_{ij}/$$

where

V_i - Daily flood fighting expenditures in each zone of the $h_i, _j$ grid in natural units multiplied by the guiding price. The considered flood fighting activity includes preparations for confinement as well as actual confinement activity, when necessary.

4.3. PROPERTY DAMAGE

Property damage (destruction or degradation of individual, business and public property including fixed and current assets) may occur mainly as a consequence of inundation but in some extent as a result of increased load due to intensive emergency operations.

Assessment were prepared in the basin for each economic unit. Properties were classified according to their water resistance (constructions, buildings, machines, different materials, etc.).

Annual property damage in the flood plain basin was determined as

$$f_3 = \sum_{s} \sum_{ij} /N_s \cdot \gamma_{ij} \cdot q_{ij}/$$

where

N_s - value of property classified according to their water resistance in each economic unit

$\gamma(h_i, \tau_j)$ - mean ratio of damage depending on stage and duration of inundation for each class of properties

4.4. COSTS OF RESCUE AND EVACUATION

The determination of this factor of damages includes:

- costs of rescue and evacuation, surplus in costs of sanitary services and supply for the evacuated, costs of resettling;

- in case of actual breach in the defence costs of cleansing and disinfection.

Annual costs of evacuation were determined as

$$f_4 = \sum_{ij} /M \cdot q_{ij}/$$

where

M - natural volume of rescue and evacuation activity depending on flood stage and duration, according to the plans of confinement and evacuation of the flood plain basin, multiplied by guiding price.

5. Determination of the economical efficiency of the raising of the standard of flood defence

Combination of the above generated loss functions results in the integrated loss function which indicates the annual flood losses at the actual development level of the flood defence for particular flood plain basins.

$$G_{p-1} = f_1 + f_2 + f_3 + f_4$$

The same equation is to be determined for the state after development

$$G_p = f'_1 + f'_2 + f'_3 + f'_4$$

Improving the safety or capacity of flood defence structures will shift, evidently, the stage ranges of probable flood losses towards the higher stages of lower frequency of occurrence (see Fig. 4.). For this reason, improvement projects will reduce appreciably the losses/costs burdening economy or other interests (see Fig. 5.).

Reduction in annual flood damage equals

$$E = G_{p-1} - G_p$$

Regarding the reduction of losses as a benefit of flood defence improvement and relating this benefit to the costs of improvement the cost-efficiency and the return period of investment can be estimated.

$$\rho \ = \ \frac{E}{B} \ , \quad \text{and} \quad TR = \frac{1}{\rho}$$

where

B   - the costs of investment/development

Analysis of the flood plain basins in Hungary have been carried out with the help of this simplified model since the middle of the 80-s. The collection and verification of data on estimated damage of the individual business is the most difficult and time demanding task.

Characteristic economic data of the Hungarian flood plain basins are given in Table 2.

REFERENCES

1. Yevjevich, V. (1974) 'Systematization of flood control measures', ASCE Journal of Hydraulics Division, Vol. 100, No. HY11, pp. 1531-1548

2. Balo, Z. (1979) 'Determination of flood plain basins in Hungary ', VITUKI Bulletins No. 23., Budapest

3. Dr. Ress, S. - Karolyine, K. (1991) 'The present state of flood defence in Hungary, conditions of operation', R+D Report of ECO Inc. to the Ministry of Transport, Communication and Water Management, Budapest. Manuscript.

4. Toth, S. (1993) 'Overview of flood defence problems in Hungary' Proceedings of the UK/Hungarian Workshop on Flood Defence, Budapest. pp. 33-56.

5. Moser, D. A. (1992) 'Assessment of the economic effects of flooding', Proceedings of the NATO ASI on "Coping with Floods", E. Majorana Centre, Erice, Sicily

6. Zorkoczy et al. (1987) 'Flood defence ' Manual. VIZDOK, Budapest. pp. 247-248.

7. Dr. Ress, S. et al. (1983) 'Optimization of the development of flood protecting systems' R+D Report. VGI, Budapest.

Table 1.

CHARACTERISTIC TECHNICAL DATA
OF THE FLOOD PLAIN BASINS OF HUNGARY

Specification	Unit	Danube Valley	Tisza	Total
Flood plain	1000 km2	5,6	15,6	21,2
- protected	1000 km2	5,3	15,2	20,5
- unprotected	1000 km2	0,3	0,4	0,7
Number of floodplain basins	piece	55	96	151
Mean value of extension	km2	106	163	140
Extension - of the smallest basin	km2	0,32	0,48	
- of the largest basin	1000 km2	2,3	1,8	
Number of basins exceeding 1000 km2 of territory	piece	2	6	8
Extension of flood plain in the basins exceeding 1000 km2 of territory	1000 km2	3,3	6,2	9,5
- proportion of the total	%	59	40	45
Length of flood protecting constructions	km	1310	2910	4220
Extension of flood plain protected by 1 km embankment	km2	4,2	5,2	4,9

Table 2.

CHARACTERISTIC ECONOMIC DATA
OF THE FLOOD PLAIN BASINS OF HUNGARY

Specification	Unit	Danube Valley	Tisza	Total
National property	M Ft/km2	49,7	61,2	52,7
- residences	"	17,9	24,4	19,6
Production	"	35,9	40,8	37,1
Total economic value	"	85,6	102,0	89,8
Economic damage caused by single inundation (p = 1 %)	"	26,0	38,7	29,3
Threatened population	cap/km2	118,0	123,0	119,5
Value of fixed assets of flood protection	M Ft/km2	0,97	1,27	1,08

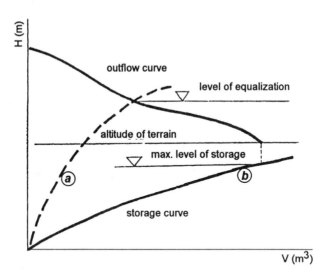

Fig. 1. Outflow and storage in (a): small, (b): simple large basin

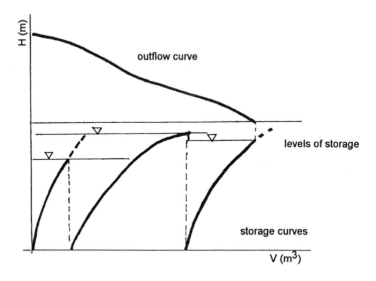

Fig. 2. Outflow and storage in compound large basin

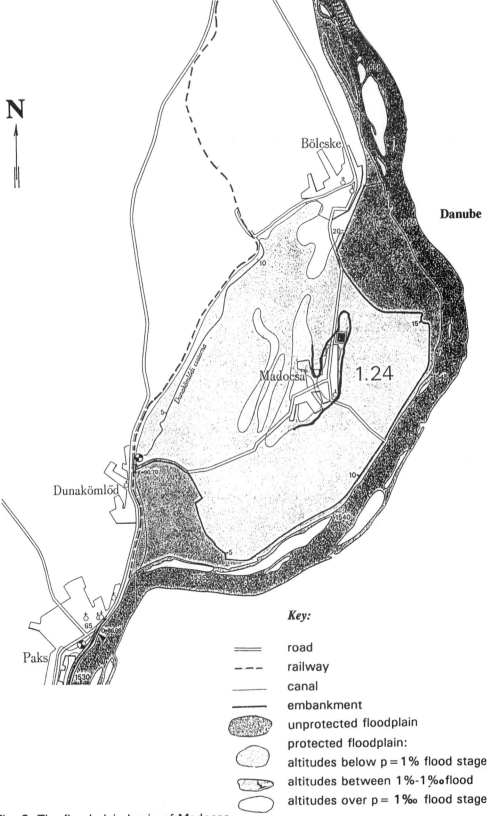

N

Bölcske

Danube

Madocsa

1.24

Dunakömlőd

Paks

Key:

═══	road
---	railway
──	canal
▬▬	embankment
	unprotected floodplain
	protected floodplain:
	altitudes below p = 1% flood stage
	altitudes between 1%-1‰ flood
	altitudes over p = 1‰ flood stage

Fig. 3. The flood plain basin of Madocsa

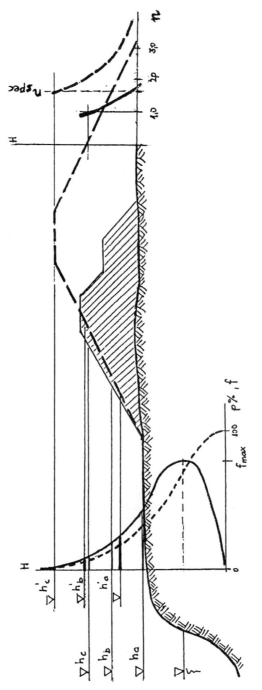

Fig. 4. Demonstration of characteristic flood stages
inducing typical economic impacts

Flood plain basin N⁰. 2.58

Kocsord gauge

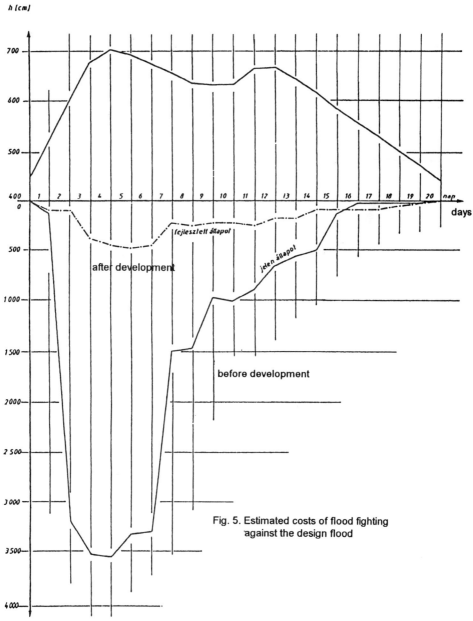

Fig. 5. Estimated costs of flood fighting against the design flood

215

RIVER FLOOD HYDRAULICS
22–25 March 1994: York, England

A Review of the Hydraulic and Environmental Performance of River Schemes in N. Ireland

H. T. Johnston[+], N. N. J. Higginson[*] and T McCully[*]

[+]Civil Engineering Department, The Queen's University of Belfast
[*]Watercourse Management Division, Department of Agriculture for N. Ireland

Summary

Environmental and hydraulic performance indicators assessed before and after the completion of major schemes on two large river systems in N. Ireland are used to examine the impact of such works. Changes in the flora within the catchment were recorded but it was found that these were mostly in the intermediate hydrology classes. Measures taken to limit the impact of drainage works on fish stocks have shown encouraging results.

The effect of the drainage schemes on river flood flows was examined by checking variations in the mean annual flood magnitudes derived by analysis of flood partial series at a number of recording stations on each river. The magnitude of this characteristic parameter was observed to increase with progress of the works, producing a ultimate increase of 50 to 90%. A parametric study showed evidence of a change in the exponential distribution of floods on one river.

It was concluded that the environmental impact of rivers schemes can be mitigated by incorporating remedial measures in the drainage works but the increase in flood risk must be carefully assessed.

Introduction

Two major river schemes have been carried out in the last decade in on the Main and Blackwater rivers N. Ireland to provide flood protection to urban and industrial areas as well as improved drainage to agricultural land. The water level within Lough Neagh, which is the largest freshwater lake in the British Isles, was lowered in 1955 and this gave the impetus to land drainage schemes on the principal catchments draining into the Lough. The schemes improved the drainage of 10,000 hectares and were designed to give agricultural land protection against 1 in 3 year flows. The extent of the drainage works in each catchment is shown on the catchment maps in Fig. 1. In one scheme a Public Inquiry stipulated that a rising sector gate be used for flood control and that specified industrial sites be given high degrees of flood protection. The arterial drainage works on both rivers involved regrading and realigning the channel together with underpinning or reconstruction of bridges at a total expenditure of £50M.

2nd International Conference on River Flood Hydraulics. Edited by W. R. White and J. Watts

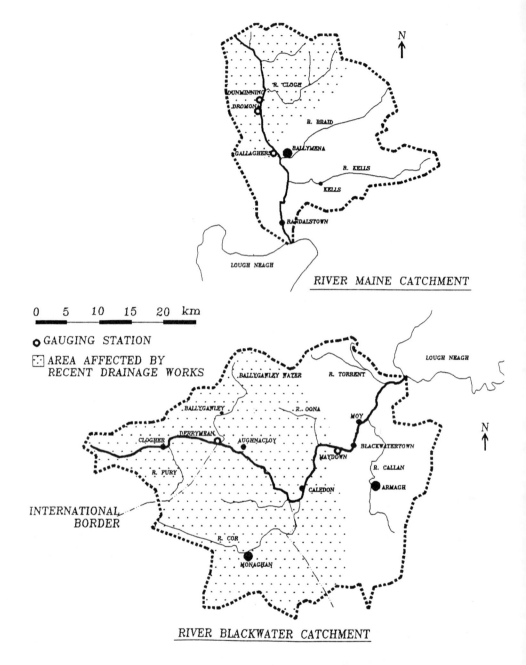

Figure 1. Catchment maps showing the extent of the areas affected by the drainage works.

River Main Scheme

The catchment of the River Main is some 700 km² with a main stream length of 51 km. A major feature of this river, which rises on the Antrim Plateau, is the extensive areas of peat bog in its upper reaches where the gradients are very shallow at 1 in 10,000. In the middle reaches where the river descends from the plateau the gradients are up to 1 in 200. The River Main intercepts the Braid and Kells Water rivers before entering the north-eastern corner of Lough Neagh.

The report of the Public Inquiry (Hutton, 1972) into the proposed drainage scheme made a number of recommendations including:
1. Special protection be given to the faces of floodbanks where a velocity exceeding 3 m/s was predicted.
2. Use of brushwood filters to diminish suspended solids in the water.
3. The longitudinal profile of the river to be retained where possible.
4. Recreate pools in which fish can shelter.
5. Groynes be installed where they would operate to scour pools and prevent them filling with material carried by the river.
6. Replace boulders to provide shelter for fish.
7. Replace gravel in the river where it had been removed for excavation work.
8. Work on alternate banks to leave trees and vegetation untouched on one bank.
9. Retain bends where possible.
10. Construct fish passes where necessary.
11. Replace trees and shrubs to provide cover and shade as well as a supply of flies for fish.

In the implementation of the scheme, a 3 m high weir, at the downstream end of the flat upper reaches of the river, was removed and replaced with a rising sector gate to allow improved drainage of agricultural land and yet retain the use of the floodplain storage to attenuate major floods. In the middle reaches of the river, flood protection measures included the construction of a two-stage channel and a by-pass channel at two industrial sites.

Impact of River Main Scheme

Between 1945 and 1985, there was a policy in N. Ireland of bringing unproductive or marginal land into agricultural production. Drained grasslands generally support a lower diversity of plants and animals than wetlands and hence a habitat loss may occur as a result of land drainage. When the River Main scheme was approved, the Public Inquiry specified that some environmental monitoring would be carried out. The Department of Agriculture instituted monitoring of changes in the flora and changes in the water table and this is still on-going.

Flora

In the Glarryford Bog, which forms a major part of the upper reaches of the river, six line transects were marked across the floodplain. Plant species were recorded along these transects in 1975 prior to the commencement of the river scheme. The transects were again surveyed in 1985 when channel works on the scheme had been completed in the Bog region and a further survey is planned for 1993. In 1985, of the total of some 200 species recorded in the original survey, 90 were found to be absent but 100 new species were recorded. Most of the species found to be absent were in the intermediate hydrology classes and only two (*Potamogaton natans* and *Callitriche stagnalis*) were wetland species. Both of these are relatively common plants of open waters. The new species found in the area were generally those which favoured dry conditions, indicating a loss of the wetland characteristics of the bog. It should be noted that the method of line transects is liable to recording error and so two dimensional quadrats were laid down and recorded in 1985 as a better baseline for future reference.

River Blackwater Scheme

The River Blackwater outfalls into the southern end of Lough Neagh and has a trapezoidal shaped catchment covering an area of 1490 km². The catchment boundary is formed by hills ranging from 230 m to 380 m AOD. The area has been subject to glaciation which resulted in the formation of a drumlin topography within the catchment. The land use within the catchment is mostly grassland pastures. It was established that some 3520 hectares of land in the catchment were severely affected by poor drainage and many areas were inundated for prolonged periods. The annual rainfall in the area is high, averaging 1030 mm. The soils in the area which would benefit from a drainage scheme were potentially rich with large areas of brown earths and low humic clays. It was considered that improvement to the drainage would lead to desirable biological changes in these soils which coupled with improved bearing capacities arising from lowered water tables would enable the land to be farmed to its potential.

The fishery potential of the rivers in the catchment was recognised and the need to preserve or even enhance the fish stocks became a requirement of the design. The wildlife and amenity interests in the area were acknowledged and discussions were held with interested parties. The two main parameters in the river scheme design were:

1.   Watercourses had to be capable of passing a 1 in 3 year flood.
2.   In the dry season the water level in the channel had to be sufficiently below surrounding field levels to allow free discharge of field drainage systems.

Fishery Measures in River Blackwater Scheme

The fishery value of the River Blackwater and the need for conservation measures significantly influenced working practices on the scheme. Measures taken included the construction of several fish passes and numerous fish weirs and groynes. Despite these measures it was felt that the river would not be fully restored to its former fisheries potential. It was decided that further fishery measures would be incorporated in the scheme based on recent research findings, Kennedy (1988), to restore the fishery habitat to at least its pre-scheme value. A large number of potential sites were examined and over 350 were chosen on which habitats suitable for fish breeding were constructed.

The natural spacing of pool - riffle sequences in rivers was investigated (Higginson, 1992) to develop suitable design parameters for the fishery measures. Gravel retaining groynes were placed in such a manner as not to impede drainage, blend into the local environment and stabilise the spawning gravel which would otherwise move downstream during floods. The design of the fishery habitat measures has been modified as a result of a number of problems which were encountered during the first 15 months of operation in 1990-91. These, which are illustrated in the schematic diagram Fig. 2, are;

(a)   The length of spawning beds for rivers with bed widths less than 4 m has been increased from 1 to 4 times the channel width.
(b)   Two additional gravel retaining groynes have been placed below the spawning bed at

MODIFICATIONS TO FISHERY HABITAT

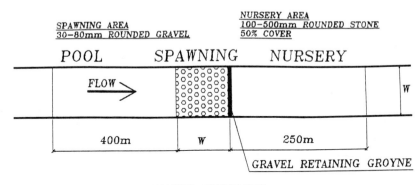

SPAWNING AREA
30–80mm ROUNDED GRAVEL

NURSERY AREA
100–500mm ROUNDED STONE
50% COVER

POOL   SPAWNING   NURSERY

FLOW →

W

400m   W   250m

GRAVEL RETAINING GROYNE

ORIGINAL SCHEMATIC

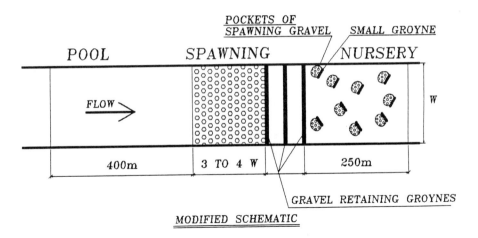

POCKETS OF
SPAWNING GRAVEL   SMALL GROYNE

POOL   SPAWNING   NURSERY

FLOW →

W

400m   3 TO 4 W   250m

GRAVEL RETAINING GROYNES

MODIFIED SCHEMATIC

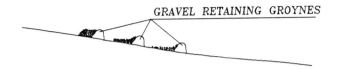

GRAVEL RETAINING GROYNES

Figure 2. Schematic representation of fishery measures based on gravel retaining groynes.

a separation of 2 m.

(c)   Small pockets of spawning gravel are placed behind short groynes throughout the nursery where the local depth and velocity are sufficient for spawning.

(d)   Gravel retaining groynes may be placed diagonally instead of perpendicular to the banks.

(e)   In the holding pools, large boulders of 1 tonne size are placed at 10 m intervals. This serves as a self-cleansing mechanism, cleaning silt from parts of the pool.

The bed material in the spawning area is coarse gravel and the banks are formed of sands and clays. The groynes are formed of imported angular boulders ranging in size from 300 to 600 mm. This work was spread throughout the entire river system. Within four months of spawning beds being laid, over 30 redd were noted on 12 sites, both trout and salmon.

Effect of River Schemes on Qbar

The effect of the river works on the flow characteristics was investigated by carrying out a peaks-over-threshold (POT) analysis (Floods Studies Report, 1975) on each river. On each of the rivers, a number of flow gauging stations had been established and records were available which covered the pre-scheme conditions, the period of river works and a three year period of post-scheme flows.

River Blackwater

Two stations were chosen on the River Blackwater, the first of which was at Maydown in the lower reaches and this included 951 km^2 of the catchment. The second station was in the upper reaches at Derrymeen, the last area in which drainage works were done, and had a catchment area of 175 km^2. To test the repeatability of the POT analysis based on a partial series, the period of record prior to the commencement of river works in each case was divided into two periods of similar length to the post scheme records.

All the independent flood events above a threshold value were extracted for each year from the stage hydrograph records. The stage values were converted to discharges by applying the rating equations which had been developed for the flow gauging station over the appropriate period. The mean annual flood, Qbar, for each period was then calculated using the Flood Studies equations:

$$\hat{\lambda} \quad = \quad M/N \tag{1}$$

$$\hat{\beta} \quad = \quad q \quad - \quad q_0 \tag{2}$$

and

$$Qbar \quad = \quad q_0 \quad + \quad \hat{\beta}\ln\hat{\lambda} \quad + \quad 0.5772\hat{\beta} \tag{3}$$

where   M is the number of abstracted flood peaks in N years of record
          q is the mean of the flood peaks
          q_0 is the threshold flow chosen to give 3 or 4 exceedences per year
          $\hat{\lambda}$ is the average number of exceedences per year
          $\hat{\beta}$ is the average exceedence.

The magnitude of the Qbar values at each station were compared to examine the influence of the channel works on the flood flows.

Maydown

The flow records were divided into four periods: 1970 to 1974 and 1975 to 1979, both of which were pre-scheme; 1986 to 1989, a period when most of the channel works were completed; and 1990 to 1992 which could be considered as post scheme. The magnitudes of the calculated Qbar values are shown in Fig. 3. It can be seen that the magnitudes of Qbar calculated for the pre-scheme periods of 1970-74 and 1975-79 agreed to within 5% at 77.9 and 81.9 m³/s. The similarity in the values gave confidence in the quality of the records and the repeatability of the use of the POT method of analysis. However, when river works were undertaken, the value of Qbar increased in the period 1986-89 by 70% to 133.6 m³/s. The change in the

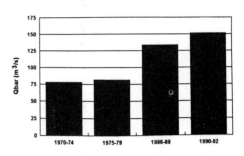

Figure 3. Qbar magnitude Changes with time at Maydown, River Blackwater.

magnitude Qbar can be attributed to the increased drainage of the catchment. In the post scheme period of 1990-92 there was a further increase in Qbar to 151.2 m³/s, an increase of more than 90%. The annual stage hydrographs for the pre-scheme year1983 and the post-scheme year 1992 , Fig. 4, show the increased frequency of high stage flows.

The increase in Qbar at Maydown resulting from the scheme on the River Blackwater was compared with the Irish growth curve shown in the Flood Studies Report. A multiplication of Qbar of this magnitude corresponds to a flood of approximately 100 year return period.

Derrymeen

Channel works on the sub-catchment contributing flow to the river at Derrymeen were completed in the later period of the river scheme. The flow records for this station were divided into three periods,1979 to 1981, 1982 to 1984 and 1990 to 1992. The first two periods can be classed as pre-scheme and the third as post-scheme. The magnitudes of Qbar calculated for the three periods are shown in Fig. 5. Again it can be seen that the pre-scheme magnitudes are in close agreement at 31.7 and 33.1 m³/s, a difference of 4%. However the post-scheme value of Qbar was found to be 59.7 m³/s which represents an increase of over 90%.

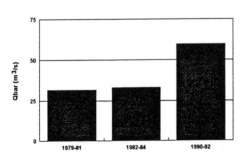

Figure 5. Qbar magnitude changes with time at Derrymeen, River Blackwater.

For both the flow gauging stations on the River Blackwater, the increase in the mean annual flood which was determined from the POT analysis was of similar order at approximately 90%. Bailey and Bree (1981) examined the effect of improved land drainage on catchment in Ireland and proposed a prediction equation based on the 3 year return period pre- and post-scheme floods,

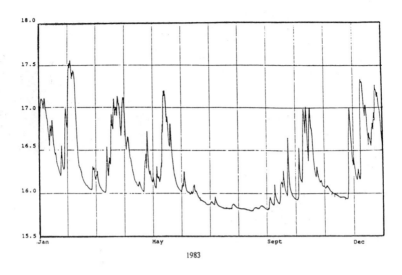

a) Stage hydrograph for Maydown, River Blackwater prior to commencement of drainage works.

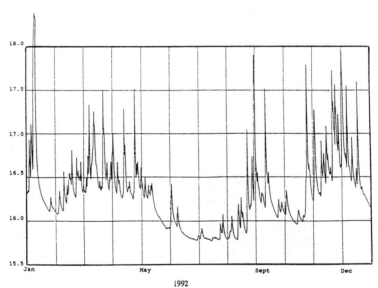

b) Stage hydrograph for Maydown, River Blackwater after completion of drainage works.

Figure 4. Pre- and post-scheme annual stage hydrographs.

$$Q_{3\,post} = 1.6\,Q_{3\,pre} \hspace{4cm} (4)$$

The difference between Qbar, which has a return period of 2.33 years, and Q_3 is small and therefore direct comparison between the ratios of the pre- and post-scheme floods can be made. It can be seen that this equation would under-predict the effect of the drainage scheme on the Blackwater catchment by some 50%.

River Main

A similar examination of the effect of the river scheme in the Main catchment on the magnitude of Qbar was carried out. In this case, the records from three flow gauging stations were used. The first of these stations was at Dunminning where the river left the boglands of the plateau and a weir was removed. The catchment area at this location was 208 km². The second was at Dromona, just after a weir which was in place throughout the period of study and which causes frequent flooding, where the catchment area was 229 km². The third station chosen for study was at Gallaghers where a two stage channel was constructed. There was a shorter period of record at Gallaghers as flow measurement at this station commenced in 1984 and there were only two years of record prior to channel works.

Dunminning

Three periods of record were examined at this station as shown in Fig. 6. It can be seen that there was a gradual increase in the values of Qbar with 13% change in the second period and a 29% increase in the third period relative to the pre-scheme value. This corresponds well with the rate of progress of the drainage works on the catchment. However, overall there was a considerably lower increase in the magnitude of the increase when compared to both the Blackwater River scheme and the prediction equation given by Bailey and Bree. This can be explained by the very shallow gradients in the catchment and the extensive boglands where it was observed that there little change in the water table.

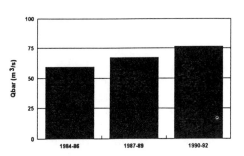

Figure 6. Qbar magnitude changes with time at Dunminning, River Main.

Dromona

The record at Dromona was divided into five periods as shown in Fig. 7. The first three periods are pre-scheme and the it can be seen that there was a high degree of similarity in the calculated Qbar values which lay within a band width of 5%. It should be noted that there were appreciable changes in the rating equation for the station during these periods. These changes resulted from alterations in the station datum and also a change in control when a weir cap was removed. In each year the rating equation current at the time was applied to the records.

The fourth and fifth periods are during the period of channel works and post-scheme respectively. It can be seen that the value of Qbar increase with time over these periods by 25 and 52 %. These increases again correlate well with the progress of work on the scheme within the catchment. The final change in the Qbar value was greater than that for the Dunminning station and corresponds well with the prediction equation given by Bailey and Bree.

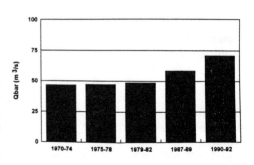

However, it was observed that the Qbar values were less than that calculated for Dunminning even though the catchment area was greater. The reason for this is the presence of a weir upstream which causes inundation of the floodplain several times per year. This floodplain storage causes attenuation of the flood and a corresponding decrease in the flood peak. this weir has recently been removed and this would indicate that there should be an increase in Qbar at this location.

Figure 7. Qbar magnitude changes with time at Dromona, River Main

Gallaghers

The records at Gallaghers were used to calculate the value of Qbar before and after the construction of the two stage channel. No pre-scheme records were available at this site and the length of record before channel works were undertaken was less than the minimum of three years specified for the POT analysis. As a check, the values of Qbar expressed in m^3/s per 100 km^2 for the two periods were calculated and were found to compare reasonably well with those calculated at Dromona. It can be seen from Fig. 8, that the effect of channel works in this reach have resulted in an increase in Qbar of 35%. This increase is greater than the increases over the corresponding periods at Dunminning and at Dromona and this may be due to the short period of record.

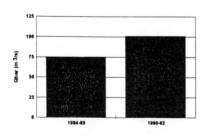

Figure 8. Qbar changes with time at Gallaghers, River Main

Effect of River Schemes on Flood Hydrographs

Hydrograph Shape
A number of flood events recorded each at each flow gauging station were abstracted and analysed to determine the influence of the river schemes on the hydrographs. The events selected were isolated flood events in which the water level rose from a recession flow to a significant peak level which was followed by a period of recession flows. The storm runoff in the event was separated from the baseflow so that the percentage runoff could be determined. Initially, the Flood Studies method of hydrograph separation was investigated. This involves determining the lag time between the centroid of rainfall and the peak flow and assumes that storm runoff continues after the peak flow for a period of four time the lag. However, it was found that this frequently resulted in a post flood baseflow which was less than that immediately preceding the event. An alternative method proposed by Wilson

(1990) was investigated. In this method, the flows on the recession limb of the hydrograph are divided by the flow six hours later and the ratio plotted against time. Two lines are fitted to the resulting curve and the point of intersection is taken as the time at which storm runoff ceased. An example of this method is shown in Figs. 9 and 10. This method was found to be suitable for use and was applied to the selected hydrographs.

The hydrograph shapes were classified in a manner similar to that used to determine the synthetic unit hydrographs in the Flood Studies Report. The time to peak and the time base of each runoff hydrograph was estimated and their ratio determined. It was found that there was no discernable difference between the ratios for the pre- and post-scheme hydrographs or between the catchments. In all cases the time base of the storm hydrograph was between 2 and 3.5 times the time to peak flow.

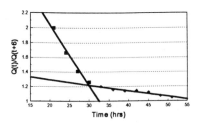

Figure 9. Plot of recession at t hrs divided by flow at t+6 hrs for hydrograph recession limb.

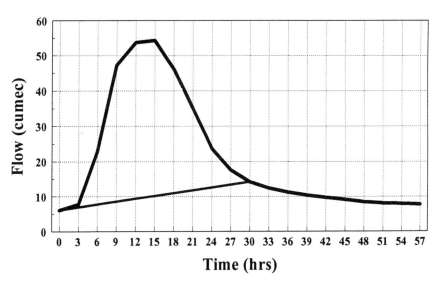

Figure 10. Flood hydrograph showing the estimated line separating the baseflow from the storm runoff

Flood Frequency
A flood of given frequency, or return period, can be estimated using the Flood Studies Report equation:

$$Q_T = q_0 + \hat{\beta}\ln\hat{\lambda} + \hat{\beta}\ln T \qquad (5)$$

where Q_T is the magnitude of the flood whose return period is T. This equation is dependent on two parameters which may be altered by drainage works, the threshold value q_0 and the exponential distribution parameter $\hat{\beta}$. Bailey and Bree (1981) examined the change in $\hat{\beta}$ due to drainage works on a number of catchments and concluded that it was not significant. They therefore attributed the increase in the post-scheme flood magnitudes to an increase in the threshold, q_0. This implies that all floods will increase by a constant amount and hence low frequency floods will be relatively less affected by drainage works.

Examination of the partial flood series used in the derivation of the Qbar values in the River Main showed that at each of the stations there was little change in the value of $\hat{\beta}$ over the periods of flow records analysed. The changes in the mean annual flood were therefore due to changes in the threshold flood, q_0. This would support the findings of Bailey and Bree. However, when the values of $\hat{\beta}$ for the stations on the River Blackwater were examined it was found that, while the pre-scheme magnitudes were similar, the post-scheme values showed a threefold increase. The increase in the threshold flood value, q_0, was found to be between 30 and 50%. This implies a greater change in the low frequency floods than would be predicted by Bailey and Bree and would appear to be due to the higher percentage of the catchment improved by river scheme than was the case in the Main catchments or those studied by Bailey and Bree. The records for Maydown in the Blackwater catchment were examined and a threshold was chosen to give 4 exceedences in the period 1970 to 1974 and 5 exceedences in the period 1975 to 1979. When this threshold was applied to the post scheme periods of 1986 to 1989 and 1990 to 1992, the number of exceedences were 21 and 19 respectively. This change from an average of about 1 exceedence per year to 5 to 6 per year shows the increase in the lower frequency floods.

The changes in the magnitude of flood flows of given frequency and the increase in the frequency of flood flows of a given magnitude (especially the lower ones) will have a considerable impact on the watercourse. The associated increase in velocities must be carefully considered, especially when designing bank protection and fishery measures. The extent of the drainage works must be considered when assessing flood risk as this would appear to affect the distribution of flood flows as well as incrementing the threshold values.

Conclusions

This review of the effects of major river schemes has shown that they have a significant impact on the catchment environment as well as on the flow regime. The environmental impact on the flora in one of the catchments was found to be a change in the diversity of species recorded rather than a reduction and, in fact, an increase in the number of species was found. The main change in the species up to 1986 was from those of the intermediate hydrology classes to species favouring dry conditions. The magnitude of the impact of the river schemes on predicted flood flows was to be significant and it was observed that the exponential distribution of flood flows could be altered by extensive drainage works. The damage caused by the river works on fishery habitats can be mitigated by the installation of carefully designed spawning and nursery habitats in the river.

References

Bailey, A. D. and Bree, T. (1981) "Effect of improved land drainage on river flood flows", ICE. Flood Studies Report - Five Years On, Thomas Telford Ltd., London, pp. 131-142

Flood Studies Report, (1975), Natural Environment Research Council, London.

Higginson, N. N. J. (1992) "Evaluation of Hydraulic Resistance in Single and Two-stage Rivers", PhD Thesis, The Queen's University of Belfast.

Hutton, J. (1972) "Report of Public Inquiry into Proposed River Main Drainage Scheme", HMSO, Belfast.

Kennedy, G. J. A. (1988) "The ecology of salmonoid habitat reinstatement following drainage schemes", Report to DANI, Fisheries Research Laboratory, Coleraine.

McAdam, J. (1992) "Effects of large scale drainage on the flora of the River Main catchment", Memorandum, Department of Agriculture (NI).

Wilson, E. M. (1990) "Engineering Hydrology", 4th Ed., Macmillan Press Ltd., London.

Acknowledgement

The authors are grateful to Department of Agriculture for N. Ireland for giving permission to publish the data in this paper.

Extended protection concepts of mountain streams-
experiences on extreme floods

F. Schöberl

Institut für Wasserbau, University of Innsbruck

1. to the problem

The extreme destructiveness of mountain stream floods is primarily due to the flow attendant morphological reactions. The vicinity to the centres of erosion create the high potential of fluvio-morphological changes. It is the mixture of water, sediments and logs that cause the extent of damage.

Despite the pratically compacted regulation of our alpine rivers it becomes evident that these training works are outfunctioned much more frequently and easily than designed. Particularly there exist sites which are mainly sensible to such flow attacks.

It is to be questioned whether the non-calculable complexity of events alone can be made responsible for the observed failures or if some important process principles of convenient protection measures may ignored.

What happens during flood processes is directly connected with the laws governing the transport of sediments. The understanding of the physical foundations seems therefore a basic requirement.

2. channel forming processes

The laws of the flow and its transport capacity have always been a main pillar of river training concepts. Nevertheless the aspects of free adjustment in all three dimensions were ignored for a long time. The ideas of a functional stream bed were unconsciously influenced by the necessary simplification for the development of the bed load theories. The idealisations seemed to be one of the most persistent reasons leading to the enforcement of linear patterns of training measures.

Contrary to this engineering approach, a natural river is free to choose its width, depth and slope development. Only in the balance of affecting forces and existing constraints, the river determines its space and its longitudinal profile.

According to this view, the river bed is the result of a historical evolution process. Shape and the alignment of a natural bed appear as external features and are in direct relation to the existing sediment supply.

The sediment load of rivers is the result of numerous fluvial denudation processes. Beside bed erosion, the supply conditions are dominated by auto-motion and mass slides in the upper zones of the catchment, Bunza (1975). In alpine catchments, glaciers and the removability of moraines play also an important role. Especially the sediment inputs from torrents occur very irregularly and mostly in form of debris flows partly depositing before reaching the main river in form of alluvial fans. The rest of the material remains able to interfere with the regime of the main river. Therefore the alluvial bed does not behave as a rigid boundary, but permanently undergoes changes due to over- and underloading conditions.

River beds adjust to the material supply by exchange processes and subsequently by creation of

2nd International Conference on River Flood Hydraulics. Edited by W. R. White and J. Watts
© 1994 HR Wallingford Ltd. Published by John Wiley & Sons Ltd

typical bed forms. Depending on slope, discharge and material properties, the bed deformations adopt different shapes and structures. In narrow channels the formation and propagation of longitudinal sequences have been studied intensively, Yalin (1977). In wider channels alternate variations of the basic forms can emerge since initial disturbances start to spread laterally to the main direction as well. In trained gravel bed rivers, the formation of alternate bars is wide-spread. If the banks are erodible and if the bed is not fixed to a certain width, the river shape changes due to local failures of bank zones to the form of a meandering channel. At higher slopes and higher bed load, the meander becomes instable and the channel starts to split into several arms. Criterias determined by slope, bed width and material have been given by several scientists, Parker (1976). Of special interest are observations on the effect of high transport rates and their contribution to abrupt changes of bed forms. A great burst of material supply can force a stable meandering channel into a braided form. The global collected results support the fact that regime jumps can occur independent of the local erosion potential and the kind of substratum. Extreme events exceeding present regime limits can always cause effective alterations of the river shape, Schumm (1979), Harvey (1987).

According to the criteria of thresholds between braided and meandering channels, you may expect most of the alpine alluvial reaches to belong to the braiding category. Looking back for 150 or 200 years, maps of the historical landscape confirm this statement. By introducing fixed banks, the hydroengineers succeeded in extrapolating the type of a slightly meandering channel from the low land into the upper reaches. Although this kind of transport system is very effective for continuous sediment transport it cannot cope with sudden sediment inputs. The nearer the reaches lie to the sources of sediment supply the more the limits of narrow regulations, concentrating the transport system, become evident.

3. experiences of extreme floods

In the alpine valleys of Austria a consequent flood-plain management was not established for a long time and the protection of the valleys was mainly attained by the help of training works. In the last 3 decades, severe floods hit different parts of the alpine area, calling for an improvement of the convenient design approach. Two particular examples will be briefly presented.

3.1 Lower Isel

The Isel river is situated in East-Tyrol and forms a main tributary of the Drau river, draining an area of 1100 km2 of the southern zone of the central-alpine massive. The highest destructive floods appeared in 1965 and 1966 and showed impressively how strongly the river regime is influenced by high rates of sediments. These events drastically reformed the specific shape of the fluvial landscape. In batches, the river occupied the whole wide valley floor. Influxes of debris flows dominated the character of the reaches and provided for a significant change in the composition of the bed.

The training concept was based on the preparation of a series of the depositional zones, enabling the river to temporarily aggregate the surplus of material and gradually remove the deposits, Thenius (1975). The balancing function was accomplished by widening the river bed up to a 3 to 5 fold of the normal width so that the river could - at least in parts - regain its original dynamic. Although the flood in 1987 was remarkable, no negative impacts have been observed.

3.2 Ötztaler Ache

A sidevalley of the river Inn in North-Tyrol underwent particular severe floods in 1985/87, while other valleys like Ziller and Sellrain were free of damage, due to the provision of large hydro power reservoirs.

Characteristically, the longitudinal profile of the Ötz-Valley is marked by a series of huge steps in consequence of young geological land slides which caused the sedimentation of 3 different valley floors. Dramatic bank and bed erosion in steep reaches resulted in outbursts of the river at each

exit, reactivating a channel bed with braiding arms, Aulitzky (1988). The return to braiding conditions at different points ensured the function of straightened reaches along several villages.
Due to the dense expansion of tourist resorts, a consequent multiple reopening of all such braided stretches becomes difficult. But on the other hand, only linear training efforts merely to close the existing gaps will not be sufficient.

4. extended protection concepts for alpine rivers

In alpine valleys the traces of heavy erosion processes are to be observed persistently and can only marginally be influenced by mankind. Extreme events raising the sediment yield and forcing an immediate adjustment of the river bed have to be accepted as natural boundary conditions.
This specific background should lead to a river training approach better adjusted to the necessities of the regime. River engineering in reaches prone to regime jumps which does not allow for local expansions of the bed, can only be assessed as temporary solutions.

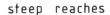

steep reaches

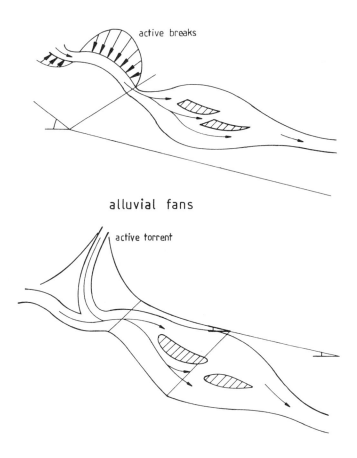

alluvial fans

Fig. 1   tendency for the formation of braided reaches

Especially braided reaches in succession to active erosion zones and to conjunctions of torrents are to be classified as morphological necessity to meet the large amounts of sediment supply, see Fig. 1. These zones act as important buffers balancing the transport conditions of different events. In view of the general shortage of space in alpine valleys, a certain voluntary renunciation of land may seem paradoxical to the layman, but is the inevitable basis for the more effective protection of the remaining area. The consequent application of morphological principles call for the restoration of all too narrowly trained reaches downstream of active erosion zones.

Morphologically based training measures will help to reduce the risk of unexpected failure, but they are limited to a certain control threshold, see Fig. 2. When the design limits are exceeded, damage becomes unavoidable, so that the protection concept has to concentrate on the consequences of flooding and on the minimization of impacts.

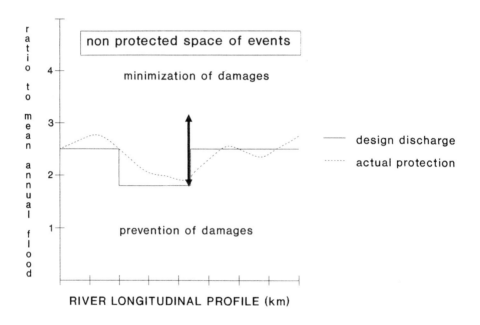

Fig. 2   protection objectives below and beyond the design discharge

Consequently, successful river engineering must be based on additional prevention. Beside a morphologically sound training, the control of all space occupying measures becomes a further important component of protection policy, see Fig. 3. In the alps, much stronger then elsewehre, the correlation of all interventions becomes apparent.

Therefore an effective concept has to include area planning and the integral coordination of all engineering measures.

extended protection concept
in alpine river engineering

* area planing directives
  hazard zoning

* coordination of measures
  for minimization of damages

* morphological adequate
  adjustment of the river course

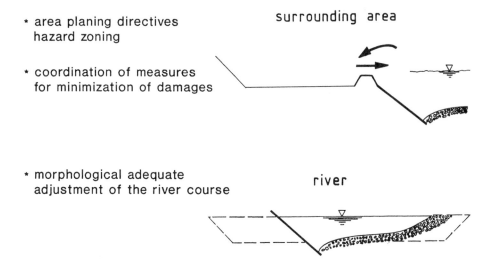

Fig. 3   components of an extended protection concept

Many of the individual operations to expand the valley development may provoke an additional destructive potential. Bridge constructions often prove as trigger for flooding by narrowly designed profiles. Also, the course of roads may have a lasting influence. Long levees without hydraulic precautions, emerge frequently as traps for overflowing water, cutting off natural drainage and unintentionally raising the damages to a higher order. This fact has been impressively demonstrated in the Ötz Valley in 1987. Similar experience has been made in the Reuss Valley/Switzerland, Jäggi (1988).

Only early recognition can avoid severe negative consequences. For floods exceeding the design capacity we have to aim at the minimization of damages in the surrounding area of the river.

references

Aulitzky H.(1988):   Sommerhochwasser 1987 in Tirol - Naturkatastrophen oder
                        fehlende Vorbeugung ? Österr. Wasserwirtschaft 40, H. 5/6

Bunza G.(1975):   Klassifizierung alpiner Massenbewegungen als Beitrag zur
                        Wildbachkunde; Interpraevent Innsbruck, Bd. 1

Jäggi,M.(1988):   Sicherheitsüberlegungen im Flußbau; Wasser, Energie Luft; 80, H. 9

Harvey A.M.(1987):   Sediment Supply to Upland Streams: Influence on Channel
Adjustment; in Sediment Transport in Gravel-bed Rivers; New York:
John Wiley

Parker G.(1967):   On the Cause and Characteristic Scales of Meandering and Braiding
in Rivers; J.Fluid Mech. 76,H.3

Schumm S.A.(1979):   Geomorphic Thresholds: the Concept and its Application.
Trans. Inst. Brit. Geogr. New Series 4

Thenius A.(1975):   Schutzwasserbau in Osttirol; Österr. Wasserwirtschaft 27 ,H.7/8

Yalin M.S.(1977):   Mechanics of Sediment Transport; 2.Ed., Oxford:Pergamon Press

RIVER FLOOD HYDRAULICS
22–25 March 1994: York, England

Modelling the Lower River Severn

By R J Mains-Smith BSc, C Eng, MICE, MIWEM
and D Ramsbottom BSc, C Eng, MICE, MIWEM

Abstract

The paper traces the development of hydraulic modelling work carried out between 1975 and 1992 covering 112km of the River Severn from Worcester down to Avonmouth in the estuary. An extensive computational model study was carried out between 1975 and 1980 to investigate flood defence options. The results were used in the design of the Severn Tidal Defences Scheme which started construction in 1983 and is ongoing.

The model was updated in 1990 and used to re-assess the Severn Tidal Defences Scheme. It was also used to provide boundary conditions for a detailed physical model of the Gloucester area, which was constructed to investigate the effects of the proposed A40 trunk road extension on water levels in the flood plain and assist the NRA in examining possible flood protection for 233 properties in Gloucester. The results of the physical model were used to construct a computational sub-model covering 18km of the Severn through Gloucester. This sub-model was subsequently reinserted into the Worcester to Avonmouth model.

The primary purpose of the paper is to demonstrate the complimentary role of physical and computational models in the Lower River Severn studies.

1   Introduction

Political pressure led the National Rivers Authority (NRA) Severn-Trent Region's predecessor body Severn-Trent Water Authority (STWA) to investigate improvements to the standard of protection afforded to the agricultural flood plains downstream of Tewkesbury on the River Severn. A computational model of the River Severn from Worcester down to Avonmouth in the estuary was constructed as part of a major study carried out between 1975 and 1980, which also included an agricultural benefit assessment (STWA, 1981). The investigations resulted in the comprehensive Lower Severn Improvement Scheme receiving Ministry of Agriculture Fisheries & Food (MAFF) 'approval in principle' for grant aid on the £12.7M scheme at June 1980 prices. The layout of the Severn between Worcester and Avonmouth is shown on Figure 1.

The study concluded that apart from the replacement of some outfalls upstream of Gloucester, embankment reconstruction would be confined to downstream of Gloucester. Construction commenced in 1983 in the Arlingham area and is ongoing. The scheme was renamed the Severn Tidal Defences Scheme in 1990.

Parts of the city of Gloucester are prone to flooding, and in 1985 a desk study was carried out to examine outline proposals for the alleviation of flooding in the low lying parts of the city. The two main options identified were a flood relief channel with embankments and high level flood relief channels across Alney Island, together with combinations of these (HR, 1985).

In 1990, it was decided to update the original model to take account of changes to embankment levels resulting from maintenance works and the Severn Tidal Defences Scheme, and developments in the flood plain (HR, 1991). At the same time the Department of Transport (DoT) announced their plans for the A40 extension. The NRA and DoT agreed to jointly fund the construction of a physical model of the Gloucester Area (Figure 2). Thus the effects of the road on water levels in the flood plain and possible flood protection for the flood prone properties in Gloucester could both be examined (HR, 1992A).

2nd International Conference on River Flood Hydraulics. Edited by W. R. White and J. Watts
© 1994 HR Wallingford Ltd. Published by John Wiley & Sons Ltd

Advantage was taken of the physical model to produce a more refined computational sub-model for the Gloucester area. The sub-model was inserted into the Worcester to Avonmouth model, which was then re-calibrated (HR, 1992B) and utilised in the benefit reassessment of the £20m outstanding flood protection works in the estuary. One further advance was the construction of a truncated computational model from downstream of Gloucester to Avonmouth. This latter model has a run time of 4 minutes compared to 4 hours for the main model.

2   Background

The Problem

Upstream of Gloucester the River Severn has floodbanks in rural areas which will contain the estimated 5 year flood between Worcester and Tewkesbury, and the estimated Mean Annual flood between Tewkesbury and Gloucester. For larger floods the valley bottom is inundated. The flood plain storage attenuates flows and reduces the risk of flooding in the urban areas of Upton, Tewkesbury and Gloucester, none of which have flood defences since they are largely situated on high ground.

Between Gloucester and Avonmouth 2500 properties and 128km^2 of agricultural land rely on embankments and walls for protection. Tidal flooding of some agricultural areas can occur at a 1 in 2 year frequency, and extensive flooding occurred during the tidal surges of December 1981 and February 1990.

The worst flooding in recent years occurred in March 1947 when the level reached at Gloucester Docks was 10.93 AOD. It was a predominantly fluvial flood with an estimated return period of just over 100 years. It is still the current standard for the definition of flood plain extent and for setting of reasonably safe building levels. More recently there was extensive fluvial flooding in January and February 1990 which received much media coverage. The level reached at Gloucester Docks on this occasion was 10.37m AOD which had an estimated return period of about 40 years.

Hydraulic Aspects

Between Worcester and Tewkesbury, the River Severn has a surface width of 60m and a bankfull capacity of 350m^3/s and the flood plain is generally 1km wide. The River Teme joins the Severn just south of Worcester and their maximum recorded discharges are 450m^3/s and 670m^3/s respectively.

The River Avon joins the Severn at Tewkesbury and has a maximum recorded discharge of 450m^3/s Downstream of Tewkesbury the channel capacity increases to 500m^3/s and the flood plain widens to 1.5km until Ashleworth where it narrows down to a few hundred metres for the next 3.5km to Upper Parting, north of Gloucester. The estimated 1 in 100 year flood flow here is about 1030m^3/s.

At Upper Parting and Severn divides around Alney Island into two channels which join together again at Lower Parting. There are navigation weirs on each of the channels which restrict tidal propagation upstream although the effects of spring tides have been recorded as far upstream as Worcester. Under flood conditions about 70% of the total flow passes down the west channel but under extreme low flow the east channel carries the total discharge. Below Lower Parting tidal effects become progressively more important until at Epney the water levels are almost completely dominated by the tide. The lower reaches downstream of Gloucester have a very shallow gradient and are bordered by extensive flood plains up to 4km wide.

The tidal range at Avonmouth is 14.5m. Spring tides rise significantly faster than neap tides and have a longer ebb period. This is caused by the funnel shaped geometry of the Bristol Channel. The tide level can be enhanced by surges generated under certain meteorological conditions, and such surges have enhanced the high water level by over 2m.

Estuary Design Standards

In the Lower Severn Improvement Scheme, embankment levels downstream of Westbury were designed for the higher of 0.5m above the estimated 1 in 30 year tide (8.5m at Avonmouth) or the level predicted from seawall overtopping considerations with a 1 in 30 year tide and a force 9 gale. This was estimated to correspond to 1 in 100 year protection based on the data available at the time, which was considered necessary due to the number of properties at risk in Avonmouth.

The embankment profile provides for a crest width of 3m and 1 in 4 side slopes and an average height of 2m. From 1990, the NRA decided to make provision for global warming by increasing design levels by 0.25m (ie 5mm/year over a 50 year design life). It was reasoned that this would avoid unnecessary future disturbance to the fabric of the embankment and also to the landowners and tenants.

In 1992, MAFF required a reassessment from first principles of benefits for all outstanding works. New farmer surveys and urban benefit assessments were carried out, and numerous runs were made using the new Worcester to Avonmouth model to provide level and frequency parameters at each point along the estuary.

Since overtopping of the unimproved defences occurred twice in 1990, the level-frequency relationship at Avonmouth was re-examined. This had the effect of reducing the design standard down to approximately 30 years for the reconstructed defences.

Development in Gloucester

Gloucester was historically the lowest bridge point on the River Severn. The city developed on the river bank of the east channel where westward expansion was constrained by the river and its flood plain. It has therefore spread eastwards and southwards over the catchment areas of local drainage channels which enter the River Severn.

To the north of Gloucester the Severn is navigable under the control of British Waterways. At Gloucester Docks, which are adjacent to the east channel, there is a connection to the Gloucester to Sharpness Canal. Upstream of the navigation weirs, river water level is maintained at a minimum level of 6.3m AOD.

In the early 1980's the A40 trunk road was diverted along a new route from Longford to Over, the Gloucester Northern Bypass. Over roundabout is a very large intrusion into the flood plain on Alney Island and links the A40 with the A417, which goes northwards to Maisemore and southwards to the city centre.

The South Wales main railway line crosses Alney Island on a combination of high-level embankment and viaduct. In addition, the now unused docks branch line crosses the Island from Over to Llanthony on a combination of low-level embankment and viaduct.

Flooding in the Gloucester area may be caused by both fluvial and tidal events. Flood plain flow passes through the various bridge and culvert openings in the causeways, but these impede flows and produce very complex flow patterns on the flood plain.

In December 1990, the Department of Transport, as part of its Trunk Roads Programme, published its plans to create an additional crossing of Alney Island from Longford to just south of Maisemore to take the A40 traffic to Newent. This was obviously of concern to both locals and the NRA with regard to its effects on flood levels. The physical model was used to optimise the alignment, flow openings and compensatory works required to ensure that no increase in flood water levels occurred.

Modelling Strategy

Computational techniques are the only practical means of modelling the Severn from Worcester to Avonmouth. These provide an approximate hydraulic representation of the river and flood plains. The computational model was not however suitable for detailed modelling of the Gloucester area to assess the effects of the proposed A40 extension and flood alleviation measures on flood water levels. It was therefore decided to use a physical model for this part of the river system. Particular features for which the physical model was considered necessary include:

- meandering channels and channel junctions with significant overbank flow
- interaction between the numerous causeways and flood openings on the flood plain
- structures on bends and groups of bridges in close proximity.

Results from the physical model were subsequently used to improve the computational model representation of the Gloucester area.

3   Worcester to Avonmouth model

The 1981 model

Part of the original Lower Severn Study involved the development of a computational model which would simulate flooding on the Severn. The resulting model included the following features:

- Separate flow paths for the main river channels and flood plains
- Embankments between channels and flood plains modelled as weirs
- Separate calculation of flood plain storage volumes
- Outfall structures in embankments, to enable simulation of flood plain emptying after the passage of a flood
- Embankments across flood plains, including culverts.

The updated model

After the completion of the study, the software was further developed to include the following additional features:

- Improved representation of loops and branches in the river system
- Division of the flood plains into two dimensional networks of "cells", allowing more flexible modelling of flood plains.

The resulting program was used for updating the Worcester to Avonmouth model. All flow calculations for channels and flood plains were based on a one dimensional application of the St Venant equations for unsteady open channel flow (Samuels P G, 1983). The computational model may therefore be described as "quasi two-dimensional", in which one dimensional equations are used to represent the flow in a two-dimensional layout of channel and flood plain cells.

The model was calibrated for three flood events: The December 1981 tidal surge; the February 1990 tidal surge; and the February 1990 fluvial flood. It was therefore necessary to update the model to 1981 conditions for the first calibration event and then to 1990 conditions for the other two events. Both of the observed surge tide events produced considerable flooding of the flood plains downstream of Gloucester. The February 1990 fluvial flood event lasted for about two weeks and completely inundated the flood plain from Worcester to downstream of Gloucester.

The purpose of updating the Worcester to Avonmouth model was to provide the NRA with a model for re-assessing the Severn Tidal Defences Scheme, and provide boundary conditions for the physical model study of the Gloucester area. It was necessary to define flood events to be used in these studies.

In view of the wide range of combinations of river flows and tidal conditions which produce floods of different return periods, it was decided to base the return period of flood events at Gloucester on the long term water level record at Gloucester Docks. A range of design flood events were derived from model tests which were similar in character to major observed events on the Severn, and which produced peak water levels of specified return periods at Gloucester.

4   Gloucester Physical Model

<u>Construction and calibration</u>

The physical model represents an area measuring 4km by 2.5km as shown on Figure 2. The horizontal scale of the model was 1:200 and the vertical scale was 1:50, giving a vertical exaggeration of 4.

Major flood events at Gloucester are dominated by fluvial events where the variation in river flows and flood water levels is small at the peak of the event. It was therefore decided to use steady flow modelling, as tests are much quicker and simpler to perform.

Detailed flood plain maps with contours at 0.25m intervals were used to mould the flood plains. 65 river cross sections were surveyed in a detailed river channel survey undertaken specifically for the study. Before the study was carried out there were only two water level gauges in the Severn at Gloucester, including the continuous recorder at Gloucester Docks. In order to obtain more detailed calibration information continuous water level recorders were installed at Upper Parting and Lower Parting together with eight staff gauges elsewhere in the river channels. In addition, twenty maximum water level recorders were installed on the flood plains. Data from these gauges were used to calibrate the model.

The model was also calibrated for the major fluvial flood which occurred in February 1990, based on limited observed water level information and the observed flooded outline. Discharges were gauged at Gloucester during flood events on the main river channels and at openings through embankments on the flood plains. Discharges at these locations were measured on the model during the calibration process to check that the distribution of flow was correct.

When an acceptable calibration had been obtained, eight design events were run on the model to obtain base sets of water levels which represent existing conditions. Boundary conditions were obtained from the flow and water level hydrographs predicted by the computational model at the appropriate river channel and flood plain cross sections. Boundary conditions used in the physical model included:

- stage in the Severn at the downstream end of the model

- discharge out of the left and right bank flood plains at the downstream end of the model

- discharge into the Severn and the left and right bank flood plains at the upstream end of the model

- Discharge into the River Leadon.

It was not possible to obtain an exact match between the two models because the predicted distribution of flow between the channels and flood plains was slightly different in each case. In addition, flow in the computational model was unsteady whereas flow in the physical model was steady. Iteration involving several physical model runs was necessary to obtain a satisfactory set of boundary conditions for each design event.

Flood alleviation

A range of flood alleviation options were tested on the model, including:

- Removal of parts of the redundant dock branch railway embankment
- Removal of the complete docks branch railway embankment
- Flood protection barriers around urban areas in the flood plain
- Flood relief channels across Alney Island
- Combinations of the above.

Changes in water levels for each option were recorded, and used in the benefit cost assessments of flood alleviation measures.

Proposed A40 crossing

The model was also used to assess the effects on flooding of the proposed A40 crossing of the Severn flood plain just north of Gloucester as indicated on Figure 2. The flood plain is about 3km wide at the crossing point. A junction was required between the new road and the existing A417, which runs along the west side of Alney Island. A large number of road options were tested on the model, including different river bridges, flood openings, and road junction arrangements.

In order to ensure that the road crossing would not produce a worsening of the already serious flood situation in the Gloucester area, it was necessary to include flood mitigation measures in the road scheme. The purpose of these measures was to produce reductions in flood water levels which, when combined with the road crossing, meant that the overall scheme would not increase flood water levels. A range of flood mitigation options were tested including removal of parts of existing embankments, realignment of existing roads, enlargement of existing flood openings, and earthworks on the flood plain.

During the physical model study, flow visualisation techniques including float tracking and dye injection were used to identify the distribution of flow on the flood plains. These were particularly useful in helping to identify suitable locations for flood openings in new embankments, and the identification of flood mitigation and alleviation measures. Flow patterns identified using float tracking are shown on Figure 3.

5   Gloucester Computational Model

Results from the physical model were used to improve the computational model representation of the Gloucester area. The improvements were carried out on a computational sub-model of the Severn from Ashleworth to Minsterworth, which was subsequently inserted into the main Worcester to Avonmouth model. The layout of the model was improved taking account of the flood plain flow patterns observed on the physical model. The model was then calibrated against the physical model for four events including an observed bankfull event and three of the design flood events, where overbank flow occurred.

A key element in the calibration process was to match the distribution of discharge between the two river channels and the flood openings. The river channels were calibrated for the bankfull event by adjusting the channel roughness and structure discharge and drowning coefficients. Changes required to the calibration of the river channels in the computational model included the following:

- reductions in roughness on the east channel upstream of Llanthony weir from (typically) $k_s = 0.45$m to values of k_s in the range 0.01 to 0.05m, where k_s is the Colebrook-White roughness length

- reductions in roughness on the west channel upstream of Over bridges from (typically) $k_s = 0.20$m to values of k_s in the range 0.002 to 0.09m. These low values reflect the smooth nature of silt river beds in the Severn estuary

- increases in weir discharge coefficients and drowning ratios

- increases in bridge afflux scaling coefficients (ie the afflux was generally greater in the physical model than the computational model).

Flows on the flood plains were controlled to a large extent by flood openings in embankments. The three design flood events were calibrated in the computational model by adjusting discharge coefficients and drowning ratios for these structures, and flood plain embankments where they are overtopped.

6   Results

Maximum water levels predicted by the Worcester to Avonmouth computational model were used to predict the required level of new or improved flood defence embankments, and estimate the standard of protection provided by existing embankments.

The flood alleviation options for Gloucester tested on the physical model did not reduce water levels significantly. The best option was the removal of the redundant docks branch railway but even that only yielded a benefit/cost ratio of 0.3. Thus there are no viable solutions to protect the widely spread out low lying properties.

Numerous different options for the A40 road crossing were tested in order to develop a design which reduced maximum water level increases upstream of the crossing to about 0.04m for the estimated 1 in 100 year fluvial flood. The design included a 144m long bridge over the west channel, a 100m long bridge over the East Channel, and a 430m long viaduct on Alney Island. By the introduction of flood mitigation options it was possible to produce an overall reduction in flood water levels. The proposals produced a redistribution of flows between the west and east channels and separate investigations were carried out to estimate the effects this will have on scour, particularly at bridges.

The study highlights some of the difficulties encountered in the computational modelling of river and flood plain systems. The modeller has to select values of roughness coefficients for channels and flood plains, and discharge coefficients and drowning ratios for embankments and structures. The selection is normally based on a limited amount of calibration information in the river channels, with little or no information on flood plain water levels or flow patterns.

The authors wish to emphasise the importance of detailed and reliable water level and flow information, both for the calibration of the models and the determination of design events. 28 water level gauges were installed in the Gloucester area and flows were gauged in the river channels and flood openings for a number of flood events, in order to provide information for model calibration and verification.

7   Acknowledgements

The development of the computational and physical models has been an interactive process between the NRA and HR Wallingford, and with the DoT and Parkman Consulting Engineers for the road crossing. The improved Worcester to Avonmouth model is currently being used for designing the remaining Severn Tidal Defences and for testing future development proposals. The permission of the NRA and DoT to publish this paper is gratefully acknowledged.

8   References

HR, 1985 "Gloucester Flood Alleviation Scheme. Preliminary desk study of hydraulic aspects". Report EX 1336, Hydraulics Research Ltd, August 1985.

HR, 1991 "River Severn Flood Plain. Avonmouth to Worcester. Computational model study". Report EX2252, HR Wallingford, March 1991.

HR, 1992A "Gloucester Flood Alleviation Study". Report EX 2644, HR Wallingford, September 1992.

HR, 1992B "River Severn at Gloucester. Computational Model". Report EX 2578, HR Wallingford, September 1992.

Samuels P G, 1983 "Computational modelling of flood flows in embanked rivers". International Conference on the Hydraulic Aspects of Floods and Flood Control, London, UK, 13-15 September 1983.

STWA, 1981 "River Severn, Avonmouth to Worcester flood alleviation study". Severn Trent Water Authority (six volumes).

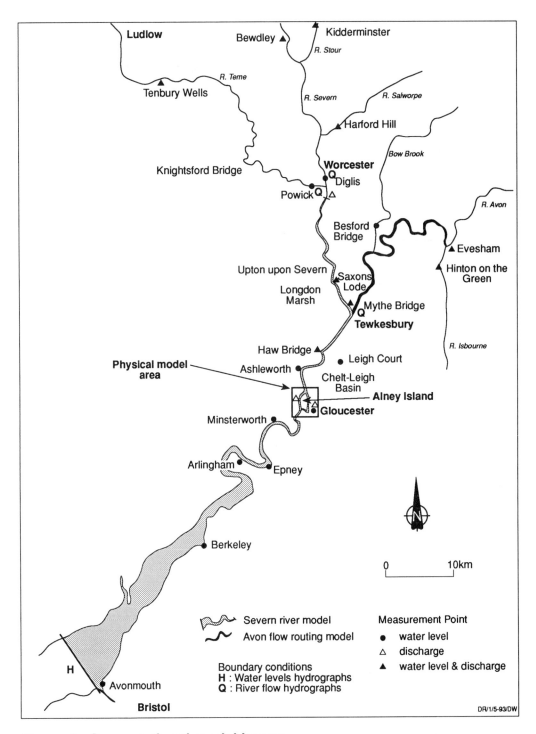

Figure 1 Computational model layout

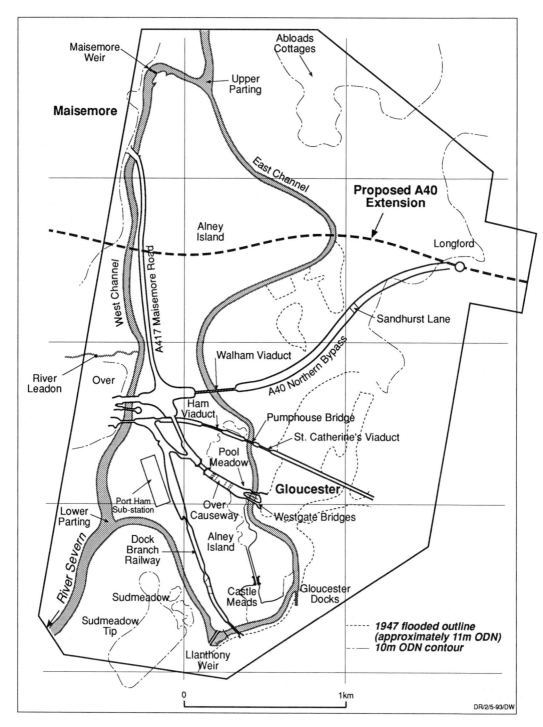

Figure 2 Physical model layout

Figure 3   1 in 100 year flood. Existing conditions

FLOOD CONTROL IN HUNGARY AND PIPING FAILURES
AT RIVER LEVEES

Sándor TÓTH M. Sc.

Counsellor

Ministry of Transport, Communication

and Water Management

75-81 Dob St.

H-1077 Budapest

Hungary

ABSTRACT. This paper is going to introduce briefly the experience of Hungarian researchers in the field of hydraulic failures of foundation soil of levees, which was mainly observed at the intersections of ancient river bed.

1. Brief introduction of flood control in Hungary

Hungary is situated in the deepest part of the basin formed by the Carpathian Mountains and the eastern foothills of the Alps The total area of the country is 93.000 km2, 52 % of which are plains, and the rest is hilly country. Mountains higher than 500 m above sea level take up only 1 % of the territory of Hungary.

The catchment area of our main rivers is outside the country in the surrounding high mountains of the Carpathians and the Alps. Thus 96 % of our surface water resources as well as the floods of the rivers come from abroad. In the catchment area the interaction of the climatic effect of the Atlantic Ocean, that of the Mediterrainean Sea and the continent itself may induce extraordinary precipitation. Due to the geographic and climatic features of Hungary floods may occur in any period of the year. Characteristic data of the regime of our rivers is shown in Table 1.

2nd International Conference on River Flood Hydraulics. Edited by W. R. White and J. Watts
© 1994 HR Wallingford Ltd. Published by John Wiley & Sons Ltd

Since the territory of Hungary is mainly flat and the rivers have a lower course character with a low longitudinal gradient, as can be seen in Table 2., flood protection has been carried out by major bed training, with the construction of embankments at both sides of the rivers.

The comparison of Europe's largest flood protection works (see Fig. 1.) points at the special importance of flood control in Hungary. The floodplain takes up the 23 % of the country with a total extension of 21.200 km^2. This total amount of flood plains consists of 151 separate flood plain basins, 55 of which are along the Danube and it's tributaries, 96 can be found in the Tisza Valley representing 72,9 % of the total floodplain. The smallest basin covers only 0,32 km^2, the greatest - which is situated by the Danube - is as large as 2.287 km^2. In the Tisza Valley there are further 5 basins exceeding 1.000 km^2 of territory, the largest has an extension of 1.783 km^2.

In the floodplain of Hungary are:

- 1,8 million hectares of valuable agricultural land, that is one third of the arable land of the country;

- 32 % of the railways, 15 % of the main roads and more than 2000 industrial plants;

- more than 700 settlements with more than 2,5 million residents;

- produced 30 % of the GDP, the accumulated national wealth makes round 20 billion USD, flood damage may reach 32,6 % of the total economic value that can be found in the affected area.

As long as the end of the 1940-s the levees were built manually, transverse transporting the earth to the smallest possible distance from the borrow pits opened near the levees. Later their height has been raised, their crest has been widened, their slopes has been flattened and one or more berms have been built on the protected side.

So far 97 % of the floodplain are protected. The remaining 700 km^2 represents the floodplains in the narrow valleys of some smaller rivers. Due to their economic-geographical conditions flood prevention of these flood plain basins is not considered to be economically feasible now. Only the protection of some settlements situated completely or partly in these valleys may be carried out as the investment of the interested with the support of the government [1].

2. Rupture of levees as a consequence of the increased head on the foundation soil

As a consequence of the continous hightening of the levees the type of rupture during floodings has been changed: while in the earlier period of the history of flood protection the main danger and cause of damages was overtopping of the river dikes which was followed by the complete erosion of the dike body itself, the hightened profile increased the load to the foundation soil.

Decades of observations have proved that the failures of otherwise properly built levees were caused in a great part by piping (hydraulic failure of the subsoil).

2.1. CONVENTIONAL PIPING/SAND BOIL PHENOMENON

Fig. 2. shows the structure and the process of the conventional piping/sand boil phenomenon [3]. The levee is built upon a relatively thin impermeable covering layer, underneath of which can be found a layer of fine sand, and the undermost layer is a relatively thick aquifer consists either of coarse sand, graveled sand, or sandy gravel. In the covering layer, on the protected side of the dike a channel arises for certain reasons, like a decayed root or a hole of a fieldmouse, etc. The water coming out concentrated has a relatively high velocity exceeding the critical gradient of the fine sand. There is an erosion process starting, transporting the fine sand and building a crater from it on the surface around the hole. As the sand is being washed out from under the covering layer, the length of the channel is growing towards the riverside. This results in the continous increasing of the initial Δ H/L ratio. The channel growing under the dike reduces the stability of the covering layer and the dike itself: a sliding of the slope or a subsidence of the levee may occur, causing levee breach.

It is very important that in this process the amount of water that transports the fine sand originates from seepage process. On the other hand the critical gradient of the fine sand is i = 0,8 - 1,0. But the value of Δ H/L along our levees is round 1/8-1/12. So the initial gradient of a piping phenomenon must be considered as Ha/d, its value may reach or exceed the critical gradient so the process of erosion may start. Simultaneously the surface of the channel is growing, but the amount of water coming from seepage will not increase considerably, so the velocity will decrease. These are the reasons why this phenomenon may be called as "slow" piping, and fighting against is rather possible, usually there is left time enough after their observation for the countermeasures like it is shown in Fig. 3.

251

Nevertheless, conventional or "slow" piping is always a subject to fight against, because there are never any guarantee against a harmful degeneration of the phenomenon.

2.2. RAPID PIPING PHENOMENON

There were some levee breaches in the past decades in Hungary and in some of our neighbouring countries caused by hydraulic failure of the foundation soil of the dike, where and when there was no chance to fight against them because of the very rapid process that occured.

One of the last ruptures like that occured at the right bank of Kettős-Körös (Double-Körös) river in 1980 [2]. The flood wave hydrograph, the longitudinal profile of the section, including the soil stratification as well as the particle distribution curve can be seen in Fig. 4. The guards that were to check the conditions along the levee section periodically, did not observe any harmful phenomenon during this flood until the early morning of July 28, 1980. Then, at 6.35 am. about 100 m away from the approaching guards a sudden and very strong eruption of water was observed. The water was reported "black and densely muddy". The dike broke through in some five minutes. The width of the rupture increased rapidly, at 7.00 am it reached 10 m, the final width was as much as 78 m.

The investigations [4] that were carried out have proved, that a "rapid" piping phenomenon occured. As can be seen in Fig. 4. in the subsoil there was a lense-formed layer of a badly graduated (uniformity coefficient is mostly less than 3) loose (e = 0,79 !) sandsoil. This layer was in communication with the river bed itself. The increasing hydraulic pressure broke suddenly and intensively the relatively thick clay layers, because they were still stiff: the torrential flood wave did not enable the clay to get saturated, which could have turned it into elastic state. So, the saturated and pressed sand layer lost its support and the channel of this sand layer got liquefied in its whole length. This lead to the very quick rupture of the levee. The process and the rapid change of piezometric pressure is shown in Fig. 5.

Similar levee breaches were observed in Hungary at Szigetköz by the Danube in 1954, in the vicinity of it, but at the left bank of the Danube in Czechoslovakia as well as in Yougoslavia, also by the Danube in 1965.

3. Measures taken in order to identify the sections prone to hydraulic failure along the levees

The above mentioned dangerous phenomena, including conventional or "slow" piping are expected to develop in special stratification conditions, usually in the three-layered stratification that was shown in Fig. 2. Such conditions are due first of all to the differing stratification of the subsoil within a shorter section from that of the neighbouring sections.

Further investigations [5] have proved that these anomalies in the stratification are expected, and all the mentioned hydraulic failures along the dikes occured in those points, where the track of the levee has intersected ancient river bed that had disconnected and silted up several hundred or possibly several thousand years ago. These ancient river beds are easily identifiable in black and white aerial photographs.

An interpretation of ancient river bed system along the Körös river as well as the scheme of stratification at the concave bank of a silted river bend can be seen in Fig. 6.

With a help of an interpretation of the ancient river bed we are able to identify the intersections of them with the levees, as well as to evaluate the weak points of the levee at these intersections from morphological point of view.

The particular characteristics that must be considered are:

- the distance of intersection from the mean bed;
- the shape of the mean bed in the vicinity of the intersection
  (straight, convex or concave bank, inflexion);
- the shape of the ancient bed in the intersection.

This morphological classification [6] completed with the exploration of continous stratification of subsoil by the means of horizontal geoelectric probing can be a proper method for identifying and determining the characteristic and individual sections.

4. Methods of reinforcement of the stability of the subsoil of levees

Since the major cause of damage to the levees at the intersections with ancient river bed is liquefaction of sand layers, construction of counterweight structures as well as decreasing the head to the foundation soil by the means of ground improvement or of lowering the groundwater table during floods were among the countermeasures considered. Of course, further basic requirements were: restoration of the original function of the levees, applicability to all the levees, economical solution, including not only the execution, but the maintenance of the construction as well.

Combination of the following countermeasures can be suggested as can be seen in Fig. 7.:

- construction of counterweight berm or basin;
- installation of sheet pile walls;
- installation of drains and/or wells;
- application of insulation facing or layer.

REFERENCES

1. Zorkóczy, Z. and Tóth, S. (1988) 'Long-term development plan of the flood protection system of Hungary' Vízügyi Közlemények (Hydraulic Engineering) 1985/4, pp 513-534.

2. Report of the Experts' Committee (1980. Oct.) 'On the investigation of the conditions of the levee breaches at the left bank of Berettyó river and at the right bank of Kettős-Körös river'

3. Dr. Szepessy, J. and Fehér, Á. (1981) 'Investigation of hydraulic failure phenomena, suggestions to the improvement' VITUKI report

4. Dr. Szepessy, J. (1983) 'Erosion and liquefaction of sedimental and cohesive soils in flood protecting dikes. The degree of the danger and its reduction' Hidrológiai Közlöny (Bulletin of Hydrology) 1983/1, pp 11-20.

5. Baló, Z. (1983) ' Investigation of the intersections of levees with ancient river bed with the help of arial photographs and maps' Hidrológiai Közlöny (Bulletin of Hydrology) 1983/1. pp. 21-23.

6. Fehér, Á. (1983) ' Classification of the intersections of levees with ancient river bed. Computing of the stability of the foundation soil ' Hidrológiai Közlöny, 1983/1. pp. 24-27.

All references in Hungarian !

Table 1.

CHARACTERISTIC DATA OF THE REGIME OF THE MAJOR RIVERS IN HUNGARY

River	Staff gauge	Range of tide, cm	Q_{min} m^3/s	Q_{max}	Q_{max}/Q_{min}
Danube	Rajka	698	570	10300	18
	Budapest	794 /875/	615 /580/	8600	14
	Mohacs	902	618	7850	13
Raba	Sarvar	622	6,5	800	123
Ipoly	Balassagyarmat	493	3,5	360	103
Drava	Barcs	666	185	3050	17
Tisza	Zahony	1060	47	3750	80
	Szolnok	1181	60	3820	64
	Szeged	1210	95	4700	49
Szamos	Csenger	998	8	1350	169
Bodrog	Sarospatak	672	4	1250	313
Sajo	Felsozsolca	513	2,4	545	227
Feher-Koros	Gyula	996	1	610	610
Fekete-Koros	Sarkad	1041	1	810	810
Kettos-Koros	Bekes	1106	2,3	905	393
Harmas-Koros	Gyoma	1034	4,5	1800	400
Maros	Mako	725	22	2450	111

Table 2.

LONGITUDINAL GRADIENT OF MAJOR RIVERS IN HUNGARY

River	Section of rivers	Longitudinal gradient, per mil
Danube	Rajka - Gonyu	0,6 - 0,2
	Gonyu - southern boundary	0,1 - 0,04
Raba	Szentgotthard - Sarvar	0,5 - 0,4
	Sarvar - Varkeszo	0,7 - 0,5
	Rabacsecseny - mouth of river	0,3 - 0,2
Drava	Mouth of Mura river - southern boundary	0,4 - 0,3
Tisza	Tiszabecs - Vasarosnameny	0,3 - 0,2
	Vasarosnameny - Tokaj	0,2 - 0,1
	Tokaj - southern boundary	0,1 - 0,03
Koros - -Berettyo river system	Along the upper national reach	0,2 - 0,13
	Along the lower national reach	0,08 - 0,03
Maros	National reach only	0,2 - 0,08

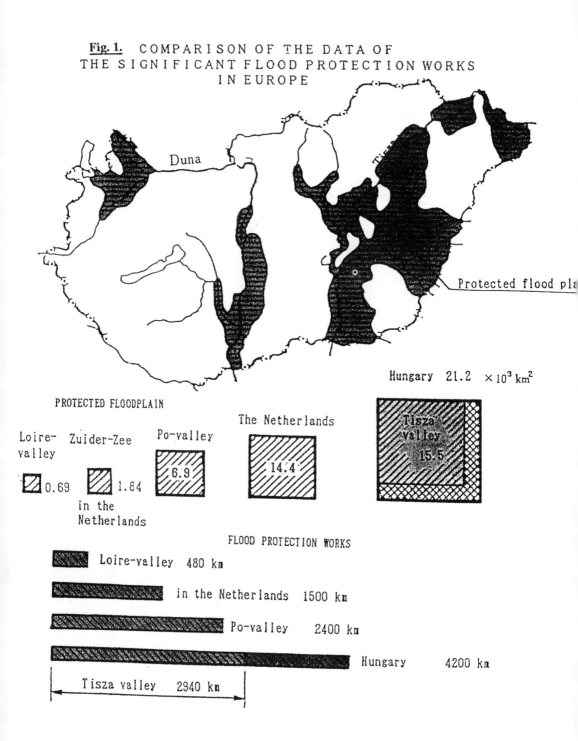

Fig. 1. COMPARISON OF THE DATA OF THE SIGNIFICANT FLOOD PROTECTION WORKS IN EUROPE

Duna

Protected flood pla

Hungary 21.2 $\times 10^3$ km^2

PROTECTED FLOODPLAIN

Loire-valley

Zuider-Zee

Po-valley

The Netherlands

Tisza valley 15.5

0.69

1.84 in the Netherlands

6.9

14.4

FLOOD PROTECTION WORKS

Loire-valley 480 km

in the Netherlands 1500 km

Po-valley 2400 km

Hungary 4200 km

Tisza valley 2940 km

258

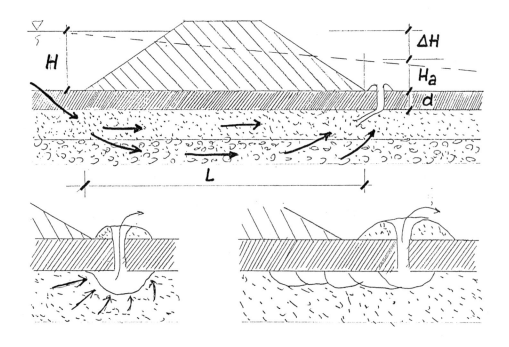

Fig. 2. Schematic diagram of a conventional or "slow" piping

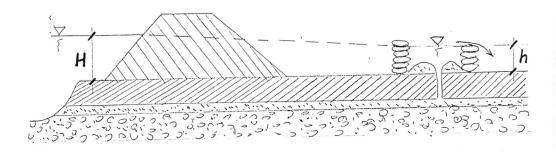

Fig. 3. Schematic diagram of the countermeasure during flood fighting against piping

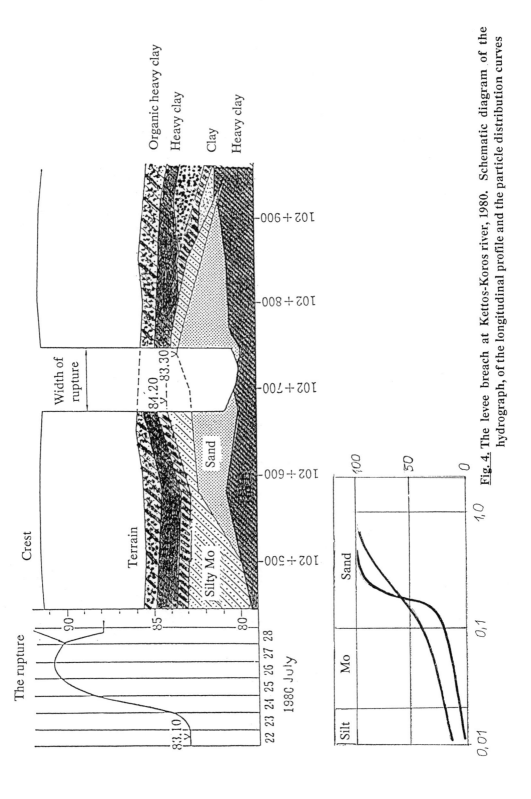

Fig. 4. The levee breach at Kettos-Koros river, 1980. Schematic diagram of the hydrograph, of the longitudinal profile and the particle distribution curves

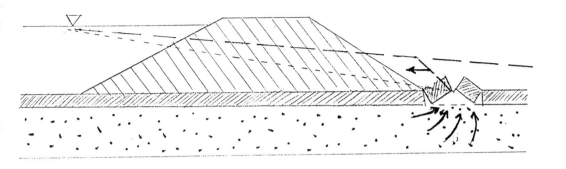

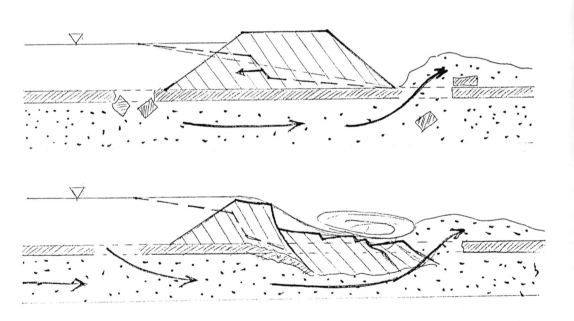

Fig. 5. Schematic diagram of a rapid piping

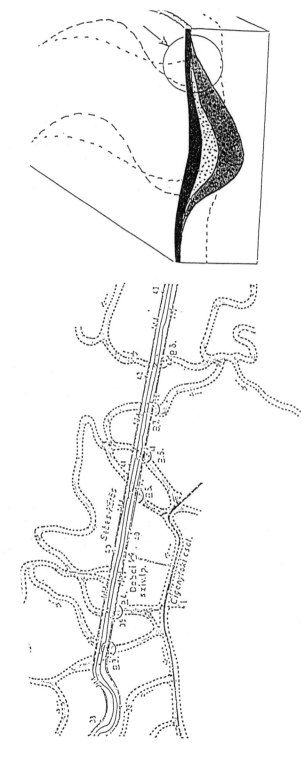

Fig. 6. Ancient river bed system along the Sebes-Koros river and scheme of stratification of soil at the concave bank of a silted river-bend

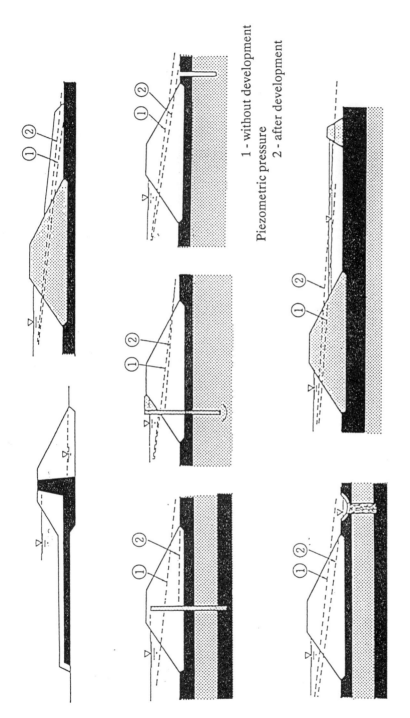

1 - without development
2 - after development
Piezometric pressure

Fig. 7. Improvement of the stability of the foundation soil

2nd International Conference on
RIVER FLOOD HYDRAULICS
22–25 March 1994: York, England

The Yorkshire Humber Estuary Tidal Defence Strategy

David Pelleymounter, B.SC., C Eng., FICE, FIWEM
National Rivers Authority, Northumbria & Yorkshire Region

ABSTRACT

This paper describes the process used by the National Rivers Authority
(NRA) to develop a framework to progress tidal defence works on the
Humber and its tributaries within the area controlled by the Yorkshire
Regional Flood Defence Committee (RFDC). A number of studies were
undertaken to establish the dimensions of the work required. These
studies included the condition of the existing defences, the frequency
of high tidal levels, the rate of relative land/sea rise, an estuary
habitat survey and an assessment of the impact of tidal flooding. By
drawing on this information, the flood defence needs of the estuary
and its tributaries were identified and works prioritised and
programmed. This work formed a strategy for which funds were sought
and on which wider consultations were undertaken. A short review of
success of the Strategy is included.

KEY WORDS

Humber, Tidal Defences, Sea Level Rise, Prioritisation, Probability.

BACKGROUND

The Yorkshire RFDC has statutory powers in respect of the tidal
defences on the North bank of the Humber and on the tributaries of the
Rivers Ouse. The whole of the tidal reaches of these rivers have
manmade flood defences with the exception of a short length of high
ground near North Ferriby. There are 80,000 ha of land protected by
these defences including much high grade agricultural land. In this
area lies the City of Hull and the towns of Goole and Selby together
with a number of villages. In total some 400,000 people live and work
in this flood risk area with high tides regularly 3m to 4m above
ground level. Although the impact of wave action reduces up the
estuary, effects remain a significant factor up to Trent Falls.

In 1989, at the time of the creation of the National Rivers
Authority, the five year plan for capital flood defence works included
only two projected tidal schemes on the Humber and Ouse with a total
estimated cost of £2 million.

CONDITION SURVEY

In 1990, the NRA decided to undertake a national survey of Sea
Defences. This survey considered the condition of each length of
defence and each component of the defence in each length. Details of
this national survey are given in the NRA report "The Sea Defence
Survey, 1990/91" (3).

In the Yorkshire Region the length of Sea Defence amounts to only
22km of which 16km are within the Humber Estuary itself. An early

---

decision was made to extend the survey to cover the Tidal Defences. This entailed covering a further 230km of flood defence on the Rivers Ouse, Don, Aire, Derwent, Hull, Esk and the Humber. A summary of the condition surveys for the Humber, Ouse, Aire and Don is given in Table I. The surveys revealed that, for the Humber, Ouse, Don and Aire, the condition of the defences was generally satisfactory with only 9.4% in Class 3 or Class 4 condition.

At the same time as the condition surveys were being undertaken, a level survey of tidal defences was being carried out.

TABLE I. SEA AND TIDAL DEFENCE SURVEY 1991
CONDITIONS OF PRINCIPAL DEFENCE ELEMENTS
HUMBER (NORTH BANK), RIVER OUSE, RIVER DON,
RIVER AIRE

DEFENCE	CONDITION					
	Class 1 km	Class 2 km	Class 3 km	Class 4 km	TOTAL km	%
PRIMARY DEFENCE						
EMBANKMENTS	6.04	155.76	9.41	4.66	175.87	84.83
PILING	0.25	10.41	1.06	0.04	11.76	5.67
WALLS	1.40	13.32	1.98	2.99	19.69	9.50
TOTAL	7.69	179.49	12.45	7.69	207.32	100.00
%	3.71	86.58	6.00	3.71	100.00	
SUPPORT ELEMENT						
REVETMENTS	0.35	35.55	11.84	9.23	56.97	

ELEMENT CONDITION
Class 1 - Condition as built   Class 3 - Moderate works required
Class 2 - Some signs of wear   Class 4 - Significant works needed

TABLE II. EXTREME EVENT FREQUENCY - BLACKTOFT
EXTREMES BASED ON ANNUAL MAXIMA

RETURN PERIOD (In Years)	1990 * WATER LEVEL	2000 WATER LEVEL	2010 WATER LEVEL	2030 WATER LEVEL	2100 WATER LEVEL
2	5.124	5.194	5.254	5.384	6.014
10	5.384	5.454	5.514	5.644	6.274
50	5.554	5.624	5.684	5.814	6.444
100	5.613	5.683	5.743	5.873	6.503
1000	5.765	5.835	5.895	6.025	6.655
FUTURE TREND ALLOWANCE**		0.07	0.13	0.26	0.89

* Data adjusted for Historical trend
** IPCC global mean sea level rise and local allowance

HISTORIC AND FUTURE SEA LEVELS

A study of high tides in the Humber was carried out by Commander Suthons in a report for the British Transport and Docks Board in 1973. This was partly updated by Graff (4) in his study of annual sea level maxima around Great Britain in 1981. These studies established that a rise was taking place of sea level relative to adjacent land levels in the Humber. Suthons' work was used in the design of the Hull Barrier where, a conservative allowance of 7.6mm/year for sea level rise was included.

In 1989 an internal report considered the tide level record at a number of Humber locations. The study used annual maxima from 7 tide gauges of varying record length between 1920 and 1987. Suthons' work was confirmed and significant variations shown in rate of sea level rise in the estuary, Immingham 1.8mm/yr. and Goole 8.2mm/yr.

In 1990 the Intergovernmental Panel on Climate Change (IPCC) (1) published its assessments of sea level rises to be expected over the next century. In the Humber Estuary, care was needed in interpreting the IPCC conclusions. Would the rise in water in the estuary be the same as general sea level rises? Would the rate of rise in levels increase or reduce further up the estuary? What was the proportion of isostatic change to sea level change?

In 1990 the NRA commissioned a study of all the historic tidal data from 18 locations on the North Sea and in the Humber Estuary. The study was a joint commission from Yorkshire, Anglian and Severn-Trent Regions of the NRA. The study involved the creation of a database containing the levels and times of all the high and low water levels from locations where significant records existed. A total of 589 years of high and low water data was collected. A first update of the database was undertaken in 1993.

Linear trend estimates were used on yearly average high tide levels to consider the rate of relative sea level rise. The IPCC reviewed the estimates of trends in mean sea levels to determine a global sea level rise. By comparing this rate with the rate of rise in the Humber, local effects were identified.

The extremes analysis used the Generalised Extreme Value Method. Two dataset types were considered, the annual maxima and the 5 highest tides in each year. Both data sets were adjusted for historic trends. Full details of the analysis were given by Parle (2).

The study had the following conclusions:-
- that average yearly high tides showed that there was a steady rise of 3.57mm/year over the past 60 years.
- that the rise was the same throughout the length of the estuary.
- that compared with the global sea level rise there was an additional local rate of 1.57 - 2.57mm/year in the Humber inclusive of isostatic change.

By using the historic trend to adjust past events, the frequency of extreme events in 1990 was found. The levels for extremes events in the years 2000, 2010, 2030, 2100 were then found by adjusting for future trends. Two future trends were considered - a continuation of the historic trend and a trend based on the IPCC business as usual scenario of future global sea level rise plus a local rate of 2.07mm/yr. Table II shows a typical extreme event frequency table for Blacktoft.

Following the publication of the report in May 1991, discussion took place within the NRA and with MAFF engineers. A future trend of 6mm/yr was agreed with the frequency of extreme events based on the analysis of annual maxima.

FORMATION OF A STRATEGY

The first suggestion of a comprehensive tidal strategy was put forward in April 1989 as an internal recommendation. Early in 1991, as the work on the Condition Survey and the Tidal Records Study was progressing, it became clear that there was a need to bring these two studies together. They made it possible to consider the flood defence needs of the Humber over the next twenty years. The limits for this "strategy" were set as the North bank of the Humber from Kilnsea to Trent falls, the tidal River Ouse, Aire and Don.

The Yorkshire Humber Estuary Tidal Defence Strategy was conceived as a framework within which the following could be achieved:-
- adequate funding and resources secured.
- balance of Flood Defence needs with other needs.
- a prioritised programme of Capital and Maintenance works.
- a complementary tidal flood warning service.

COST OF WORKS

To arrive at an estimate of the total costs in improving flood defence to an acceptable standard a number of assumptions were made:-
- The design standard would be based on the 1 in 100 year still water level in 2030 from the Tidal Records study.
- An additional local wave allowance based on exposure and fetch, with a minimum of 500 mm. No further freeboard allowance.
- All improvement works would be completed by 2010.
- Flood defences would be improved on their existing line.
- Improved banks profile minimum 3 to 1 side slope, 2m crest width, where the height is over 3m, a back berm 3m wide to be provided.
- Landscaping and high quality finishes in urban areas.
- Heavy stone revetment on exposed reaches below Goole.

The area covered by the Humber Strategy was divided into seven sectors. Each sector is topographically independent with discreet boundaries and no internal defences or high ground. A breach within a sector could, if unrepaired, allow flooding to spread throughout the sector.

The total cost of works is estimated at £110 million. As the construction programme would be phased over 20 years, the Net Present Value of the works is £62 million.

IMPACT OF FLOODING

In assessing the impact of flooding in most situations the assumption is that the risk is static. Rising mean sea levels result in a progressive increase in the frequency of a given high tide level. There will be an associated increase in the annual losses due to flooding as flood defences are overtopped or breached more frequently.

An assessment of the cost of flood damages for the strategy area was undertaken in order to assess the overall benefits from improving flood defences. Full detailed benefit studies would be undertaken on each sector.

Damages were considered in 1990, 2010 and 2030 assuming flood defences at the same level as in 1990. No attempt was made to evaluate the losses due to traffic disruption, communication failure, costs of emergency service or public authorities. When overtopping of defence up to 250mm deep was being considered, a simple relationship of depth/time/length of overtopping resulting in a depth and area of flooding was used. Such flooding was assumed to last less than 12 hours. When depths of greater than 250mm were being considered, a breach of the defences was deemed to have occurred with resulting flooding extending over several tide cycles.

The costs of flood damage are well distributed over the whole of the estuary both in space and in time. It was therefore concluded that a phased programme of construction covering discreet topographical units would be practicable in execution and effective in meeting flood defence needs. Annual losses rise from £3 million in 1990 to £32 million in 2030. The Net Present Value of these costs was calculated as £123.5 million.

PRIORITIES AND PROGRAMME

A programme of works reflecting the priorities needed to be drawn from the studies into the flood defence needs of the Humber. Priorities had to reflect the condition of the main defence, the current standard of protection, and the economic consequences of defence failure. Proposed works were placed in four priority groups, defined as follows:-

First Priority Major Improvement Schemes   £20 million
    Generally over 0.5 km in length
    Defence elements in Class 3 and Class 4 condition
    Defence standard less than 1:20 years or high value land use
First Priority Minor Improvement Schemes   £1 million
    As Major but less than 0.5 km in length.
Second Priority Improvement Schemes   £19 million
    As First Priority Major Schemes but Defence standard greater
than 1:20 years.
Low Priority Improvement Schemes   £70 million
    All remaining flood defences which would not provide a 1:100
    year protection in the year 2030 without improvement.
Figure 1 shows the Humber with first, second and low priority flood defences

HABITAT SURVEY

The works suggested to meet the flood defence needs by the Yorkshire Humber Estuary Tidal Defence Strategy are seen by the NRA as an opportunity for the enhancement of the coastal habitat. It was recognised from its inception that the strategy would give rise to legitimate concerns for the ecology of the estuary and adjacent land.

Large areas of the estuary are designated as Sites of Special Scientific Interest (SSSI) as shown on Figure 1. In the near future areas are also likely to be designated under the International Ramsar Convention and under the EC Directive on Special Protection Areas for

Figure 1
HUMBER ESTUARY TIDAL DEFENCES
STRATEGY PRIORITIES

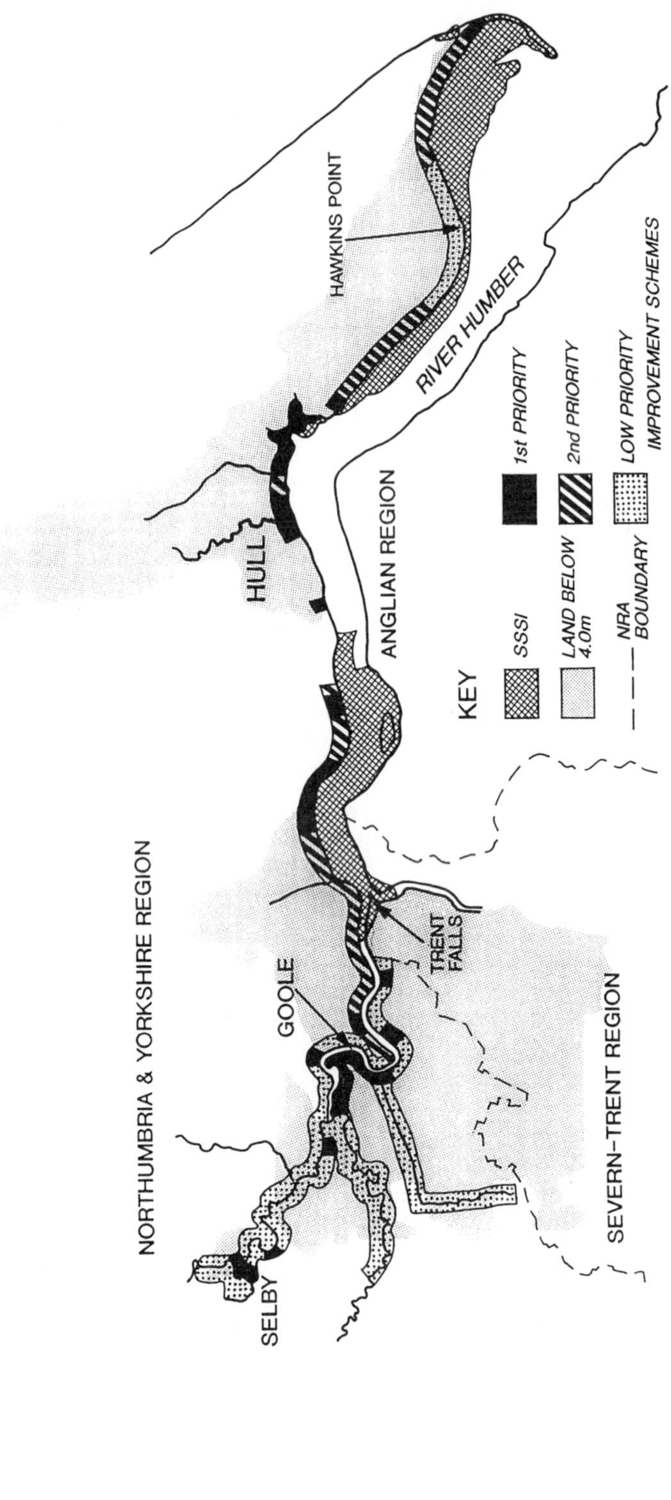

NORTHUMBRIA & YORKSHIRE REGION

SELBY

GOOLE

TRENT FALLS

HAWKINS POINT

RIVER HUMBER

HULL

ANGLIAN REGION

SEVERN-TRENT REGION

KEY

SSSI

LAND BELOW 4.0m

NRA BOUNDARY

1st PRIORITY

2nd PRIORITY

LOW PRIORITY IMPROVEMENT SCHEMES

270

the conservation of wild birds.

In order for the NRA to gain a fuller understanding of the estuary, a habitat survey was commissioned. The principal element of this study was a botanical and zoological survey of the north bank of the Humber and River Ouse. The botanical survey was a field survey carried out between May and October 1991. The zoological survey was collated from data collected by consulting animal and ornithological groups and from the many years of biological monitoring undertaken by the NRA and its predecessors.

The study gave advice on a number of subjects related to the engineering works. Suggestions were made on the time of year when works would have the minimum impact at certain key locations. Phasing of engineering works over a number of years would also assist re-colonisation. Suggestions on where the excavation of borrow material might be acceptable and where this should be avoided were made. Locations where habitat creation might be possible were also identified either by developing borrow areas or realignment of flood defences.

The habitat survey was an integral part of the scoping exercise required to develop the tidal defence strategy. It allowed the ecological factors to form part of the overall framework of needs and limitations within which the engineering works could be designed.

FLOOD WARNING

Although the Strategy provides a programme of prioritised improvement works, it will be a number of years before even the first priority schemes will be completed. As part of the Strategy, the NRA was determined to use the data collected by the various studies to develop a comprehensive flood warning system for the areas at risk from tidal flooding.

Using the tidal records database, a comprehensive tidal warning system for Yorkshire was developed. The Meteorological Office, mainly through the Storm Tide Warning Service (STWS), provides forecasts of tidal surges, wind speed and direction and North Sea wave height and direction. The core of the tidal forecasting system developed was based on relating this forecast data to local flood risk areas.

The STWS provides forecast tidal surge information at three locations adjacent to Yorkshire - North Shields, Whitby, and Immingham. By correlating high tide records at these locations with records at other locations, a local forecast of still water levels could be made.

By relating North Sea wave height forecast or Wind forecasts to foreshore conditions a prediction of local in shore wave heights can be made. A local high tide forecast consists of the forecast still water level plus half the forecast local wave height. This is then related to an NRA Yellow, Amber or Red flood warning for a particular tidal zone.

Following full liaison with the adjacent regions of the NRA, the Police and the District Councils, the Yorkshire Tidal Warning System became operational in August 1992. It is intended that regular reviews will be undertaken to reflect improvement to the defences as they are completed and also to improve warnings as they are compared with actual events.

PROMOTION OF STRATEGY

In July 1991 a paper was presented to the Yorkshire RFDC, entitled "Yorkshire Tidal Defences - Humber Strategy". This paper was the first public indication of the significant tidal defence needs in the Yorkshire region. This paper was followed in January 1992 with a further paper to the Yorkshire RFDC entitled "Priorities for Tidal Defence Improvements". The four groupings of priorities as detailed above were approved together with a programme required to complete first priority schemes within five years.

At the same committee, the Goole Sector Comprehensive Scheme was approved. Each sector within the Strategy formed the basis of a Comprehensive Scheme upon which a detailed cost/benefit exercise would be undertaken. Such Comprehensive Schemes, following approval by the RFDC are submitted to MAFF to be approved for grant aid. The works are then split into phases, for detail design, and construction.

The Goole Sector showed the pressing need for works estimated at some £9 million. The remaining £9 million of works however would not be justified until after the year 2000. These further works included the possibility of tidal barriers at the mouths of the Don and the Aire.

In May 1992 Yorkshire Region hosted a seminar to launch the Strategy. Presentations were made on the Strategy to an invited audience of representatives from local authorities, internal drainage boards, industry, conservation groups, English Nature, MAFF, land owners and other bodies with an interest in the Estuary. A short video covering the strategy was produced, together with an exhibition and a pamphlet. This Seminar publicly announced the wish of the NRA to be open as to the flood defence needs of the estuary and to welcome debate on balancing these needs with other interests. The seminar was followed by a series of meetings with individual local authorities in which NRA staff explained the impact of the Strategy in local areas. Meetings also took place with other interested groups. Debates with conservation groups were particularly intense and useful.

In Goole a public exhibition was staged making use of the video and display material prepared for the Seminar. This exhibition, focusing on the work in the Goole Sector, was manned by NRA Staff. The Public showed interest and support for the scheme. The urban nature of the land behind the flood defences, with roads, houses and industry sited close at hand, left little alternative but to raise the defences on their existing line.

REVIEW OF STRATEGY

The Yorkshire Humber Tidal Defence Strategy was conceived in 1990 and developed in 1991. By May 1993 it is possible to review the strengths of its approach and where it could have been improved.

The Humber is split for Flood Defence between Yorkshire, Anglian and Severn-Trent Regions of the NRA, and within Yorkshire it was, until 1993 split between two Areas. The weakness of this situation has been recognised by the NRA. It is a situation that is repeated across the country with other estuaries being split by regions, areas, and functions. The current movement within the NRA towards organising on a multifunctional Area basis and developing Catchment Management Plans has direct relevance to the Humber. The importance of the NRA determining a strategy for all of its functions for the whole of the estuary cannot be stressed enough. The development of a Yorkshire tidal defence strategy is an important element in developing a multifunctional, inter-regional Humber plan. Such strategies will contribute to a Humber Plan and be revised as necessary.

In 1990 a major step was taken in deciding to look at all the Yorkshire Tidal Defences rather than simply progressing those reaches where important works had already been identified. The Strategy has been successful in securing funding in the short term. The total MAFF grant aided capital expenditure for Yorkshire has risen from £5.15 million p.a. in 1991/92 and to a projected £6.8 million p.a. in 1993/94. The Strategy calls for a continued rise in expenditure levels to over £9 p.a. million from 1995 onwards. This increase would require significant extra commitment by either Local Authorities or by MAFF or both.

The implementation of the Tidal Warning System for Yorkshire is a direct result of the Strategy. It allowed the significant risks of tidal flooding to be recognised both within the NRA and by the Police forces and Local Authorities. Although considerable work is still needed to ensure an integrated emergency response to tidal flooding, the Strategy provided a platform from which such a response could be developed.

The publication of the strategy coincided with a national debate on "Managed Retreat." The strategy assumed that defences would be improved on their existing line for the purposes of broad brush assessment of costs and benefits. Although the options would be considered for each section as that sector was developed in detail, generally status quo for defence alignment was equated to status quo for the environment. Opportunities to provide local enhancements would be taken and these could include managed retreat where it was the most appropriate cost effective engineering solution.

This approach does not allow for concern expressed over "Coastal Squeeze". By raising defences on their existing line, rising sea level could eventually result in the loss of inter tidal habitat. The sector by sector approach to dealing with alignment options does not allow for a consideration of a change in processes impacting on the estuary as a whole. In 1993, MAFF published two documents under the general title of "Coastal Defence and the Environment", a strategy guide and a guide to good practice (5). In these guides emphasis is laid on understanding the impact of flood defences on coastal and estuarine processes and on the need to consider alternative lines of defence. Work on the Humber Strategy has continued to develop. It now reflects MAFF guidance with collaborative work on estuarine processes covering the whole of the Humber. It has to be accepted that the conclusions of this work could change the original outline costing's and benefits of the strategy.

The target minimum standard of defence for the strategy of 1 in 100 years may need to be reconsidered as costs and benefits are examined in detail. Although every effort was made to be generous with cost and conservative with benefit the strategy ratio of 2 could be eroded as detailed design proceeds. Should the optimum standard of defence in terms of cost benefit ratio prove less than the strategy target, then the target NRA land use levels of service would be considered as the minimum acceptable .

CONCLUSIONS

The formation of the Yorkshire Humber Estuary Tidal Defence Strategy was an essential step in providing for the flood defence needs of the area. It drew together the available information and presented a picture of the flood defence needs. That picture could be understood in terms of timing, funding and impact. It allowed an informed response from both within and outside the NRA and was, to a large degree, successful in facilitating progress.

The Strategy must remain flexible in embracing issues as they are brought into focus. There is a challenge for the NRA in keeping interested parties fully informed as development and change take place.

The NRA needs to link in a more formal way the tidal defence activities on the Humber undertaken by the three Regions covering the area. The integration of the Yorkshire Strategy and other tidal defence proposals in the Humber area could yield improvements and possibly savings. Proposals for NRA multifunctional planning for the whole of the Humber are already in progress.

The proposals for inclusion of major habitat creation within the Strategy must be sustainable. The physical processes at work in the estuary will need to be understood, so that the impact of changes can be anticipated with confidence.

The NRA must strike the right balance between planning and progress. There is a time scale to the rise in sea level and the deterioration of defences. Planning should ensure that the next generation do not have cause to regret our decisions. Progress must ensure that today's families do not suffer the misery and cost of major tidal flooding.

ACKNOWLEDGEMENTS

The author wishes to thank Mr R Hyde, Regional General Manager, NRA, Northumbria and Yorkshire Region for permission to publish this paper. The author also wishes to acknowledge the assistance of the Flood Defence staff from Northumbria and Yorkshire Region.

REFERENCES

(1) INTERGOVERNMENTAL PANEL ON CLIMATE CHANGE, Working Group 1, 1990, "Scientific Assessment of Climate Change, Section 9, Sea Level Rise" Cambridge University Press
(2) PARLE P, 1991 "Sea Level Trends in the Humber Estuary: A Case Study" Proceedings International Conference on Coastal Engineering, USA
(3) NATIONAL RIVERS AUTHORITY 1991 "Sea Defence Survey 1990/91"
(4) GRAFF J, 1981 "An Investigation of the Frequency Distributions of Annual Sea Level Maxima at Ports around Great Britain" Estuarine Coastal and Shelf Science (12), 389-449
(5) MAFF 1993 "Coastal Defence and the Environment: A Strategic Guide and A Guide to Good Practice."

River flood protection in the Netherlands
by
Wijbenga J.H.A., J.J.P Lambeek, E. Mosselman,
R.L.J. Nieuwkamer and R.H. Passschier[1]

Abstract

River-dike improvement along the rivers Rhine and Meuse has caused large-scale protests in the Netherlands due to its harmful impact on the riverine landscape and the natural and cultural values of the river dikes. A Government Commission was set up to assess the present policy for river-dike improvement, such as: the required safety level, the design methods and the procedures used to involve local and general interest groups in the design process.

To support the advice of the Commission, a study was commissioned by the government of the Netherlands to DELFT HYDRAULICS and RAND's European-American Center for Policy Analysis (RAND/EAC) to analyze all design and institutional aspects related to river-dike improvement. A part of the study was related to the elaboration of a starting point for the load on the dikes. Based on frequency analyses a reduced design discharge could be recommended. Historical data with respect to the occurrence of ice-jamming in and subsequent flooding of the river were analyzed. The design height of dikes must be based on high river discharges. Strategies to reduce the design water levels are not feasible as regards the reduction of the length of the dikes to be improved. Locally, however, some measures may contribute to reduce the difficulties for dike sections that are considered problematic.

1   Introduction

In 1958, only a few years after the flood disaster of 1953, the Government of the Netherlands decided to improve the dikes along the non-tidal part of the main rivers Rhine and Meuse. The design discharge with a return period of 3,000 years was estimated at 18,000 m^3/s and levee heights were assessed accordingly. The implementation of newly designed dikes had an enormous effect on the riverine landscape, and on natural and cultural values. Once this became public, wide-spread opposition against the plans ensued, leading to the installation of a River Dikes Commission (Becht Commission, 1977). To mitigate the impact of dike reinforcement the Commission advised to reduce the design discharge to 16,500 m^3/s (return period 1,250 years).

---

[1] DELFT HYDRAULICS, Delft, The Netherlands

2nd International Conference on River Flood Hydraulics. Edited by W. R. White and J. Watts

The results of the Becht Commission had only a temporary effect on public acceptance. Moreover, analysis of historical data, see Bervaes 1991, showed that the major floodings along the rivers prior to 1870 had been caused by ice-jamming and not by excessive discharges. Due to the increasing opposition the Minister of Public Works, Transport and Watermanagement established another River Dikes Commission (the Boertien Commission) in July 1992. A policy analysis study was assigned to the combination DELFT HYDRAU-LICS/(RAND/EAC). A description of this study is given by Breusers and Vis (1994). Part of this study was the assessment of boundary conditions for the river-dike system and the evaluation of flood-protection measures that will reduce the load on the dikes to be built. Although the whole study was performed for the non-tidal part of the River Rhine and the River Meuse, see Figure 1, we will restrict ourselves here to the River Rhine.

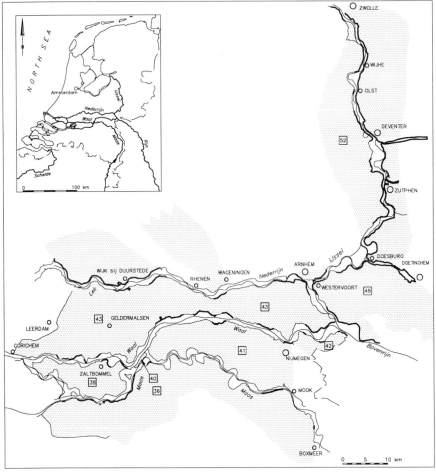

Figure 1   Study reach

In chapter 2 we will describe the estimation of the design discharge based on a frequency analysis of high river discharges and the chosen safety standard. In chapter 2 we will estimate the return period for flooding due to ice-jamming in the Dutch main river. For a balanced dike-improvement plan, there should be no discrepancy between safety standard for high discharges and the frequency of flooding due to ice-jamming.

In chapter 4 we will describe the evaluation of possible measures to lower the design water levels.

2   Frequency analysis

From an economic point of view the optimum safety standard should be in the order of 1/10,000 per year, but the Boertien Commission recommended to maintain the current safety standard of 1/1,250 per year (return period of 1,250 years), see Breusers and Vis (1994).

Once the safety standard is set, the design discharge linked to this standard has to be assessed. This should be based on a frequency analysis of historic discharges, supplemented by an analysis of the behaviour of the Rhine catchment under flood conditions with a hydrologic/ hydraulic model. For the River Rhine such a model is not available, so only frequency analyses could be applied.

The use of frequency analyses is only warranted with homogeneous data. Inhomogeneity may be caused by systematic errors in discharge measurements, changes in river catchment (changes in river geometry, urbanisation, de- and reafforestation, and so on) and climatic changes. Statistical tests of homogeneity are often not selective enough to detect inhomogeneity, but the historic record of the River Rhine indicates thorough changes in the river geometry. However, the impact of these changes can only be assessed with a hydraulic study of the river, which was not yet possible.

We decided to apply frequency analyses on the original set of data, except for some minor changes for obvious overestimations in the peak discharges.

Frequency analysis can be applied to peak over threshold data (partial series) and to annual maxima. For both methods a specific group of distributions exists. As there is no consensus on the preferable method, we decided to base our choice of distributions on the visual acceptance of the fitting of the distribution to the data. Subsequently, the design discharge was calculated as the average of the extrapolated values with the selected distributions.

Analysis based on peak discharges

The use of distributions with peak discharges assumes absence of interdependency between subsequent peaks. This is approached by using a certain threshold discharge as lower limit of acceptance and a minimum time period between subsequent peaks. For the River Rhine, this period is assumed to be 15 days. However, for large and complex river catchments such as the River Rhine, this is no guarantee for independency and we prefer the approach with annual maxima.

For the recorded peak discharges the general Pareto and the exponential distributions were applied. On visual inspection, the exponential distribution was rejected. The general Pareto-distribution showed an acceptable fit.

Analysis based on annual maxima

For the analysis of annual maxima use was made of the Gumbel distribution (with a lower limit of 7,000 m^3/s), the (3-parameter) log-normal, the Pearson III- and the log-Pearson III distributions. After visual inspection only the latter was rejected.

From the extrapolations with the selected frequency distributions, the discharge for the return period of 1,250 years was estimated at 14,500 m^3/s. In order to apply a correction for the impact of changes in the river geometry upstream of the Dutch border, an estimate was made based on the results of preliminary German studies. An addition of approx. 500 m^3/s was made to the original value, resulting in a final design discharge of 15,000 m^3/s.

During the Becht Commission in the seventies, the design discharge was estimated at 16,500 m^3/s, based only on the extrapolation with the exponential distribution.

An attempt was made to account for the impact of future climatic changes. However, the scale of modelling with the Global Circulation Models (GCM) is such that the size of the whole catchment of the River Rhine may fall within one grid cell. More detailed regional models are being developed, but their boundary conditions have to come from the GCM. As the results from different GCM on the future directions in climatic change still differ widely, the predictions with these models can not yet form a reliable basis for the study of the impact of climate change.

3   Flooding due to ice-jamming

Digging into the history of the town of Zaltbommel on the River Waal, the main branch of the River Rhine, Bervaes (1991) found historical descriptions of river floodings, recorded by the "Society of Nijmegen". The first records of the water levels at a small number of locations and the occurrence of ice in the river dates back to 1757. From 1879 onwards this information had been recorded and reported by the Directorate-General for Public Works and Water Management (Rijkswaterstaat).

Summaries of floodings in the Dutch Delta had been given by Glimmerveen (1856), Weelden and Mingelen (1864) and Gottschalk (1971 and 1977). Only the Publications by Gottschalk are internationally accessible as it was printed in a dual language edition (Dutch and English). Numerous studies about ice in the rivers have been published, but they are only available in Dutch.

Bervaes (1991) pointed out that in the period from 1720 to 1870 river flooding due to ice(-jamming) occurred approximately once every 11 years. (An ice jam is defined as an accumulation of fragmented ice or frazil that restricts the flow.) After 1870, however, no floodings due to ice-jamming in the river occurred. Bervaes explained that it was the result of small cyclic changes (period approx. 100 years) in the climatic changes. After 1870 the winters were less harsh, but harshness of the winters may increase in the near future. Although Rijkswaterstaat had reshaped the rivers in the period 1850-1890, Bervaes expects that the frequency of flooding due to problems with ice will be much greater than the present safety standard (1/1,250 per year) for flooding due to high river discharges. In the public discussion the occurrence of ice played an important role.

We analyzed the hypothesis that the harshness of a single cold period during a winter nowadays is less than in the years before 1880. First of all we made an inventory of ice-jamming in the main rivers after 1880 to 1992. The frequency of flooding caused by ice-jamming appeared to be higher than Bervaes has brought forward, namely once in 4.2 years for the period 1757-1880. However, after 1880 no more floodings due to ice-jamming occurred.

Furthermore, we characterized the harshness of single cold periods for the years 1657 to 1991 with a Cold Period Index (CPI) as defined by Haas (1986a and 1986b), see Figure 2. The CPI is defined as the sum of all averaged daily temperatures below zero in a prolonged frost period. In short periods of melt the summation is continued when a another cold period follows, provided that the temperatures were not too high during the melt period. In Figure 2 the years before 1880 when ice-jamming resulted in flooding are marked, together with the years after 1880 when ice-jamming occurred without flooding. There is no significant difference between the CPI-values before and after 1880, so we concluded that there are other reasons why ice-jamming had not caused flooding after 1880. The main reasons are: improved flow conditions in the river, heat emission, changed characteristics of ice-jamming, improved mitigation possibilities and increased dike heights.

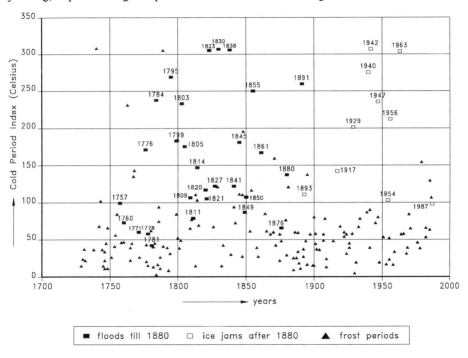

Figure 2   Cold Period Index for the years 1757-1991

The frequently occurring floods led to the establishment of the Rijkswaterstaat. From the years 1850 to 1890 the main rivers were reshaped from a river with multiple channels to a river with one channel only. For low flow conditions the width of this channel is more or less constant. The constant width enables an easier transport of ice in the downstream direction. The heat emission due to increased population and increased energy consumption resulted in shorter periods of ice covers on the rivers. As the periods during which ice can form in the river are shorter, less-thick fragmented ice is found. The stability of ice-jams formed with this less thick fragmented ice is decreased. Ice jams break up more easily nowadays than they did before 1880.

There are two types of ice-jams, namely, freeze-up and break-up jams. A freeze-up jam occurs when a large accumulation of frazil ice restricts the normal flow of the river. A break-up jam occurs when positive air temperatures and melting snow and rain cause the water levels to rise thus releasing the ice cover and moving it down-river. The ice cover breaks up in many pieces as it travels and can accumulate at such locations as sharp bends, islands, bridges, and so on. Before 1880 both types of ice jamming must have occurred. Especially the break-up type must have frequently caused flooding. After 1880, the ice-jamming is from the freeze-up type, that can be removed in time with ice-breakers from the downstream end or that will break up spontaneously due to lack of stability (reduced ice thickness).

For the River Waal a stage-discharge analysis was carried out based on the HEC-2 Water Surface Profiles computer program, developed by the United States Army Corps of Engineers (USACE 1990). The computational procedure is based on the solution of the one-dimensional energy equation, accounting for the frictional energy losses of the riverbed and the ice cover. The model showed that stable ice-jams in the River Waal were not to be expected for discharges greater than 5,000 m^3/s. The return period for such a discharge during the formation of an ice-cover is estimated using a frequency analysis (log-normal distribution) at approx. 1/1,100 per year. This return period is well in balance with the safety standard of 1/1,250 per year for high river discharges. The risk of flooding due to ice-jamming can further be reduced by early-warning systems based on the Cold Period Index and mitigation methods such as ice-breaking.

4   Measures to lower design water levels

Instead of reinforcing and raising the dikes it is also possible to reduce the design water levels in the river by river engineering measures. A wide variety of measures can be thought of for the reduction of the load on the dikes. We applied a policy-analysis approach in order to structure the analysis. The process of identification, impact assessment and evaluation of these measures consisted of the following phases:

1.   Brainstorm session.
2.   Qualitative impact assessment and first screening.
3.   Quantitative assessment of the effectiveness of the measures.
4.   Second screening and strategy design.
5.   Impact assessment.
6.   Selection of best strategy.

The result of the Brainstorm session was the design tree depicted in Figure 3. The purpose of the design tree is to get an overview as complete as possible of all types of river engineering measures. However, this set of alternatives is so great that not all alternatives can be assessed in much detail. Besides, many of these alternatives do not look very promising. That is why a special meeting was organized in which a team of experts assessed qualitatively each alternative. For this qualitative assessment we used the following criteria:

—   effectiveness;
—   technical feasibility;
—   time until the desired effect occurs;
—   administrative feasibility;
—   social feasibility.

The effectiveness is the expected water-level reduction (in metres) compared with the costs of a measure. A water-level reduction of 0.1 m or less was considered not enough, whereas a reduction of more than 0.5 m was considered very attractive. The measure "cutting-off river bends", for instance, was dropped because of its little effect and the very high investment costs.

Some measures were proposed, which are technically not feasible. An example of such a measure is a tunnel which carries the excess water under high pressure from the town of Lobith to the sea. Besides, the reliability of such a tunnel system with pumping-stations can be an even bigger problem.

An example of a measure rejected from the analysis due to the third and fourth criterion is afforestation of the river basin in Germany and Switzerland. Afforestation will reduce the design discharge, but it would take too long before any effect could be noticeable. Besides, it is questionable whether such a measure is administratively feasible, since the largest part of the river basin is situated in Germany. The Netherlands will never have complete control over activities in the upstream river basin. Of course this makes upstream alternatives less attractive.

The last criterion, social feasibility, indicates whether or not an alternative is worse than the current dike improvement schemes. An example of an alternative that was dropped because of this criterion is an additional lateral canal which carries the water from Lobith to the sea. Such a canal needs much more space and its own new dikes. So, it would have a much greater an impact than the current dike-improvement schemes.

The result of the qualitative assessment was that the most promising measures are the ones between the existing main dikes in the Netherlands.

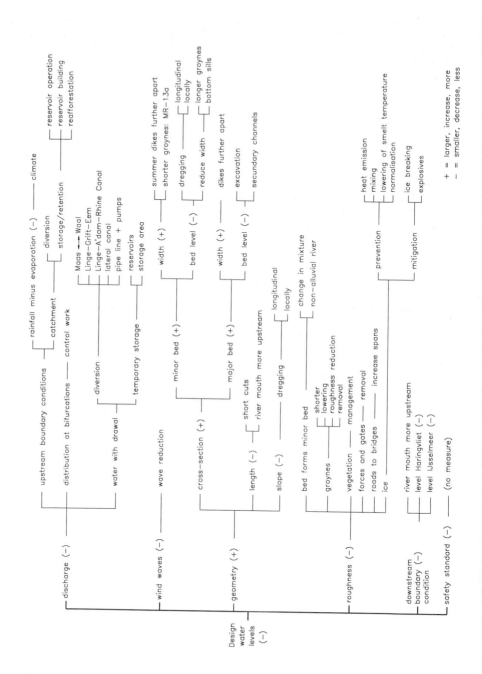

Figure 3.   Design tree for the identification of alternatives for reducing the design water levels

282

The next phase of the analysis was the quantitative assessment of the resulting measures. For this purpose we built a one-dimensional mathematical model of the river Rhine and its branches (see Figure 4). Based on the results of the model computations we decided to elaborate on three types of river-engineering measures, namely: lowering of the bed of the main river channel, lowering of the floodplains, and adjustment of the groynes. It is clear that lowering the bed level of the main channel and the floodplain will reduce the water levels. The groyne adjustment, however, aims at reducing the hydraulic head loss in the river. This will also yield lower water levels.

These three measures were combined into three "design water-level reduction strategies":

1. Groyne adjustment and lowering of the bed level of the main channel.
2. Lowering of the floodplains in combination with 25% of the floodplains covered with floodplain forest.
3. Combination of strategy 1 and 2.

Strategy 2 was considered socially acceptable only if it would be done within the framework of ecological rehabilitation of the river Rhine. Therefore, this strategy includes the growth of floodplain forest which partly reduces the effect of the lowering of the bed level of the floodplain.

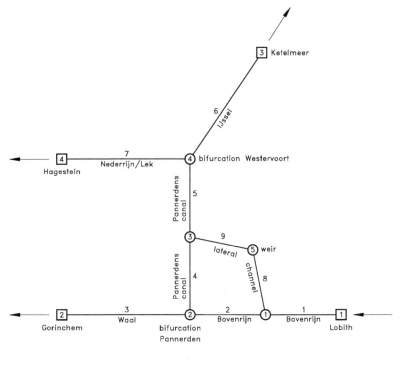

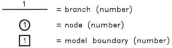

Figure 4.   The 1-D river model

In the impact assessment phase we looked at the effects of these three strategies on:

— design water levels;
— costs of the strategy;
— navigation;
— water distribution at the bifurcations;
— existing infrastructure (weirs, locks, etc.)
— nature and landscape.

The results of the analysis were presented in a score card (Table 1).

Criteria	Unit	Strategy		
		1	2	3
Change of design water levels	m	0,4 à 0,7	0,45 à 0,9	0,6 à 1,1
Construction costs	Mfl	990	pm	990 + pm
Change of navigation costs	Mfl/j	-67	0	-67
Change of Waal discharge	m^3/s	15	0	15
Change of IJssel discharge	m^3/s	-15	0	-15
infrastructure adjustment costs	Mfl/j	much more than 8	a little less than 8	much more than 8
conservation of existing nature and landscape values		--	--	--
possibilities for the development of new nature and landscape values		--	+ +	0

Table 1. Score card for water-level reduction strategies

The conclusions from these results are:

1. Strategies including groyne adjustment are not feasible due to the high costs.
2. Excavation of the floodplains is the most promising strategy, mainly because it is thought that the sand- and clay-mining industry would be eager to excavate the floodplains on a commercial basis. However, due to the huge scale of the measure, the long execution time and the only small reduction of the dike length to be improved (from 372 km to 342 km), strategy 2 is not a real alternative for the dike-improvement schemes.
3. It is possible though, that local excavation of the floodplains can be a mitigating measure for problematic dike sections.

References

River Dike Commission, 1977: Report of River Dikes Commission (in Dutch). Ministry of Public Works, Transport and Water Management, The Hague, The Netherlands

Bervaes, J.C.A.M., 1991: The River Waal at Zaltbommel in the period 1832 till 1983, origins of flooding, (in Dutch). Van Voorn tot Loevestein, Historical Society Bommelwaard.

Breusers, H.C.N. and M. Vis, 1994: Policy Analysis of River-Dike Improvement in The Netherlands. 2nd International Conference on River Flood Hydraulics, York, England.

Glimmerveen, D.J. 1856: Historical description of the most known extremely high floods, breaches and floodings which have distressed North and South Holland from early times till present. Weyting and Van der Haart, Amsterdam The Netherlands.

Gottschalk, M.K.E., 1971: Storm Floods and River Floodings in The Netherlands, part I and II, Van Gorcum, Assen, The Netherlands.

Gottschalk, M.K.E., 1971: Storm Floods and River Floodings in The Netherlands, part III; The period between 1600 and 1700. Van Gorcum, Assen/Amsterdam, The Netherlands.

Haas, A.W. de, 1986a: Ice discharge problems for the main rivers and Rhine delta; general part and ice discharge strategy (in Dutch), Ministry of Public Works and Watermanagement, Directorate of Lower Rivers, AX38/ml.

Haas, A.W. de, 1986a: Ice discharge problems for the main rivers and Rhine delta; special topics (in Dutch), Ministry of Public Works and Watermanagement, Directorate of Lower Rivers, AX18/ml.

USACE, 1990: HEC-2, Water Surface Profiles User's Manual. U.S. Army Corps of Engineers, Hydrologic Engineering Center, Davis, CA, USA.

Chapter Six

Sediment Transport

MATHEMATICAL MODEL FOR RESERVOIR SEDIMENTATION

By SHARGHI Abdolali[1] and BERLAMONT Jean[2]

ABSTRACT

The phenomenon of reservoir sedimentation poses serious problems, as the storage capacity of many reservoirs all around the world has seriously decreased.

One of the methods or techniques for recovering lost storage, which has been applied successfully for the reservoir in several countries, such as Russia, China, India and Iran is known as "Flushing". Deposited sediments are flushed away with water available in the reservoir, by opening the bottom outlets and consequently lowering the water level abruptly. In order to plan flushing operation and to predict the efficiency, one should be able to predict the magnitude and distribution of sediment deposits in the reservoir. It is therefore important to develop a mathematical model for simulating both velocity fields and sediment movements. In this paper a mathematical model is presented which describes the unsteady flow of water and entrainment of sediments in a reservoir. The compound flow model approach is used to predict the magnitude and lateral distribution of the sediments in the reservoir. The differential equations for simulating the gradually varied unsteady flow , the continuity and momentum equations for sediment laden water and the continuity equation for the sediment are solved by a finite differences method.

The model has been verified with laboratory data. The experiments were conducted in a 9.0 m long, 0.40 m wide and 0.40 m deep tilting flume using sand with $d_{50}=1.0$ mm. The experimental results for a lateral expansion of the flume show a reasonable agreement with the computed and measured bed profiles both for flushing and accumulation.

1. INTRODUCTION

Reservoir sedimentation creates major problems in the planning, design and operation of water resource systems. The useful life time of a reservoir can reduce rapidly because of high sediment yields from drainage basins, and the number of reservoirs which have deteriorated due to complete silting up with sediments is continuously increasing. In order to fight reservoir sedimentation, two basic possibilities are available: one is to prevent sediment from entering the reservoir and the other is let it enter and to extract it afterwards.

---

[1] Graduate student, Laboratory of Hydraulics, Catholic University of Leuven (K.U.L.), Belgium.
[2] Professor, Civil Engineering Department, Catholic University of Leuven (K.U.L.), Belgium.

2nd International Conference on River Flood Hydraulics. Edited by W. R. White and J. Watts
© 1994 HR Wallingford Ltd. Published by John Wiley & Sons Ltd

As far as the sediment which could not be prevented from entering the reservoir is concerned, again two possibilities are available: one is to pass the sediment on before it starts to settle and the other is to remove it after settling. One of the methods for recovering lost storage, which has been applied for reservoirs is known as flushing. Usually by the end of the irrigation period, some water remains in the reservoir and this water can be used to flush out sediment which has been deposited during the year.

Prediction of the sediment distribution pattern in reservoirs is a complex task and depends on many interrelated factors, such as: size and texture of the sediment particles, seasonal variations in river and sediment flow, size and shape of the reservoir and its operation schedule. The mathematical model affords the engineer a technique to explore the interrelationship between the important variables of the process and it also offers a good opportunity to study long-term system responses. In order to simulate the deposition of sediment in a reservoir and also to plan the flushing operation, it is important to develop a mathematical model for simulating both velocity fields and sediment movements.

The objective of this paper is to present a computational model that is capable of predicting the magnitude and distribution of the sediment in the reservoir and to verify the mathematical model by using laboratory data.

2. GOVERNING EQUATIONS

The basic equations that govern the flow are differential equations for simulating the gradually varied unsteady flow in a natural alluvial channel:

Momentum equation for sediment - laden water:

$$\frac{\partial(Q\rho)}{\partial t} + \frac{\partial(\rho\beta Q V)}{\partial x} = -gA\frac{\partial(\rho y)}{\partial x} + \rho gA(S_x - S_f) + \rho q_l V_l \tag{1}$$

Continuity equation for sediment - laden water:

$$\frac{\partial Q}{\partial x} + \frac{\partial A}{\partial t} + \frac{\partial A_d}{\partial t} - q_l = 0 \tag{2}$$

Continuity equation for sediment:

$$\frac{\partial Q_s}{\partial x} + (1 - \lambda)\frac{\partial A_d}{\partial t} + \frac{\partial(AC)}{\partial t} - q_{sl} = 0 \tag{3}$$

Sediment transport relation:

$$Q_s = mV^n \tag{4}$$

in which Q = the discharge of sediment - laden water; ρ = the density of the sediment - laden water given by $\rho = \rho_w(1 - c) + \rho_s c$; ρ_w = the water density, ρ_s = the sediment particle density; v = the mean flow velocity; c = the sediment concentration in cross section on a volume basis; g = the gravitational acceleration; β = the momentum correction factor for velocity distribution; A = the cross-sectional area of the channel; y = the flow depth; s_x = the bed slope; s_f = the friction slope given by the Manning equation = $Q^2 n^2 / A^2 R^{4/3}$; q_l = the lateral inflow of sediment - laden water into stream; v_l = the velocity component of the lateral flow in the x - direction; A_d = the volume of deposition or erosion of sediment on unit length of channel bed; Q_s = the total sediment load in units of volume per unit time; λ = porosity of sediment in bed layer($0 \le \lambda \le 1$); q_{sl} = the lateral sediment inflow into the stream; and m and n = constants that depend on the sediment and flow characteristics.

Equations (1) - (3) are a set of nonlinear first - order partial differential equations of the hyperbolic type. They contain two independent variables x and t and three dependent variables, Q, y, A_d; the remaining terms are functions of the three basic unknowns. Equation (4) is an empirical relation based on laboratory and field measurements under steady - uniform flow conditions, and it is considered a good first approximation for moderate changes in the total sediment load.

The compound flow model approach developed by Dass (4) and modified by Lopez (2,3) to solve the governing equations is modified and used to route the flow of water and sediment through the river - reservoir system. The river - reservoir system in this study is shown in Figure 1. The model considers a reservoir formed by a dam which has been constructed on a river course. The river is presented by a single channel; one - dimensional flow phenomena are predominant, whereas a set of multiple channels is used to simulate the river and the flood plains in the reservoir.

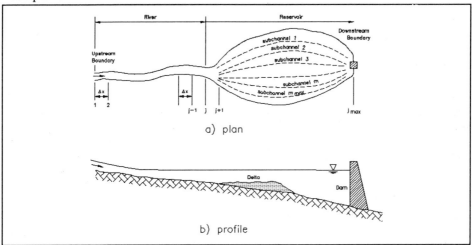

FIG. 1 Schematic of the River - Reservoir System

This development is based on dividing a nonuniform cross section into a set of subsections in such a way that each subsection can be treated as uniform within itself. Therefore, the basic equations (1) - (3) are solved by first treating the whole river reach as a single channel and then solving the sediment continuity equation by considering a multiple channel approach. In this way the variations of bed deviations with time for each individual subsection can be determined. The following assumptions based on the compound flow model approach procedure have been used in the mathematical model: (1) the term $\partial A_d/\partial t$ is much smaller than $\partial A/\partial t$; and (2) within a short time period the change in channel geometry due to sediment routing is not significant enough to warrant the simultaneous solution. The calculation procedure then is summarized as follows. First equations (1) and (2) are solved for two unknowns Q and y at each cross section in the reach. The next step is to determine the value of these unknowns for each individual stream by using the equation: $Q = Q_m(K_m/K)$, in which Q_m and K_m are the water discharge and conveyance for any subchannel at the known cross section (such as mth subsection) and Q and K are the total discharge and conveyance of a cross section. Then the flow continuity equation, equation (1), is rewritten as follows at each individual mth stream to solve the lateral flow transfer:

$$\frac{\partial Q_m}{\partial x} + \frac{\partial A_m}{\partial t} - q_m + q_{m-1} = 0 \tag{5}$$

Noting that Q_m and A_m are known from the flow continuity calculations and that q_{m-1} for $m = 1$ is specified in advance, then the only unknown is q_m. Finally the sediment continuity equation at each individual stream which is to be solved for the variation in bed elevations will be introduced as follows:

$$\frac{\partial Q_{s_m}}{\partial x} + (1 - \lambda)_m \frac{\partial A_{d_m}}{\partial t} + \frac{\partial (A_m C_m)}{\partial t} - q_{s_m} + q_{s_{m-1}} = 0 \tag{6}$$

When the river enters the reservoir is comparable to a submerged plane jet flow discharge from a slot of width equal to the width of the river. The two dimensional equations for velocities in a submerged turbulent jet discharging into a fluid of the same density have been given by Albertson and others (1,5). With reference to Figure 2, they distinguish two basic zones in their theory.

The first zone is called the zone of flow establishment, in which the fluid undergoes lateral diffusion and deceleration as a direct result of the turbulence generated at the border of a submerged jet. The constant - velocity core of the jet will steadily decrease in lateral extent. The limit for this initial zone of flow establishment (which is almost equal to five times the width of the river) is reached when the mixing region is penetrated to the centre line of the jet. The second zone is the zone of established flow, in which the diffusion process continues without essential change in character.

The velocity field in the no diffusion zone:

$$V_{(x,y)} = V_0 \tag{7}$$

The velocity field in the zone of flow establishment:

$$V_{(x,y)} = V_0 \exp\left[-42.084\left(0.096 + \frac{y - \frac{B_0}{2}}{x}\right)^2\right]$$ (8)

The velocity field in the zone of established flow:

$$V_{(x,y)} = V_0 \sqrt{\frac{B_0}{x}} \exp\left[0.812 - 41.58\frac{y^2}{x^2}\right]$$ (9)

For simulation of the flushing technique in this study, close to the dam, the velocity field is approximated by the following expression:

$$V_{(x,y)} = U_0 \sqrt{\frac{D}{x}} \exp\left[0.812 - 41.58\frac{y^2}{x^2}\right]$$ (10)

In which v_0 = the mean velocity at the mouth of the river; B_0 = the river width; v_0 = the velocity of the orifice = $c_v\sqrt{2gh}$; D = the bottom outlet diameter; c_v = the velocity coefficient; and x and y = the longitudinal and transverse coordinates depicted in Figure 2. From the integration of the velocity distribution equations, correction factors for the water discharge distribution at each section are obtained and incorporated in the compound flow model.

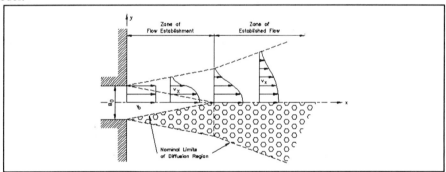

FIG. 2 Schematic Representation of Jet Diffusion

The distribution of sediment in the reservoir highly depends on the shape of the basin. If the reservoir is regular in shape, deposits will normally spread almost uniformally along the axis. On the other hand, if the shape of reservoir is irregular, the sediment deposition might be distributed in irregular patterns. In narrow reservoirs, the incoming flow spreads evenly across the pool and therefore the jet effect is not significant but if the stream enters a wide reservoir, the flow tends to act like a jet with a considerable effect.

In this mathematical model, nonuniform grain size distribution is treated by considering different size fractions separately and by calculating the transport capacities for each grain size. Then, the total variation in bed elevations can be obtained by superimposing the results obtained from the sediment routing for each sediment fraction. In this way the sorting process and its effect in the delta formation can be investigated.

3. NUMERICAL SCHEME

Equations (1) - (3) are a set of nonlinear hyperbolic equations, and closed - form solutions are available only for idealized cases. Therefore, they are solved by numerical schemes. In this model, an implicit finite difference scheme developed by Preissmann (7) is used.

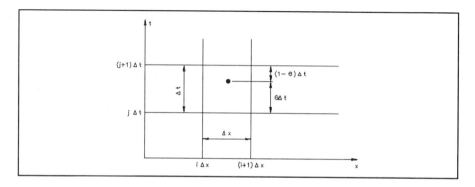

FIG. 3 Finite Difference Scheme

According to this scheme, a variable, say f, and its derivatives are discretized as follows:

$$f(x,t) \approx \frac{1}{2}\left[\theta(\Delta f_{i+1} + \Delta f_i) + f_{i+1}^j + f_i^j\right] \qquad (11)$$

$$\frac{\partial f}{\partial x} \approx \frac{1}{\Delta x}\left[\theta(\Delta f_{i+1} - \Delta f_i) + f_{i+1}^j - f_i^j\right] \qquad (12)$$

$$\frac{\partial f}{\partial t} \approx \frac{1}{2\Delta t}(\Delta f_{i+1} + \Delta f_i) \qquad (13)$$

In which f represents Q, A, T, etc.; $\Delta f_i = f_i^{j+1} - f_i^j$; Δx and Δt = the length and time increments, respectively; i =node along x-axis; j =node along t-axis (Figure 3); and θ =a weighting factor. All the variables are known at all nodes of the network on the time line t^j.

The unknown values of the variables on time line t^{j+1} can be found by solving the system of linear algebraic equations formulated from substitution of the finite-difference approximations, equations (11), (12), and (13), into the basic governing equations, in conformance with prescribed initial and boundary conditions by the double sweep method (7). Once the values of water elevation and discharge at a new time step were known, the bed level z^{j+1} was computed by solving continuity equation for sediment (3) with an explicit finite difference scheme.

4. EXPERIMENTAL SET-UP AND PROCEDURE

In order to test the feasibility of the mathematical model, the experiments were conducted in a 0.40 m wide, 0.40 m deep and 9.0 m long recirculatory tilting flume located in the Hydraulics Laboratory of the Catholic University of Leuven, Leuven, Belgium. The general view of the flume is shown in Figure 4.

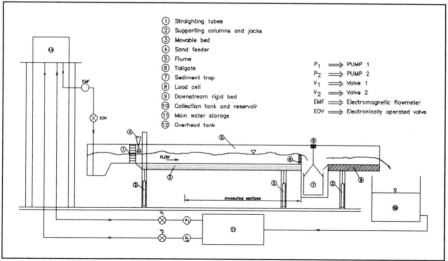

FIG. 4 The Experimental Set - Up

A small channel, 0.20 m wide and 3.0 m long, was built to create a lateral sudden expansion in the channel. Variations in water surface elevations were produced by using a sluice gate downstream to control the flow conditions in the channel (Figure 5). The sand forming the bed and the injected material had a median diameter of 1.0 mm.

4.1 Sediment deposition experiment

The experiments procedure for this part of the study consisted of the following: (1) Constant depth of flow was established by setting the gate as soon as possible after full discharge was reached; (2) the discharge was kept constant throughout the run and water was allowed to recirculate through the system; (3) after recording initial conditions, the corresponding time was noted as the starting time of the experiments; (4) the sediment supply by means of a sediment feeder, was used to feed the sediment at the upstream end of the flume at a constant rate; (5) the bed and water surface profiles were recorded at selected sections along the channel at certain intervals of time. The run was continued until the aggradation front reached close to the end of the flume. The total sediment transport rate was measured at the downstream end of the flume by using a total load sampler. The sediment transport rate so measured was practically equal to that before addition of sediment thereby indicating that all the sediment had been deposited in the flume itself. The data from the uniform flow experiments were utilized to determine the value of m and n in power relationship between the sediment discharge and the flow velocity, used in the mathematical model.

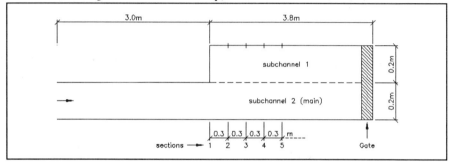

FIG. 5 The Lateral Sudden Expansion in Laboratory Flume

4.2 Flushing experiment

For this part of the study, the experimental procedure consisted of the following steps: (1) Constant depth of flow was established by setting the gate as soon as possible after full discharge was reached; (2) the discharge was kept constant through the run and water and sand were allowed to recirculate through the system; (3) after recording initial conditions, the specially designed outlet was completely opened and the corresponding time was noted as the starting time of the experiment; (4) during the whole experiment at certain intervals of time, the bed elevations were measured and recorded at selected sections along the channel bed. The total sediment transport rate was measured by using the sediment trap connected to the load cell at the downstream end of the flume. Once more the value of m and n in the sediment transport relationship used in the mathematical model were determined from the uniform flow experiments data.

5. EVALUATION OF THE MODEL

In this section, the feasibility of the mathematical model is evaluated by using the experimental results to see if the model is able to simulate with reasonable accuracy the distribution of the sediment in sudden expansion.

The lateral sudden expansion channel, as it has been shown in Figure 5, was divided into two subchannels along with 13 sections. The space increment was selected to be 0.30 *m* and a time increment of 1/2 min was selected to insure the stability of the numerical scheme. The variations in the bed elevations were recorded at all sections for each subchannel. The bed elevations observed together with the computed bed profiles at different time intervals both for accumulation and flushing are indicated in Figure 6 and 7 respectively.

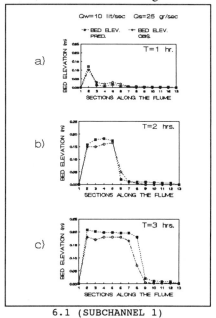

6.1 (SUBCHANNEL 1)

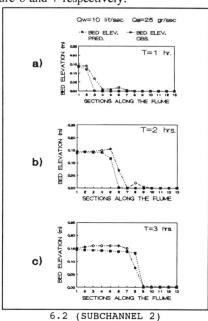

6.2 (SUBCHANNEL 2)

FIG. 6 Variation in Bed Elevations (Accumulation)

According to Figure 6.2(a), which shows the bed profile of subchannel 2 one hour after implementation of the experiment, the delta shaped bed profile has reached sections 2 and 3. At the same time, sediment deposition in subchannel 1, shown in Figure 6.1(a) is less compared to subchannel 2. This is due to sudden expansion of the river at the mouth of the reservoir. Two hours after the start of the experiment, when the sediment passes the mouth of the reservoir, the bed elevations in subchannel 1 (Fig. 6.1(b)) have increased compared to subchannel 2 (Fig. 6.2(b)). This difference of bed elevations is accompanied by lower velocity in subchannel 1. The laboratory experiments show that the bed profile is

297

montonically moving downstream in both channel with increase in distance. The computed bed profiles from the mathematical model shows the same trend as the measured values.

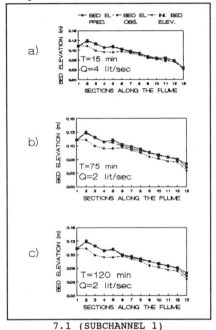 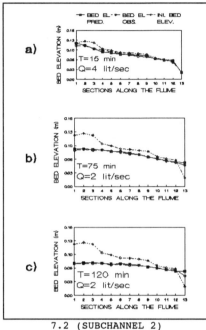

| 7.1 (SUBCHANNEL 1) | 7.2 (SUBCHANNEL 2) |

FIG. 7 Variation in Bed Elevations (Flushing)

When the bottom outlet is opened, the water level in the flume starts to come down, and an unsteady regime is generated towards the bottom outlet. According to Figure 7.1 and 7.2, 15 minutes after the start of the experiment the changes on bed profiles have taken place along subchannels 1 and 2. The velocity of the flow has increased and the delta-shaped bed profile has been forced to wash away completely in subchannel 2. By applying the flushing technique, the laboratory experiment and the computed results from the mathematical model show, there is no big change in the bed profile of subchannel 1; instead, a low level of the sediment accumulation has occurred on subchannel 1 (Fig. 7.1). This is due to low water elevation in the flume and to lower velocity in subchannel 1 compared to subchannel 2. During the flushing process, from the mouth of the river, where the sudden expansion started, a tunnel-shaped channel has developed in subchannel 2. Initially the width of this tunnel is equivalent to the width of the subchannel 2, after which it increases. Also, the laboratory experiments show that the bed profile at sections 1, 2, 3 and 4 was higher than water elevation 45 minutes after the starting of the experiment on subchannel 1. This development continued up to section 6, after which the width coincides with the width of the flume. The results obtained by the mathematical model show the same trend as the observed values for both subchannels.

6. MODEL LIMITATIONS

Due to simplification and numerical solution, the accuracy of any mathematical model is to some degree restricted and limited. In this study, the model limitations are as follows:
1) The material which formed the bed in this model is assumed to be noncohesive.
2) The model is applicable to predict the sediment distribution in a reservoir in which the effect of density currents may be neglected.
3) The uncoupled procedure is used in the model in the sense that the flow and sediment routing are solved independently. Therefore, in the flow routing procedure, the geometry of the river - reservoir system without any sediment movement is assumed to be constant. Similarly, during the calculations made for sediment routing, the water surface profiles are assumed to be unchanged.
4) This model can be applied only for water and sediment routing in subcritical flows.

7. CONCLUSIONS

A mathematical model is presented for studying the unsteady flow of water and entrainment of sediment in a reservoir. The model considers a reservoir formed by a dam which has been constructed on a river course. The river is presented by a single channel, whereas a set of multiple channels, is used to simulate the reservoir. The compound flow model approach, together with a two dimensional jet theory, is used to predict the magnitude and lateral distribution of the sediment in the reservoir. A simple equation for the sediment discharge as a power function of flow velocity is used.

In order to determine the feasibility of the model, the experiment was conducted in a laboratory flume. The computed bed profiles were compared with the measured bed profiles. The agreement between them is satisfactory, both for flushing and accumulation. The model may well be used by incorporating seasonal variations in the flow of water and sediment for studying the long-term responses in the river-reservoir system. Also it can be applied as a predictive tool for reservoir sedimentation. Satisfactory results of the model for flushing suggest that the model can be used also to develop operational methods by which the maximum amount of sediment can be flushed with the available amount of water in the reservoir.

REFERENCES

1. Albertson, M. L., Dai, Y. B., Jensen, R. A., Rouse, H., "Diffusion of Submerged Jets," Transaction, ASCE, Vol. 115, Paper No. 2409, pp. 2041-2060, 1950.
2. Annandale, G. W., "Reservoir Sedimentation," Developments in Water Science, Elsevier, Amsterdam, Holland, 1987.

3. Chen, Y. H., Lopez, J. L., Richardson, E. V., "Mathematical Modelling of Sediment Deposition in Reservoir," J. Hydr. Div., ASCE, Vol. 104, No. HY12, pp. 371-389, 1978.
4. Dass, P., "Water and Sediment in nonuniform Channels," thesis presented to Colorado State University, at Fort Collins, Colorado, 1975.
5. French, R. H., "Open Channel Hydraulics," McGraw-Hill Book Company, 1985.
6. Graf, W. H., "The Hydraulics of Reservoir Sedimentation," J. Water Power & Dam Construction, Vol. 35, No. 4, pp. 45-52, 1983.
7. Liggett, A. J., Cunge, J. A., "Numerical Methods of Solution of the Unsteady Flow Equations," Vol. 1 (Mahmood, et al., ed.), pp. 89-182, Fort Collins, Colorado, 1975.
8. Sharghi, A., Berlamont, J., "Reservoir Sedimentation," 3rd Iranian Congress of Civil Engineering, Shiraz, Iran, 1990.
9. Sloff, C. J., "Reservoir Sedimentation," A Literature Survey, Report No. 91-2, Faculty of Civil Engineering, Delft University of Technology, Delft, Holland, 1991.
10. Yalin, M. S.: Mechanics of sediment transport, Pergamon Press Ltd., Headington Hill Hall, Oxford, 1972.

2nd International Conference on
RIVER FLOOD HYDRAULICS
22–25 March 1994: York, England

Sand waves in alluvial channels and their influence on sediment transport

Wang shiqiang

(Professor, Department of Hydraulic Engineering,
Tsinghua University, Beijing, P.R. China)

Abstract

In this paper new relations between the parameters of dunes or ripples and the flow intensity, the diameter of bed material are proposed. They are in close agreement with the variation of alluvial resistance. The bed load transport rate can be determined by measuring or calculating the height and the migrating velocity of dunes or ripples. The change of size distribution of the bed material close to the bed surface is dependent not only upon the prosess of scour or deposition but also upon the thickness of the exchanging layer of the bed material. The latter mainly depends on the vertical migrating velocity of sand waves. It has a great influence on the rate of degradation or aggradation of alluvial streams.

Introduction

The parameters of the shape and the movement of sand waves are very important in analysing or calculating alluvial resistance, size distribution of bed material and sedimeat transport rate. So far, there have been a large number of research results about height, length and their ratio of ripple and dunes, for example, Yalin(1964, 1979), Ranga Raju et al (1976), Van Riji(1984), but they are only applicable to limited cases. Errors in calculated results are too large when they are used to the Yangtze River or the Yellow River in China. On the other hand, there are quite a few relations for migrating velocity and movement period of sand waves.

The bed load transport rate can readily be obtained by measuring or computing the height and the migrating velocity of ripples or dunes, but the magnitude of the coefficient has not been determined satisfactorily (Shinohara et al (1959), Peter et al (1980)).

The bed material in natural rivers is generally a mixture of graded sediment. Its size distribution changes as scouring or deposition of the bed occurs. The rate at

2nd International Conference on River Flood Hydraulics. Edited by W. R. White and J. Watts

which bed material becomes coarser or finer is dependent not only on the intensity of scouring or deposition but also on the thickness H_b of the exchanging layer in which grains of different sizes exchange their relative positions during fluvial processes. So far H_b has been taken as an empirical constant in most sediment routing models. In the HEC-6 model its computed value increases with increasing discharge per unit width for gravel bed (Thomas (1980)). It has a great influence on the composition of bed material and sediment transport rate, particularly for a long-term scour. This is a very important problem for sediment routing model, but its physical process still has not been well understood. A physical model for the exchanging layer and a formula for its thickness are given in this paper.

Prediction of parameters of sand waves

Migrating velocity of ripples and dunes   In Figure 1 $V_{sx} / \sqrt{g D_{50}}$ is plotted against Θ'_* and H / D_{50}, where the data are taken from S.Wang (1990), S. Wang & W R White (1993), Guy et al (1966), and the field measurement for Lower Yangtze River and Lower Yellow River. In the figure V_{sx} represents the migrating velocity of ripples or dunes, Θ'_* is a dimensionless shear stress due to grain $(= r R'_b S / (r_s - r) / D_{50})$, H is the water depth, D_{50} is the sediment diameter for which 50% by weight of the sample is finer, S is the energy slope, g is acceleration of gravity, r and r_s are the specific gravity of water and sediment grains respectively, R'_b is the hydraulic radius due to grain resistance which can be computed by

$$\frac{V}{\sqrt{g R'_b S}} = 2.5 ln(\frac{11 R'_b}{K'_s}) \tag{1}$$

where V is the mean flow velocity, K'_s is the grain roughness height given by

$$K'_s = D_{65} \qquad\qquad (D_{50} > 0.1mm)$$
$$K'_s = 0.5 D_{65} \qquad\qquad (D_{50} \leqslant 0.1mm)$$

where D_{65} is the sediment diameter for which 65% by weight of the sample is finer. By analysing the data shown in Figure 1, a relation for the migrating velocity is proposed in the form of

$$\frac{V_{sx}}{\sqrt{g D_{50}}} = K_v \Theta'^2_* \tag{2}$$

$$K_v = 5600(\frac{D_{50}}{H})^{1.5} \qquad\qquad (\frac{H}{D_{50}} \leqslant 7000)$$

$$K_v = 0.01 \qquad\qquad (\frac{H}{D_{50}} \geqslant 7000)$$

The above equation shows that the migrating velocity is directly proportional to the fourth power of the mean velocity and decreases with increasing value of H / D_{50} when $H / D_{50} < 7000$.

Migrating period of dunes $T / \sqrt{D_{50} / g}$ is plotted against Θ'_* in Figure 2_b and 2_a for flume and field data respectively, where T is migrating period of dunes. Analysing the data shows that the migrating period increases with the increase of water depth H for a given value of Θ'_* and with the decrease of Θ'_* for a given value of H, it has a much larger value in natural rivers than in flumes. For sandy rivers the migrating velocity can be expressed as

$$\frac{T}{\sqrt{D_{50} / g}} = \frac{9.5 \times 10^7}{\Theta'_*} \qquad\qquad (3)$$

The value of T equals 3.1 day for $D_{50} = 0.08$mm and 4.3 day for $D_{50} = 0.15$mm by (3) when Θ'_* equals 1.0. The former value represents a common case in the Lower Yellow River and the latter one in the lower Yangtze River.

Height of dunes and ripples   Figure 3 shows the relation of Δ / D_{50} to Θ'_* and H / D_{50}, where Δ is height of dunes or ripples. It shows that for a given value of H / D_{50}, the value of Δ / D_{50} at first increases and then decreases with increasing Θ'_*. The maximum Δ_{max} / D_{50} for a given H / D_{50} increases with increasing H / D_{50}. New relation for the height of dunes or ripples for sandy rivers are proposed as follows:

$$\frac{\Delta}{D_{50}} = 1052(\frac{\Theta'_*}{0.04} - 1)^{1.13} \qquad (0.04 \leqslant \Theta'_* \leqslant 0.7) \qquad (4)$$

$$\frac{\Delta}{D_{50}} = 11730(\frac{2}{\Theta'_*} - 1)^{1.23} \qquad (0.7 \leqslant \Theta'_* \leqslant 2.0)$$

$$\frac{\Delta_{max}}{D_{50}} = 25000 \qquad (\Theta'_* = 0.7)$$

The value of Δ_{max} equals 2m for $D_{50} = 0.08$mm and 3.75m for $D_{50} = 0.15$mm by (4). They correspond to the measured data of the Lower Yellow River and the Lower Yangtze River respectively.

Based on the research results on alluvial resistance by Wang et al (1993), the critical values of Θ'_* for forming ripple or dunes and for flat moving bed are 0.04

and about 2.0 respectively. These results are used together with the data in Figure 3 to obtain equ.(4). According to the equation of bed load transport rate q_b by Wang and Zhang (1987), q_b is directely proportional to $D^{3/2}\Theta'^P_*$, and the power P equals approximately 2.0 for $\Theta'_* = 0.7$ and decreases with increasing Θ'_*. Another equation for q_b by the authos and others (Wang(1988), Shinohara et al (1959)) is given below:

$$q_b = Kr_b V_{sx} \Delta \tag{5}$$

where r_b is the specific gravity of dry sediment deposition, K is a coefficient reflecting the shape of sand waves. In equation (5) replacing q_b by $D_{50}^{3/2}\Theta'^P_*$ and V_{sx} by $D_{50}^{1/2}\Theta'^2_*$ we obtain $\Delta/D_{50} \sim \Theta'^{P-2}_*$. P equals 2 when Θ'_* is 0.7, Θ'_* corresponding to the maximum value of Δ_{max}/D_{50} for natural sandy rivers is also 0.7. It shows that equation (4) is consistent with other formulas of migrating velocity and bed load transport rate.

Relation between height of dunes or ripples and alluvial resistance

According to author's research (Wang(1990)) the friction coefficient due to bed forms mainly depends on four parameters of the size and shape of sand waves: Δ/H, Δ/L, Δ/L_b and Δ/Δ_b, where L, L_b and Δ_b are length, back length and average height of bed surface above the trough of sand wave respectively (see Fig.5).

Figure 4 shows the relation of Θ_* to Θ'_* for various values of R_b/D_{50} and three different values of D_{50} from author's equations (Wang & White (1993)), where $\Theta_* = rR_b s/(r_s - r)/D_{50}$, R_b is the hydraulic radius due to bed.

By comparing Figures 4 with 3 some similarities can be observed. The critical value of Θ_* from static flat bed to ripples or dunes are all 0.04 for different values of D_{50} and H. The maximum value of $\Theta''_* (= \Theta_* - \Theta'_*)$or Δ and the corresponding values of Θ'_* all increase with increasing R_b/D_{50} or H/D_{50}. The critical values of Θ'_* for which Δ or Θ''_* is zero also increase with the increase of H/D_{50} or R_b/D_{50}. These similarities between these two figures show clearly that alluvial resistance due to bed forms depends mainly on the height of ripples or dunes in the lower and transition regime. Further comparison between these two figures shows that two values of Θ'_* corresponding to the maximums of Θ''_* and Δ respectively are not equal, the former is 0.2 and the latter is 0.7 for natural rivers. It shows that Δ is not a unique factor which affects alluvial resistance due to bed forms.

Movement of sand waves and transprort of bed load

The variation of q_b with position and time is shown in Figure 5 where symbol $+$ expresses same direction of the bed boad transport and the flow, t is the time, x is the longitudinal coordinate direction, and z is the elevation of bed surface.

According to Wang's (1988) research results, the difference of q_b at any two points on the bed surface with sand waves is directely proportional to the migrating velocity V_{sx} and the difference of their elevation, the average bed load transport rate q_b in a wave period T or in a wave length L can be determined by

$$q_b = q_{bz} - r_b V_{sx} Z \qquad (6)$$

when the bed forms are ripples or dunes in lower or transition flow regime the point of flow reattachment is a specific point at which q_{bA} is zero (point A in Fig.5). Meantime let $z = -K\Delta$, the equation (6) becomes (5). Fig.6 shows the relation between q_b and $r_b V_{sx}\Delta$ by plotting flume data of Guy et al (1966) and Wang et al (1986) where the coefficient K changes from 0.36 to 0.7 with an average value of 0.52. Following formula may be used to predict q_b,

$$q_b = 0.52 r_b V_{sx} \Delta \qquad (7)$$

The value of coefficient $K = 0.52$ is in a good agreement with the river data in Hunan province, China by collecting the bed load in a trough across river bed. Since great deviation are usually unavoidable when a bed load sampler or a general transport formula is used to measure (to predict) q_b, equ. (7) will give a result that is quite comparable with those obtained from other formulas and measuring devices. Particularly, V_{sx} and Δ can be readily measured, and equ. (7) will predict q_b quite accurately. In the upper flow regime, no specific point at which q_{bz} is known is apparent, so equ. (7) is only suitable to alluvial bed with ripples or dunes, the criterion has been presented by Wang and White (1993).

Exchanges of bed material and movement of sand waves

As reservoir discharges clear water the bed material coarsens and the bed surface even may form armour. It results in greatly decreasing the capacity of sediment transport and the rate of degradation. Conversely, when deposition occurs, the bed material becomes finer, and the sediment transport capacity increases and the rate of aggradation decreases. The rate of change of size distribution of sediment on the bed surface is dependent on the thickness of the exchange layer H_b besides the intensity of deposition or scouring. If H_b is smaller, the rate of degradation or aggradation will be larger than that for larger H_b.

305

By observing sediment movement in flumes and analysing both the laboratory and field data, it is noted that the exchange of bed material between the bed surface and the layer below is mainly a consequence of the sand waves movement. If the bed material is absolutely uniform, then the supply of sediment from the bed surface is theoretically unlimited for bed load during scouring process, but it is limited in case of nonuniform bed material. Fine particals in deeper layers will be exposed on bed surface while coarse grains on bed surface will fall to the trough as the sand waves move on. So the thickness H_b should depend on the vertical migrating velocity V_{sy} of sand waves and the computing or exchanging duration dt. The maximum value of H_b should not exceed the height Δ of sand waves. Therefore we may write

$$H_b = V_{sy} \, dt = \frac{\Delta}{T} dt \qquad\qquad (dt \leqslant T)$$
$$H_b = \Delta \qquad\qquad\qquad\qquad (dt > T) \qquad\qquad (8)$$

Where the period T and the height Δ of dunes in natural sandy rivers can be determined by equ. (3) and (4) respectively.

The movement of sand waves is a basic reason for the exchange of bed material, but it is not the only one. The wriggle of meanders and sand bars in alluvial streams are the other reasons. So it is impossible for H_b to be zero. But no relationship of Δ and T for antidunes in upper regime is available. In the author's sedimeut routing model the values of Θ'_* in the equ. (3) and (4) are taken temporarily and empirically as 1.8 for $\Theta'_* > 1.8$ to determine T, Δ and H_b for the moving flat bed and antidunes.

The new size distribution of bed material can be predicted by the following equation,

$$P_b(I) = [(H_b - dz)P_{b0}(I) + dz \cdot P_{bs}(I)] / H_b \qquad (H_b > dz) \qquad (9)$$
$$P_b(I) = P_{bs}(I) \qquad\qquad\qquad\qquad\qquad\qquad (H_b \leqslant dz)$$

where dz is the average computing thickness of deposition or scour, dz>0 for deposition and dz<0 for scour, I is the size fraction index, $P_{bs}(I)$ is its fraction by weigt for deposition or scour, $P_{b0}(I)$ is its fraction by weigt in the thickness (H_b-dz) for original bed material, $P_b(I)$ is its fraction by wheigt in the thickness H_b after deposition or scour. As the deposition occurs and $dz>H_b$, $P_b(I)=P_{bs}(I)$. It means that if the rate of deposition is larger than V_{sy}, the movement of sand waves does not affect the size distribution of bed material on bed surface. If the preliminary calculated intensity $(-dz \cdot P_{bs}(I))$ of scour is quite large and $P_b(I)$ becomes less than zero, it means that the supply of bed material for a size fraction I from bed is not enough, in other words, it is limited. Since this is incorrect, it should be calculated repeatedly by changing the size distribution of bed material untill $P_b(I) > 0$. It is to be noted that $dz \cdot P_{bs}(I)$ is a secondary variable which is also dependent on the magnitude of H_b or the supply from the bed material. Above equations have been applied in author's sediment routing model to compute the degradation and the aggradation in Yellow River, and the computed results are in a good agreement with the abserved data.

Conclusions

Based on the proposed new relations of the parameters of dunes or ripples, it is found that the migrating velocity V_{sx} is directly proportional to Θ'^2_* or V'^4_* and inversly to water depth H, the period T increases with increasing H and decreasing Θ'_*, the height Δ is directly proportional to H and first increases and then decreases with increasing Θ'_*, and the maximum Δ for sandy river is alout 25000 D_{50} when $\Theta'_* = 0.7$. The variation of Δ with respect to Θ'_* and H / D_{50} are similar to that of Θ''_*. It seems that Δ is the most important factor affecting the alluvial resistance due to bed forms but it is not the unique factor.

The bed load transport rate is directly proportional to V_{sx} and Δ of ripples or dunes, the average value of the coefficient equals 0.52. This approach is applicable only for the lower and the transition regime. If V_{sx} and Δ can be readily measured, the prediction of bed load transport rate will be more accurate.

The movement of sand waves results in the exchange of graded bed material of which the thickness is directly proportional to the vertical migrating velocity of the sand wave. It has a great influence on the change of size distribution of the bed material and the rate of degradation or aggradation.

Acknowledgement

A part of data used in this paper are taken from the flume experiments carried out at hydraulics Research, Wallingford, where the author was a visiting scholar in 1986 and 1990. Special thanks must go to Dr. W R White and Dr. R Bettess. The author would like also to acknowledge the help of Professor Xia Zhenhuan.

References

Guy H P et al, 1966. Summary of alluvial channel data from flume experiments, 1956-61. U. S. Geo. Survey, professional paper 462-I.

Peter E and Lau Y L, 1980. Computation of bed load bathymetric data. ASCE,

Vol. 106, No. HY3, pp. 369−380.

Ranga Raju and Soni J P, 1976. Geometry of ripples and dunes in alluvial channels. J. Hyd. Res. IAHR, Vol.14, No.3, pp. 241−249.

Shinohara K and Tsubaki T, 1959. On the characteristics of sand waves formed upon the beds of the open channels and rivers. Rep., Res. Inst. Applied Mech., Kyushu Univ. Japan, Vol.7. No.25, pp 15−45.

Thomas W A, 1980. Calculation of sediment movement in gravel bed rivers. Workshop on eng. probleme on the manag. of gravel bed rivers, newtown, Wales, UK.

Van Rijn L C, 1984. Sediment transport, part III : bed forms and alluvial roughness. J. Hyd. Eng. ASCE. 110(12), pp. 1733−1754.

Yalin M S. 1964. Geometrical properties of sand waves. J. Hyd. Div. ASCE, 90(HY5), pp. 105−119.

Yalin M S and Karahan E, 1979. Steepness of sedimentary dunes, J. Hyd. Div. ASCE, 105(HY4), pp. 381−392.

Wang Shiqiang, White W R and R Bettess, 1986. Experiments on alluvial friction. HR, Report. SR83, Wallingford, UK.

Wang Shiqiang and Zhang Ren, 1987. A New equation of bed load transport. proc. 22nd cong. IAHR.

Wang Shiqiang, 1988. The movement of sand waves and the measurement of bed load. J. Sediment Research, No.4. Beijing.

Wang Shiqiang, 1990. Experimental study of hydraulic resistance of alluvial streame. J. Hydraulic Eng., No. 12, Beijing.

Wang Shiqiang and White W R, 1993. Alluvial resistance in transition regime. J. hyd. Eng. ASCE, Vol 119 (HY6).

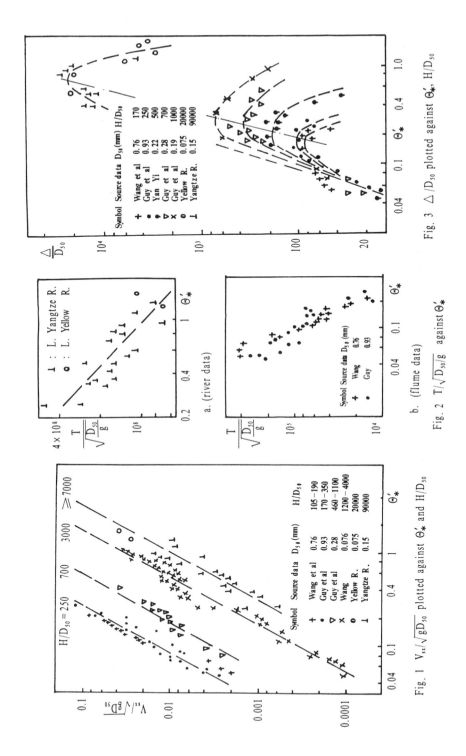

Fig. 3 $\triangle/D_{50}$ plotted against Θ'_*, H/D_{50}

Symbol	Source data	D_{50}(mm)	H/D_{50}
+	Wang et al	0.76	170
•	Guy et al	0.93	250
•	Yan Yi	0.22	500
▽	Guy et al	0.28	700
×	Guy et al	0.19	1000
○	Yellow R.	0.075	20000
⊥	Yangtze R.	0.15	90000

a. (river data)

⊥ : L. Yangtze R.
○ : L. Yellow R.

b. (flume data)

Symbol	Source data	D_{50} (mm)
+	Wang	0.76
•	Guy	0.93

Fig. 2 $T/\sqrt{D_{50}/g}$ against Θ'_*

Symbol	Source data	D_{50}(mm)	H/D_{50}
+	Wang et al	0.76	105 – 190
•	Guy et al	0.93	170 – 350
▽	Guy et al	0.28	460 – 1100
×	Wang	0.076	1200 – 4000
○	Yellow R.	0.075	20000
⊥	Yangtze R.	0.15	90000

Fig. 1 $V_{ss}/\sqrt{gD_{50}}$ plotted against Θ'_* and H/D_{50}

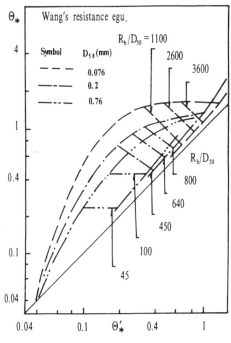

Fig. 4 Θ_* aginst Θ_*', R_b/D_{50} and D_{50}

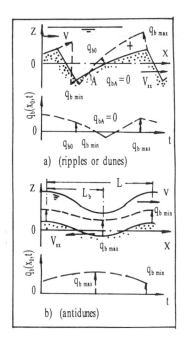

Fig. 5 Variation of q_b on sand bed

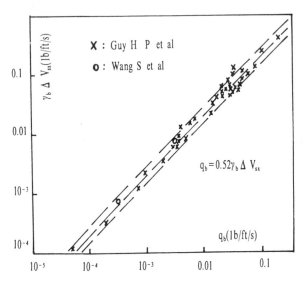

Fig. 6 Relatino between q_b and $\gamma_b \, \Delta \, V_{sx}$

2nd International Conference on
RIVER FLOOD HYDRAULICS
22–25 March 1994: York, England

NUMERICAL MODELLING OF SUSPENDED
SEDIMENT TRANSPORT IN COMPOUND CHANNELS
by

B.Westrich, Xu Yichun, S.AL-Zoubi
Institut für Wasserbau, Universität Stuttgart

1. INTRODUCTION

Flood events may have a considerable influence on a river bed morphology as a result of sediment transport. Sedimentation of contaminated suspended sediments may cause severe pollution of flood plains which has to be taken into account for land use.
When overbank flow occurs, the flow characteristics and suspended sediment transport of a river with a flood plain are very different from one without a flood plain. The interaction mechanism between the main channel and the flood plain has an influence on the velocity and dispersion and results in an increased momentum and mass exchange between the main channel and the flood plain. The effect of the lateral transport depends on the velocity gradient, water depth ratio, and concentration gradient at the interface. Therefore, a semi-empirical diffusive term for lateral suspended sediment transport is presented in this paper. The paper provides a new method which combines a 1-D multiple strip flow model with a 2-D depth-averaged suspended sediment transport model. The numerical model is tested for different types of channel geometries. The results are then compared with some basic laboratory experiments by James (1985) and Kohane (1991).

2. FLOW MODEL

For a flood flow calculation of a river with compound section, a 1-D multiple strip model is used:

$$\frac{dQ_T}{dx} = q_s \tag{1}$$

$$\frac{d}{dx}\left(\frac{\beta Q_T^2}{A_T}\right) + gA_T\frac{dh}{dx} = -gA_T J \tag{2}$$

2nd International Conference on River Flood Hydraulics. Edited by W. R. White and J. Watts
© 1994 HR Wallingford Ltd. Published by John Wiley & Sons Ltd

$$J = \frac{Q_T |Q_T|}{\left(\sum\limits_{i=1}^{n} kst_i A_i R_i^{2/3} \right)^2} \tag{3}$$

$$\beta = \frac{\left(\sum\limits_{i=1}^{n} kst_i^2 A_i R_i^{4/3} \right) A_T}{\left(\sum\limits_{i=1}^{n} kst_i A_i R_i^{2/3} \right)^2} \tag{4}$$

where, Q_T = total discharge, q_s = lateral discharge, A_i and R_i = area and hydraulic radius in a strip, respectively, A_T = total discharge, kst_i = roughness coefficient in stripe, β = Boussinesq coefficient, h = water surface elevation, x = longitude direction, and J = energy slope.

By using these equations flow parameters of the main channel and flood plain can be calculated separately. Kohane(1993) developed a multiple strip numerical model which accounts for the lateral momentum exchange between conected flow strips and therefore, it is superior for more irregular cross section.

3. SEDIMENT TRANSPORT MODEL

For steady flow the 2-D depth average suspended sediment transport equation in the orthogonal natural coordinate system have been written by Yotsukura (1976):

$$\frac{\partial}{\partial x}(m_z huC) + \frac{\partial}{\partial z}(m_x hvC) = \frac{\partial}{\partial x}\left(\frac{m_z}{m_x} hD_x \frac{\partial c}{\partial x}\right) + \frac{\partial}{\partial z}\left(\frac{m_x}{m_z} hD_z \frac{\partial c}{\partial z}\right) + \frac{\dot{E}}{h} - \frac{\dot{S}}{h} \tag{5}$$

where, x, z = streamline and lateral directions, respectively, u, v = local velocities in x and z directions, h = average water depth, D_x, D_z = dispersion coefficient in x and z directions, C = local concentration. m_x and m_z are metric coefficients. In some cases, where the streamline curvature is small and the width of the river does not vary greatly, m_x=1, and m_z=1 can be used as a useful approximation. When m_x=1, m_z=1, the above equations can be written as follows:

$$\frac{\partial}{\partial x}(huC) + \frac{\partial}{\partial z}(hvC) = \frac{\partial}{\partial x}\left(hD_x \frac{\partial c}{\partial x}\right) + \frac{\partial}{\partial z}\left(hD_z \frac{\partial c}{\partial z}\right) + \frac{\dot{E}}{h} - \frac{\dot{S}}{h} \tag{5a}$$

SEDIMENT AND EROSION TERMS

Sediment rate S and erosion rate E in kg per unit area and time are described as:

$$\dot{S} = \omega_s C \left(1 - \frac{\tau}{\tau_{cs}}\right) \tag{6}$$

$$\tau_{cs} = \frac{(\rho_s - \rho) \, gh\omega_s C}{T_K u} \tag{7}$$

$$\dot{E} = M\left(\frac{\tau}{\tau_{cr}} - 1\right) \tag{8}$$

where, τ = bottom shear stress. τ_{cs}, τ_{cr} = the critical shear stress of sedimentation (Westrich, B and Juraschek, M. 1985) and erosion, ω_s = fall velocity, ρ_s and ρ = the densities of the sediment and water. T_K = an efficient parameter depending on the deformation and mobility of the river bed, the value of T_K used was 0.0016. M = an empirical coefficient, the value used is 0.0000008 - 0.0000025 kg/m^{2}s.

DISPERSION

The dispersion caused by bottom shear is assumed to be:

$$D_x = \beta_x U_* h \tag{9a}$$

$$D_z = \beta_z U_* h \tag{9b}$$

where, U_* = bottom shear velocity, $U_* = (\tau/\rho)^{\frac{1}{2}}$, β_x and β_z = empirical coefficient, which were assumed to 6 and 0.35.

In a river with compound sections, there is a big difference between the lateral velocity distribution at the interface of the main channel and the flood plain. When flow over the banks occurs, there is a strong interaction between the deep flow region to the shallow flow region, and therefore, the lateral dispersion of suspended sediment transport increases.

For the shear in the interaction zone Evers (1980) and Kohane (1991) have found:

$$\tau_s = 2\rho\alpha_1 (u_m - u_p) \cdot |u_m - u_p| \tag{10}$$

where, τ_i = shear stress at the interface between the main channel and the flood plain. α_1 = coefficient, u_m and u_p = velocities of the main channel and flood plain, respectively. For practical application, Evers suggested α_1 equal to 0.01, Kohane proposed α_1 to be 0.02.

From $v_t = \dfrac{\tau}{\rho \frac{du}{dz}}$, the following expression for momentum coefficient v_t can be found:

$$v_t = \frac{2\rho\alpha_1 (u_m - u_p)^2}{\rho \frac{du}{dz}} \tag{11}$$

If du/dz is taken as the ratio of the velocity difference (u_m - u_p) and B as a charactristic mixing length in the interaction zone, and it is considered as momentum and mass dispersion coefficient :

$$D_i = 2\alpha_2 B \cdot |u_m - u_p|$$

$$(12)$$

The mixing in the interaction region is caused by large eddies which have a mixing length of the order of magnitude (B-d). Rajaratnam and Ahmudi (1981) found:

$$B = 6 \ (D-d)$$

$$(13)$$

where, D and d = water depth in a main channel and a flood plain, respectively. From equation (12) and (13):

$$D_i = \alpha |u_m - u_p| \cdot |D-d|$$

$$(14)$$

where, α is equal to 0.12 - 0.24.
From (9b) and (14), the resulting lateral dispersive coefficient can be written as follows:

$$D_z = \beta_z U_* h + \alpha |u_m - u_p| \cdot |D-d|$$

$$(15)$$

4. MODEL TEST

COMPARISON WITH EXPERIMENTS
The channel section of James' laboratory experiment (James, C. S. 1985) is shown in Fig. 1(a). The model is 38 cm wide and 10 m long with a bed slope of 0.004. The mean diameter of sand used in the experiment is 0.25 mm. For each test, deposited sediment distribution was measured on the flood plain over two 0.5 m long sections. The sediment was classified into four groups according to particle size. The flow parameters used in James' experiment and the calculations are shown in the table 1.
The calculation simulates the deposition, mass and relative distribution on the flood plain. The results for the relative distribution are shown in Fig.1. It can be seen that the relative deposition distribution upstream and downstream agrees with the results of James' experiment. The deposited mass agrees well at the upstream sampling section.

BACKWATER
The model is a channel with a rectangular compound section (Kohane, R 1991). The geometry, flow condition for calculating sediment transport is shown in Fig 2.
Fig. 2(a) shows the backwater curve and the highest lateral discharge q is at the beginning of the gradually varied flow which coinciders with Kohane experimental data. Fig. 2(b) and Fig. 2(c) show longitudinal and lateral sediment concentration distributions. Sediment concentration at the beginning of the section is 0.3 kg/m³ in the main channel and zero in the flood plain. Fig. 2(b) and Fig. 2(c) show that lateral diffusive transport is very large in the first 50 metres. After this the concentrations in the main channel and flood plain will

Table 1

	test Nr.	Q	H	u_m	u_p	kst_m	kst_p
		m^3/s	m	m/s	m/s	$m^{1/3}/s$	$m^{1/3}/s$
experi-	2	0.0219	0.145	1.00	0.42		
ment	3	0.0099	0.120	0.90	0.20		
	4	0.0095	0.100	0.75	0.30		
calcula-	2	0.0219	0.145	0.85	0.39	49.0	49.0
tion	3	0.0147	0.120	0.77	0.23	50.0	50.0
	4	0.0120	0.100	0.68	0.30	50.0	50.0

Note: James' hydraulic data could not be reproduced by our calculation.

gradually become the same. Fig. 2(d) is the ratio of the lateral convective rate to the lateral diffusive rate. It shows that this ratio is greater at the beginning of the gradually varied flow. This agrees with the line q/qmax in Fig. 2(a) (see also Kohane, R. and Westrich, B. 1994). As the lateral transverse flow in this case is very small, the convective rate is smaller than the dispersive rate. If the channel diverges, the lateral discharge will increase and convective rate will also increase.

The calculation of the suspended sediment concentration in the Neckar river from Lauffen to Besigheim (distance of 11 km) has been carried out as a case study. Comparison of the results of the measured sediment and calculated values show that the model satisfactory simulates the sediment transport in the river.

D_i is derived for rivers with compound sections, but it also can be used for channels with large difference water depths. The percentage of difference between D_i and D_z has been calculated in order to show its influence on diffusion. The results show that for a channel with a compound section, D_i is about 0.0 - 0.001, this is 10 - 50 percent of D_z at the interface (in backwater situation). At the interface it has a peak value (see Fig. 3). For the Neckar river, in the main flow D_i is very small and is about 0.0001-0.01, but near the banks it will increase too about 0.15, 30 - 40 percent of total lateral dispersion D_z.

Using the 1-D multiple strip model, one can obtain the transverse distribution of flow parameter. The more strips there are, the better the results will be. In order to use the advantages of this simply, quick method and to save computational time and memory the optimal number of strips should be found. The calculated results show that generally, if the river is not very wide and the geometry is not variable, calculations using 12 - 15 strips can describe the flow situation. When the river width changes and geometry are complicated, more strips are needed.

5. CONCLUSION

The 1-D multiple strip flow numerical model and the 2-D averaged water depth suspended sediment transport model provide a good method for simulating sediment transport in a river with a compound section. By Using 1-D multiple strip model one can easily obtain flow parameters for sedimentation transport calculations. It is accurate enough to predict lateral distribution of concentrations and geometrical changes for engineering applications. This model is easy, simply and saves computer time and capacity.

As momentum exchange exists due to the great difference in lateral velocities near the interface between the main channel and the flood plain, a new formula to describe this diffusion is introduced in this paper. The calculation shows that $\alpha \mid u_m - u_p \mid \cdot \mid D - d \mid$ is about 10 - 50 percent of the total lateral dispersion at the interface of the main channel and the flood plain.

5. REFERENCES

Evers, P. (1983). Untersuchung der Strömungsvorgänge in gegliederten Gerinnen mit extremen Rauheitsunterschieden. Mitteilungen Heft 45, Institut für Wasserbau und Wasserwirtschaft, Rheinisch-Westfälische Technische Hochschule Aachen.

JAMES, C. S. (1985). Sediment transfer to overbank sections. Journal of Hydraulic Research, VOL. 23, 1985, NO5.

Kohane, R. (1991). Berechnungsmethoden für Hochwasserabfluss in Fliessgewässern mit Oberströmten Vorländern. Mitteilungen Heft 73, Institut für Wasserbau, Universität Stuttgart.

Kohane, R and Westrich, B (1994). Modelling of Flood Hydraulics in Compound channels. 2nd Internation Conference on river flood hydraulics, March 1994, York, England.

Lam Lau, Y. Krishnappan, G. B. (1978). Transverse Dispersion in Rectangular Channels. Journal of the Hydraulics Division, ASCE, VOL. 103, No. HY10, 1977.

Lam Lau, Y. Krishnappan, G. B. (1978). Modelling Transverse Mixing in Natural Streams. Journal of the Hydraulic Division, ASCE, VOL. 107, No. HY2, 1981.

Ogink, H. J. M.(1985) The Effective Viscosity Coefficient in 2-D Depth-Averaged Flow Models. 21st IAHR Congress, Melbourne, Australia, 1985.

Rajaratnam, N. and Ahmadi, R (1981). Hydraulics of Channel with Flood-Plains. Journal of Hydraulic Research, VOL. 19. 1981, NO. 1.

Westrich, B. , and Juraschek, M (1985). Flow transport capacity for suspended sediment. 21st IAHR Congress, Melbourne, Australia, 1985, P591.

Yotsukura, N., Fischer, H. B. and Sayre, W. W. (1970). Measurement of mixing characteristics of the Missouri River between Sioux City, Iowa, and Plattsmotuth, Nebraska. U.S. Geol. Surv. Water Supply Pap. 1899-G, 1970.

Yotsukura, N. Quality, S. W. (1976). Transverse Mixing in Natural Channels. Water Resources Research, VOL. 12, 1976, NO4.

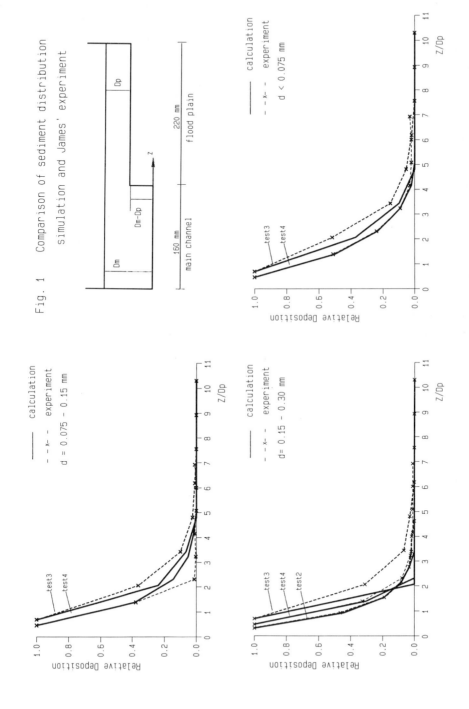

Fig. 1 Comparison of sediment distribution
simulation and James' experiment

317

(a) Lateral discharge distribution vs longitudinal coordinate

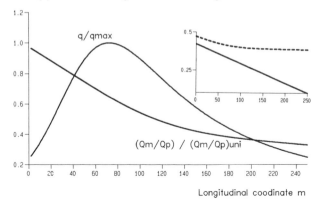

Longitudinal coodinate m

(b) Concentration distribution vs longitudinal coordinate

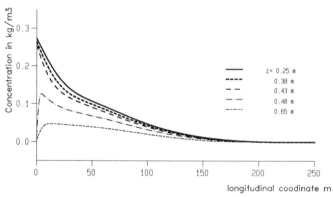

longitudinal coodinate m

(c) Concentration distribution vs lateral coodinate

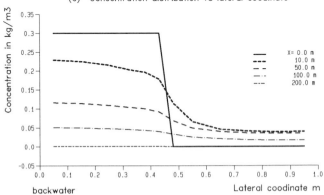

backwater

Lateral coodinate m

318

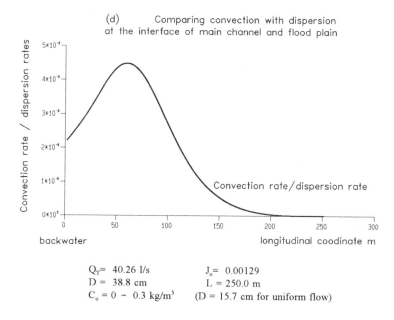

(d)   Comparing convection with dispersion
at the interface of main channel and flood plain

Convection rate/dispersion rate

backwater   longitudinal coodinate m

Q_T= 40.26 l/s J_o= 0.00129
D = 38.8 cm   L = 250.0 m
C_o = 0 ~ 0.3 kg/m^3 (D = 15.7 cm for uniform flow)

Fig. 2   Effect of backwater

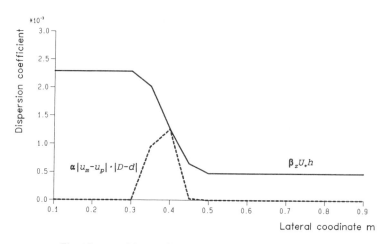

$\alpha|u_m-u_p|\cdot|D-d|$ $\beta_z U_* h$

Lateral coodinate m

Fig. 3   Dispersion coefficient vs lateral coodinate

Equilibrium scour in rivers with sandbeds

A Rooseboom[**] and A le Grange[*]
[**]*Department of Civil Engineering, University of Stellenbosch, Private Bag X5018, Stellenbosch 7599, South Africa*
[*]*BKS Consulting Engineers, P O Box 3173, Pretoria, South Africa*

Abstract

Severe floods caused extensive scour along sand-bedded rivers in Natal during 1984 and 1987. Recorded information on the extent of scour as well as peak flood discharges was analysed in an attempt to develop relationships which could be used to predict scour depths and flood levels in future.

Contrary to expectations, all the indications are that viscosity comes into play together with absolute roughness in determining limiting transporting capacity when maximum flood levels are approached.

By deforming their beds through the formation of dunes and other bed formations, the sediment transporting capacity of rivers is decreased. This means that rivers possess a built-in mechanism through which excessive downward scour is prevented when extreme floods occur. The relationships which have been derived can be used to calculate maximum scour depths as well as associated absolute roughness values for rivers with sandbeds.

Introduction

Severe floods caused extensive damage to river systems in south eastern Africa during 1984 and 1987 (Kovács et al, 1985; Van Bladeren and Burger, 1989). The floods which occurred in the Komati, Mkuze, Black Mfolozi and White Mfolozi Rivers during 1984 together with the 1987 flood in the Mhlatuze River were the largest on record at the gauging stations on these rivers. Their respective estimated return periods ranged from at least 20 years to more than 200 years (Table 1).

2nd International Conference on River Flood Hydraulics. Edited by W. R. White and J. Watts
© 1994 HR Wallingford Ltd. Published by John Wiley & Sons Ltd

Table 1: Site and flood characteristics

River	Unit	Komati	Mkuze	Black Mfolozi	White Mfolozi	Mhlatuze
Site		Trading site	Morgenstond	Game Reserve	Game Reserve	Riverview (W1H009)
Catchment Area (CA)	km^2	8 040	2 647	3 396	4 776	2 409*
Mean Annual Runoff (MAR)	x 10^{6}m^2		95	343	255	178
Mean Annual Precipitation (MAP)	mm		898	965	791	996
Bed Slope (from 1:50 000 maps)	m/m	0,00062	0,00125	0,0012	0,00152	0,0013
Flood Data						
Date (1984)		31-01-1984	31-10-1984	31-01-1984	31-01-1984	31-01-1984
Method of Flood Peak Measure		SA	SA	SA	SA	SA
Flood Peak (Q)	m^2/s	2 640	5 500	10 000	6 500	2 400**
Flood Line Slope (S)	m/m	0,00061	0,00163	0,0012	0,001	0,003
Storm rain (p)	mm	285	480	580	445	370**
Return period (T)	yr	20-50	50-200	0,93 RMF	50-200	20-50**
Sediment size (mean)	mm	1,33	0,243	0,12	0,38	0,2
Date (1987)		-	29-09-1987	29-09-1987	29-09-1987	29-09-1987
Method of Flood Peak Measure			SA	SA	SA	SA
Flood Peak (Q)	m^3/s	-	1 060	1 740	2 150	3 600
Flood line Slope (S)	m/m	-	0,00188	0,00183	0,0022	0,00223
Storm rain (p)	mm	-	165	262	247	436
Return Period (T)	yr	-	< 10	10	15	50 to 100
Sediment size (mean)	mm	-	0,43	0,425	0,61	0,27

* Catchment excluding Goedetrouw Dam (1980) = 1 336 km^2
** Refer to CA at Goedetrouw Dam
SA = slope area
CA = catchment

Extensive bank erosion occurred and a large number of bridges were either destroyed or severely damaged.

Shortly after the floods had occurred, the South African Department of Water Affairs performed topographical surveys of specific reaches (Fig. 1) along these rivers. Maximum flood levels that had been reached were recorded at the same time. It was thus possible to calculate the peak discharges that had occurred and to compare these values with the depths and widths to which the sandbed river channels had been eroded in an attempt to establish criteria which could be used in future to predict equilibrium scour conditions.

Sediment loads in southern African rivers are typically availability limited even where flows pass over sandbeds (Rooseboom 1992). It might be expected therefore that when extremely large floods occur, sand-bedded reaches of rivers will be scoured out in order to provide the additional sediment that the rivers are capable of transporting. The experience has been however that although sideways scour occurred on a large scale, limited downward scour was observed along the main channel beds under consideration. (This was confirmed by subsequent geotechnical investigations.) In contrast, deep scour depths were observed during the same floods at bridge sites. It must be accepted therefore that the downward erosive capacity remains limited during flood events along unconstricted, uniform river reaches.

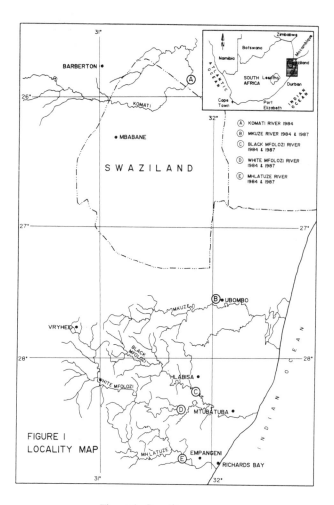

Figure 1: Locality map

It was concluded in a previous publication (Rooseboom and le Grange 1992) that laminar boundary conditions prevail when the maximum scouring depth is reached within a sand-bedded river during a major flood event. Further development of the theory has led to a well-defined relationship which links the absolute roughness of the deformed river bed to the role that viscosity plays when the maximum scour depth is reached. The apparent anomaly that the limiting sediment transporting capacity of streams that are obviously rough-turbulent, is linked to viscosity, is thereby resolved.

It is interesting to note (Yalin 1988) that amongst 20 sets of regime equations, none include fluid viscosity for determining flow depth. This proves that it has been generally accepted that viscosity does not come into the picture when riverbeds are scoured by flood discharges.

A satisfactory explanation of the role that fluid viscosity plays in determining limiting transporting conditions was only found after reconsidering the basic hydraulic relationships.

Theoretical background

It might be expected that when extremely large floods with limited sediment supplies and high sediment carrying capacities occur in rivers with erodible bed and bank materials, scour will continue to take place until the erosive capacity of the stream approaches the minimum value required to transport the available material.

A number of criteria have been developed which depict the critical stage where a stream's transporting capacity becomes sufficient to transport the available material. Classical examples of such criteria are represented by the Hjülstrom (1935), Shields (1936) and Liu (1957) diagrams. Whilst these diagrams were developed primarily on an intuitive basis, rigorous theoretical analysis of flow transporting capacity and sediment transportability (Rooseboom, 1974; 1992) leads to the type of relationships represented in the Liu diagram. The success of this (applied power) approach is attributed to the fact that both flow transporting capacity and sediment transportability can be expressed in directly comparable scalar terms. This approach has been developed further in order to quantify the influence that fluid viscosity and bed roughness have on sediment transporting capacity.

It can be argued that whenever alternative modes of flow exist, that mode which requires the least amount of unit power will be followed. Accordingly fluid flowing over movable material would not transport such material unless this would result in a decrease in the amount of unit power which is being applied. Alternatively, if two modes of yielding exist, yielding will take place according to that mode which offers the least resistance.

Where flow takes place over movable material and the relatively large amount of unit power required to maintain motion along the bed becomes greater than that which would be required in the process of deformation of the bed, the stream should begin to transport the bed material rather than persist in its existing mode of flow. The applied power required per unit volume to suspend a particle with density ρ_s

and settling velocity V_{ss}, in a fluid with density ρ, equals $(\rho_s - \rho) \; g \; V_{ss}$.

In rough turbulent flow the unit stream power applied in maintaining motion along an even bed consisting of particles with diameter d is proportional to (Rooseboom 1974; 1992):

$$\frac{\rho gsD\sqrt{gDs}}{d}$$

(representing the applied unit stream power $\tau dv/dy$ along the bed)

with:

ρ = fluid density
g = acceleration due to gravity
s = energy slope
D = flow depth
d = particle diameter ($\approx$ to the absolute bed roughnes for an even bed)
τ = shear stress
dv/dy = velocity gradient

In terms of the concept of minimum applied power, the stream will begin to entrain particles when the power required to suspend the particles becomes less than the power required to maintain the status quo.

At that stage:

$$(\rho_s-\rho) \; g \; V_{ss} \quad \propto \quad \rho gsD\frac{\sqrt{gDs}}{d} \qquad \cdots \cdots \cdots (1)$$

According to the general equation for settling velocity (Graf, 1971):

$$V_{ss} \quad \propto \quad \left[\frac{(\rho_s-\rho)gd}{\rho c_d} \right]^{\frac{1}{2}} \qquad \cdots \cdots \cdots (2)$$

and assuming that c_d, the drag coefficient, is a constant, which is true for larger diameters, then from (1) and (2), the condition of incipient sediment motion under rough turbulent flow conditions is depicted by:

$$\frac{\sqrt{gDs}}{V_{ss}} = \text{constant} \qquad \cdots \cdots \cdots \cdots (3)$$

As can be seen in Fig. 2, this relationship fits measured data as compiled by Yang (1973) well, with the value of the constant = 0,12, for values of:

$$\frac{\sqrt{gDs}\; d}{\nu} \;>\; 13$$

with:

ν = kinematic viscosity of the fluid

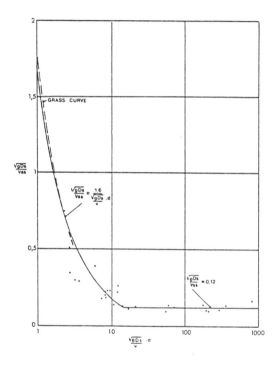

Figure 2: Mathematical relationships for true laminar and turbulent critical boundary layer conditions

Similarly, with laminar boundary conditions in smooth turbulent flow as well as in completely laminar flow the unit applied stream power equals:

$$\frac{(\rho gsD)^2}{\rho\nu}$$

326

The corresponding equation for settling velocity (Graf, 1971) under viscous conditions states that:

$$V_{ss} \propto d^2 g \frac{(\rho_s - \rho)}{\rho \nu} \qquad \cdots\cdots\cdots\cdots (4)$$

Accordingly, the relationship for values of

$$\frac{\sqrt{gDs} \cdot d}{\nu} < 13,$$

calibrated with data by Grass (1970) and Yang (1973) is found to be (Fig. 2) (Rooseboom 1974; 1992):

$$\frac{\sqrt{gDs}}{V_{ss}} = \frac{1,6}{\dfrac{\sqrt{gDs}}{\nu} \cdot d} \qquad \cdots\cdots\cdots\cdots (5)$$

Two distinct relationships are thus identified (Eqs. 3 and 5) which are valid for describing incipient transport conditions along even beds consisting of particles with diameter d. As long as the value of $\dfrac{\sqrt{gDs} \cdot d}{\nu} > 13$ boundary flow conditions are completely turbulent whilst laminar boundary conditions prevail when $\dfrac{\sqrt{gDs} \cdot d}{\nu} < 13$.

However, when the bed is not even, the particle diameter d is no longer representative of the absolute roughness k and the power applied along the bed becomes proportional to:

$$\frac{\rho gsD\sqrt{gDs}}{k} \quad \text{instead of} \quad \frac{\rho gsD\sqrt{gDs}}{d}$$

As the even bed of a river is deformed through the formation of ripples, dunes and other bed forms, the absolute roughness k increases proportionally with the size of the eddies being formed inbetween the bed forms. A specific size of turbulent eddies is generated for a given value of the shear stress being applied (Rooseboom 1974; 1992). A movable bed is deformed so that the size of the bed undulations are in harmony with the size of the turbulent eddies being generated along the bed. As the size of the eddies and k increases, the unit applied stream power along the bed, which is proportional to $\rho gDs\sqrt{gDs}$, will decrease until this value

$$\frac{}{k}$$

drops below the value required to entrain sediment particles.

At the same time, the maximum sediment concentration which can be carried in suspension just above the bed is

$$\propto \left(\frac{\rho gDs\sqrt{gDs}}{k}\right)^z \qquad \text{with} \qquad z = \frac{5\sqrt{2\pi}V_{ss}}{6\sqrt{gDs}}$$

(Rooseboom 1974; 1992). This means that the larger the values of k, the lower the sediment transporting capacity of the stream.

Field results

Table 2 contains the most important values which were measured as well as derived for the different river reaches under consideration. More comprehensive information is contained in le Grange and Rooseboom (1993).

Table 2: Sediment characteristics and flow parameters

Site	River	Year	Representative Particle Diameter d_{85} (mm)	Absolute Roughness[1] k (m)	Settling Velocity V_{ss} (m/s)	$\dfrac{\sqrt{gDs}}{V_{ss}}$	$k\sqrt{\dfrac{1}{gDs.d}{d} \ \ \nu}$	$\dfrac{k}{d_{85}}$
A	Komati	1987	2,33	1,3	0,217	1,33	0,85	485
B	Mkuze	1984	0,429	1,5	0,063	6,52	4,46	3 497
		1987	0,88	1,28	0,113	2,53	2,40	1 455
C	Black Mfolozi	1984	0,205	1,48	0,028	16,3	8,78	7 220
		1987	0,530	0,89	0,076	3,84	3,30	1 679
D	White Mfolozi	1984	0,605	1,16	0,085	4,14	3,00	1 917
		1987	1,7	0,8	0,178	1,81	0,93	471
E	Mhlatuze	1984	0,368	1,11	0,055	8,63	4,16	3 016
		1987	0,471	0,87	0,069	6,61	2,93	1 847

[1] According to estimates by the Department of Water Affairs.

Whereas one tends to assume in terms of the parameters in the Liu diagram (Fig. 2) that the value of the $\dfrac{\sqrt{gDs}}{V_{ss}}$ function should be constant for cases where critical turbulent boundary conditions ought to prevail, the recorded values of this function displayed in Table 2 vary significantly.

By plotting the values on the modified Liu-curve (which includes the transition from fully laminar to fully turbulent boundary conditions) (Fig. 3) the variation in $\dfrac{\sqrt{gDs}}{V_{ss}}$ follows the same pattern as for laminar boundary conditions. All the evidence seems to indicate that somehow, even under such extreme flood conditions, laminar boundary conditions develop below the highly turbulent flows that prevail above. The hypothesis is that a laminar boundary layer develops below the (large) turbulent eddies that are formed to fit the undulations along the bed.

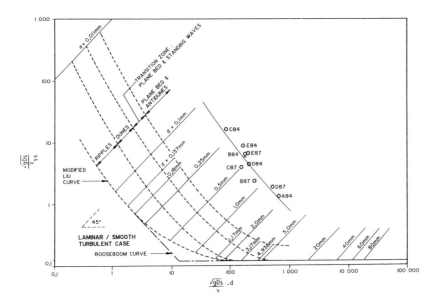

Figure 3: Modified LIU-digram

To test whether this hypothesis is true, the basic relationship for critical conditions with laminar boundary conditions was reconsidered under these conditions:

At the boundary between the turbulent eddies and the laminar boundary layer, the unit applied stream power is proportional to:

$$\dfrac{\rho gsD\sqrt{gDs}}{k}$$

and in turn this is proportional to the unit stream power required to suspend the sediment particles $(\rho_s - \rho) g V_{ss}$.

Substitution of V_{ss} for laminar suspension from Eq. 4 leads to:

$$\frac{\sqrt{gDs}}{V_{ss}} \propto \left[\frac{k}{d} \cdot \frac{1}{\dfrac{\sqrt{gDs} \cdot d}{\nu}} \right]^{\frac{1}{2}} \quad \ldots \ldots (6)$$

describing the situation when the applied power becomes too low to entrain sediment particles in the laminar region below the turbulent eddies after which further downward scour should cease even though the sand waves may still progress downstream or upstream along the bed. Independent estimates of k-values were used by the Department of Water Affairs for calculating peak discharge rates. These same k-values were substituted into Eq. 6 and the resulting function values are given in Table 2 and plotted in Fig. 4.

Conclusions

There is strong evidence in Fig. 4 that this linear relationship holds good with the slope of a straight line, fitted through the origin, $\approx 1{,}6$ (More data is obviously required for more accurate calibration of the relationship). It is also interesting to note in Fig. 3 that with an even bed it is not possible to have turbulent critical boundary layer conditions for bed particles smaller than say 2 mm in diameter, i.e. it is not possible to have particles smaller than 2 mm at rest on an even bed as long as turbulent boundary layer conditions prevail. Scouring of particles smaller than about 2 mm can therefore only stop when laminar boundary layer conditions develop.

It is clear from the foregoing that large increases in the absolute roughness of river beds lead to vastly decreased transporting capacities. By creating sand waves along its bed a river virtually armours itself and prevents the much deeper scour that should have taken place if the bed had remained even. The size of the absolute roughness when scour equilibrium is reached can be calculated by relating the functions which represent applied unit power required for critical laminar entrainment with the power being applied along the bed under turbulent boundary layer conditions.

Starting with an even river bed, increasing discharge will lead to increasing values of $\dfrac{\sqrt{gDs}}{V_{ss}}$ which in turn lead to undulations increasing in size until the peak discharge is reached.

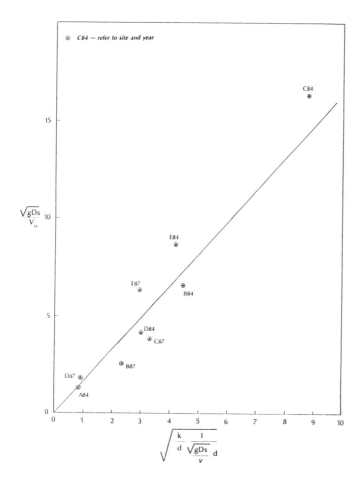

Figure 4: Limiting entrainment relationship for laminar boundary conditions on an uneven bed

In the case of rivers which are often completely dry, their beds tend to be quite even when flow ceases. When a flood passes through, sediment transport and deformation will begin when

331

$$\frac{\sqrt{gDs}}{V_{ss}} = \frac{1,6}{\dfrac{\sqrt{gDs}.d}{\nu}}$$

and with gradually increasing discharge the transporting capacity, represented by $\sqrt{gDs}$, will increase whilst the value of k will also increase as the bed is deformed. As long as

$$\frac{\sqrt{gDs}}{V_{ss}} > 1,6 \left[\frac{k}{d} . \frac{}{\dfrac{\sqrt{gDs}.d}{\nu}} \right]^{\frac{1}{2}} \quad \ldots\ldots\ldots (7)$$

scouring as well as deformation of the bed should proceed. If change takes place gradually enough for near equilibrium to prevail, then at any time

$$\frac{\sqrt{gDs}}{V_{ss}} \approx 1,6 \left[\frac{k}{d} . \frac{1}{\dfrac{\sqrt{gDs}.d}{\nu}} \right]^{\frac{1}{2}} \quad \ldots\ldots\ldots (8)$$

and when the peak discharge and maximum $\sqrt{gDs}$ values are reached, then both the maximum flow depth and maximum k-value can be established. This can be done by combining Eq. 8 with the continuity and energy equations to provide the three seperate equations that are required to solve for the variables velocity, depth and roughness, given the discharge per unit width.

Calculations of channel width proves to be problematic in terms of the role that vegetation can play. Regime-type relationships at this stage probably provide the best estimates of channel widths (le Grange and Rooseboom 1993).

It is likely that pseudo-viscous boundary layers of high sediment concentration would play a role in limiting the power being applied along the bed, as in the case of true laminar boundary layers, especially when transition takes place from dune to antidune bed forms (Rooseboom 1974; 1992). Such conditions could be represented mathematically by high k-values.

After the peak discharge and associated maximum degree of deformation of the bed has been reached, the size of the bed undulations will no longer be in equilibrium with the rate of energy dissipation along the bed, as represented by the applied stream power. As the discharge decreases, smaller and smaller undulations will be formed until the bed becomes even again and the sediment transporting capacity eventually drops below the lower critical value.

Acknowledgments

The authors wish to acknowledge the financial support recieved from the Water Research Commission for the work undertaken by Mr le Grange.

A very special word of recognition is due to Messrs Z P Kovács, D van Bladeren, D B du Plessis and their colleagues at the South African Department of Water Affairs and Forestry. Their stirling efforts in documenting extreme flood events are proving to be of great value to those working in this field.

References

GRAF, WH (1971) *Hydraulics of Sediment Transport.* McGraw Hill.

GRASS, AJ (1970) The initial instability of fine sand. *Proc ASCE J Hydr Div.* Vol 96, No HY3.

HJüLSTROM, F (1935) The morphological activity of rivers as illustrated by River Fyris. *Bull. Geol. Inst.* Uppsala. Vol 25.

KOVáCS, ZP, DU PLESSIS, DB, BRACHER, PR, DUNN, P and MALLORY, GCL (1985) Documentation of the 1984 Demoina Floods. Technical Report No 122, Department of Water Affairs, South Africa.

LE GRANGE, A, ROOSEBOOM, A, (1993) The development of a model to simulate channel deformation in alluvial rivers. Water Research Commission Report, Pretoria, South Africa.

LIU, HK (1957) Mechanics of sediment ripple formation. *J. Hydraul. Div. Am. Soc. Div. Engrs.* No HY2, 1957.

ROOSEBOOM, A (1974) Open channel fluid mechanics. Technical Report No 62, Dept of Water Affairs, Pretoria, South Africa.

ROOSEBOOM, A (1992) Sediment Transport in Rivers and Reservoirs. A southern African Perspective. Water Research Commission, Pretoria, South Africa. Rep. no. 297/2.

ROOSEBOOM, A, LE GRANGE, A, Equilibrium scour in rivers with sandbeds (1992). Water SA, Vol 18, No 4. October 1992.

SHIELDS, A (1936) Anwendung der Aehnlichkeits-mechanik und der Turbulenzforschung auf die Geschiebebewegung. *Mitt. der Preuss. Versuchsanst. für Wasserbau und Schiffsbau.* Berlin.

VAN BLADEREN, D and BURGER, CD (1989) Documentation of the September 1987 Natal floods.

Technical Report No 139, Department of Water Affairs, South Africa.

YALIN, MS (1988) Dimensional approach to the formulation of regime channels. Proc. of the International Conference on Fluvial Hydraulics. Budapest.

YANG, CT (1973) Incipient motion and sediment transport. *Proc. Am. Soc. Civil Engrs.* Vol 99, No HY10, October 1973.

Chapter Seven

Computational Modelling— Methods

2nd International Conference on
RIVER FLOOD HYDRAULICS
22–25 March 1994: York, England

NUMERICAL SIMULATION OF RAPIDLY VARYING FLOWS
IN NONPRISMATIC CHANNELS

Wei ZHANG[*] and Bernhard H. SCHMID
Institut für Hydraulik, Gewässerkunde und Wasserwirtschaft
Technische Universität Wien, A-1040 Vienna, Austria

Abstract
A numerical model of one-dimensional, rapidly varying flows in nonprismatic channels is presented. The approach is based on the explicit, shock-capturing, two-step MacCormack scheme, applied to the equations of mass and momentum conservation. Net pressure forces due to the variation in width are specially accounted for. A description of the model properties is given. The method was used to simulate the outcome from laboratory and field experiments, respectively. Recorded and computed hydrographs matched well.

1. Introduction
In hydraulic engineering rapidly varying open channel flows may be encountered in a variety of situations of practical interest. Hydropower development of river reaches, for instance, entails the possibility that, intentionally or not, surges may develop and subsequently propagate along the channel, and so may hydraulic jumps. In order to keep the associated impacts within tolerable limits, the properties of these flows have to be computed beforehand. Another field, in which such flows may play an important role, is that of dambreak-induced waves. It is obvious that emergency plans must rely heavily on the results of modelling studies, either mathematical or experimental.

In the absence of analytical solutions for most cases of practical interest, numerical tools have to be developed to deal with this class of hydraulic engineering problem. If the case of interest is characterized by one space dimension, the analysis can be based on a suitably chosen form of the de St. Venant equations, this in spite of the fact that rapidly varying free surface flows may be associated with distinct local deviations from hydrostatic pressure distribution

[*] On leave from: Nanjing Hydraulic Research Institute, Nanjing, China

2nd International Conference on River Flood Hydraulics. Edited by W. R. White and J. Watts
© 1994 HR Wallingford Ltd. Published by John Wiley & Sons Ltd

(Basco, 1989; Gharangik and Chaudhry, 1991).

Unlike most other problems in computational river hydraulics rapidly varying flows are often characterized by the appearance of discontinuities, which
call for specially adapted numerical solution techniques. An adequate scheme
must, therefore, be able to handle shocks, and fairly small time steps will be
required for reasons of accuracy, regardless of stability considerations. In contrast to gradually varied flows, these arguments make explicit finite difference
schemes competitive here.

The modelling effort described below is based on a shock-capturing, explicit predictor-corrector technique, the MacCormack scheme. As flows in nonprismatic channels were felt to be of major practical importance, the ability of the
model to handle such cases was given particular attention.

2. Basic equations

Considering that discontinuities may appear, the basic equations must represent the conservation of mass and momentum, whereas energy will be dissipated. In differential form the governing relations are (Cunge et al., 1980):

$$\frac{\partial A}{\partial t} + \frac{\partial Q}{\partial x} = 0 \tag{1}$$

and

$$\frac{\partial Q}{\partial t} + \frac{\partial}{\partial x}\left(\frac{Q^2}{A} + gI_1\right) = gI_2 + gA(S_0 - S_f) \tag{2}$$

with

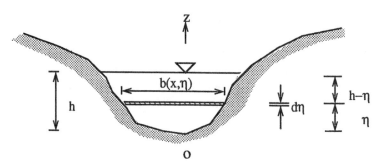

Fig.1: Definition sketch

$$I_1 = \int_0^{h(x,t)} [h(x,t)-\eta] b(x,\eta) d\eta \qquad (3)$$

and

$$I_2 = \int_0^{h(x,t)} [h(x,t)-\eta][\partial b(x,\eta)/\partial x] \Big|_{h=const.} d\eta \qquad (4).$$

S_o denotes bed slope, S_f friction slope, A wetted cross-sectional area, Q discharge, g gravitational acceleration, x space- and t time coordinates, respectively. Definitions of geometry-related parameters can be seen from Fig.1. The integral term I_2 is zero for flows in prismatic channels. It reflects the pressure force exerted on the control volume due to the variation in width.

Using vector notation equations (1) and (2) may be expressed as:

$$\frac{\partial F}{\partial t} + \frac{\partial G(F)}{\partial x} = S(F) \qquad (5)$$

with

$$F = (A, Q)^T, \quad G(F) = (Q, Q^2/A+gI_1)^T \qquad (6a)$$

and

$$S(F) = [0, gI_2+gA(S_o-S_f)]^T. \qquad (6b)$$

Equation (5) is written in conservation law form, which allows both continuous and weak solutions to be determined. Equation (2) being a statement of momentum conservation, the weak solutions obtained will be physically meaningful.

3. Explicit finite difference model
As mentioned above, a version of MacCormack's two-step explicit difference

339

scheme was employed to obtain numerical solutions to equation (5) or equations (1) and (2), respectively.

The predictor step yields:

$$A_j^* = A_j^k - \Delta t (Q_{j+1}^k - Q_j^k)/\Delta x \tag{7}$$

$$Q_j^* = Q_j^k - \Delta t [(Q^2/A + gI_1)_{j+1}^k - (Q^2/A + gI_1)_j^k]/\Delta x$$
$$+ g\Delta t [I_2 + A(S_0 - S_f)]_j^k \tag{8}$$

and the corrector step:

$$A_j^{**} = A_j^* - \Delta t (Q_j^* - Q_{j-1}^*)/\Delta x \tag{9}$$

$$Q_j^{**} = Q_j^* - \Delta t [(Q^2/A + gI_1)_j^* - (Q^2/A + gI_1)_{j-1}^*]/\Delta x$$
$$+ g\Delta t [I_2 + A(S_0 - S_f)]_j^* \tag{10}$$

The "new" values of A and Q are finally computed from:

$$A_j^{k+1} = (A_j^k + A_j^{**})/2 \tag{11}$$

$$Q_j^{k+1} = (Q_j^k + Q_j^{**})/2. \tag{12}$$

The order in which backward and forward differences are used may be exchanged. Analogous expressions can be written for the case of variable grid spacing ($\Delta x_- \neq \Delta x_+$).

The above equations were applied to points within the computational domain ("inner" points), whereas boundary conditions were treated by means of characteristics. This aspect of the MacCormack scheme is not described here, as it was discussed in detail previously elsewhere (Garcia-Navarro and Saviron, 1992).

Discretization as given by equations (7) to (10) is straightforward, with the exception of the term I_2. This term cannot be computed separately for each cross-section, like I_1, as it contains a spatial derivative (see equation (4)).

$\partial b(x,\eta)/\partial x$ may be approximated using central differences, but this is favourable only for inner points. Instead, the following procedure was chosen:

$$(I_2)_j^k = \int_0^{h_j^k} (h_j^k-\eta)\{[b_{j+1}(\eta)-b_j(\eta)]/(\Delta x)+O(\Delta x)\}\,d\eta \qquad (13)$$

(predictor step), which is equivalent to:

$$(I_2)_j^k = \int_0^{h_j^k} (h_j^k-\eta)b_{j+1}(\eta)/(\Delta x)\,d\eta - \int_0^{h_j^k} (h_j^k-\eta)b_j(\eta)/(\Delta x)\,d\eta+O(\Delta x). \qquad (14)$$

Comparison of the terms of equation (14) with the definition of I_1, equation (3), finally permits $(I_2)_j^k$ to be written as:

$$(I_2)_j^k = [(I_1)_{j+1}(h_j^k)-(I_1)_j(h_j^k)]/\Delta x+O(\Delta x) \qquad (15)$$

In this context it shall be noted that the space index of the depth-dependent width b, and therefore also that of I_1, may differ from the index attached to depth h, the limit of integration.

For the corrector step analogous reasoning yields:

$$(I_2)_j^* = [(I_1)_j(h_j^*)-(I_1)_{j-1}(h_j^*)]/\Delta x+O(\Delta x) \qquad (16)$$

While each single step (equations (15) and (16), respectively) is first-order accurate, it can be shown (Zhang, 1992) that, taken together, the two expressions yield a second order approximation, provided the grid spacing considered is constant.

4. Model properties

The difference scheme described above was analysed with respect to consistency, stability and convergence. A somewhat lengthy derivation including the integral term I_2 proved the scheme to be of order 2 for constant grid interval and of order 1 else (Zhang, 1992; Zhang and Schmid, 1993).

For Δx = const. von Neumann's method gave the condition of stability as

$$|Cr| = |c\Delta t/\Delta x| \le 1.0 \qquad (17)$$

which is a Courant-Friedrichs-Lewy (CFL) condition as mentioned by Garcia-Navarro and Saviron (1992). Cases with variable grid spacing were studied by means of an error-tracking technique and the modified condition

$$|Cr| = |\Delta t(c/\Delta x)_{max}| \le 1.0 \qquad (18)$$

was shown to be adequate.

Convergence was assumed to follow from Lax's equivalence theorem, although the authors are aware that this theorem is strictly valid only for linear systems (Richtmyer and Morton, 1967). Deviations may, therefore, arise from certain nonlinearities inherent in the equations treated, and, more importantly, in the vicinity of shocks (Abbott, 1979; Schmid, 1990). There, stable parasitic oscillations may appear, which are undesirable, though of limited extent. Test runs using equidistant grids were performed to study the parameters influencing these oscillations. First, the rule that the direction of differences (forward or backward) used in the predictor step should coincide with the direction of shock propagation (see e.g. Garcia-Navarro and Saviron, 1992) was confirmed. Secondly, the oscillations strongly depend on the value of the Courant number immediately "behind" the discontinuity. $|Cr| = 1.0$ yielded the best results. This can give rise to problems if variable grid spacing is employed. In such cases the global maximum of $Cr \approx 1.0$ may not be reached at the location of the shock, but somewhere else with Δx sufficiently small. $|Cr|$ distinctly below 1.0 in the vicinity of the shock then leads to more pronounced oscillation than would be encountered with Δx = const. Therefore, besides the usual discretization error argument, there is one more reason to keep variations in grid spacing as small as possible.

5. Model validation

This section presents a comparison of modelling results with data obtained from laboratory experiments (Bellos et al., 1991). The experimental setup is shown in Fig.2.

The channel considered is nonprismatic, with rectangular cross-sections and a roughness given by Manning's $n = 0.012$ s/m$^{1/3}$ (smooth surface). The impounded water-depth h_s of interest here is 0.30 m. A constant grid interval was chosen to be $\Delta x = 0.25$ m, the time step was adjusted so that max $|Cr| = 1.0$. Downstream of the dam a small fictitious water-depth of 0.5 mm was assumed.

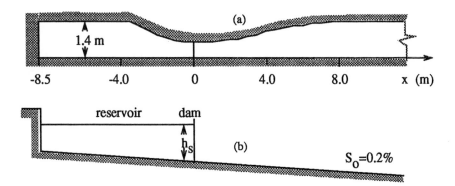

Fig.2: Experimental setup, (a) plan view; (b) longitudinal section

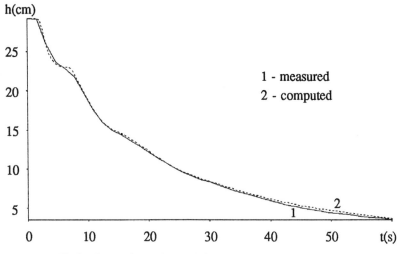

Fig.3   Comparison of recorded and computed water-levels
versus time, upstream of dam site, x = -4.0 m

Fig.3 shows measured and computed water-levels upstream of the dam side, plotted against time after dam failure. As can be seen, the agreement is excellent.

Fig.4 displays the corresponding curves for a location downstream of the dam. Again, simulated and measured values of water-level elevation agree well.

The recorded recession limb is, however, characterized by a number of small

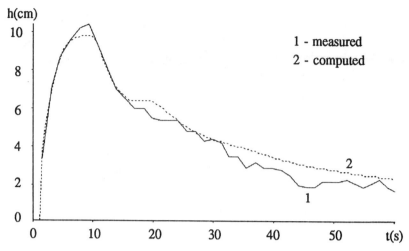

Fig.4: Comparison of recorded and computed water-levels
versus time, tailwater, x=2.5 m

"bumps", which, according to Bellos et al. (1991), are due to twodimensional effects. Consequently, this feature was not reproduced by the onedimensional model discussed here.

6. Field experiment

In the course of alteration works to the power canal of the Austrian Rosegg/St. Jakob hydropower plant a 1:1 surge wave experiment was carried out by Österreichsche Draukraftwerke A.G. (Baumhackl, 1991). A layout of the situation is shown in Fig. 5.

The power canal measures some 3.5 km in length. Canal cross-sections vary, but are generally trapezoidal in shape. Manning's n was given as $0.015 \text{ s/m}^{1/3}$ (Baumhackl, 1991), which reflects a very smooth surface, mainly consisting of asphalt cover.

As the object of the field investigation was to carry out a worst-case surge wave study, discharge at the power station Rosegg was increased from original-ly 150 m^3/s to 425 m^3/s prior to the experiment. The establishment of pseudo steady-state conditions was followed by a rapid shut-down (zero discharge within 6 seconds). The ensuing surge wave was monitored at several sites dis-tributed along the canal. The location of gauging site M_6 is shown in Fig.5.

The wave generated by the shut-down moved in upstream direction until it reached the upper end of the power canal, where it was partly reflected. After that, a negative surge travelled down. Recorded and computed hydrographs for

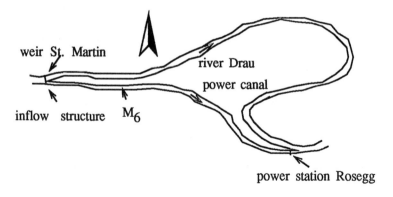

Fig.5: Layout plan

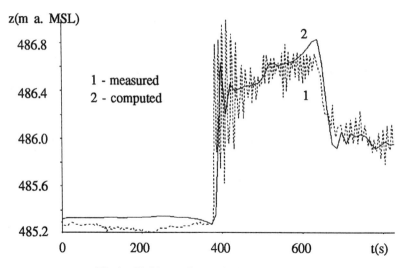

Fig.6:   Field experiment: hydrographs at site M_6

site M_6 are displayed in Fig.6.

   As can be seen from the above plot (and others not shown here for brevity of presentation) the model fairly accurately simulates both the hydrograph features and the arrival times of the surge. Expectedly, the observed disintegration of the wave into several wavelets and the wave run-up on inclined embankments are not reproduced. With regard to the latter problem, however, it may be added the modelling results may be used to subsequently obtain order-of-magnitude estimates of wave run-up in accordance with the guidelines given by Benet and Cunge (1971). In the course of the case study reported here, this procedure proved successful.

7. Summary and Conclusion

The model presented is based on the explicit, two-step MacCormack scheme, which has been adapted for application to one-dimensional, rapidly varying flows in nonprismatic channels. Since the basic equations are adequate forms of the conservation laws of mass and momentum, discontinuous, "weak" solutions computed are also physically meaningful. Results obtained from validation runs show good agreement with measurements and demonstrate the adequacy of the approach. The paper ends with a brief description of a case study, the simulation of a field-scale surge wave experiment in an Austrian power canal.

References

Abbott, M. B.: Computational hydraulics; Elements of the theory of free surface flow. Pitman Publishing Ltd., London, England, 1979.

Basco, D. R .: Limitations of de Saint Venant equations in dam-break analysis. Journal of Hydraulic Engineering, ASCE, Vol. 115, No. 7, pp. 950-965, 1989.

Baumhackl, G.: Schwallversuch am Oberwasserkanal des KW - Rosegg / St. Jakob. Report, Österreichische Draukraftwerke A.G., Klagenfurt, Austria, 1991 (in German).

Bellos, C. V., J. V. Soulis and J. G. Sakkas: Computation of two-dimensional dam-break induced flows. Advances in Water Resources, vol. 14, no. 1, pp. 31-41, 1991.

Benet, F. und J. A. Cunge: Analyse d'expériences sur les ondulations secondaires dues aux intumescences dans les canaux trapézoidaux. Journal of Hydraulic Research, vol. 9, no. 1, pp. 11-34, 1971.

Cunge, J. A., F. M. Holly and A. Verwey: Practical aspects of computational river hydraulics. Pitman Publishing Ltd., London, England, 1980.

Garcia-Navarro, P. and J. M. Saviron: McCormack's method for the numerical simulation of one-dimensional discontinuous unsteady open channel flow. Journal of Hydraulic Research, vol. 30, no. 1, pp. 95-105, 1992.

Gharangik, A. M. and M. H. Chaudhry: Numerical simulation of hydraulic jump. Journal of Hydraulic Engineering, ASCE, vol.117, no. 9, pp. 1195-1211, 1991.

Richtmyer, R. D. and K. W. Morton: Difference methods for initial value problems. Interscience Publishers, New York, 2nd ed., 1967.

Schmid, B. H.: A study on kinematic cascades. Wiener Mitteilungen Wasser-Abwasser-Gewässer, vol. 90, Vienna, Austria, 1990.

Zhang, W.: Zur hydraulisch-numerischen Modellierung eindimensionaler, stark veränderlicher Gerinneströmungen. Doctoral thesis, Technische Universität Wien, Vienna, Austria, 1992 (in German).

Zhang, W. and B. H. Schmid: Ein Verfahren zur Berechnung diskontinuierlicher Strömungen in natürlichen Gerinnen. Österreichische Ingenieur- und Architekten-Zeitschrift, 138. Jahrgang, Heft 3, pp. 96-100, 1993 (in German).

2nd International Conference on
RIVER FLOOD HYDRAULICS
22–25 March 1994: York, England

ENERGY CONSERVATION IN OPEN CHANNEL FLOW

CAROLINE P SKEELS
Lecturer, University of the West of England,
Department of Mathematical Sciences,
Frenchay Campus, Coldharbour Lane, Bristol BS16 1QY, U.K.

ABSTRACT

One dimensional open channel flow may be simulated using various finite difference schemes to approximate the St. Venant equations. All hydraulic models should conserve energy in the special case of steady, frictionless flow. Discretisations which conserve energy in the steady, frictionless case should be implemented in general modelling problems with the exception of modelling hydraulic jumps. This paper examines the variation in calculated energy for some standard St. Venant equation discretisations of the Abbott–Ionescu and Preissmann implicit finite difference schemes.

For each space–centred discretisation of the momentum flux term, if the momentum coefficient is set to one then it is possible to conserve energy using a specific discretisation of average area. Numerical models comparing one of these new discretisations with a standard discretisation demonstrate the validity of the theory.

No consistent method of space–weighting allows computational conservation of energy. This implies that schemes should be centred in space.

HYDRODYNAMIC EQUATIONS

Application of Newton's principles to the motion of one dimensional unsteady flow leads to the coupled partial differential equations formulated by St. Venant (de St. Venant, 1871). Thus the St. Venant equations are frequently taken to represent bulk flow in natural and artificial channels. In the simple model used in this analysis no distinction is made between the storage and the computational width (Abbott and Ionescu, 1967), the velocity is assumed to be constant across a section, water density is assumed constant, and the free surface wind stress and the lateral inflow are omitted. The non–conservative momentum equation considered in this paper assumes the water surface and the bed level are continuous functions of x and that $\partial h/\partial x$ is independent of y. Under these assumptions, the mass and momentum equations for unsteady one dimensional flow in natural channels of arbitrary shape may be written

$$\frac{\partial A}{\partial t} + \frac{\partial Q}{\partial x} = 0 \tag{1}$$

and

$$\frac{\partial Q}{\partial t} + \frac{\partial}{\partial x}\left(\frac{\beta Q^2}{A}\right) + gA\left(\frac{\partial h}{\partial x} + s_f\right) = 0 \,. \tag{2}$$

where x, y and z are cartesian coordinates which have directions horizontal towards the flow, horizontal perpendicular to flow and vertical respectively, t is time, A is the wetted cross–sectional area, Q is the discharge, g is the acceleration due to gravity, β is the momentum coefficient, s_f is the friction slope and h is the water surface level above datum (stage). $\partial(Q^2/A)/\partial x$ represents net momentum flux due to the channel flow and $gA\partial h/\partial x$ represents the momentum due to the surface slope.

ENERGY CONSERVATION

In an idealised world of a channel with a fixed bed and no friction, energy remains constant along the channel if the upstream and downstream variables of the flow remain steady, that is constant in time. For frictionless flow, the steady St. Venant equations may be written

$$\frac{dQ}{dx} = 0 \tag{3}$$

and

$$\frac{d}{dx}\left(\frac{\beta Q^2}{A}\right) + gA\frac{dh}{dx} = 0 \,. \tag{4}$$

Considering Q^2/A as QU, where U is the mean average velocity, differentiating by the product rule, substituting equation (3) into equation (4), and dividing through by A gives

$$U^2\frac{d\beta}{dx} + \beta U\frac{dU}{dx} + g\frac{dh}{dx} = 0 \,. \tag{5}$$

Note that the momentum coefficient is defined as

$$\beta(x,t) = \frac{A(x,t)}{Q^2(x,t)}\left(\int_{L_b(x,t)}^{R_b(x,t)} \int_{h_b(x,y)}^{h(x,y,t)} u^2(x,y,z,t)dzdy\right),$$

$$= \frac{\overline{u^2}}{U^2},$$

where u is the fluid velocity in the positive x–direction, L_b and R_b are the left and right banks respectively, h_b is the bed level and barred variables are averaged over the cross–sectional area A (note that $U = \bar{u}$). In reality the momentum coefficient is never exactly one due to internal friction effects due to boundary conditions. Setting friction to zero requires that the momentum coefficient is one. Subsequently integrating equation (5) with respect to x gives

$$\frac{U^2}{2} + gh = E \,, \tag{6}$$

where E represents constant energy. The energy equation (6) is used by Arakawa (1966) and Morton (1970) among others to motivate the development of special differencing of the non–linear terms. Since equations (3) and (4) necessarily imply equation (6), steady, frictionless flow conserves energy. Numerical models of equations (3) and (4) should be chosen to conserve energy. These energy conserving discretisations should be implemented in the corresponding terms of numerical models of equations (1) and (2) and their integral form. This analysis is only appropriate to the non–conservative form of the momentum equation, which is not considered as accurate as the conservative form in modelling transitional flow (Whitlow and Knight, 1992).

THE NUMERICAL SCHEMES

The Abbott–Ionescu (1967) and Preissmann (1961) schemes are implicit and currently are used to model unsteady flow in open channels (MIKE11 scientific documentation, 1988; ONDA user manual, 1992; SALMON-F user manual, 1992).

The Abbott–Ionescu scheme is a six point, space staggered scheme. It centres the continuity equation in space at j where stage is calculated, while it centres the dynamic equation at $(j - \frac{1}{2})$ where discharge is calculated. First order time and space derivatives, time and space integrals and average function values of a general variable p may be implicitly approximated in a space and time weighted version of the Abbott–Ionescu scheme as follows:

$$\frac{\partial p}{\partial t} \simeq \frac{1}{\Delta t}[P_k^{n+1} - P_k^n] \,,$$

$$\frac{\partial p}{\partial x} \simeq \frac{1}{\Delta x}[\theta(P_{k+\frac{1}{2}}^{n+1} - P_{k-\frac{1}{2}}^{n+1}) + (1 - \theta)(P_{k+\frac{1}{2}}^n - P_{k-\frac{1}{2}}^n)] \,,$$

$$\int_{n\Delta t}^{(n+1)\Delta t} p|_{x_k} dt \simeq \Delta t[\theta P_k^{n+1} + (1 - \theta)P_k^n] \,,$$

$$\int_{(k-\frac{1}{2})\Delta x}^{(k+\frac{1}{2})\Delta x} p|_{t^n} dx \simeq \Delta x P_k^n \,,$$

$$\bar{p} \simeq [\theta P_k^{n+1} + (1 - \theta)P_k^n] \,,$$

where $P_k^n \simeq p(k\Delta x, n\Delta t)$, θ is the time–weighting coefficient and in the continuity equation $k = j$, while in the dynamic equation $k = j - \frac{1}{2}$. When the variable is not available at k, a space–weighted arithmetic average may be taken using variables at $k - \frac{1}{2}$ and $k + \frac{1}{2}$.

The Preissmann scheme uses values of stage and discharge at four corners of a computational box in the (x, t) plane. First order time and space derivatives, time and space integrals and average function values of a general variable p may be implicitly approximated in the Preissmann scheme as follows:

$$\frac{\partial p}{\partial t} \simeq \frac{1}{\Delta t}[\phi(P_{j+1}^{n+1} - P_{j+1}^{n}) + (1 - \phi)(P_{j}^{n+1} - P_{j}^{n})] ,$$

$$\frac{\partial p}{\partial x} \simeq \frac{1}{\Delta x}[\theta(P_{j+1}^{n+1} - P_{j}^{n+1}) + (1 - \theta)(P_{j+1}^{n} - P_{j}^{n})] ,$$

$$\int_{n\Delta t}^{(n+1)\Delta t} p|_{x_j} dt \simeq \Delta t[\theta P_{j}^{n+1} + (1 - \theta)P_{j}^{n}] ,$$

$$\int_{j\Delta x}^{(j+1)\Delta x} p|_{t^n} dx \simeq \Delta x[\phi P_{j+1}^{n} - (1 - \phi)P_{j}^{n}] ,$$

$$\bar{p} \simeq \theta[\phi P_{j+1}^{n+1} + (1 - \phi)P_{j}^{n+1}] + (1 - \theta)[\phi P_{j+1}^{n} + (1 - \phi)P_{j}^{n}] .$$

Note that this paper only analyses steady equations. The time dependent variables are only included for completeness.

ENERGY CONSERVING DISCRETISATIONS

From equation (6), energy is conserved from one grid position to the next if and only if

$$gh_{j+1} - gh_j + \frac{(U_{j+1}^2 - U_j^2)}{2} = 0 . \tag{7}$$

More appropriately for the Abbott–Ionescu scheme, equation (7) is equivalent to

$$gh_{j+1} - gh_j + \frac{1}{2}\left(\frac{Q^2}{A_{j+1}^2} - \frac{Q^2}{A_j^2}\right) = 0 , \tag{8}$$

since, from equation (3), discharge is uniform.

Conservative Form of the Momentum Flux Term

By algebraic manipulation and using the fact that $Q = Q_{j+1} = Q_j$, space-centred Abbott–Ionescu and Preissmann discretisations of equations (3) and (4) may be rewritten in the form

$$gh_{j+1} - gh_j + \frac{\mathcal{F}(A_{j+1}, A_j)}{2}\left(\frac{Q^2}{A_{j+1}^2} - \frac{Q^2}{A_j^2}\right) = 0 , \tag{9}$$

where $\mathcal{F}(A_{j+1}, A_j)$, the energy factor, is some function of the variables A_{j+1} and A_j: $\mathcal{F}(A_{j+1}, A_j) = 1$ for conservation of energy. One standard Abbott–Ionescu and Preissmann space–centred discretisation of equations (3) and (4) is

$$\left(\frac{Q^2}{A_{j+1}} - \frac{Q^2}{A_j}\right) + \frac{g}{2}(A_{j+1} + A_j)(h_{j+1} - h_j) = 0 , \tag{10}$$

where Q is the constant discharge. Equation (10) may be rearranged into equation (9) when

$$\mathcal{F}(A_{j+1}, A_j) = \frac{4A_{j+1}A_j}{(A_{j+1} + A_j)^2} \ .$$

(11)

Equation (11) (and also (19)) is given for the Preissmann scheme by Samuels (1985). This energy factor is equivalent to one if neighbouring cross–sectional areas are equivalent or if, instead of discretising the average cross–sectional area term in equation (4) as $A \simeq (A_{j+1} + A_j)/2$, the area discretisation is

$$
\begin{aligned}
A & \simeq \frac{1}{2}(A_{j+1} + A_j)\mathcal{F}(A_{j+1}, A_j) \\
& = \frac{2A_{j+1}A_j}{(A_{j+1} + A_j)} \ .
\end{aligned}
$$

(12)

Thus, in place of equation (10), an energy conserving discretisation is

$$\left(\frac{Q^2}{A_{j+1}} - \frac{Q^2}{A_j} \right) + \frac{2gA_{j+1}A_j}{(A_{j+1} + A_j)}(h_{j+1} - h_j) = 0 \ .$$

(13)

The translation of these discretisations to the unsteady form is straight-forward for the Preissmann scheme. The Abbott–Ionescu scheme requires interpolation of the discharge term or the use of a differentiated momentum flux term.

Differentiated Form of the Momentum Flux Term

In many engineering applications (Preissmann, 1961), equation (4) has been written in a differentiated form

$$\frac{2Q}{A}\frac{dQ}{dx} - \frac{Q^2}{A^2}\frac{dA}{dx} + gA\frac{dh}{dx} = 0 \ ,$$

(14)

where the first term is zero from equation (3). Two discretisations of the term Q^2/A^2 are studied here, the first previously studied by Cunge, Holly and Verwey (1980, pp. 102–103). With the discretisation

$$\frac{Q^2}{A^2} \simeq \frac{1}{4}\left[\left(\frac{Q}{A} \right)_{j+1} + \left(\frac{Q}{A} \right)_j \right]^2 \ ,$$

(15)

the standard discretisation for equation (14) is

$$-\frac{1}{4}\left[\left(\frac{Q}{A_{j+1}} \right) + \left(\frac{Q}{A_j} \right) \right]^2 \frac{(A_{j+1} - A_j)}{\Delta x} + \frac{g(A_{j+1} + A_j)(h_{j+1} - h_j)}{2\Delta x} = 0 \ .$$

(16)

This may be rearranged into the form of equation (9), where $\mathcal{F}(A_{j+1}, A_j) = 1$. Thus equation (16) conserves energy.

The second discretisation is not quite as straightforward. Substituting the discretisation

$$\frac{Q^2}{A^2} \simeq \frac{1}{2}\left[\left(\frac{Q^2}{A^2_{j+1}} \right) + \left(\frac{Q^2}{A^2_j} \right) \right]$$

(17)

351

for discretisation (17), in equation (14), gives

$$-\frac{1}{2}\left[\left(\frac{Q^2}{A_{j+1}^2}\right)+\left(\frac{Q^2}{A_j^2}\right)\right]\frac{(A_{j+1}-A_j)}{\Delta x}+\frac{g(A_{j+1}+A_j)(h_{j+1}-h_j)}{2\Delta x}=0\,. \quad (18)$$

This may be rearranged into the form of equation (9), where in this case

$$\mathcal{F}(A_{j+1},A_j)=2\frac{(A_{j+1}^2+A_j^2)}{(A_{j+1}+A_j)^2}\,. \quad (19)$$

Although it appears from this analysis that the first discretisation of Q^2/A^2 is the more accurate for energy, the constancy of energy could be recovered by modifying the average for the area. Instead of using $A \simeq (A_{j+1}+A_j)/2$, the area discretisation

$$\begin{aligned} A &\simeq \frac{1}{2}(A_{j+1}+A_j)\mathcal{F}(A_{j+1},A_j) \\ &= \frac{(A_{j+1}^2+A_j^2)}{(A_{j+1}+A_j)}\,, \end{aligned} \quad (20)$$

maintains constant energy.

So either discretisation of the diffentiated momentum flux term Q^2/A^2 can be used as long as there is the corresponding discretisation of the averaged area term A.

COMPUTATIONAL MODEL OF ENERGY

The computational example taken considers the steady, frictionless St. Venant equations, with the conservative form of momentum flux given by equations (3) and (4). The standard space–centred discretisation (10) and an energy conserving discretisation (13) are both coded into a computer. The channel has a rectangular cross–section with the breadths changing at every node, bar the last, between the values of 2 and 20 metres. The space step is 500 metres. The input discharge is constant at $8\ m^3/s$. The graphical output of the energy at each node is illustrated by figure 1.

It can be seen that, even for such a low discharge, the numerical error in modelling energy using standard discretisations is approximately seven percent.

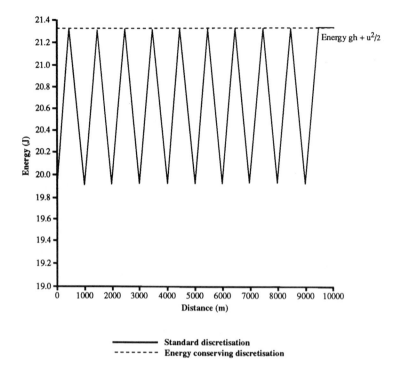

Figure 1: Numerical Approximations of Energy

SPACE-WEIGHTING

Conservative Form of the Momentum Flux Term

One standard Abbott–Ionescu and Preissmann space–weighted discretisation
of equations (3) and (4) is

$$\left(\frac{Q^2}{A_{j+1}} - \frac{Q^2}{A_j} \right) + g(\phi A_{j+1} + (1 - \phi)A_j)(h_{j+1} - h_j) = 0 , \qquad (21)$$

where Q is the constant discharge. Equation (21) may be rearranged into
equation (9) if

$$\mathcal{F}(A_{j+1}, A_j) = \frac{2A_{j+1}A_j}{(A_{j+1} + A_j)(\phi A_{j+1} + (1 - \phi)A_j)} . \qquad (22)$$

Equation (21) conserves energy if the cross–sectional areas are the same or
if the area discretisation is

$$\begin{aligned}
A &\simeq (\phi A_{j+1} + (1 - \phi)A_j)\mathcal{F}(A_{j+1}, A_j) \\
&= \frac{2A_{j+1}A_j}{(A_{j+1} + A_j)} ,
\end{aligned}$$

which is equation (12). Thus energy is not conserved if the average term is weighted.

Differentiated Form of the Momentum Flux Term

The standard discretisation of equation (14) with the discretisation

$$\frac{Q^2}{A^2} \simeq \left[\phi \left(\frac{Q}{A} \right)_{j+1} + (1 - \phi) \left(\frac{Q}{A} \right)_j \right]^2 , \tag{23}$$

can conserve energy if the average area discretisation is replaced by

$$A \simeq \frac{2(\phi A_j + (1 - \phi)A_{j+1})^2}{(A_{j+1} + A_j)} . \tag{24}$$

The average space–weighting for discharge and area are incompatible: discharge is weighted the opposite way to area.

The discretisation

$$\frac{Q^2}{A^2} \simeq \left[\phi \left(\frac{Q^2}{A_{j+1}^2} \right) + (1 - \phi) \left(\frac{Q^2}{A_j^2} \right) \right] \tag{25}$$

can be used to conserve energy in equation (14) if the average area

$$A \simeq \frac{2(\phi A_j^2 + (1 - \phi)A_{j+1}^2)}{(A_{j+1} + A_j)} . \tag{26}$$

Again the average space–weightings for discharge and area are incompatible.

It should be noted that a fully space centred scheme has been known to lead to oscillating solutions. This problem may be resolved by choosing a space weighting parameter slightly above 0.5, but this does lose complete energy conservation.

CONCLUSIONS

When modelling one dimensional hydraulics using the standard St. Venant equations, energy conservation

1. may be verified in a model by setting (i) no variation in time, (ii) the friction slope to zero and (iii) the momentum coefficient to one.

2. requires the Abbott–Ionescu and Preissmann schemes centred in space.

3. is possible for every space–centred Abbott–Ionescu and Preissmann discretisation if average area is appropriately discretised.

4. is straightforward to implement by adapting the standard discretisations and does not affect the solution procedure.

REFERENCES

1. ABBOTT, M.B. AND IONESCU, F., 1967. On the numerical computation of nearly horizontal flows. *J. Hyd. Res.*, **5**, pp. 97–117.

2. ARAKAWA, A., 1966. A computational design for the long term integration of the equations of atmospheric motion. *Journal Computational Physics, 1*, 119.

3. CUNGE, J.A., HOLLY, F.M., AND VERWEY, A., 1980. *Practical aspects of computational river hydraulics*, Pitman Publishing Ltd., London.

4. DE SAINT VENANT, B., 1871. Théorie du mouvement non–permanent des eaux avec application aux crues des rivières et à l'introduction des marées dans leur lit. *Acad. Sci. Comptes rendus*, **73**, pp. 148–154, 237–240.

5. *MIKE 11 scientific documentation*, 1988. Danish Hydraulics Institute, 1988–10–20.

6. MORTON, K.W., 1970. The design of difference schemes for evolutionary problems. *Numerical solution of fluid problems in contiuum physics*, (eds. Birkoff, G., and Varger, R.S.), SIAM-AMS, Proc. 2, pp. 1-10.

7. *ONDA user manual*, 1992. William Halcrow and Partners.

8. PREISSMANN, A., 1961. Propagation des intumescences dans les canaux et rivières. *1st Congrès de l'Assoc. Française de Calcul., Grenoble*, pp. 433–442.

9. RICHTMYER, R.D. AND MORTON, K.W., 1967. *Difference methods for initial value problems,* 2nd edition, Interscience Publishers, New York.

10. *SALMON-F version 1.0 user manual*, 1992. Hydraulics Research Limited, Nov.

11. SAMUELS, P.G., 1985. Modelling open channel flow using Preissmann's scheme. *2nd International Conference on the Hydraulics of Floods and Flood Control*, British Hydraulics Research Association, Sep.

12. WHITLOW, C.D. AND KNIGHT, D.W., 1992. An investigation of the effect of different discretizations in river models and a comparison of non–conservative and conservative formulations of the de St. Venant equations. *Proceedings of the second international conference on hydraulic and environmental modelling of coastal, estuarine and river waters,* (eds. Falconer, R. A., Shiono, K., and Matthew, R. G. S.), Ashgate Publishing Group, Aldershot, England, **2**, part 1 (Flow processes), no. 10, pp. 115–126.

Parameter Uncertainty
in Dam-Break Flood Modelling

Xiao-Liang Yang & Chen-Shan Kung

Royal Institute of Technology (KTH)
Hydraulics Laboratory
S - 10044 STOCKHOLM Sweden

ABSTRACT: One source of uncertainty in dam-break simulation is associated with river-valley hydraulic parameters. This embraces errors in description of cross-sectional geometry from topographical maps and errors in estimation of Manning's roughness coefficient from historical floods. Monte Carlo method is used to examine their effects on dam-break flood routing. In accordance with uniform distribution, techniques are developed to adjust base profile co-ordinates and roughness coefficients within prescribed ranges. The findings show that the resultant uncertainty in both discharge and time to peak stage increases further downstream along the river. The variation in (peak) flood stage depends heavily on the cross-sectional profile and size. A narrower river course results in larger uncertainty. The range of variation in discharge, water depth and time to peak stage resulting from river parameter uncertainty should be examined in detailed dam-break flood simulations and contingency evacuation planning.

1. INTRODUCTION

The consequences of a dam-break flood are often catastrophic in the context of losses of human life and property damage. Accurate dam-break flood modelling is essential for a clearer understanding of their prediction, risk-zone mapping and contingency evacuation planning.

Despite the improvements in the dam-break flood models that have evolved over the last decade, dam-break simulation is still subject to great uncertainty. Several sources of error limit the accuracy of prediction of the time and magnitude of flooding occurrence at any specified location downstream of a breached dam. One source of error results from the uncertainty of river-valley hydraulic parameters. These include errors due to cross-sectional geometry, and errors in estimation of Manning's roughness coefficient. When topographic maps are used to determine stream cross-sections at certain spacings, errors in both vertical and horizontal co-ordinates are present. The great amplitude of dam-break floods makes it impossible to fully calibrate Manning's coefficient based on the previous

2nd International Conference on River Flood Hydraulics. Edited by W. R. White and J. Watts

flood information. Its estimation in dam-break flood simulation also gives rise to uncertainty.

This paper reports the findings of a study aiming at evaluation of the effects of river-valley parameter uncertainty in a hypothetical dam-break event. The dam designated is Tvärön, an earthen dam located at Stornorrfors in the lower reaches of the Umeälven river, Sweden.

2. BACKGROUND & SIMULATION STRATEGY

Data information needed for determining cross-sectional geometry of a river catchment is usually obtained from topographical maps. These maps are generated through aerial photogrammetry methods. Errors to a varying extent are always present in the description of the cross-sectional properties of a natural river course (Fread 1981, Burnham and Davis 1990). The main sources of error regarding cross-section uncertainty are field measurement error; errors inherent in the assumed linear change between contour intervals on topographical maps; and manual errors introduced when distances between contour intervals are measured. The second and third sources of error depend upon the scale of the map used, all these errors occur if topographical maps are employed. Both vertical and horizontal errors in cross-sectional co-ordinates are involved.

Manning equation is usually used in the shallow-water equations to calculate frictional head losses. Manning's roughness coefficient is a comprehensive representation of channel resistance to flow in rivers, and direct measurement is not possible. For precipitation-generated floods, Manning's values are usually estimated by field observation, and calibrated using observed high water marks from historical flood events. However, for a dam-break flood, its much larger magnitude makes it impossible to fully calibrate Manning's coefficient based on any previous flood information. Coefficients derived from historical floods often need to be increased so as to account for additional energy losses associated with dam-break floods. The uncertainty arises regarding to what extent it can be increased. The contributing factors that lead to increased Manning's coefficients were summarised by Fread (1981).

Monte Carlo simulation technique is employed to examine the effect of uncertainty due to cross-sectional geometry and hydraulic roughness on dam-break flood routing. Errors in the river geometry or the roughness are considered spatially un-correlated and randomly distributed. For simplicity, uniform probability distribution is used for all error estimations.

River cross-sections measured from the topographical maps at certain spacings along the river are taken as base profiles. Each profile is defined by a couple of co-ordinate points at map contour intervals. Based on these base profiles, techniques are developed to generate stochastic profile co-ordinates in accordance with prescribed uniform distribution. The uncertainty of a particular cross-sectional profile is defined as the difference between its base profile and the profile formed by the adjusted co-ordinate points. Uncertainty in both vertical and horizontal co-ordinates (i.e. elevation and channel top-width) is considered, however with different error ranges.

The hydraulic roughness of the river is treated in a similar way. Manning's roughness coefficients calibrated from historical extreme floods are increased, and those are taken as mean values. They are adjusted within acceptable ranges based on engineering judgement and other dam-break simulation data. Coefficients at different locations along the river are also spatially un-correlated.

3. DATA & CONDITIONS OF SIMULATION

3.1 Computer program

The BOSS DAMBRK™ program, developed by Fread (1984) at US National Weather Service (NWS) and supported by BOSS Corporation (1988-91), is designated for use in the study.

In the program, a parametric approach is used to describe the breaching process of a dam. For overtopping failure, the breach starts at a point on the dam crest, then enlarging with a given constant side slope until the prescribed terminal bottom elevation and width are reached at the end of the prescribed failure time. The initial water-surface elevation and elevation at the start of the breach in the reservoir are specified by the user. For piping failure, piping centreline elevation should also be specified.

The complete Saint-Venant equations for one-dimensional unsteady open-channel flow, written in conservation form, is used. The numerical algorithm is the weighted, four-point implicit scheme. The resultant non-linear equations at each time step are solved by the Newton-Raphson iterative procedure.

3.2 Dam & river

The Tvärön earthen dam on river Umeälven is assumed to fail due to piping. The crest elevation of the dam is 78 m MSL, and the maximum height is 18 m. Its crest length is 230 m. The reservoir has a regulation storage of 9.72×10^6 m^3 between elevations 73.5 and 75 m MSL, corresponding to an average surface area of 6.48 km^2. The design inflow at the dam is 1800 m^3/s, and the maximum spillway capacity is 3200 m^3/s.

The length of the river from the dam to the river month is 30 km. The longitudinal profile has two different slopes. The first 8 km has an average slope of 5 m/km, while the average slope of the rest 22 km is only 0.27 m/km. A 3-D representation and its plan view of the river produced from the program is plotted in Figure 1. Along the upstream 15 km, the river bank is steep and the valley is narrow, with typical top widths of 600 - 800 m. Thereafter, the river becomes much wider and flatter, a typical type of flood plain. At the river mouth, the river has a maximum top width of about 8,000 m.

3.3 Input data specification

The scale of the topographical maps used is 1.10,000, with 5-meter contour intervals. Cross-sectional properties are specified for 26 locations along the river. A total of 279 cross-sections (user entered plus program interpolated) are used in the calculation. Six top widths are used to describe each cross-section.

Level pool routing is used for the upstream reservoir, while dynamic routing is used for the downstream river valley. The effect of backwater at the dam on breach outflow is taken into account. Lateral inflow from the river bank or outflow into the bank is neglected throughout the river valley. Dynamic loop rating is specified at the downstream extremity. The flow into the reservoir is constant, 1100 m³/s. The initial turbine flow is 1045 m³/s. During the dam break, the spillway does not function, and no overtopping occurs over the dam. Total simulation time is 15 hours.

The piping centreline elevation is set at 70 m MSL. The terminal breach bottom elevation is 61 m MSL, with a terminal base width of 45 m. The breach side slope is vertical. The initial level in the reservoir and the level at the time of breach are the same, 76 m MSL. The breaching process is linear, with formation time of one hour.

3.4 Monte Carlo data generation

Uncertainty of cross-sectional geometry involves errors in both elevation and horizontal distance. According to the mapping industry standard, aerial survey accuracy for topographical maps should satisfy certain criteria. For vertical (elevation) accuracy associated with map contours, the following criterion generally applies: at least 90% of all contours shall be within one-half contour interval of their true positions. Although there are certain exceptions to this criterion, it is used in this study and treated this way: *all contours are within one-half contour interval of their true positions.* For 5-meter interval contours used herein, they will be within a range of 2.5 m. Take elevation 50 m MSL for example, it will be within 48.75 - 51.25 m MSL. Thus, its true elevation will be obtained by successively adjusting it within this range from uniform distribution.

Horizontal errors for cross-sectional co-ordinates are not so significant as vertical ones. *The location of a contour on topographical maps is considered to have a horizontal error dependent on the map scale.* In this study, 0.05-cm map error is designated. For maps of 1:10,000, the location of a contour will have an error of 0.05 x 10,000 = 500 cm = 5m. For example, if the distance of one of the contours of a river cross-sectional profile measured from a reference point is

360

75.5 m, then its true location will be within 75.5 ± 2.5 m = 73 - 78 m. Random values will be generated within this range from uniform distribution.

Based on historical flood information of the river, Manning's roughness coefficient 0.050 is chosen as the base (mean) value. This is adjusted by $\pm 20\%$, thus corresponding to a range of 0.040 - 0.060. The 30-km long river is divided into 25 parts by 26 cross-sections, and roughness values of each part are treated independently. Random values are generated within this prescribed range in accordance with uniform distribution for each of the 25 parts.

To reduce simulation error and obtain statistically reliable results, one hundred replicates are produced for each cross-sectional profile and for roughness coefficient of each part. Parameter sets used in the simulation are formed by random combinations of the generated values of both profile and roughness. For a given parameter set, the simulation process is deterministic. Accordingly, 100 sets of deterministic results are obtained.

4. RESULTS & DISCUSSIONS

Downstream of the dam, three representative locations, 10.07, 16.30 and 24.08 km, are chosen to demonstrate the effects of the uncertainty on discharge and water stage. Peak discharge, peak water stage and time to peak stage along the river are also illustrated.

4.1 Uncertainty in discharge

Discharge hydrographs at these three locations are given in Figure 2. The hydrograph of each location consists of 100 sets of results. The figures show that the range of deviation in discharge at location 16.30 km is larger than that at 10.07 km, and the range at 24.08 km is even larger than that at 16.30 km. Compared with their local deterministic values, the relative ranges of change in peak discharge are $\pm 1.5\%$, $\pm 2\%$ and $\pm 3\%$. The discharge becomes more divergent further downstream along the river. This can also be seen through the peak discharge summary along the river, which is given in Figure 3. The relative change at the downstream end of the river is $\pm 4\%$. This manifests that, due to the uncertainty in geometry and roughness, larger uncertainty can be expected further in the downstream reaches.

4.2 Uncertainty in water depth

Water depth hydrographs and a summary of maximum water depth along the river are provided in Figures 4 and 5. The variations in peak flow depth at the 3 positions, from upstream to downstream, are ± 0.27, ± 0.21 and ± 0.11 m respectively. The range becomes even larger along the first 5 km downstream of the dam, about ± 0.95 m. The change of flood depth along the river is closely related to the geometry and size of the river channel. In the upper reach, as shown in Figure 1, the river course is narrow, with typical top widths of 600-800 m. While in the lower reach, the river becomes wider, with increased width all the way to the downstream. At the mouth, the river channel is 8,000 m wide. Adjustment in the Manning roughness and in the cross-sectional profiles for the upper narrower reaches can result in a larger change in the flow passage, thus giving rise to larger range of variation in flow depth.

Therefore, for a non-uniform river course, larger uncertainty in water stage can be expected at narrower locations. Normally, the lower reach of a river is wider, and the resulting level of uncertainty will be lower.

4.3 Uncertainty in time to peak stage

The time of arrival for peak flood stage at different locations along the river is shown in Figure 6. Time is accounted from the start of the dam break. It takes about 7.3 hours for the peak stage to travel from the dam to the downstream end of the river.

At locations 10.07 and 16.30 km, the ranges of variation are 20 and 35 minutes, respectively. At the downstream extremity, 30 km from the dam, it is 55 minutes, corresponding to a relative change of $\pm 6.3\%$. Largely, the shadowed range becomes wider further downstream along the river, implying greater uncertainty in time to peak flood stage in the lower reach of the river.

5. CONCLUDING REMARKS

Dam-break flood modelling is subject to several sources of uncertainty. This paper addresses one of them, i.e., the effects of uncertainty of river-valley hydraulic parameters. Both cross-sectional geometry and hydraulic roughness are contributing factors.

The resulting uncertainty in flood discharge or time to peak water stage increases farther downstream along the river. The range of uncertainty in water stage is dependent upon cross-sectional geometry and channel width. Larger variation can be expected at narrower sections of a river.

It is recommended that, for detailed dam-break modelling and contingency evacuation planning, the effect of uncertainty in cross-sectional geometry and roughness should be examined.

ACKNOWLEDGEMENT

The study reported herein is part of a research program in river flood hydraulics. It is financed by the Swedish Association of River Regulation Enterprises (VASO) and also by the Swedish Council for Building Research (BFR). These supports are gratefully acknowledged.

REFERENCES

Burnham, M.W. and Davis, D.W. (1990). Effects of data errors on computed steady-flow profiles. J. of Hydraulic Engineering, ASCE, 116 (7), 914 - 929.

Boss Corporation (1988-91). BOSS DAMBRK User's Manual.

Fread, D.L. (1981). Some Limitations of dam-break flood routing models. ASCE Fall Convention, St. Louis, Missouri.

Fread, D.L. (1984). DAMBRK: The NWS dam-break flood forecasting model. U.S. National Weather Service (NWS), Maryland.

Johnson, F.A. and Illes, P. (1976). A classification of dam failures. Water Power and Dam Construction, December 1976, 43 - 45.

Kung, C.S. and Yang, X.L. (1993). Dam-break flood simulation and river parameter uncertainty. Report No.65, Hydraulic Laboratory, Royal Institute of Technology, Stockholm.

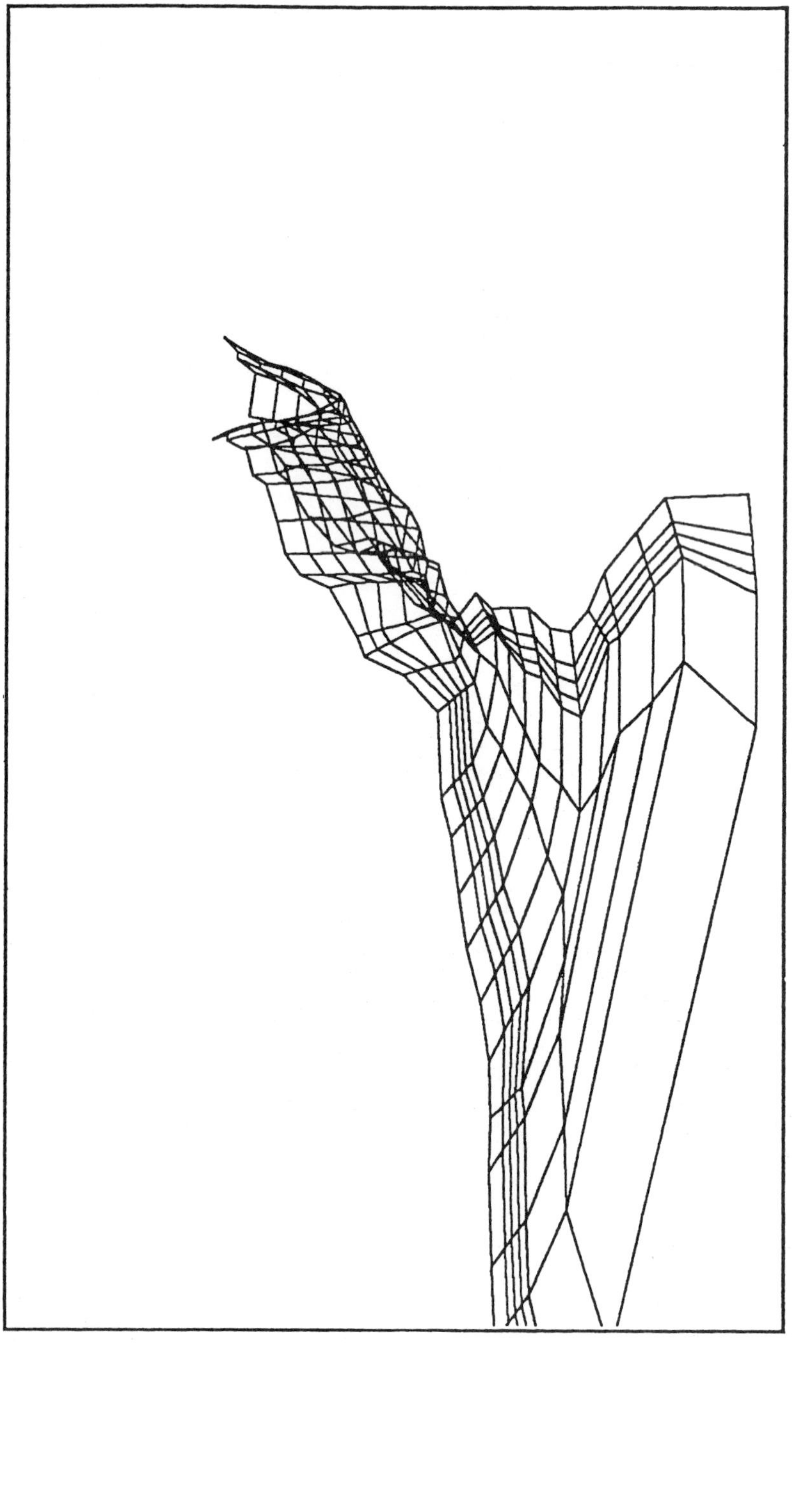

Fig. 1a 3-D representation of the river channel

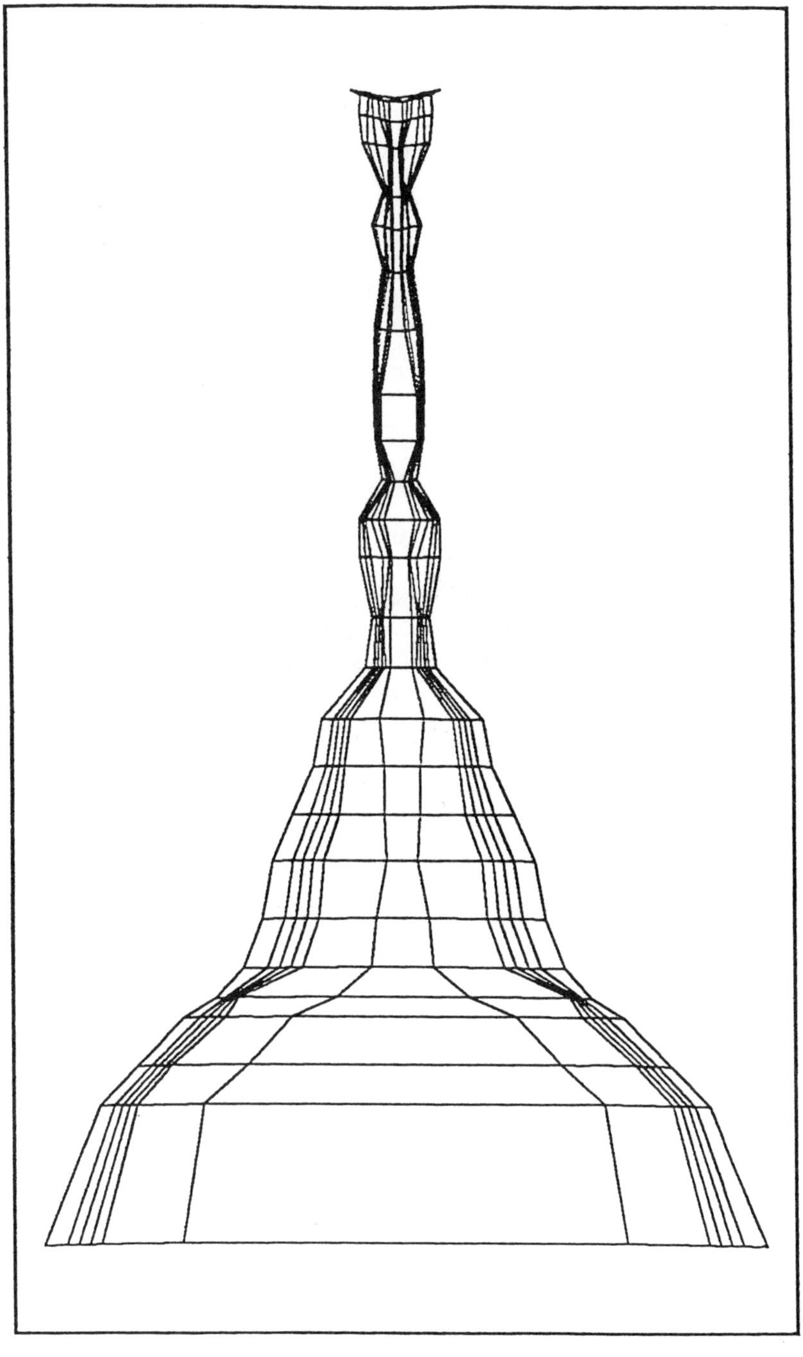

Fig. 1b Plan View of the river channel

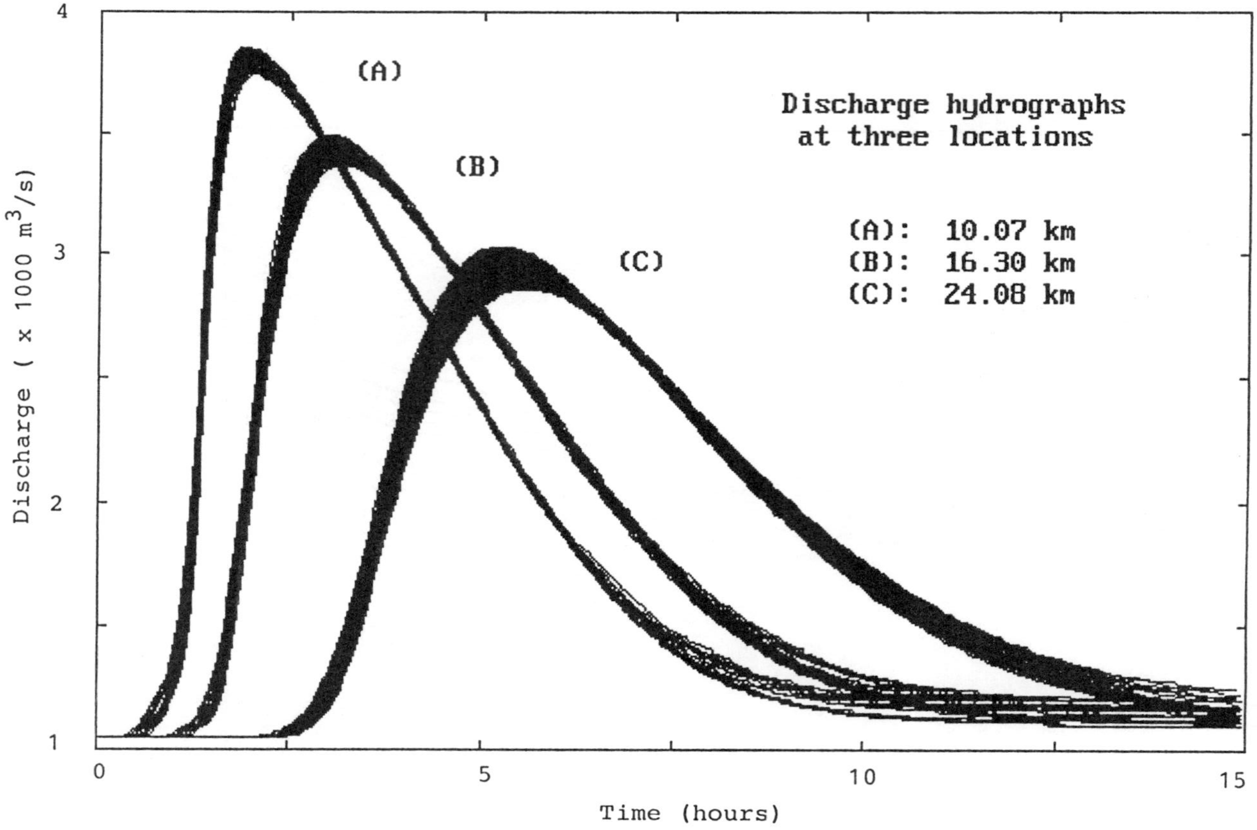

fig.2 Discharge hydrographs at 3 selected locations

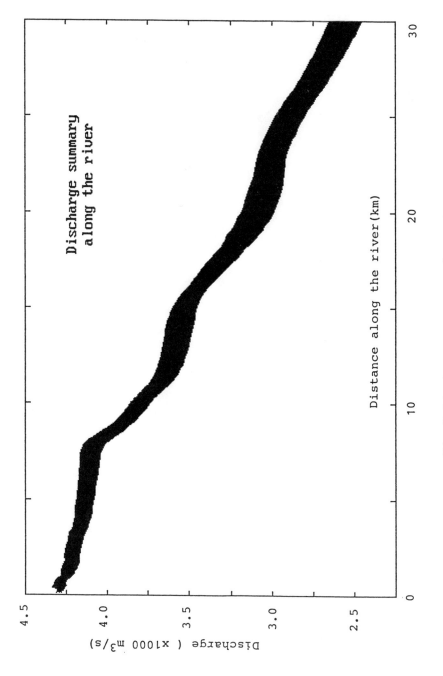

Fig.3 Discharge summary along the river

367

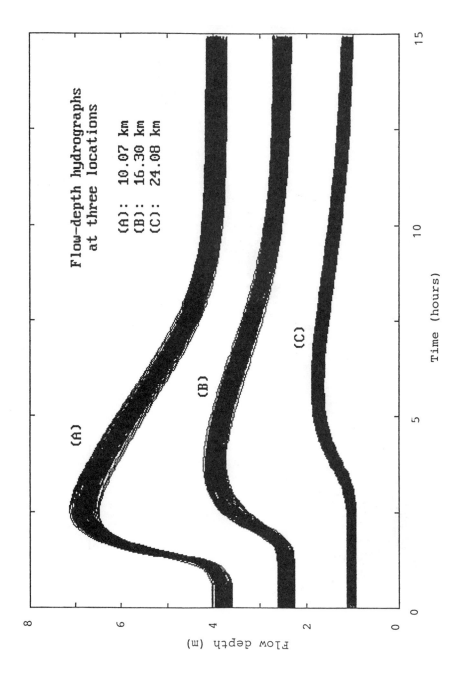

Fig. 4 Flow-depth hydrographs at 3 selected locations

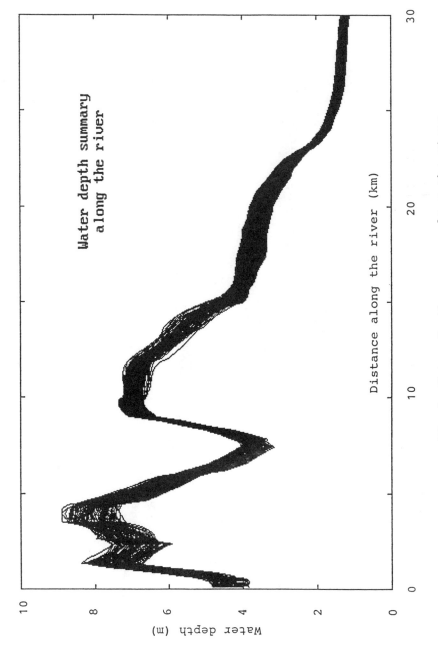

Fig.5 Water depth summary along the river

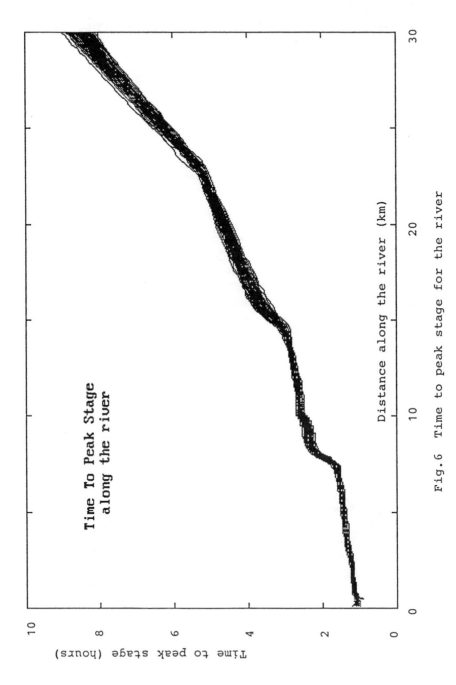

Fig.6   Time to peak stage for the river

RIVER FLOOD HYDRAULICS
22–25 March 1994: York, England

DEVELOPMENTS IN THREE DIMENSIONAL NUMERICAL
MODELLING OF RIVER FLOWS

G.Pender[1] and J.R.Manson[2]

ABSTRACT

The paper reviews progress to date on a research programme to develop a fully three dimensional mathematical model of river flows. The need for such a model is discussed followed by a description of the revelant physical processes which have to be captured by the model. The numerical method used has distinct advantages of flexibility for dealing with free surface flows Results are presented for the application of the model to flow over a trench which demonstrates similarities to flow in the cross-over region of meandering two-stage channels. Results are also presented for preliminary applications to a meandering two-stage channel. These demonstrate that the model is capable of reproducing the flow patterns which occur in such channels. More research effort is required before the model could be used in a predictive capacity.

INTRODUCTION

Increasing environmental awareness has resulted in river engineers being required to design flood alleviation schemes that preserve and even enhance riverside habitat. Such schemes often include the retention or construction oᶠ areas of flood plain and river meanders. The term two-stage channel is used to describe flood alleviation schemes where the inner channel is designed to contain only the smaller spates with water from larger floods being allowed to spill onto purpose designed flood plains. During over bank events flows are highly three-dimensional with circulation patterns varying widely depending on the ratio of flood plain to main channel depth. The accurate prediction of these circulations at the design stage is important as their strength and sense can significantly affect energy losses. This controls the stage-discharge relationships through the channel. Velocity distributions are also of importance in determining the transport, dispersion, erosion and deposition characteristics within the two-stage channel.

The lack of detailed knowledge of these flows led to the Science and Engineering Research Council and HR, Wallingford sponsoring the Flood Channel Facility. The results of this major physical modelling research programme have been widely discussed by Knight and Shiono (6), Elliot and Sellin (1), Greenhill and Sellin (3), Willetts and Hardwick (4), Sellin,Ervine and Willetts (16). While producing valuable insight into the flow mechanisms that occur in both straight and meandering two-stage channels the data was limited to simplified main channel and flood plain geometries. The one study undertaken using natural channel data indicated a significant increase in the complexity of the flow mechanisms in such circumstances, Sellin et al (12). Clearly, as engineers wish to design natural river features there is a great need for a method of extending the physical model data to more general situations. One method of achieving this is to employ numerical modelling techniques which have the distinct advantage of ease of modification to different channel geometries.

---

[1] Lecturer, Department of Civil Engineering, University of Glasgow, Glasgow G12 8LT, Scotland.

[2] Research Assistant, Same department

2nd International Conference on River Flood Hydraulics. Edited by W. R. White and J. Watts
© 1994 HR Wallingford Ltd. Published by John Wiley & Sons Ltd

Such a numerical model for simulating over bank flows in two-stage channels and natural rivers is being developed at the University of Glasgow. The model, employing an operator splitting finite difference solution technique, is fully three-dimensional and incorporates a choice of linear or non-linear two-equation turbulence models.

HYDRODYNAMIC EQUATIONS

River flows are governed by the laws of conservation of momentum in the three orthogonal axes and conservation of mass. Making the assumptions that the water is incompressible and of uniform density the following equations can be written in a cartesian tensor notation.

$$\frac{\partial u_j}{\partial x_j} = 0 \tag{1}$$

$$\frac{\partial u_i}{\partial t} + \frac{\partial(u_j u_i)}{\partial x_j} + \frac{1}{\rho}\frac{\partial p}{\partial x_i} = \frac{1}{\rho}\frac{\partial \tau_{ij}}{\partial x_j} + f_i \quad i = 1,2,3 \tag{2}$$

where $x_{1,2,3}$ are the co-ordinate axes (x, y and z respectively), t is the time, $u_{1,2,3}$ are the Reynolds averaged velocity components in x, y and z, ρ is the water density, p is the pressure, τ_{ij} is the interfacial shear stress tensor and f_i are components of some external forces per unit mass. The interfacial stresses may be represented as,

$$\tau_{ij} = \rho v \left(\frac{\partial u_i}{\partial x_j} + \frac{\partial u_j}{\partial x_i} \right) - \rho \overline{u'_i u'_j} \tag{4}$$

In which u'_i represents the fluctuating part of the x_i velocity. The $-\overline{u'_i u'_j}$ terms are the Reynolds stresses.

TURBULENCE MODEL

The standard (or linear) k-ε model is described by Rodi (9). Turbulent stresses are represented by the Boussinesq's eddy viscosity assumption to give,

$$-\overline{u'_i u'_j} = v_t 2 D_{ij} - \frac{2}{3} k \delta_{ij} \tag{5}$$

where,

$$D_{ij} = \frac{1}{2} \left(\frac{\partial u_i}{\partial x_j} + \frac{\partial u_j}{\partial x_i} \right) \tag{6}$$

$$v_t = c_\mu \frac{k^2}{\varepsilon} \tag{7}$$

The turbulence quantities are k, the kinetic energy of turbulent fluctuations per unit mass, and ε its rate of dissipation. These quantities are given by the transport equations,

$$\frac{\partial k}{\partial t} + \frac{\partial(u_i k)}{\partial x_i} = \frac{\partial}{\partial x_i}\left(\frac{v_t}{\sigma_k}\frac{\partial k}{\partial x_i}\right) + Prod - \varepsilon \tag{8}$$

$$\frac{\partial \varepsilon}{\partial t} + \frac{\partial(u_i \varepsilon)}{\partial x_i} = \frac{\partial}{\partial x_i}\left(\frac{v_t}{\sigma_\varepsilon}\frac{\partial \varepsilon}{\partial x_i}\right) + c_1 \frac{\varepsilon}{k} Prod - c_2 \frac{\varepsilon^2}{k} \tag{9}$$

$$Prod \ = -\overline{u'_iu'_j}D_{ij} \qquad\qquad [10]$$

The constants c_μ, σ_k, σ_t, c_1 and c_2 are given by Rodi (1980).

The linear k-ε model has some well-documented drawbacks, Younis (18), in particular, it performs poorly in predicting the normal Reynold's stresses. Consequently it fails to reproduce turbulence driven secondary motions in planes normal to the main direction of flow and fails to accurately predict the point of re-attachment in recirculating flows. It has remained popular however owing to ease of implementation in Navier-Stokes solvers which allow for a variable viscosity. The authors' have been experimenting with non-linear stress-strain relationships which relax the Boussinesq assumption. These have been proposed in different forms by Baker (14) and Speziale (13),

$$-\overline{u'_iu'_j} \ = \ v_t\,2\,D_{ij} \ - \ c_{ij}k\delta_{ij} \ + \alpha v_t\omega(2\,D_{ij})^2 \qquad Baker \qquad\qquad [11]$$

$$-\overline{u'_iu'_j} \ = \ v_t\,2\,D_{ij} \ - \ \frac{2}{3}k\delta_{ij} \ + 4C_DC_\mu v_t\omega(D_{im}D_{mj} - D_{mn}D_{mn}\frac{\delta_{ij}}{3}) \qquad\qquad [12]$$

$$+ \ 4C_EC_\mu v_t\omega(D'_{ij} - D'_{mm}\frac{\delta_{ij}}{3}) \qquad Speziale$$

The constants α, c_{ij}, C_D and C_E are given by Baker (14) and Speziale (13). In these expressions, D'_{ij} is the Oldroyd derivative and ω is the specific dissipation (k/ε). The first of these relationships is semi-empirical but simple and numerically robust. The second relationship is much more theoretically sound but prone to numerical instability in regions of high velocity gradients. These non-linear relationships make better predictions of the normal Reynolds stresses than the standard k-ε model and thus enable prediction of turbulence driven secondary motions in straight channels. They also provide a more accurate prediction of re-circulation lengths.

NUMERICAL SOLUTION

The equations are solved by a fractional step projection method on a cartesian grid, see Viollet et al (11). The velocities and all scalar quantities are defined at the computational cell corners while the pressure is defined at the cell centre, see figure 1. The velocities and pressure are computed in three steps.

1. Velocities are advanced to an auxiliary velocity field at each computational node by a finite difference method which represents the advection terms explicitly and the diffusion type terms implicitly. The resulting matrix is solved by an iterative relaxation method with the non-linear terms introduced as source terms.

$$\frac{u_i^{aux} - u_i^n}{\Delta t} \ = \ [\ -\frac{\partial(u_ju_i)}{\partial x_j} \ ]^n \ + \ [\ \frac{1}{\rho} \ \frac{\partial\tau_{ij}}{\partial x_j} \ ]^{aux} \quad i = 1,2,3 \qquad [11]$$

2. This velocity field does not necessarily satisfy continuity and the error in continuity is used as a source for a Poisson equation for the future pressure field. The Poisson equation is solved with Neumann boundary conditions to give the future pressure field.

$$\frac{D^{aux}}{\Delta t} \ = \ [\ \frac{1}{\rho}\frac{\partial^2 p}{\partial x_j\partial x_j} \ ]^{n+1} \qquad\qquad [12]$$

where,

$$D^{aux} = [\frac{\partial u_j}{\partial x_j}]^{aux} \qquad [13]$$

3. The auxiliary velocity field is then corrected by the pressure gradient based on the now known future pressure field to give the future velocity field.

$$\frac{u_i^{n+1} - u_i^{aux}}{\Delta t} = [-\frac{1}{\rho} \frac{\partial p}{\partial x_i}]^{n+1} \qquad i = 1,2,3 \qquad [14]$$

In the above expressions $[ ]^n$ is taken to mean the discretised form of the differential expression within the square brackets at time level n. The turbulence quantities are advanced in a similar way but require an additional computation for the turbulent source terms. Boundary conditions must be prescribed at the inlet, outlet, free surface , bed and sidewalls. At the inlet a fully developed flow profile is specified. At the outlet it is assumed that advection is dominating. The free surface is replaced by a rigid lid where a non-zero pressure may develop and which represents the height to which the water level would achieve if the surface were free. At the free surface a symmetry condition is applied for all variables except ε. The bed and sidewalls a wall law is applied as described by Rodi (9).

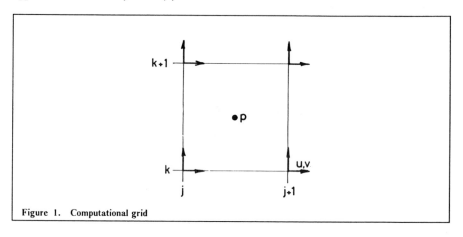

Figure 1. Computational grid

MODEL APPLICATION

The numerical model has been applied to a number of simplified two and three dimensional flow situations. Some of which are discussed below.

Backward Facing Step Tests

Physical model studies of two-stage channel flow, see for example Kiely (5), Lorena (7), Ervine and Lorena (2), have identified the importance of secondary circulations in determining energy losses and channel capacity. These circulations are driven by flood plain flow crossing over the main channel flow and in cases where channel aspect ratio is greater than 7 the flow mechanisms show some similarity to flow over a backward facing step. Prior to applying the model to the complex three-dimensional geometries described in references 2,5 and 7 comparitive tests were undertaken to compare linear and non-linear turbulence model results against experimental measurements by Nakagawa and Nezu (8). The results of these tests are discussed in Pender, Manson and Ervine (17). As expected the linear model under predicts the re-attachment length by around 20%, see Thangam and Speziale (10), whereas, the non-linear turbulence model shows a significant improvement in predicting the point of re-attachment.

Flow Across a Trench

To test the models ability to simulate enclosed circulation when the flow both expands and contracts, flow across trench was simulated as a two-dimensional problem. This is similar to the cross-over region during out of bank flow in two-stage channels. The trench was 1.8 m. wide at the top, 1.2 m. wide at the bottom with sides sloping at an angle of 45 ° This was represented in the numerical model using a grid of 101 x 61 with Δx = 0.03 m. and Δz = 0.03 m.. The model does not yet possess a boundary fitted grid capability so the boundaries were represented as closely as possible using a staircase approximation as by McGuirk and DePalma (19). A number of simulations were undertaken with varying unit flows. The results presented are for a unit flow of 0.27 m³/s/m. Figure 3 shows the computed velocities and turbulence parameters for this problem.

Meandering Two-Stage Channel

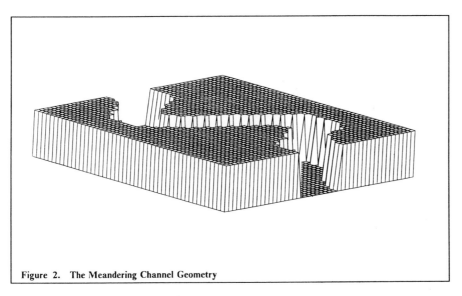

Figure 2. The Meandering Channel Geometry

To demonstrate the full three dimensional capability of the model results from small two-stage meandering channel are presented below. An isometric view of the channel is shown in figure 2. The qualitative results presented below are an indication of the models possibilities. We are presently working on quantifying the results. The principle flow mechanisms occurring in these types of two-stage meandering channels are described by Sellin, Ervine and Willetts (1993). Figure 4 shows velocity vectors computed by the model on a horizontal plane just above the bankfull level. The deflection of these vectors compare qualitively with those presented by Sellin, Ervine and Willetts (1993). Figure 4 also shows the contours of velocity magnitude for a cross-section at at the bend apex. The channel was modelled using a 51 x 48 x 17 grid with Δx = 0.1m. Δy = 0.1 m. and Δz = 0.05 m.

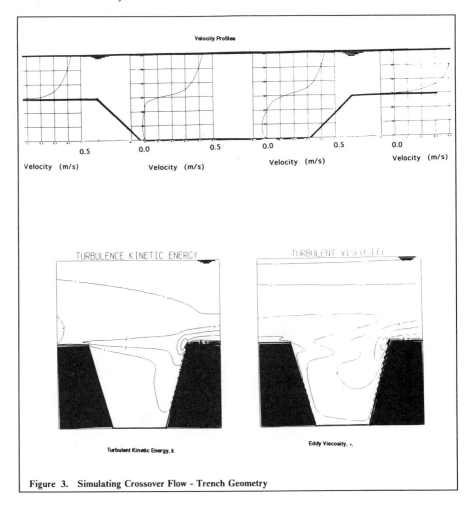

Figure 3. Simulating Crossover Flow - Trench Geometry

CONCLUSIONS

The current state of a numerical model for simulating three-dimensional flows in two-stage channels has been presented. Qualitive examination of the results obtained to date indicate that the model is capable of reproducing the essential features of two-stage channel flow. Two further developments are required to allow full verification of the model:

- Pre-processing software needs to be developed to enable quantitive analysis of the numerical models performance with physical model data.

- Computing turn-around needs to be improved either by porting the to a faster linear processor or re-writing the code to take advantage of parallel processing machines which are now becoming available at the desktop level. The 41616 solution node three dimensional example presented in this paper required about 20,000 C.P.U. seconds on an I.B.M. 3090-VF to reach a steady state. Representing the SERC flood channel facility using a similar grid size would require many more solution nodes thus requiring much more computer time. Of course, computational enhancements and the adoption of a more efficient solution grid system could reduce this time but the computational times will still be extremely high for these fully three dimensional simulations.

Other longer term developments of the model are also desirable:

1. At present the free surface is represented by a rigid lid against which pressure can increase or decrease from the hydrostatic value. Evidence suggests that the major flow mechanisms in two-stage meandering channels are 'pressure driven' (16). Clearly in such circumstances the validity of the rigid lid assumption requires to be investigated.

2. Grid aspects in particular the investigation of boundary fitted grid systems is required.

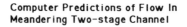

Computer Predictions of Flow In
Meandering Two-stage Channel

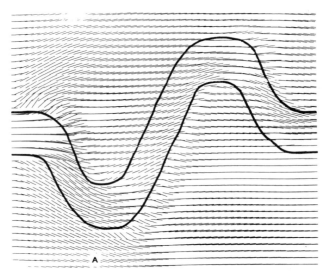

**Velocity Patterns on Horizontal Plane Just Above
Bankfull Level**

Velocity Contours at section A-A

Figure 4.   Preliminary Results for Flow in Meandering Two-stage Channel

REFERENCES

1. Elliot,S.C.A. and Sellin,R.H.J.(1990) "SERC Flood Channel Facility: Skewed Flow Experiments", Journ.of Hyd.Res. Vol.28

2. Ervine,D.A. and Lorena,M. (1992) "Conveyance of Meandering Compound Channels" Proceedings of the Second International Conference on Hydraulic and Environmental Modelling of Coastal, Estuarine and River Waters, Bradford

3. Greenhill,R.K. and Sellin,R.H.J.(1993) "Development of a Simple Method to Predict Discharge in Compound Meandering Channels", Proc.Inst. Civ.Engrs. - Water,Maritime and Energy, Vol.101 Mar pp37

4. Willetts,B.B. and Hardwick,R.I.(1993) "Stage Dependancy for Overbank Flow in Meandering Channels", Proc.Inst. Civ.Engrs. - Water,Maritime and Energy, Vol.101 Mar pp45

5. Keily,G. (1989) "An Experimental Study of Overbank Flow in Straight and Meandering Compound Channels", A Thesis Submitted to University College, Cork for the Degree of Doctor of Philosophy.

6. Knight,D.W. and Shiono,K.(1990) "Turbulence Measurements in a Shear Layer Region of a Compound Channel", Journ.of Hyd.Res., Vol.28, No.2

7. Lorena,M. (1992) "Meandering Compound Flow", A Thesis Submitted to University of Glasgow for the Degree of Doctor of Philosophy.

8. Nakagawa,H. and Nezu,I. (1987) " Experimental Investigation on Turbulent Structure of Backward Facing Step Flow in an Open Channel", Journal of Hydraulic Research, Vol.25, No 1.

9. Rodi,W. (1980) "Turbulence Models and their Application in Hydraulics " I.A.H.R. Specialist Publication

10. Thangam,S. and Speziale,C.G. (1992) "Turbulent Flow Past a Backward-Facing Step: A Critical Evaluation of Two-Equation Models.", AIAA Journal Vol.30, No.5, May.

11. Viollet,P.L.et al (1987) "The Modelling of Turbulent Recirculating Flows for the Purposes of Reactor Thermal-Hydraulic Analysis", Nuclear Engineering and Design vol.99 pp365-377.

12. Sellin,R.H.J. et al (1990) "Post-implementation Appraisal of a Two-stage Channel in the River Roding, Essex", Journ.Inst.Water & Env. Management, Vol.4 No.2 Apr pp119-130

13. Speziale,C.G. & Ngo,T. (1987) "Numerical Solution of Turbulent Flow Past a Backward Facing Step Using a Non-Linear k-ε Model", ICASE Report 87-74

14. Baker,A.J. & Orzechowski,J.A. (1983) "An Interaction Algorithm for Three Dimensional Turbulent Sub-sonic Aerodynamics Juncture Region Flow", AIAA Journal, Vol.21, No.4.

15. Golay,M.W. & Boyle,D.R. (1983) "Measurement of a Recirculating, Two Dimensional, Turbulent Flow and Comparison to Turbulence Model Predictions. 1:Steady State Case", Journal of Fluids Engineering, Vol.105, December 1983, pp439-446

16. Sellin,R.H.J., Ervine,D.A. and Willetts,B.B. (1993) "Behaviour of Meandering Two-stage Channels", Proc.Inst. Civ.Engrs. - Water,Maritime and Energy, Vol.101 Mar pp37

17. Pender,G., Manson,J.R. and Ervine,D.A. (1993) "Application of two-equation turbulence models to flows in two-stage channels", Proc. of the 5th International Symposium on Refined Flow Modelling and Turbulence Measurements. 7-10 Sept. Paris, France.

18. Younis,B. (1992) "Some Turbulence Models" in 'Is Turbulence Modelling of Any Use ?', I.A.H.R. Conference April, 1992 - at I.C.E. London

19. McGuirk,J.J. and DePalma,J. (1992) "Calculations of the Dilution in an Annular Gas Turbine Combustor", AIAA Journal Vol.30 No.4 April, 1992.

Chapter Eight

Compound Channels

RIVER FLOOD HYDRAULICS
22–25 March 1994: York, England

COMPARISONS BETWEEN MEASURED AND NUMERICALLY MODELLED UNSTEADY FLOWS IN A COMPOUND CHANNEL USING DIFFERENT REPRESENTATIONS OF FRICTION SLOPE

J F Lyness,   Dept of Civil Engineering and Transport,
                University of Ulster
W R C Myers,   Dept of Civil Engineering and Transport,
                University of Ulster

SYNOPSIS

Unsteady flow hydrographs have been obtained at either end of an 805 m reach of a compact compound channel on the River Main in Northern Ireland. Using the hydrographs two measured floodwaves have been extracted and used as data for comparisons between measured and computed hydrographs obtained from a numerical model. Three methods are used to calculate the friction slope in the St Venant equations on which the model is based – single channel conveyance, divided channel conveyance and depth varying global Manning's n. Using bankfull Manning's n, as the basis for calculating single channel and divided channel conveyances, the errors in total flow depth and floodplain flow depth were plotted. The single channel method overestimated floodplain flow depth by up to 90% for shallow floodplain flow and the divided channel method underestimated floodplain flow depth providing its optimum accuracy for floodplain flows in the relative depth range $0.15 < Y_r < 0.35$.

NOTATION

A	Cross sectional area of flow
h	Water level
K	Channel conveyance function
K_i	Conveyance function for section i of divided channel
n	Manning's n
q	Lateral inflow/unit length
Q	Cross section discharge
R	Hydraulic radius of cross section
S_f	Friction slope
t	Time
x	Distance downstream
Y_r	Relative depth of flow on floodplain

INTRODUCTION

Natural and man made river channels can often be described as two stage or compound channels, flow in the full channel cross section occurring only during the passage of flood waves. Numerical models based on steady and unsteady flow equations are used to analyse such channels for the purposes of flood mitigation design and flood hazard identification. The numerical models used have been described by Cunge, Holly and Verwey [1] and for realistic assessment of effects during the passage of a

2nd International Conference on River Flood Hydraulics. Edited by W. R. White and J. Watts

flood wave an unsteady flow model is used. The St Venant equations form the basis for unsteady flow modelling and, for accurate representation of flow resistance during the passage of the flood through a river reach of compound section, alternative techniques are available. The compound section may be treated as a single channel section, or as a divided channel section as shown in Fig 1, with the channel partitioned into main channel and left and right flood plains. The roughness coefficient used for these methods is Manning's n at bankfull. This is used frequently in practice because of the absence of data from overbank flows.

Using the divided channel method conventionally, with channel divisions as shown in Fig 1, hydraulic radii for the separate divisions are calculated using the wetted perimeters measured around the bed of the channel without taking into account the floodplain/main channel interface. For any water depth the conveyance of the compound section is then the sum of the main channel and floodplain conveyances.

An alternative method used is to treat the compound section as a single channel. This method is often used by river engineers in situations where floodplains are relatively narrow and the roughness of the compound section is homogeneous. The conveyance for any water depth is then calculated using the single channel wetted perimeter.

The present study assesses the errors using single and divided channel conveyances and the use of global Manning's n by modelling measured unsteady river flows. Flood hydrographs have been obtained at each end of an 805 m reach of the River Main in Northern Ireland using datalogged diaphragm pressure transducers. Bankfull and global Manning's n for a range of flow depths have been obtained from a previous study by Martin and Myers [2].

NUMERICAL SOLUTION METHOD

The numerical solution method is similar to that used in several proprietary software packages for modelling unsteady flow and is based on the St Venant equations given below:

$$\frac{\partial A}{\partial t} + \frac{\partial Q}{\partial x} = q \tag{1}$$

$$\frac{\partial Q}{\partial t} + \frac{\partial}{\partial x}\left(\frac{Q^2}{A}\right) + gA\left(\frac{\partial h}{\partial x} + S_f\right) = 0 \tag{2}$$

Finite difference discretion of the St Venant equations follows the Preissmann "box" scheme and the solution of the finite difference equations uses the application of the Newton-Raphson

FIG.1 COMPOUND CHANNEL ANALYSIS METHODS

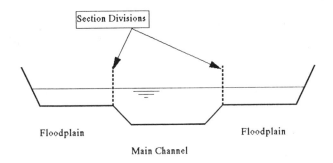

FIG.2 VARIATION OF MANNING'S n
WITH RELATIVE DEPTH Yr

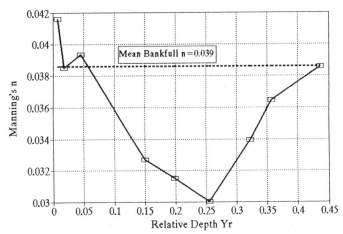

Method as described by Amein and Fang [3]. The reach of the River Main analysed did not contain tributary or lateral inflows so that boundary conditions for the model comprised time varying upstream discharge and downstream water depth.

FLOW RESISTANCE

The effects of flow resistance are described using the friction slope turn, S_f, in the St Venant equation (2). In this study three methods are used to calculate S_f.

(i)   Depth varying global Manning's n

$$S_f = Q|Q| \left(\frac{n}{AR^{2/3}} \right)^2 \tag{3}$$

(ii)   Single channel depth varying conveyance using bankfull Mannings's n

$$S_f = \frac{Q|Q|}{K^2} \tag{4}$$

(iii)   Divided channel depth varying conveyance using bankfull Manning's n

$$S_f = \frac{Q|Q|}{\left(\sum_{i=1}^{i=3} K_i \right)^2} \tag{5}$$

The previous study of this reach by Martin and Myers [2] provided bankfull and global Manning's n values. Fig 2 shows the variation of global Manning's n with relative depth, Y_r, for the upstream section which is similar in form to that described by Knight [4].

$$Y_r = \frac{\text{Flow Depth on Floodplain}}{\text{Total Flow Depth}} \tag{6}$$

It can be seen from Fig 2 that Manning's n reaches a minimum value at a relative depth of approximately $Y_r = 0.25$ for overbank flow. The mean bankfull value of Manning's n used for the calculation of single channel and divided channel conveyances was n = 0.0386.

EXPERIMENTAL DATA

Flood wave records have been obtained using calibrated pressure diaphragm transducers at either end of an 805 m reach of the River Main in Co Antrim, N Ireland. A typical cross section of the experimental reach is shown in Fig 3. The river has been

FIG.3 TYPICAL CROSS-SECTION Section 14
Upstream Boundary

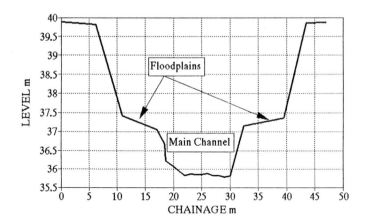

reconstructed as a two stage channel by the Department of Agriculture for Northern Ireland. Using dataloggers the transducer signals were recorded at 300 sec intervals and converted using calibration constants, mean bed levels and transducer levels into depth hydrographs [5]. The dataloggers were synchronised at the start of each recording period of 28 days and produced a maximum time error of 20 seconds at the end of a recording period. Eight suitable synchronised overbank flood hydrographs with different peak magnitudes were available in spreadsheet file format.

A topographical survey of the reach provided data on variation of cross sectional area and wetted perimeter for eight levels on each cross sections. Flow gauging was carried out to enable stage discharge relationships to be derived at upstream and downstream limits of the reach. A steady flow computational model was employed to derive flow resistance data in the form of Manning's roughness coefficients.

RESULTS

Two overbank flood waves from the hydrograph record were simulated using the unsteady flow model based on the Preissmann scheme. The overbank flood wave durations were 30 and 10 hours with peak values of Y_r = 0.45 and 0.23 respectively. Boundary conditions were obtained from the upstream and downstream datalogger records. The upstream boundary condition was time varying discharge and the downstream boundary condition was time varying depth. The geometry of 805 m reach of the river was described in the model using 5 cross sections at approximately 200 m spacing, each section geometry was described by cross sectional areas and wetted perimeters at 8 levels. Section flow resistance was described using either mean bankfull Manning's n for the single and divided channel conveyances or global depth varying Manning's n defined at 24 levels of which 8 were overbank.

Figure 4 shows the results obtained at the upstream boundary of the model using the three representations of flow resistance compared with measured flow depths for the two flood waves. It can be seen from the figures that the single channel conveyance gives greater flow depths than measured for both flood waves. The divided channel method underestimates flow depths generally within a closer range to the measured depths than the single channel method for the relative depth range $0.05 < Y_r < 0.40$.

Figures 5 and 6 show the errors in computed flow depths and floodplain flow depths at the upstream boundary. Both graphs contain points from the large and small overbank flood waves. It should be noted on figure 6 that no points are plotted below second bankfull level of the section for clarity.

The use of the single channel method produces a maximum overestimation of flow depth of 12% at relative depth $Y_r = 0.19$ and the error then declines with increasing depth to approach zero. This is also shown in figure 6 in terms of errors in floodplain flow depth where the maximum error of 100% overestimation occurs at $Y_r = 0.10$.

The use of the divided channel method underestimates flow depths providing best accuracy in the range $0.10 < Y_r < 0.35$. Errors are large for very shallow floodplain flows then decline to underestimation of less than 5% at $Y_r = 0.24$ before increasing again with increasing depths.

As stated previously the upstream boundary condition was discharge with the same discharge hydrographs being used for the single and divided channel methods. Because the downstream boundary condition of the model is time varying depth the deviations, between computed and measured depths, declined along the reach to zero at the downstream boundary. The overestimation of computed depth, by the single channel method, in the relative depth range shown, is therefore an underestimation of the channel discharge capacity. Similarly the divided channel computed depths represents an overestimate of section discharge capacity. This is consistent with the observations on the two methods made by Ackers [6]. The discharges at the downstream boundary of the model confirmed the order of section discharge capacities.

CONCLUSIONS

A commonly used one dimensional unsteady flow model using different representations of channel conveyance has been applied to a reach of compound section. The compound section can be described as compact having narrow floodplains of similar roughness to the main channel. The use of the single channel conveyance method underestimates channel discharge capacity in the relative depth range of $0 < Y_r < 0.45$ producing greater floodplain flow depths than measured. The maximum overestimation error of floodplain flow depths is approximately 90% at relative $Y_r = 0.10$. Errors decline for depths $Y_r > 0.10$ to approach zero.

FIG.4 COMPUTED WATER DEPTHS vs TIME
Upstream Boundary - Peak Yr=0.45

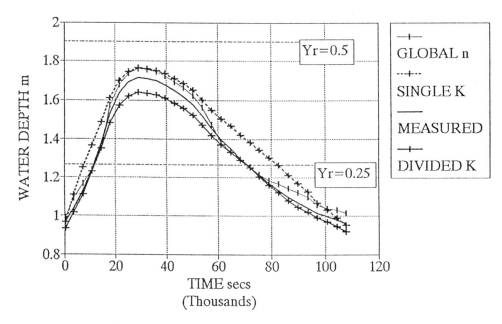

Upstream Boundary - Peak Yr=0.23

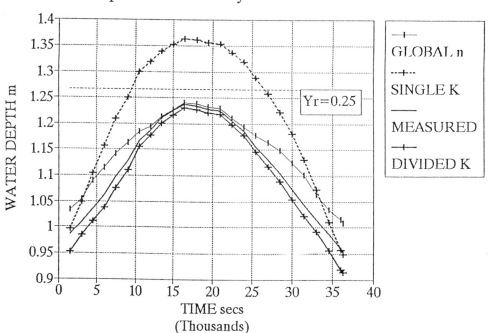

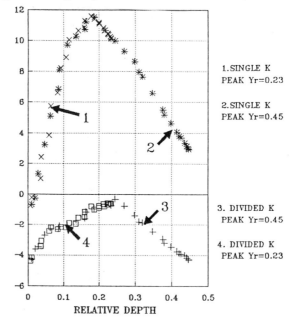

FIG 5 ERROR IN COMPUTED DEPTH vs Yr

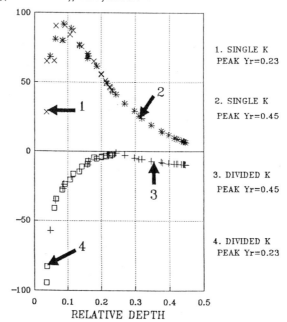

FIG 6 ERROR IN COMPUTED FLOODPLAIN DEPTH vs Yr

The divided channel conveyance method overestimates the discharge capacity of the section providing closest accuracy in the relative depth range $0.10 < Y_r < 0.35$. The minimum error of 5% was obtained at relative depth $Y_r = 0.24$. The use of piecewise linear global Manning's n functions at each section also underestimated channel discharge capacity though providing better accuracy than the single channel conveyance method for the relative depth range $0 < Y_r < 0.45$.

ACKNOWLEDGEMENTS

The authors gratefully acknowledge financial support for this study from the Science and Engineering Research Council. The authors would also like to acknowledge the valuable assistance given by the Department of Agriculture for Northern Ireland.

REFERENCES

[1] CUNGE, J.A., HOLLY, F.M. and VERWEY, A. Practical Aspects of Computational River Hydraulics. Pitman, London, 1980.

[2] MARTIN, L.A. and MYERS, W.R.C. Measurement of Overbank Flow in a Compound River Channel. Proc Insn Civ Engrgs, Part 2, 1991, 91, Dec, 645-657.

[3] AMEIN, M and FANG, C.J. Implicit Flood Routing in Natural Channels. J Hydr Div, ASCE, 96, No HY12, Paper 7773, Dec 1970, 2481-2500.

[4] KNIGHT, D.W. et al. Prediction of Depth Mean Velocity and Discharge in Natural Rivers with Overbank Flow. Conf on Hydraulic and Environmental Modelling of Coastal, Estuarine and River Waters, Bradford 1989, Gower Technical Press 1989, 419-428.

[5] LYNESS, J.F. and MYERS, W.R.C. Transducer Flow Records-River Main. University of Ulster, Dept of Civil Eng and Transport, 1992, Research Report CET/92/H/01.

[6] ACKERS, P. Hydraulic Design of Two-Stage Channels, Proc Instn Civ Engrs, Wat, Marit and Energy, 1992, 96, Dec, 247-257.

2nd International Conference on
RIVER FLOOD HYDRAULICS
22–25 March 1994: York, England

COMPUTATION OF DISCHARGE AND CRITICAL DEPTH
IN COMPOUND CHANNELS

Nuray (Denli) Tokyay

Introduction

It is well known that the discharge capacity of a compound channel is highly reduced due to lateral momentum transfer between the main channel and the flood plain[22]. Therefore, an accurate estimation of the discharge in a compound channel is a difficult task, especially when the flood plains are rougher than the main channel[27]. In such channels, the degree of interaction between the main channel and the flood plain increases. Therefore, the traditional methods which ignore this interaction usually overestimates the discharge with errors exceeding 50%[26]. However, in literature, there are modified methods which take this interaction into account[5,18,23,27]. Although the modified methods show significant improvement, the application is limited to the geometries they are derived from[27]. In the present study, discharge prediction in channels with rougher flood plains has been improved by introducing an equivalent Manning roughness coefficient. Furthermore, the discharge predicting methods for asymmetrical channels are also compared.

Another important problem in compound channels is the computation of critical flow. In literature, there are various definitions of critical flow[1,2,3,6,10,15,16,17,20,21]. However, the definition of critical flow should be based on whether a subcritical or supercritical flow is subject to a downstream or an upstream control, respectively. Such a definition of Froude number is given by Chaudry and Bhallamudi[3] for symmetrical channels. In compound channels, there may be more than one critical depth. Calculation of these critical depths depends on the discharge computation method used. Chaudry and Bhallamudi[3] used a discharge computation method which does not consider the momentum transfer between the main channel and the flood plain. By using a better discharge–computation method, Chaudry 's approach can be improved and also extended to asymmetrical channels.

Discharge Computation Methods

The method to compute the discharge in a compound channel is based on the assumption that the total discharge in the compound section is the summation of the discharges in the subsections. In application, the cross section is usually divided in such a way as to ensure hydraulic homogeneity in flow computations. Several methods of subdivision have been suggested in literature [8,9,23,25,27]. Whatever the subdivision is, the discharge computation methods may basically be divided into two main groups: i) Separate channel methods, and ii) Methods based on force balance within each subsection.

Separate Channel Methods:

These are the standard discharge calculation methods in which compound channel is divided either by vertical, horizontal or diagonal interfaces. Then the discharge in each subsection is computed by using the Manning equation. To account for the drag effect of flood plains, it is suggested that the interface is to be included to the wetted perimeter of the main channel, but not to that of flood plain[22]. Throughout this study, the following abbreviations are used for the discharge computation methods: SEV, SED, and SIV; where S stands for standard computational methods for symmetrical compound channels (for asymmetrical channels AS is used instead, like ASEH, ASIV, etc.); E and I if the interface is excluded from or included to the wetted perimeter of the main channel, respectively. V, H and D stand for vertical, horizontal and diagonal interfaces, respectively.

In SIV, when the interface is included to the wetted perimeter of the main channel, the Manning roughness coefficient of the main channel is used for the interface too. Although SIV gives good results in compound channels which have the same roughness both in flood plain and main channel, it gives very large errors when flood plain is rougher than the main channel [27]. When a flood plain is rougher, the lateral momentum transfer and hence the apparent shear stresses at the interface will increase. Therefore, the Manning roughness coefficient for the interface must represent the effect of both main channel and the flood plain. In the present study, by analogy to composite roughness formula given by Pavlovskii [4] and by considering the upper and lower limits, an interface Manning roughness coefficient, n_{int} is suggested as :

$$n_{int} = \sqrt{\left(n_c^2 + n_f^2 \frac{B_f}{P_f}\right)\left(\frac{Y-Y_m}{Y}\right)} \quad \text{..} (1)$$

where n_c and n_f are the Manning roughness coefficients for the main channel and the flood plain, respectively. Y is the depth of flow, and Y_m is the depth of the main channel below the flood plain. B_f and P_f are the width and the wetted perimeter of the flood plain, respectively. Since the main channel will act like a composite channel, an equivalent roughness for the main channel can be computed by using Pavlovskii's formula as:

$$n_{eq} = \sqrt{\frac{n_c^2 P_c + 2n_{int}^2 (Y-Y_m)}{P_c + 2(Y-Y_m)}} \quad \text{..} (2)$$

where P_c is the wetted perimeter of the main channel. As $Y \rightarrow Y_m$, $n_{in} \rightarrow 0$, and as $Y \rightarrow \infty$, $n_{int} \rightarrow n_c$ and hence n_{eq} becomes equal to n_c, as must be. The notation $SIV(n_{eq})$ is used to indicate that n_{eq} given by Eqs.(1) and (2) is used for the main–channel roughness.

Methods Based on Force Balance in Each Subsection

The momentum transfer between the main channel and the flood plains are taken into consideration in two methods; i) Φ–Indices Methods, and ii) Area Method[23].

Φ– Indices Methods : The Φ–indices suggested by Radojkovic[18] characterize the degree of interaction and momentum transfer between the main channel and flood plains. These Φ–indices may be used to modify the channel and flood plain discharges either by using vertical or diagonal interface planes (FIV and FID, respectively)[6,27]. In the present study, Φ–indices for asymmetrical compound channels are computed by using two different equations for the apparent shear stress ,τ_{app}, at the main channel–flood plain interface:

$$\tau_{app} = 50(\Delta V)^2 \quad \text{..} (3)$$

and

$$\tau_{app} = 3.325\Delta V^{1.451}(Y-Y_m)^{-0.354}B_f^{0.519} \quad \text{..} (4)$$

where ΔV is the difference in the average velocities in main channel and flood plain given by the Manning equation. Although, Eq.(3) is obtained for asymmetrical channels, it has been shown that the total resisting force for a given ΔV and $(Y-Y_m)$ is the same for symmetrical and asymmetrical sections[5]. Therefore, Eq.(4), obtained for symmetrical channels[27], may also be used for asymmetrical case. Only vertical interface is used for asymmetrical case and AFIVE and AFIVW stand for Φ-indices computed by using Eq.(3) and Eq.(4), respectively.

Comparison of The Methods

Let $E_r = 100 \ (Q_m-Q_c)/Q_m$ be % error, where Q_m is the measured discharge and Q_c is the one computed by using the either of the methods described, and $Y_r = (Y-Y_m)/B_f$ be the relative flood plain depth. The plot of % E_r versus Y_r for SIV in case of smooth channels $(n_r=n_f / n_c=1)$ is shown in Fig.1. This figure shows that, although the % error in SIV is high in some cases where the relative depth, Y_r is small, it is still in acceptable limits. On the other hand, E_r versus $(Y-Y_m)/Y$ for various discharge computation methods for channels having rougher flood plains than the main channel is shown in Fig.2. This figure shows that the use of n_{eq} in SIV reduces the error considerably. For example, in the data of Wormleaton and Merrett [27], the maximum error (−43.85) % in SIV reduces to (−5.33) % by using n_{eq}. In fact, for this data, SIV(n_{eq}) gives the lowest error among the other methods. For the data of Knight and Hamed[8], FIV gives the lowest error. But SIV(n_{eq}) is still comparable with FIV. Therefore the performance of SIV, which is usually preferred due to its convenience in use, is improved by the use of n_{eq} concept introduced in this investigation. The n_{eq} given by Eq.(2) compares quite well with the measured values of main channel n given by Sturm and Sadiq[24].

For asymmetrical channels, the plot of % E_r for various methods is shown in Fig.3. Accordingly, AFIVE, AFIVW, ASIV and ASED, all give similar results. However, AFIVE appears to be slightly better.

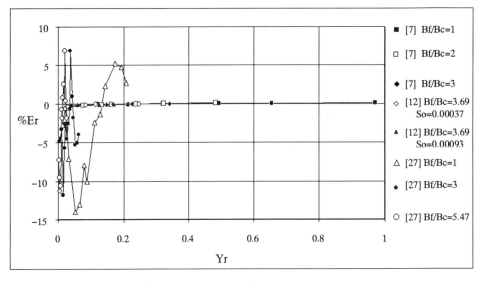

Fig.1 % Error in SIV vs Yr for smooth channels

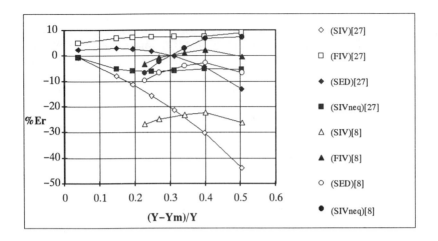

Fig.2   Comparison of % Error For Rough Flood Plains

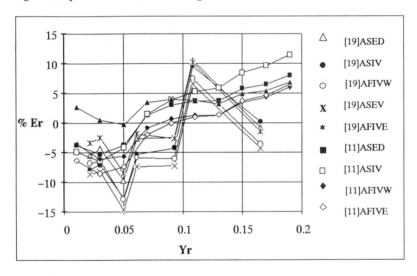

Fig.3   % Error versus Y_r For Asymmetric Compound Channels

Critical Depth For Compound channels

The basic difference between a subcritical flow and supercritical one is that; a disturbance can propagate upstream only in case of subcritical flow and hence it is subject to a downstream control. Therefore, it becomes quite important to define a Froude number for the whole section which allows to identify whether the flow in the channel is subject to an upstream or a downstream control as a whole. Chaudry and Bhallamudi[3] defined a Froude number according to the direction of propagation of a small amplitude wave for symmetrical compound channels. They used SEV to compute the discharge and hence the critical depths. In the present study it is shown that SIV together with n_{eq} gives quite good results. Also, it was discussed that SED gives quite good results not only for total discharge but also for component discharges[27]. Therefore, in the present study, Chaudry's approach is adopted both for SIV and SED. The results are compared with SEV and with the data of Petryk and Grant[15]. Furthermore, it is also applied to asymmetrical compound channels by using ASIV.

The compound channel Froude number, F_c which takes into account the direction of propagation of a small amplitude wave is given as[3]:

$$F_c = \frac{\beta V}{\sqrt{\frac{gA}{B} + V^2\left(\beta^2 - \beta + \frac{A\beta'}{B}\right)}} \quad\text{...} (5)$$

Where β is the momentum correction coefficient for compound channels and β' is the variation of β with the flow depth; $d\beta/dY$. B is the width of the free surface, A is the total flow area, and g is the acceleration of gravity. For compound channels β is given by:

$$\beta = \left(\frac{K_c^2}{A_c} + \frac{NK_f^2}{A_f}\right)\frac{A}{\left(K_c + NK_f\right)^2} \quad\text{..} (6)$$

K_c and K_f are the conveyance factors and A_c and A_f are the flow areas of main channel and flood plain, respectively. Here N is a factor which is equal to 1 for asymmetrical channels and 2 for symmetrical ones. Then the total flow area $A = A_c + (N)\,A_f$. Let

$$m = \frac{K_c}{K_c + NK_f} = \frac{1}{1 + Nn_r\left(\frac{A_f}{A_c}\right)^{5/3}\left(\frac{P_c}{P_f}\right)^{2/3}} \quad\text{...........................} (7)$$

Then β in terms of m can be written as:

$$\beta = \left(\frac{m^2}{A_c} + \frac{(1-m)^2}{NA_f}\right)A \quad\text{..} (8)$$

For critical flow, F_c must be equal to 1. Therefore Eq.(5) reduces to:

$$\frac{g}{Q^2} = \frac{\beta B - A\beta'}{A^3} \quad\text{..} (9)$$

By substituting Eq.(8) and the expression for β' obtained from it, Eq.(9) can be written as:

$$
\frac{gA}{Q^2} = \frac{1}{A_c^2}\frac{dA_c}{dY}\left\{\left[\left(m^2 + \frac{1}{N}(1-m)^2\frac{A_c^2}{A_f^2}\frac{dA_f/dY}{dA_c/dY}\right) - \frac{2}{3}m(1-m)\left(m - \frac{A_c}{A_f}\frac{1-m}{N}\right)\right.\right. *
$$

$$
\left.\left(5\left(1-\frac{A_c}{A_f}\frac{dA_f/dY}{dA_c/dY}\right) - 2\left(\frac{A_c}{P_c}\frac{dP_c/dY}{dA_c/dY} - \frac{A_c}{P_f}\frac{dP_f/dY}{dA_c/dY}\right)\right)\right]\right\} \quad\text{...............................(10)}
$$

Eq.(10) can be written in a non dimensional form by introducing the following parameters:

$$
y = \frac{Y}{Y_m} \quad\text{................(11)}
$$

$$
c_1 = \frac{dA_f/dY}{dA_c/dY} \quad\text{................(12)}
$$

$$
c_2 = \frac{A_c}{A_f} \quad\text{................(13)}
$$

$$
c_3 = \frac{A_c}{P_f}\frac{dP_f/dY}{dA_c/dY} \quad\text{................(14)}
$$

$$
c_4 = \frac{A_c}{P_c}\frac{dP_c/dY}{dA_c/dY} \quad\text{................(15)}
$$

Each c_i and m are functions of y, and take different forms depending on cross sectional shape and discharge computation method used. If the main channel–flood plain interface is not included in the wetted perimeter of the main channel $c_4 = 0$. By substituting $A = A_c + NA_f = A_c(1 + N/c_2)$ and Eqs.(11–15), Eq.(10) can be written as:

$$
\frac{gA_c^3\left(1+\frac{N}{c_2}\right)}{Q^2\frac{dA_c}{dY}} = m^2 + \frac{(1-m)^2}{N}c_1c_2^2 - \frac{2}{3}m(1-m)\left(m - c_2\frac{1-m}{N}\right)\left(5\left(1-c_1c_2\right)+2\left(c_3-c_4\right)\right)\quad\text{...........(16)}
$$

The area in the main channel can be written as $A_c = A_m + A_a$ where A_m and A_a are the areas below and above the flood plain, respectively. Let f(y) represent the right–hand side of Eq.(16), then, in terms of these variables, Eq.(16) becomes:

$$\frac{gA_m^3\left(1+\dfrac{A_a}{A_m}\right)^3\left(1+\dfrac{N}{c_2}\right)}{Q^2\dfrac{dA_c}{dY}} = f(y) \quad\text{...(17)}$$

If SEV , SIV and ASIV is used, $dA_c / dY = B_{fm}$, where B_{fm} is the width of the main channel at flood plain level. If SED is used, $dA_c / dY = B_{fm}/2$. Let

$$C = \frac{gA_m^3}{Q^2 B_{fm}} \quad\text{...(18)}$$

$$c_5 = \left(1+\frac{A_a}{A_m}\right)^3 \quad\text{..(19)}$$

If the factor N_s which is equal to 1, in SEV, SIV and ASIV and 2 in SED is introduced into Eq.(17) together with Eqs.(18) and (19), Eq.(17) becomes:

$$C = \frac{1}{N_s} F(y) \quad\text{..(20)}$$

where

$$F(y) = \frac{f(y)}{c_5\left(1+\dfrac{N}{c_2}\right)} \quad\text{..(21)}$$

In Eqs.(16) and (20), when $y \to \infty$, $m \to 0$ and hence $F(y) \to 0$, and hence $C \to 0$. Also, as $y \to 1$, $m \to 1$ and $F(y) \to 1$, however C goes to 1 or 0.5, depending on the method used for discharge computation. On the other hand, C–y curve has a maximum value which is quite important in the determination of critical depths[3]. For a given cross section and discharge Q, C will take a special value k as determined from Eq.(18). If $C = k > C_{max}$, there is only one critical depth and it is less than the depth at flood plains. If $1 < k < C_{max}$, there are three critical depths, two for $y > 1$ and one for $y < 1$. One of these critical depths occurs nearly y=1, that is on the edge of flood plain, which is also observed on an experimental study by Yuen et al[29]. However, if $k < 1$, there is only one critical depth and it is greater than the depth of main channel. The shape of specific energy curves also verifies these by having either three extrema points or only one minimum value below or above the banks[3]. However, in C–y curve obtained by using SED, since the lower limit of the curve as $y \to 1$ is 0.5, whenever $0.5 < k < C_{max}$, it would give three possible critical depths which has not been verified by specific energy curves, when it is applied to the examples given by Chaudry and Bhallamudi[3]. The value of C_{max} is also affected by the method used. This can be shown best by applying it to the data of Petryk and Grant[15], for which B = 21.95 m, B_f =182.8 m., Y_m = 1.83 m, and the side slopes of the main channel z_c and flood plain z_f are $z_c = z_f = 1$, B_{fm} = 25.60 m, and n_c=0.03 and n_f = 0.08. C–y curve is plotted in Fig.4, by using SEV, SIV and SED. As can be seen from Fig.4, the value of C_{max} for each method is different. For the computation of critical depths for Q = 142 m^3/s, the value of C = k is determined from Eq.(18) as 1.57. This value C = 1.57 does not have a point of intersection with the C–y curve if SED is used. However it has two points of intersection in case of SIV and SEV, which correspond to critical depths Y_{c1} = 1.91 m and Y_{c2} = 1.85 m for SIV and Y_{c1} = 2.10 m and Y_{c2} = 1.83m for SEV. To discuss it better, the plots of y versus non dimensional specific–energy curve, E / Y_m and the Froude number F_c, defined by Eq.(5), are obtained and shown in Fig.(5) together with C curves obtained by using SED and SIV. In Fig.(5), C = 1.57 and F_c = 1 are also shown. C = 1.57 intersects the C–y curve at two points, where y = 1.043 and y = 1.01. F_c= 1 at these depths and y = 0.87 also. Fig.(5) also shows that the specific energy has two minimum and a local maximum. The lower extrema points of specific–energy curve are coincident with the points of F_c=1 and C=1.57. For the upper minimum point the Froude number is 0.71, therefore it is not a critical point. These curves show that SED does not predict the critical depths correctly.

In computations of E/Y_m and F_c which involve computations of the energy correction coefficient α, and momentum correction coefficient β, respectively SEV, SIV and SED are all used and compared. The results showed that these values and hence E and F_c are insensitive to the method of discharge computation, only the extrema values show very slight variations, like SEV gives 3.5% higher values than SIV which gives 3 % higher values than SED.

For asymmetrical channels, C–y, F_c and E/Y_m curves are plotted by using ASIV and the data of Myers[11] and Rajaratnam and Ahmadi[19] in Fig.(6) and Fig.(7), respectively. Fig.(6) shows that for; B_m = B_{fm} = 25.4 cm, Y_m= 10.16 cm, and Q = 0.0154 m^3 /s, C = k = 2.83 > C_{max} = 1.46. Therefore, there is only one critical depth which is below the flood plain level, which is verified by F_c and E/Y_m curves too. Fig.(7) shows that for; B_m = B_{fm}= 71 cm, Y_m = 9.75 cm and Q = 0.07 m^3/s, the value of C = 0.935 is smaller than C_{max} = 1.106. Then, there is only one critical depth which is above the flood plain and y_c = 1.12 or Y_c = 10.92 cm. Specific energy and Froude number curves verify this result too.

Conclusions

1. The introduction of n_{eq} improves the performance of SIV for rough flood plains. SIV(n_{eq}) predicts the discharge with an error less than 10 %.
2. For asymmetrical channels AFIVE predicts the discharge best, but ASIV gives quite good results too.
3. The discharge computation method used affects the computation of critical depths. Therefore SIV with n_{eq} and ASIV should be used in critical flow computation.
4. Froude number defined by Eq.(5) is consistent with the extrema points of the specific–energy curve both for symmetrical and asymmetrical channels.

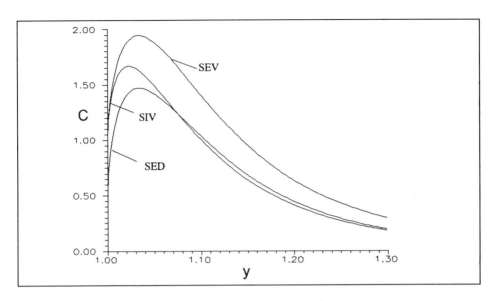

Fig.4   C–y Curve for the data of Petryk and Grand[15]

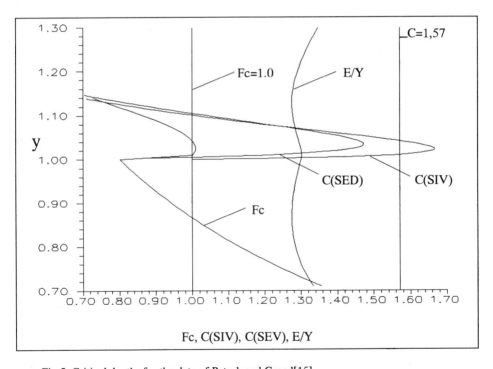

Fig.5   Critical depths for the data of Petryk and Grand[15]

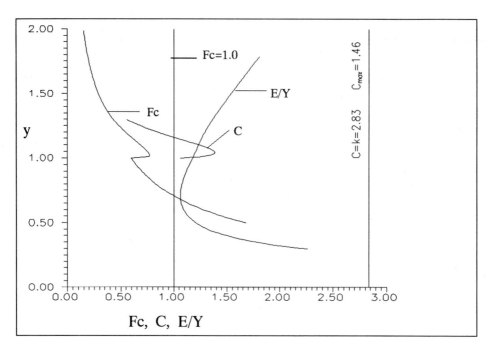

Fig.6 Fc, C-y and E/Y Curves for the data of Myers[11]

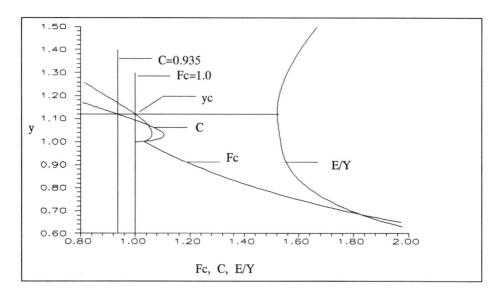

Fig.7 Fc, C-y and E/Y Curves for the of Rajaratnam and Ahmedi[19]

References

1. Black, R.G.,(1982) "Minimum Specific Energy in Compound Open Channel",Discussion of Blalock,   M.E., and Sturm, T.W., Journal of The Hydraulics Division, ASCE, 108(6), 798–800.
2. Blalock, M.E., and Sturm, T.W., (1981) "Minimum Specific Energy in Compound Open Channel", Journal of The Hydraulics Division, ASCE, 107(6), 699–717.
3. Chaudry, M.H.,and Bhallamudi,S.M.,(1988) "Computation of Critical Depth in Symmetrical Compound Channels", Journal of Hydraulic Research, 26(4),377–396.
4. Chow, V.T.,(1959) Open–Channel Hydraulics, McGraw–Hill Book Company.
5. Ervine, D.A., and Baird, J.I.,(1982) "Rating Curves for Rivers with Overbank Flow", Proceedings of the Institution of Civil Engineers, Part 2,73, 465–472.
6. Franz, D.D.,(1982) "Minimum Specific Energy in Compound Open Channel",Discussion of Blalock, M.E., and Sturm, T.W., Journal of The Hydraulics Division, ASCE, 108(6), 800–802.
7. Knight,D.W, and Demetriou,J.D.,(1983) Flood plain and Main Channel Flow Interaction",Journal of The Hydraulics Division, ASCE, 109(8), 1073–1092.
8. Knight, D.W, and Hamed, M.E., (1984) "Boundary Shear in Symmetrical Compound Channels ", Journal of The Hydraulics Division, ASCE, 110(10), 1412–1430.
9. Knight,D.W, Demetriou, J.D.,and Hamed, M.E.(1985)"Stage Discharge Relationship for Compound Channels", Channels and Channel Control Structures,ed. K.V.H Smith, Springer–Verlag,4.21–4.35.
10. Könemann,N., (1982) "Minimum Specific Energy in Compound Open Channel", Discussion of Blalock, M.E., and Sturm, T.W., Journal of The Hydraulics Division, ASCE, 108, 462–464.
11. Myers,R.C.,and Elsawy, E.M.,(1975) "Boundary Shear in Channel with Flood plain",Journal of The Hydraulics Division, ASCE, 101(7), 993–1025.
12. Myers,W.R.C., (1978) "Momentum Transfer in a Compound Channel ", Journal of Hydraulic Research , 16(2), 139–150.
13. Myers,W.R.C., 1987) "Velocity and Discharge in Compound Channels", Journal of The Hydraulics Division, ASCE, 113(6), 753–766.
14. Myers,W.R.C., and Brennan, E.K.,(1990) "Flow Resistance in Compound Channels", Journal of Hydraulic Research , 28(2), 141–155.
15. Petryk, S.,and Grant, E.U., (1978) "Critical Flow in Rivers with Flood Plains ", Journal of The Hydraulics Division, ASCE, 104(5), 583–594.
16. Price, R. K. , and Samuels, P. G., (1980) "A Computational Hydraulic Model for Rivers", Proceedings of the Institution of Civil Engineers, London, Part. 2, 69, March, 87–96.
17. Quintela, A.C.,(1982) "Minimum Specific Energy in Compound Open Channel", Discussion of Blalock, M.E., and Sturm, T.W., Journal of The Hydraulics Division, ASCE, 108, 465–468.
18. Radojkovic, M., and Djordjevic, S.,(1985) "Computation of Discharge Distribution in Compound Channels", Proceedings, 21–st Congress of International Association for Hydraulic Research, Vol.3, 367–371, Melbourne, Australia.
19. Rajaratnam, N., and Ahmadi, R.,(1981) "Hydraulics of Channels with Flood plains", Journal of Hydraulic Research , 19(1), 43–59.
20. Samuels, P. G., ,(1990) "Computation of Critical Depth in Symmetric Compound Channels", Discussion of Chaudry, M.H.,and Bhallamudi,S.M., Journal of Hydraulic Research, 28(1),121–122.
21. Schoellhamer, D.H.,Peters, J.C., and Larock, B.E.,(1985) "Subdivision Froude Number", Journal of The Hydraulics Division, ASCE, 111(7), 1099–1104.
22. Sellin, R.H.,(1964)"A Laboratory Investigation into the Interaction Between the Flow in the Channel of a River and that of its Flood plain", La Houille Blanche, 7, 793–802.
23. Stephenson,D.,and Kolovopoulos,P.(1990) "Effects of Momentum Transfer in Compound Channels", Journal of The Hydraulics Division, ASCE, 116 (12), 1512–1522.
24. Sturm, T. W., and Sadiq A., "Water Surface Profiles and The Compound Channel Froude Number for Rough Flood Plains", Environmental Hydraulics, Lee & Cheung (eds), Balkema, Rotterdam, 1991, 1383–1389.
25. Wormleaton, P. R., Allen, J., and Hadjipanos, P., (1982) " Discharge Assessment in Compound Channel Flow", Journal of The Hydraulics Division, ASCE, 108 (9), 975–994.

26. Wormleaton, P. R., and Hadjipanos, P., (1985) " Flow Distribution in Compound Channels", Journal of The Hydraulics Division, ASCE, 111 (2), 357–361.
27. Wormleaton,P.R., and Merrett, D.J.,(1990)"An Improved Method of Calculation for Steady Uniform Flow in Prismatic Main Channel–Flood plain Sections",Journal of Hydraulic Research, 28(2),157–174.
28. Wright, R. R., and Carstens, M.R., (1970) " Linear Momentum Flux to Overbank Sections", Journal of The Hydraulics Division, ASCE, 96(9),1781–1793.
29. Yuen, K. W. H., and Knight, D.W. " Critical Flow in A Two Stage Channel", International Conference on River Flood Hydraulics, edited by W.R. White, Hydraulic Research Limited, 1990. Published by John Wiley & Sons Ltd.

An application of a new procedure for estimating discharges in meandering overbank flows to field data

J B Wark Engineer, Rivers Group, HR Wallingford, Howbery Park, Wallingford, OXON OX11 8BA, UK.

C S James Associate Professor, Department of Civil Engineering, The University of the Witwatersrand, Johannesburg, Private Bag 3, WITS 2050, South Africa.

SUMMARY

The authors have developed a new procedure for estimating discharge in meandering overbank flow. The procedure was developed based on laboratory experiments in the SERC Flood Channel Facility (FCF) and the University of Aberdeen. The procedure has been applied to field data collected from the River Roding at Abridge in Essex and is shown to predict the measured stage-discharges reasonably well. The sensitivity of the method to variation in bed friction values has been investigated.

1.   Introduction

The calculation of channel conveyance is one of the most common problems in river engineering practice. It has long been recognised that the traditional methods do not account for all of the processes dissipating energy in the case of complex or compound channels. Recently experimental work has been carried out in both straight and meandering overbank flows using the 50m long by 10m wide FCF at HR Wallingford. The data from the experiments with straight compound channels (Phase A) were used by Ackers (1991) to develop an empirical design procedure for straight compound channels. The second phase of the experiments provide information on stage-discharges and flow distributions in meandering compound channels and this has been used by the authors to develop a semi-empirical procedure of estimating discharges in meandering compound channels. The details of the development of the procedure are reported in full in a technical report (James and Wark 1992) and are summarized in two journal papers (James and Wark 1993 1, 2). The main features of the procedure are described below.

2.   The procedure

The flow mechanisms in meandering compound channels are extremely complex and are incompletely understood. In order to predict discharges accurately a model should include quantitative descriptions of the important mechanisms. The procedure developed by the authors is intended to provide a simple, direct method of relating stage and discharge by approximating as many of the mechanisms as possible. Where it was impossible to formulate a predictive model the experimental data was used to develop empirical models. The procedure is as follows.

2nd International Conference on River Flood Hydraulics. Edited by W. R. White and J. Watts
© 1994 HR Wallingford Ltd. Published by John Wiley & Sons Ltd

The channel is divided into the four zones shown in Figure 1 and the various discharges are calculated and summed to give the total.

$$Q_T = Q_1 + Q_2 + Q_3 + Q_4 \qquad (1)$$

The important loss mechanisms for the various zones were identified as:

Zone 1 : main channel

- bed friction
- secondary currents due to overbank flow

The procedure is to calculate bankfull flow (Q_{bf}), either using an inbank method or from flow measurements. The bankfull discharge is then adjusted to account for the effects of overbank secondary currents. The correction factor (Q_1') is based on empirical analysis of the SERC FCF data. Figure 2 shows the resulting functions. At low overbank stages the research showed that the main channel discharge decreases linearly with relative depths up to 0.2. At higher relative depths the discharge starts to rise again. The slopes of the decrease and increase and the point of change depend were found to depend on the channel shape, relative floodplain roughness and sinuosity. The flow in Zone 1 is given by:

$$Q_1 = Q_{bf} Q_1' \qquad (2)$$

The adjustment factor (Q_1') is the **greater** of :

$$Q_1' = 1.0 - 1.69 \, y' \qquad (3)$$

or

$$Q_1' = m \, y' + K \, c \qquad (4)$$

with

$$
\begin{aligned}
m &= 0.0147 \, B^2/A + 0.032 \, f' + 0.169 &\qquad (5)\\
c &= 0.0132 \, B^2/A - 0.302 \, s + 0.851 &\qquad (6)\\
K &= 1.14 - 0.136 \, f' &\qquad (7)\\
y' &= y_2 / (A/B) &\qquad (8)\\
f' &= f_2 / f_1 &\qquad (9)
\end{aligned}
$$

Zone 2 : inner floodplain

- bed friction
- expansion and contraction of flow over the main channel

A model for the expansion and contraction losses was formulated and empirical adjustment factors were derived based on both the SERC FCF and Aberdeen data. These account for the effects of main channel cross section shape, side slope and sinuosity. The wetted perimeter for the inner flood plain is defined as the total wetted surface of the inner flood plain minus the term B(s-1).

The discharge for Zone 2 is given by

$$Q_2 = A_2 V_2 \qquad (10)$$

in which

$$V_2 = \left(\frac{2 g S_o L}{(f_2 L) / (4 R_2) + F_1 F_2 K_e} \right)^{1/2} \qquad (11)$$

with

$$F_1 = 0.1 B^2/A \qquad \text{for } B^2/A < 10$$

$$F_1 = 1.0 \qquad \text{for } B^2/A \geq 10 \qquad (12)$$

$$F_2 = s/1.4 \qquad (13)$$

$$K_e = C_{sl} C_{wd} (C_{sse} (1 - y_2/(y_2 + h))^2 + C_{ssc} K_c) \qquad (14)$$

$$C_{sl} = 2(W_2 - B)/W_2 \qquad (15)$$

$$C_{wd} = 0.02 (B^2/A) + 0.69 \qquad (16)$$

$$C_{sse} = 1.0 - S_s/5.7$$
(but C_{sse} not less than 0.1) $\qquad (17)$

$$C_{ssc} = 1.0 - S_s/2.5$$
(but C_{ssc} not less than 0.1) $\qquad (18)$

K_c is the basic contraction coefficient as given in Table 1.

Table 1 Contraction loss coefficients (Rouse, 1950)

$y_2/(y_2+h)$:	0.00	0.10	0.20	0.30	0.40	0.50	0.60	0.70	0.80	0.90	1.00
K_c :	0.50	0.48	0.45	0.41	0.36	0.29	0.21	0.13	0.07	0.01	0.00

Zones 3 and 4 : outer floodplains

- bed friction

Flow in the outer flood plain zones is assumed to be solely controlled by friction. The zonal discharges are calculated using an appropriate friction equation with the division lines separating these zones from Zone 2 excluded from the wetted perimeter. The flood plain slope S_o is used in the calculation.

In addition the experimental evidence shows that there is considerable bulk exchange of flow between the main channel and the floodplain. The discharge in both the main channel and inner floodplain zones vary along a wave length. However for the purposes of stage-discharge estimation it is assumed that these discharges are constant. If the effects of the non friction losses are neglected, ie $Q_1{}'$ is taken as 1.0 and the expansion contraction terms for zone 2 are ignored then the procedure becomes the divided channel method referred to as Bed Friction Only (BFO) below.

3. Application to field data

The procedure presented above was developed and verified using laboratory model data. There is very little field information available regarding the performance of full scale meandering channels with flood plains. The only detailed field investigation known at present was carried out on the River Roding in Essex, see Sellin and Giles (1989) or Sellin et al (1990). One other site is also currently being investigated by Sellin. A physical model of a 250m long section of the River Blackwater in Hampshire has been constructed in the SERC FCF at a scale of 1:5. Field measurements are scheduled to commence in early 1993 and are to run for three years. The results of this study were not available at the time of writing but should provide improved validation data.

The Roding study

The Roding is a relatively small river with a channel width and depth of about 7m and 1.5m respectively. Full details of the field and laboratory measurements carried out on this site are available in Sellin and Giles (1988) and Sellin et al (1990). The study reach lies downstream of Abridge and as part of a flood alleviation scheme a two stage channel was formed by excavating approximately 30m wide berms on either side of the main channel (Figures 3 and 4). The original channel was untouched and remained in the natural state with a bankfull capacity of approximately 3 cumecs. The resulting flood channel has a low flow channel which meanders within the berm limits with a sinuosity of 1.38 and a wave length of approximately 96m. Hence the channel does not possess outer floodplain zones. The berms were formed at a level below the surrounding floodplain and were intended to provide extra flood discharge capacity and so relieve flooding on the existing floodplain for flows with a return period of up to thirty years. Shortly after completion of the scheme it became clear that the actual capacity of the channel was less than the design value. This was partly assigned to the difference between the assumed berm vegetation (short grass) and the actual vegetation which was extremely dense. The design case assumed that the berm would be grazed by farm animals but in fact this did not happen and the National Rivers Authority (NRA) were forced to cut the growth mechanically at considerable cost.

The field and laboratory projects investigated the effects of different maintenance policies on the channel capacity. Most of the conditions investigated were with the flood berms covered, totally or partially, with extremely dense vegetation and verification of calibrated bed roughness values was not possible. The roughness values varied strongly both with stage and during the growing season. The data recorded after a full cut on the berm showed much less variation in berm roughness values and so were felt to provide the best information for validation of the author's procedure. The method was applied to the stage-discharge data from the following two cases.

P2 The berm growth was cut immediately after the summer growing season and so the berms were covered in short grass.

M2 The laboratory model data corresponding to the smooth berm case (P2 on the prototype).

In order to apply the procedure to these measurements the seven available surveyed sections were used to provide reach averaged areas, widths etc for both flow zones at stages up to 1.0m above the berm level and these are given in Table 2. The information provided by Sellin and Giles (1988) and Sellin et al (1990) combined with widely accepted guidelines, Chow(1959) and Henderson (1966) allowed the berm Manning's n values for the two cases, P2 and M2 to be estimated as 0.050 and the main channel Manning's n was estimated as 0.044. The longitudinal slope of the berm was 1.405×10^{-3}.

Table 2 Reach averaged geometric parameters

y (m)	Area (m^2)	BFO and JW methods Width (m)	Wetted Perimeter (m)	BFOVD method Area (m^2)	Wetted Perimeter (m)
Main channel at bankfull					
0.0	5.3	7.1	7.7	7.7	7.7
Zone 2 or flood plain					
0.1	2.1	20.5	10.8	1.4	13.6
0.2	4.4	25.3	15.7	3.0	18.4
0.3	7.1	27.9	18.4	5.0	21.1
0.4	10.0	29.0	19.5	7.1	22.2
0.5	12.9	29.9	20.4	9.4	23.0
0.6	15.9	30.4	20.9	11.7	23.6
0.7	19.0	30.9	21.4	14.0	24.1
0.8	22.1	31.3	21.9	16.4	24.6
0.9	25.3	31.8	22.5	18.9	25.2
1.0	28.5	32.4	23.1	21.4	25.8

The measured and predicted stage-discharge curves for these two cases are shown in Figure 5 and the mean errors in Table 3. The authors' method has been compared with two other methods: bed friction only using the authors' horizontal division (BFO) and bed friction only with the more widely used vertical division of the cross-section at the main channel edges (BFOVD). It is apparent that the present method improves the overall accuracy of the predicted discharges and that by ignoring the non-friction head losses discharge will be over-predicted by about 10% on average with the horizontal division and by about 25% with the vertical division.

Table 3 Errors in predicting overbank discharges

Case Method	P2 Mean Error (%)	Standard Deviation (%)	M2 Mean Error (%)	Standard Deviation (%)
BFO	9.5	9.0	7.3	8.6
James and Wark	-2.0	1.7	-2.2	3.2
BFOVD	24.6	29.0	19.4	33.0

Note   %Error = $100^*(Q_{calc} - Q_{meas})/Q_{meas}$

Some sensitivity tests were carried out to investigate the effect of berm roughness on the total channel capacity. Table 4 shows the variation of mean errors for both methods with berm roughness for case P2. Both methods over-predict with low berm roughness and under-predict with high berm roughness. The authors method always gives smaller discharges because the non-friction energy losses in the two zones are explicitly accounted for. The difference between the mean errors for the two methods reduces from >100% at very low roughness to about 10% at the calibrated roughness. At higher roughnesses the difference between the two methods remains approximately constant at about 10%.

Table 4 Sensitivity tests on the effect of floodplain roughness

Zone 2		Mean %Errors		Difference in Means	
Manning n	BFO	JW	BFOVD	(BFO - JW)	(BFOVD - JW)
0.01	305	142	507	163	365
0.02	122	78	204	44	126
0.03	61	40	102	21	62
0.04	31	16	51	15	35
0.05	10	-2	22	12	24
0.06	1	-10	1	11	11
0.08	-14	-25	-24	11	1
0.10	-24	-33	-39	9	-6
0.18	-40	-47	-66	7	-22
0.30	-48	-58	-80	10	-22

These results show that as the floodplain becomes smoother the two methods diverge more. Thus the effect of increased flood plain roughness is to make the non-friction head losses less important. Bed friction is likely to be the most important single source of energy loss in natural rivers and remains a potential source of significant error in conveyance predictions. The estimation of bed friction factors is largely subjective even given the comprehensive guidelines presented in standard texts such as Chow (1959) and Henderson (1966). Thus it is not possible to give general guidelines on the choice of bed friction value as site specific aspects are likely to govern the relative importance of the various loss mechanisms. Tests should be carried out for each application to gauge the sensitivity of the solution to variations in roughness values.

4. Conclusions

The authors have developed a new procedure for calculating conveyance in meandering channels with overbank flow. The procedure explicitly accounts for non-friction energy losses and was developed and verified against laboratory model data.

The new procedure is based on a horizontal division of the cross-section. This represents a significant change to the current practice of using vertical divisions to separate the main channel and flood plains.

The procedure has been applied to the best field data available and has been shown to give improved predictions compared to current practice.

The sensitivity of the results to variations in bed roughness value has been investigated. The non-friction energy losses are shown to be less important as the floodplain is roughened. Bed friction remains the most significant source of energy loss in rivers with overbank flow.

Acknowledgements

The work presented was done under contract for the National Rivers Authority. Their permission for its publication is gratefully acknowledged. The work was done during the first author's sabbatical visit to HR Wallingford, for which additional financial support was provided by the Foundation for Research Development and the Murray and Roberts Charles Skeen Fellowship. The contributions made by Dr Paul Samuels, Dr Nigel Walmsley and Mrs Mary Johnstone are greatly appreciated. The assistance of Mr A Pepper, of the NRA, in providing the surveyed river sections is gratefully acknowledged.

Notation

A	cross-sectional area
A	unsubscripted, cross-sectional area of main channel
B	top width of main channel
C_{sl}	length coefficient for expansion and contraction losses, zone 2
C_{ssc}	side slope coefficient for contraction loss, zone 2
C_{sse}	side slope coefficient for expansion loss, zone 2
C_{wd}	shape coefficient for expansion and contraction losses, zone 2
c	coefficient in equation for zone 1 adjustment factor
F_1	factor for non-friction losses in zone 2 associated with main channel geometry
F_2	factor for additional non-friction losses in zone 2 associated with main channel sinuosity
f	Darcy-Weisbach friction factor
f'	ratio of flood plain and main channel Darcy-Weisbach friction factors
g	gravitational acceleration
h	hydraulic depth of main channel, $= A/B$
K	coefficient in equation for zone 1 adjustment factor
K_e	factor for expansion and contraction losses in zone 2
K_c	contraction coefficient
L	meander wavelength
m	coefficient in equation for zone 1 adjustment factor
Q	zonal discharge
Q_{bf}	main channel bankfull discharge
Q_T	total discharge
Q_1'	adjustment factor for zone 1 discharge
R	hydraulic radius
S_o	flood plain gradient
S_s	cotangent of main channel side slope
s	channel sinuosity
V	flow velocity

W_2	width of zone 2
y_2	flow depth on flood plain at main channel bank
y'	dimensionless flow depth on flood plain, $= y_2/(A/B)$

Subscripts

| 1 | zone 1 |
| 2 | zone 2 |

References

Ackers P (1991) The hydraulic design of straight compound channels, Report SR 281, HR Wallingford, UK.

Chow V T (1959) Open-Channel Hydraulics, International Student Edition, McGraw-Hill.

Henderson F M (1966) Open Channel Flow, Macmillan.

James C S and Wark J B (1992) Conveyance estimation for meandering channels, HR Wallingford, Report SR 329, December.

James C S and Wark J B (1993) Conveyance estimation for meandering compound channels, Part 1 Development, Submitted to Jrnl. Hydr. resch.

James C S and Wark J B (1993) Conveyance estimation for meandering compound channels, Part 2 Application and verification, Submitted to Jrnl. Hydr. resch.

Rouse H (Ed) (1950) Engineering Hydraulics, John Wiley and Sons, New York.

Sellin R H J and Giles A (1988) Two stage channel flow, Final Report for Thames Water Authority, Department of Civil Engineering, University of Bristol.

Sellin R H J, Giles A and van Beeston D P (1990) Two stage channel flow, Post-Implementation of a two-stage channel in the River Roding, Essex, J IWEM, 1990, Vol4, pp 119, 130.

Figures

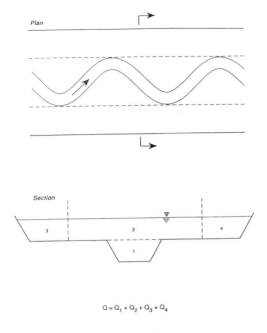

$$Q = Q_1 + Q_2 + Q_3 + Q_4$$

Figure 1 Division of meandering channel into zones

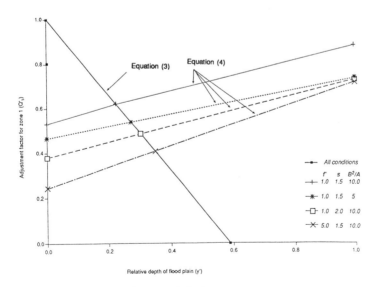

Figure 2 Adjustment factor for zone 1 discharge

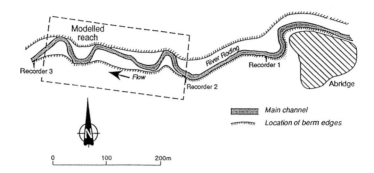

Figure 3 Location plan of the area (after Sellin et al)

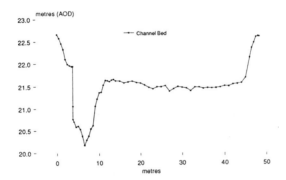

Figure 4 Sample cross section

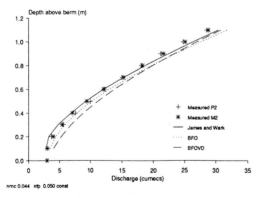

Figure 5 Stage discharges

RIVER FLOOD HYDRAULICS
22–25 March 1994: York, England

MODELLING OF FLOOD HYDRAULICS
IN COMPOUND CHANNELS

by

R. Kohane and B. Westrich
Institut für Wasserbau, Universität Stuttgart

Summary

A one–dimensional multiple strip flow model is proposed for river flood calculations. The numerical model is calibrated and validated by laboratory flume experiments with uniform and non-uniform flows. The study shows the influence of the turbulent shear acting at the interface between the main channel and the flood plain and the effect of diverging and converging levees on the tripwise flow velocity and water level.

1   Introduction

River flood hydraulics can be classified as flows in channels with compound cross sections. By the inundation of flood plains there is a significant difference of flow velocities within the flow cross section, i.e. between the deeper main channel and the shallow flood plains. For river flood management and planning of flood protection measures not only the water level but also the flow velocity and discharge capacity of the different flow compartments (i.e. main channel, flood pllains) is required. The 1D strip model is very useful for engineering application, as it accounts for dynamic interaction between the fast flowing water in the main channel and the slow flowing water on the flood plains. The mutual exchange of water and momentum is described by two specific terms expressing the convective and turbulent exchange of lateral momentum.

A multiple-strip model has been tested and verified by laboratory experiments conducted in a tilting flume (12 m long, 1 m wide) with a main channel of trapezoidal cross section and vertical walls as levees. Uniform and non-uniform (backwater) flow, and flow with converging and diverging levees have been investigated. The measurements were focussed on the mean flow parameters such as the percentage discharge in the main channel and the flood plain respectively and water depths. By changing alignment of the levees, the flow rate and the downstream water level a great variability of dynamic interaction between the main channel and the flood plains has been produced and measured for comparison with the numerical model. The evaluation of the different terms in the governing

2nd International Conference on River Flood Hydraulics. Edited by W. R. White and J. Watts
© 1994 HR Wallingford Ltd. Published by John Wiley & Sons Ltd

equations enables to illustrate the influence of turbulent and convective momentum exchange. The experimental results show the predominant influence of the non-uniformity of river flow on the momentum balance. Therefore, in many flow situations with changing alignment of levees and width of the flood plains the modelling of the interfacial shear is not required for the description of the flood hydraulics. The strip model shows a fairly good agreement with the experiments in terms of discharge per strip and water depth.

2 Flow Computation Model

When computing the flow in a channel or river of compound cross section usually one has the choice between either a one dimensional or a two dimensional approach. The model described here is a half way compromise between the two traditional approaches and is particulary suitable for long range backwater computations in compound channels which have moderate variations of cross section geometry . The model is based on a so called multiple strip method which was first introduced by Yen et al. (1985) and later further developed by the authors. Details of the method can be found in Kohane, 1990. Only an overview of the method will be given here.

Flow computation with the multiple strip method begins by subdividing each channel or river cross section along the computational reach in subsections having different flow depths and roughness caracteristics (Fig. 1). Corresponding channel subsections define channel strips extending along the reach. Each channel strip will normally have different flow conditions depending primarily on the flow depth and the roughness caracteristics. Lateral exchange of mass and momentum between neighbour channel strips will usually be present caused either by changes of the cross section geometry or by the influence of a high water surface elevation at the downstream section of the reach. The flow depth and the flow velocity of each channel strip will therefore usually vary along the channel reach.

For computing the flow along each channel strip a one dimensional momentum equation is used (Eq. 1) which includes extra terms to account for lateral turbulent momentum exchange and momentum exchange due to lateral mass transfer between channel strips.

$$\frac{d}{dx}\left(\frac{\beta Q}{A}\right) + gA\frac{dh}{dx} = -gAJ_f - \int_\sigma uq_\sigma d\sigma$$

(Eq. 1)

The bed friction in (Eq. 1) will be computed either by using the formulas of Manning-Strickler or Darcy-Weisbach. Turbulent shear stress along the vertical interface separating neighbour strips will be only considered at the interface between the main channel and the floodplains. The apparent shear stress at this interface will be computed using (Eq. 2).

$$\tau_{xy} = -2\rho\kappa \left(u_{ch} - u_p \right)^2 \qquad \text{(Eq. 2)}$$

Conservation of mass along each channel strip is imposed by specifying a continuity equation (Eq. 3) for each channel strip.

$$\frac{dq}{dx} = -\int q_o \, d\sigma \qquad \text{(Eq. 3)}$$

(Eqs. 1 and 3) apply to every channel strip resulting in a system of ordinary non-linear differential equationns which is solved simultaneously using any standard method for solving first order ordinary differential equations (e.g. 4th order Runge-Kutta method).

The computational procedure begins by assigning initial values of flow depth and partial discharge to each channel strip at the initial section. Flow computation is performed always following the direction of the flow, starting at the upstream section and moving stepwise along the reach. In each computational step the values of the flow depth and the flow discharge of each channel strip are computed for the corresponding cross section. Computing subcritical flow moving from the upstream to the downstream section has the disadvantage of not being able to account for a known water surface elevation at the downstream section of the reach. Trying to compute the flow moving in the opposite direction has proved to produce always unstable solutions (Kohane, 1990). Backwater computations with known downstream conditions can be still achieved by using a special iterative procedure.

3   Computation and Experiments

Experimental and computational investigations are carried out for different flow situations in a channel of compound cross section. Fig. 2 shows the laboratory flume in which the experiments are conduced and the channel cross section being considered. The channel cross section can be assumed to represent one half of the cross section of a symmetric channel having a central main channel with inclined banks and floodplains on both sides of it. The channel bed is artificially roughened with small gravel particles having a mean diameter of approx. 4 mm. Vertical smooth glas walls on the sides of the flume delimit the cross section of the main channel and the floodplain. Flow depths are measured in the main channel with point gages which are distributed along the channel reach at equally spaced distances. The total discharge and the partial flow of the main channel are measured at the entrance of the flume with magnetic inductive discharge meters. At the downstream end of the flume the partial floodplain flow is measured with a V-notch weir. Flow distribution between the main channel and the floodplain is also measured inside the channel reach for which a special procedure is used. The flows in the main channel and the floodplain are separated with a thin vertical wall extending from the section at which flow is to be measured to the end section of the flume. Water depths at the measuring section are adjusted to their corresponding values previously measured in the absence of the separation wall. The flow distribution is obtained by measuring the partial discharge on the floodplain side of the channel at the downstream end of the flume.

The tested flow situations are computed using two different approaches. The first approach is based on a one dimensional model which includes correction terms for computing the momentum flux and the friction slope in the compound cross section, thus accounting for the difference of flow depths, flow velocities and roughness caracteristics present in the cross section. The effect of the turbulent shear stress acting on the vertical interface between the main channel and the floodplain is considered in the one dimensional model in a simplified manner by either including or excluding the length of the vertical interface for computing the wetted perimeter of the main channel.

The second computational approach is based on the multiple strip method discussed in the previous section. The turbulent shear stress at the vertical interface between the main channel and the floodplain is calculated using (Eq. 2), where the empirical constant χ is assigned values ranging from 0.0 to 0.02. In both models the bed shear stress is calculated using Darcy-Weisbach's formula combined with Einstein-Horton's method to account for non-uniform roughness distribution along the cross sections of the main channel and the floodplain.

The investigations are carried out for two different channel geometries. First a compound channel having a prismatic main channel and a prismatic floodplain is considered. For this channel geometry both uniform and gradually varied flow situations are investigated. Experiments are carried out for different combinations of the main flow parameters defined by the total discharge, the channel slope, the uniform flow depth and the ratio of flow depth to uniform flow depth at the downstream section of the reach in the case of gradually varied flow. Results are discussed based on a comparison between measured and computed values of flow depth and ratio of partial flows of the main channel and the floodplain. The second channel geometry corresponds to a prismatic main channel and a non-prismatic floodplain. The floodplain width either increases (expanding cross section) or decreasses (contracting cross section) in the direction of the flow. Again the main flow parameters are varied and the measured and computed results are compared against each other.

4   Discussion of Results

The most important results of the investigations are summarized in the following. The computational approach based on the multiple strip method considering (Eq. 2) to compute the turbulent shear stress at the vertical interface between main channel and floodplain delivers for all tested flow situations the most accurate results.

Figs. 3 and 4 show a comparison between measured and computed values of the flow depth of the main channel and of the ratio of partial flows between the main channel and the floodplain along a backwater curve in a full prismatic channel. The influence of the turbulent shear stress between the main channel and the floodplain seems to be in this case only important when looking at the distribution of discharges or velocities within the channel cross section. For flow computations in which accurate discharge or velocity distributions are needed use of the multiple strip method with values of χ in (Eq. 2) ranging from .01 to .02 is recommended. For backwater computations aimed on determining the water surface elevation along the computational reach the influence of the turbulent lateral momentum exchange can be neglected. In such cases one dimensional models can be used.

In channels with non-prismatic floodplains use of one dimensional models may lead to inaccurate computational results of flow depth and flow distribution especially in regions where the width of the floodplain cross section increasses in the main flow direction. Fig. 5 shows that in the case of a divergent floodplain the one-dimensional model overestimates the lateral flow from the main channel to the floodplain, especially in the upstream part of the floodplain transition for small ratios of floodplain to main channel width. The results in Fig. 5 for different values of χ show that the turbulent momentum exchange term has practically no influence on the results of the flow computation.

Even in prismatic channels with backwater flows the turbulent momentum exchange between the main channel and the floodplains is much less significant than the lateral convective momentum exchange due to mass transfer as indicated by the ratio $(\tau_l/\rho)/(q\,Y_p)$ in Fig. 6.

5   Conclusions

The proposed strip flow is useful for flood flow computation of rivers with compound cross sections and can be taken as an improved description of the fractional discharge and water level elevation in rivers with irregular cross sections and backwater effects. However, the applicability is restricted to flows with moderate lateral momentum and bottom friction controlled energy loss.

References

Evers, P. (1983): Untersuchung der Strömungsvorgänge in gegliederten Gerinnen mit extremen Rauheitsunterschieden. Mitteilungen Heft 15, Institut für Waserbau und Wasserwirtschaft, Rheinisch-Westfällsche Technische Hochschule Aachen.

Kohane, R. (1991): Berechnungsmethoden für Hochwasserabfluß in Fließgewässern mit oberströmten Vorländern. Mitteilungen Heft 73, Institut für Wasserbau, Universität Stuttgart.

Wormleaton, P.R.; Allen, J.: Hadjipanos, P. (1980): Discharge Assessment in Compound Channel Flow. Journal of the Hydraulics Division, ASCE, Vol. 108, No. HY9, 1982.

Yen, B.C.; Camacho, R.; Kohane, R.; Westrich, B. (1985): Significance of Floodplains in Backwater Computation, 21st IAHR Congress, Australia, 1985.

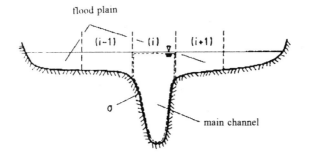

flood plain

main channel

Fig. 1   Compound flow cross section

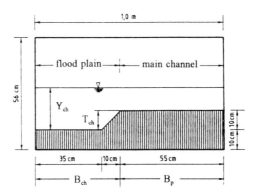

Fig. 2   Laboratory flume

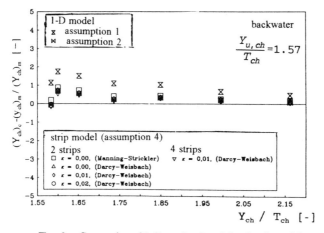

Fig. 3   Comparsion of 1-dimensional model and strip model

421

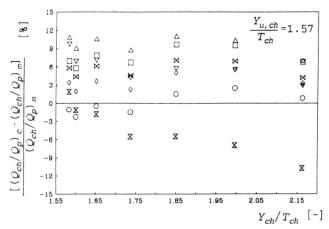

Fig. 4 Comparsion of measured and computed discharge

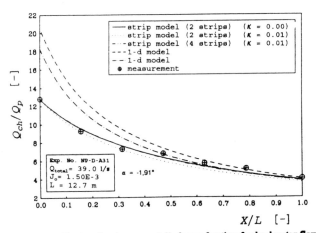

Fig. 5 Computed and measured discharge fraction for backwater flow

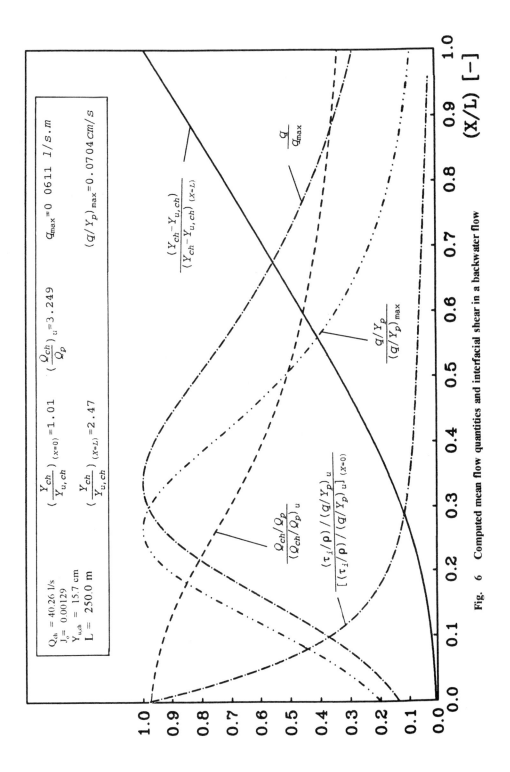

Fig. 6 Computed mean flow quantities and interfacial shear in a backwater flow

Chapter Nine

Hydraulics of Flood Flow

2nd International Conference on
RIVER FLOOD HYDRAULICS
22–25 March 1994: York, England

HYDRAULIC RESISTANCE OF RIVER BANKS
COVERED WITH TREES AND BRUSHWOOD

Prof. Dr.-Ing. Anton Nuding

Professor of Hydraulic Engineering; Dept. of Civil Engineering,
Polytechnical College Biberach, Germany
Hydraulic Expert of Lahmeyer International Consulting Engineers,
 Frankfurt, Germany;

Abstract

For flood flows in a watercourse which is in or has been modified into a natural state, a contact zone will exist between that part of flow which is running through an area containing a large amount of vegetation, normally the flood plain, and that part of flow in the main channel which is free of vegetation. In this interactive contact zone with shedding of vortices due to different flow velocities on both sides of the interface, strong eddies will be produced which hamper the main flow.

Applying the shear flow equation for free turbulence, relationships have been developed herein for the lateral distribution of flow velocity and for the resistance factor λ_T, similar to the PRANDTL-COLEBROOK friction factor. In extensive test series calibration of these relationships were carried out to describe quantitatively the hydraulic effects of the vegetation simulated by cylindric elements and by bushes.

The new empiric-mathematical model is valid for compound channel flow and different roughness in the cross section, caused either by different wall structures or by vegetation, and allows the calculation of the mean flow velocity v_m and discharge Q by using a function of basic parameters, which are independent and directly determinable. The error margin of the results is determined by the difficulties to gain the parameters necessary and is about 20% for the friction factor, but is reduced to $\pm$ 6 % for the discharge Q, owing to the

application of λ_T in the form of $\sqrt{\dfrac{1}{\lambda_T}}$.

Introduction

The problems of the hydraulic resistance of wooded river banks have been the subject of the hydraulic science for several decades, just like the accurate evaluation of the flow resistance for compound channel flow. In the early sixties, FELKEL measured a 30 % reduction of the flood discharge in a trapezoidal flume with side slopes of 1:1 and banks covered by willow trees, as compared to a rough wall boundary. About 1970 especially the "Flaechenabzugs-verfahren" spread over Germany and is used today by most of the hydraulic engineers. This procedure is based on the assumption that the vegetation area A_v does not have to be considered in the calculation of the hydraulic radius of the channel; only

2nd International Conference on River Flood Hydraulics. Edited by W. R. White and J. Watts

the wetted perimeter of the main cross section $l_{u,F}$ and, in addition, the water depths at the vertical boundary of the vegetation zones h_T are of importance:

$$r_{hy,F} = \frac{A_F}{l_{u,F} + \Sigma h_T}$$

with A_F, $r_{hy,F}$, and $l_{u,F}$ as cross section, hydraulic radius and wetted perimeter of the main channel part without the vegetation zone

The discharge Q is then evaluated by the MANNING-STRICKLER formula. A detailed consideration of the structure of vegetation and the flow pattern is not possible. Therefore, these early formulae are only a rough approximation of the complex phenomenon. In 1975 it was extended by the method of PETRYK/BOSMAJAN which analysed the flow through vegetation of flood plains. Other methods were published by OBENDORF, EVERS and WORMLEATON [1]. They also derived empirical relationships to estimate the flow resistance as a function of geometry and the different velocities between the flood plain and the main channel.

Intensified research activities were carried out between 1980 and 1985, considering the turbulent flow phenomenon. These new methods are based on the general flow equation of DARCY/WEISBACH with relationships for the friction factor λ_T as part of the total friction coefficient

$$v_m = \sqrt{\frac{1}{\lambda_{tot}}} \cdot \sqrt{8 \cdot g \cdot r_{hy} \cdot I_E} \qquad (1)$$

with:

v_m	=	average cross sectional flow velocity
λ_{tot}	=	PRANDTL-COLEBROOK resistance coefficient which is a superposition of λ_W of river bed roughness and of λ_T at the interactive vegetation boundary
r_{hy}	=	hydraulic radius
g	=	gravity acceleration
I_E	=	energy gradient

As a consequence of the high turbulent shear stresses generated at the vertical interface of the vegetation zone and the main channel, an intensive vortex and momentum transfer has to be considered in every theoretical approach. The objective of these studies therefore was to develop a one-dimensional model, based on simple turbulence assumptions. The activities culminated in the results of PASCHE, BERTRAM, MERTENS and KAISER, recently published in DVWK (German Association for Water Resources and Land Improvements) [2] and DFG (German Research Foundation) [3] bulletins.

The shortcomings of these procedures however are found in their multiple interrelations and iterations, in their coefficients closely related to their experimental arrangements and in the complications if they were to be used in practice. The sophisticated calculations, esp. of PASCHE [4], simulate an exact result not considering, however, the many other unknown influences in planning natural watercourses.

A new method is presented in this paper, based on an analysis and on additional measurements by the author. A numerical model is derived by which the flow resistance of the vegetated flood plain with trees, bushes and shrubs and even compound cross sections with respect to the flow in the main channel can

428

be predicted. Utilized as computational module in a program for water profile calculations, a number of field verifications in natural rivers were carried out. The complete theoretical description, all experimental analyses and examples for the practical application are given in [5].

Theory and Structure of Flow

The mechanism of interaction in the vicinity of the vertical interface between the flow in the vegetation zone A_V and the free flow in A_F seems to be similar to the one observed in compound cross sections. On both sides of the interface a transition region exists where an intensive mass and momentum transfer dominates the flow pattern.

In all the turbulence models, the resistance due to the momentum exchange is also analysed by subdividing the total cross section into different parts with different horizontal distribution of flow velocity v(y), as shown in Fig. 1. The new methods described in [3] deal with the interactive process along the transition region by balancing the vortex production and vortex dissipation. They assume the existence of wall turbulence based on PRANDTL's hypothesis with imaginary turbulent shear stress and the application of the logarithmic law for velocity distribution.

In this study, however, the lateral velocity variation v(y) is characterized as a function of shear flow at the boundary of a free jet entering an area of slow flow, with a turning point at the joint face. Therefore, the relationships for the horizontal distribution of v(y), the shear stress τ_T (y) and finally for the resistance factor λ_T have to be derived from the shear flow equation of free turbulence [6].

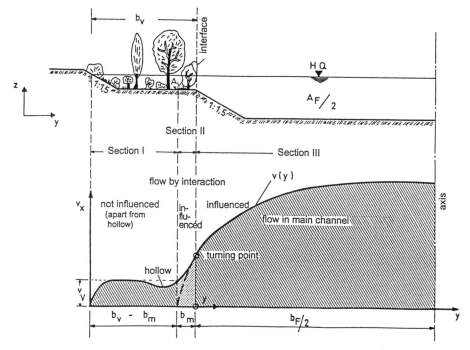

Fig. 1 Lateral distribution of velocity v(y) on both sides of an interface

The physical process of interaction between the different zones of velocities v(y) is characterized by the exchange of eddies with high turbulence levels:

- Eddies with a small longitudinal velocity v_x will be transported (or "shot") from the vegetation zone A_V into the free flow section A_F and there will reduce the flow velocity from $v_{o,F}$ to real velocity v_F ($v_{o,F}$ = fictive longitudinal flow velocity in A_F without considering the friction of the interface).
- At the same time but at other places, eddies with a higher longitudinal velocity will be transported into the vegetation zone and there will increase the velocity v_V within a small area b_m.

Flood Plain Pattern

The flood plain velocity v_V is dominated by the non-submerged roughness elements. It can be expressed similarly to the DARCY-WEISBACH equation Eq. (1):

$$v_V = \sqrt{\frac{1}{\lambda_V}} \cdot \sqrt{8 \cdot g \cdot r_{hy,V} \cdot I_E} \tag{2}$$

with: $r_{hy,V} = \dfrac{A_V}{l_{u,V}}$ ($l_{u,V}$ without h_T)

and is constant in A_V. A homogeneous velocity-distribution in vertical and horizontal direction is due to the relatively high influence of the resistance of the plants than of the resistance of the rough wall-surface. In all the measurements, a non-logarithmic velocity-distribution was yield.

For practical use, the hydraulic radius $r_{hy,V}$ may be replaced by the water depth h_T on the flood plain. The vegetation resistance factor λ_V which contains the drag coefficient c_{WR} is given according to previous investigations by LINDNER [7] and KAISER [8] and is (if, in the case of a dense vegetation, the minor wall roughness of the flood plain is neglected):

$$\sqrt{\frac{1}{\lambda_V}} = \sqrt{\frac{1}{4 \cdot \omega_p \cdot h_T \cdot c_{WR}}} \tag{3}$$

with ω_p = specific vegetation number which characterizes the density of vegetation

$$\omega_p = \frac{d_p}{a_x \cdot a_y}$$

with a_x and a_y are the spaces between the elements in longitudinal (x) and lateral (y) direction and c_{WR} is the drag coefficient which ranges from 0.6 to 2.5 according to the form of elements (normally c_{WR} = 1.0).
(d_p = diameter of vegetation elements)
ω_p is normally between 0.1 [1/m] for light vegetation arrangements and 3.0 [1/m] for dense vegetation.
The equation for the flow velocity in A_V therefore is:

$$v_V = \sqrt{\frac{2 \cdot g \cdot I_E}{\omega_P \cdot c_{WR}}} \qquad (4)$$

The area of A_V which contributes to the eddy production is of limited width. Only in a small area the reduction of the shear stress, induced at the imaginary interface, will occur where the velocity v_T at the interface is reduced to v_V, owing to the wake effect after vegetation elements (SCHLICHTING [6]). This cooperat- ing width b_m therefore depends on the wake width b_N which is found by experiments to be:

$$b_N = 3.2 \cdot \sqrt{a_x \cdot d_P} \qquad (5)$$

The width b_m is limited either by the real width of $b_V = A_V/h_T$ or is equal to a width a_y in the case of regularly arranged elements (only for tree trunk vegetation) like a "vegetation channel". Nevertheless, a minimum value for b_m was also observed, being $b_m > 0.15\ h_T$.
Hence the complete set of formulae for the width b_m is:

if:	$b_N > a_y$	:	$b_m = a_y$	
	$b_N < a_y$	:	$b_m = b_N$	(6)
	$b_m \geq b_V$	:	$b_m = b_V$	
	$b_m \leq 0.15\ h_T$	:	$b_m = 0.15 \cdot h_T$	

Main Channel Flow in A_F
The velocity distribution $v(y)$ in A_F is based on the famous equation for momentum transfer and turbulent apparent shear stress (BOUSSINESQ theorem for viscous flow):

$$\tau_T(y) = \rho \cdot e_T \cdot \frac{dv}{dy} \qquad (7)$$

with:
$\tau_T(y) =$ turbulent shear stress for interaction
$\rho \cdot \epsilon_T =$ apparent kinematic viscosity of water eddies
$dv/dy =$ lateral velocity gradient
The apparent kinematic viscosity ϵ_T can be described, according to SCHLICHTING [6], as:

$$e_T = b_m^2 \left[B^* \cdot lg \left(\frac{v_{o,F}}{v_V} \right) \right]^2 \cdot \left| \frac{dv}{dy} \right| \qquad (8)$$

The ratio of the shear velocity $v_{o,F}/v_V$ is the power or the impulse for every interactive process. It is equal to the ratio of the kinetic energy $v_{o,F}^2/2g$ with the fictive mean velocity in A_F without the hampering interaction and $v_V^2/2g$ with the mean velocity in A_V.
Replacing Eq. (7) by Eq. (8), the turbulent shear stress in A_F is:
The analysis of a number of velocity measurements in laboratory tests showed a hyperbolic curve of the apparent shear stress along the transition region:

$$\tau_T(y) = \rho \cdot b_m^2 \left[B^* \cdot lg \left(\frac{v_{o,F}}{v_v} \right) \right]^2 \cdot \left| \frac{dv}{dy} \right| \cdot \frac{dv}{dy} \tag{9}$$

$$\tau_{T,xy} = \tau_{tot}(y) = \tau_{T,max} \cdot \frac{b_m}{y} \tag{10}$$

The qualitative variation of τ_T distribution and $v(y)$ distribution is presented in Fig. 2.

With the slip velocity $\left(v_T^* \right)^2 = \frac{\tau_{T,max}}{\rho}$ at the interface, the differential equation for the lateral velocity distribution yields (according to the historical procedure of deriving the resistance law):

$$\frac{dv}{dy} = \frac{v_T^*}{B^* \cdot lg \left(\frac{v_{o,F}}{v_v} \right) \cdot \sqrt{b_m \cdot y}} \tag{11}$$

According to a dimensional analysis, B^* is replaced by:

$$B^* = \frac{2}{K} \cdot \sqrt{\frac{h_T}{r_{hy,V}}} \tag{12}$$

After a regressional analysis of experimental measurements the constant factor K was estimated to K = 2.2.
Eq. (11) was integrated along y to give the horizontal distribution of flow velocity:

$$\frac{v(y)}{v_T^*} = K \cdot \frac{1}{lg \left(\frac{v_{o,F}}{v_v} \right)} \cdot \sqrt{\frac{h_T}{r_{hy,V}}} \cdot \sqrt{\frac{y}{b_m}} \tag{13}$$

The ratio y/b_m in Eq. (13) is an imaginary roughness, similar to the y/k_s in the logarithmic law for wall turbulence [4].

Resistance Law for the Imaginary Interface
The final form of the resistance law results from dimensional analyses. Eq. (13) as a function of the depth-averaged velocity $v(y)$ yields the discharge Q_F by integration between $y = b_m$ and $y = b_F$ (for rectangular channel):

$$Q = h \cdot \int_{b_m}^{b_F} v(y) \, dy \tag{14}$$

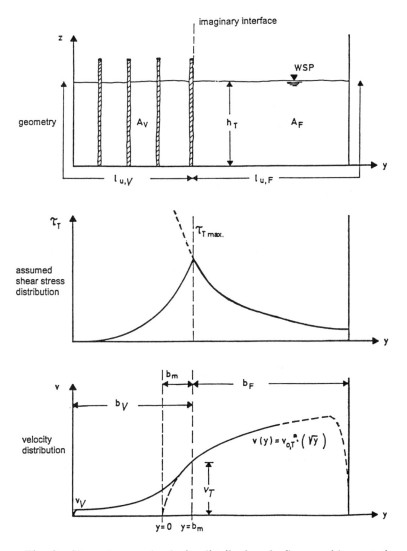

Fig. 2 Shear stress and velocity distributions in flumes with vegetation

By application of the equation for the mean velocity:

$$v_{m,F} = \frac{Q}{h \cdot b_F}$$

and the defining relationship for the friction coefficient λ_T:

$$\frac{\lambda_T}{8} = \frac{\tau_T}{\rho \cdot v_{m,F}^2} \quad ; \quad v_T^* = \sqrt{\frac{\tau_T}{\rho}} \quad ; \quad \frac{\lambda_T}{8} = \left(\frac{v_T^*}{v_{m,F}}\right)^2 \tag{15}$$

a friction formula for the imaginary wall permeable for lateral momentum transfer is obtained, which is similar to the quadratic resistance law of von KARMAN, considering however the conditions of free flow turbulence:

$$\frac{1}{\sqrt{\lambda_T}} = 0.518 \cdot \left(lg \frac{v_{0,F}}{v_V} \right)^{-1} \cdot \sqrt{\frac{h_T}{r_{hy,V}}} \cdot \sqrt{\frac{b_F}{b_m}} \qquad (16)$$

with:

$v_{0,F}$ = fictive flow velocity in the main channel, not affected by interaction

v_V = flow velocity in the flood plain (PETRYK/BOSMAJIAN)

$r_{hy,V}$ = hydraulic radius of flood plain

h_T = water depth at the vertical interface between channel and vegetation zone (or flood plain)

The parameter $\dfrac{h_T}{r_{hy,V}}$ characterizes the form of the vegetation area as space for the exchange of water masses and must not be mixed up with the cooperating width b_m for vortex production. For larger flood plains, this parameter runs to 1 because $r_{hy,V}$ is nearly h_T. The ratio b_F/b_m with $b_F = A_F/h_T$ represents the space in A_F, where the vortices may spread out unlimitedly. This ratio has high influence because of its balancing character with regard to producing and depressing vortices. For larger rivers the width b_F goes to ∞ so that the resistance factor λ_T decreases to 0 and only the bed roughness λ_W will become the dominating influence.

The adaption of Eq. (16) to the experimental data by calibration with known model results for cylindric wooden rods as tree trunk simulations of KAISER [8], PASCHE [4] and DFG [3] gives the correlation shown in Fig. 3.

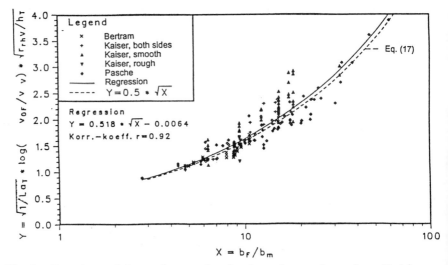

Fig. 3 Experimental data and regression for the resistance factor for cylindric vegetation simulation [3]

With minor modifications, the final resistance law to be used in practice is:

$$\lambda_T = 4 \cdot \left(lg \cdot \frac{v_{o,F}}{v_V} \right)^2 \cdot \frac{r_{hy,V}}{h_T} \cdot \frac{b_m}{b_F} \qquad (17)$$

Friction Factor of Interface at Brushwood Vegetation

To calibrate and to extend the mathematical model Eq. (17) for 3-dimensional vegetation such as brushwood, extensive tests were carried out in a laboratory flume (l/b/h = 34/2/0.6 m). Brushwood vegetation was simulated by means of wire mesh with square grids of 19 mm and $d_{P,y} = d_{P,z} = 1.35$ mm which results in $\omega_P = 0.49$ 1/m and $v_V = 0.17$ m/s at $c_{WR} = 1.87$.

The experiments were completed with tests to simulate the hydraulic effects of natural bushes. The hydraulic parameters were: $\omega_P = 0.9$ 1/m, an average $d_{P,y} = 10$ mm and $d_{P,z} = 8$ mm which gives $v_V = 0.15$ m/s and $c_{WR} = 0.9$.

Several cross sections with varying ratios of b_V/b_F under different channel bed roughness were investigated.

The field velocity in the main channel was measured by Prandtl-tubes of 3 mm dia., evaluated and registered by a micro-computer system and software for data processing.

For the basic tests, the channel bed of the flume was hydraulically smooth with an equivalent roughness of $k_s = 0.13$ mm. An artificial roughness of $0.4 < k_s < 25$ mm was created by movable bed and sand ripples.

Results and Conclusions

The resistance law Eq. (17) is valid both for brushwood and tree trunks, provided the following modifications are established:
- The calculatory diameter d_P of the vegetation elements consists of $d_{P,z}$ of the horizontal elements (spacing a_z) and of $d_{P,y}$ of the vertical elements (spacing a_y) by:

$$d_P = d_{P,y} + d_{P,z} \cdot \frac{a_y}{a_z} \qquad (18)$$

- A "vegetation channel" for limiting the cooperating width b_m does not exist for brushwood. The first limitation for b_m in Eq. (6) ($b_N > a_y$) is generally modified:

$$b_N > a_y \quad \text{and} \quad a_y > 0.3 \cdot h_T \ : \ b_m = a_y$$

The resulting friction factor λ_T therefore depends upon the water depth h_T, the widths b_V and b_m and the characteristics of vegetation, expressed by v_V. According to the tests, it ranges from $0.05 < \lambda_T < 0.25$. A comparison of λ_T at rough and smooth bed structures shows a significant difference: the friction factor for a rough bed is generally smaller than for a smooth bed. This phenomenon depends upon a reduced lateral BERNOULLI energy balance between the different cross sections, due to reduced ratios in flow velocities $v_{o,F}/v_V$ as the dominating parameter. An increased bed roughness in the main channel leads to a reduced influence of the cross section area A_T belonging to h_T at the interface ($A_T \ll A_{F,tot}$). Therefore, λ_T for very rough bed structures can be assumed to be at least $\lambda_T \geq \lambda_{bed}$.

In Fig. 4 the results of Eq. (17) are correlated with the measured data from experimental brushwood tests. The approximation may be classified as good; no systematic deviations of certain groups of simulations are observed. This result confirms the theoretically derived assumptions that in compound channels with extremely high flood plain roughness (owing to vegetation) the flow in the main channel is dominated by lateral and longitudinal processes. The interface between flood plain and main channel can be interpreted as a sectional plane covered with the sectional parameter λ_T for calculation of the main channel discharge.

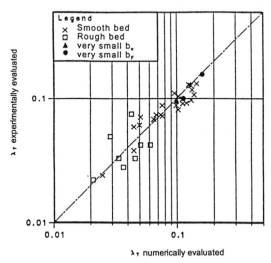

Fig. 4 Experimentally versus numerically evaluated friction factor for brushwood

Operation Formulae for Practical Handling

The calculation of the total discharge through a one-sided vegetated channel may be carried out by the following procedure:

1. Separation of the perimeter of main channel into the vegetation interface h_T and the bed perimeter $l_{u,F}$ with roughness $k_{W,F}$.

2. Determination of the hydraulic radius $r_{hy,\ F}$, $r_{hy,\ V}$ and of the cross section areas A_F, A_V and of the resistance factor λ_W according to PRANDTL-COLEBROOK

$$\sqrt{\frac{1}{\lambda_W}} = 2 \cdot lg \left(\frac{14.84 \cdot r_{hy,\ F}}{k_{W,\ F}} \right) \tag{19}$$

3. The flow velocity v_V in the vegetation zone is calculated by Eq. (4) and:

$$\omega_P = \frac{d_{P,y} + d_{P,z}\ \frac{a_y}{a_z}}{a_x \cdot a_y} \tag{20}$$

with assumed $c_{WR} = 1.0$. The discharge there is $Q_V = v_V \cdot A_V$.

4. Calculation of the fictive flow velocity $v_{o,\ F}$ (without any effect of vegetation) in main channel by Eq. (1) but without λ_T. For different parts in bed roughness, the EINSTEIN/HORTON superposition for $\lambda_{W,F}$ is necessary.

436

$$\sqrt{\frac{1}{\lambda_{W,F}}} = \sqrt{\frac{l_{u,tot}}{\Sigma(\lambda_i \cdot l_{u,i})}} \qquad (21)$$

5. Computation of resistance factor λ_T of the interface with Eq. (17) by applying Eq. (6).
6. Calculation of the total resistance factor λ_{tot} influenced by vegetation by means of Eq. (19) and iteration of

$$r_{hy,F} = \frac{\lambda_{W,F} \cdot A_F}{\lambda_{W,F,n-1} \cdot l_{u,F} + \lambda_T \cdot h_T} \qquad (22)$$

7. The real velocity v_F (affected by interaction) of the main channel is:

$$v_F = \sqrt{\frac{l_{u,W,F} + h_T}{\Sigma (\lambda_{W,F} \cdot l_{u,W,F}) + (\lambda_T \cdot h_T)} \cdot 8 \cdot g \cdot r_{hy,F} \cdot I_E}$$

and the discharge $Q_F = v_F \cdot A_F$
8. The total discharge is $Q_{tot} = Q_F + Q_V$.

References:

[1] Bretschneider, H., Schulz, A., 1985: Anwendung von Fließformeln beim naturnahen Gewässerausbau. Schriftenreihe DVWK, Heft 72

[2] DVWK (German Association for Water Resources and Land Improvements) 1991: Hydraulische Berechnung von Fließgewässern. Merkblatt 220

[3] DFG (German Research Foundation) 1987: Hydraulische Probleme beim naturnahen Gewässerausbau. Forschungsbericht Bd. 2; Schwerpunkt: Anthropogene Einflüße auf hydrologische Prozesse, VCH-Verlag Weinheim

[4] Pasche, E., Rouvé, G., 1985: Overland flow with vegetatively roughened flood plains. Journal of the Hydraulics Division, ASCE, Vol. 111, No.9

[5] Nuding, A., 1991: Fließwiderstandsverhalten in Gerinnen mit Ufergebüsch. Wasserbau-Mitteilungen der TH Darmstadt, Heft 35

[6] Schlichting, H., 1968: Boundary Layer Theory. 6th edition, MacGraw Hill Co. New York

[7] Lindner, K., 1982: Der Strömungswiderstand von Pflanzenbeständen. Mitteilung des Leichtweiß-Institutes für Wasserbau der TU Braunschweig, Heft 75

[8] Kaiser, W., 1984: Fließwiderstandsverhalten in Gerinnen mit durchströmten Ufergehölzzonen. Wasserbau-Mitteilungen der TH Darmstadt, Heft 23

RIVER FLOOD HYDRAULICS
22–25 March 1994: York, England
Impact of aquatic vegetation cutting

KR Fisher & Dr CE Reeve
HR Wallingford, UK

Abstract
Water levels within a river can be influenced by the spatial variations in bed roughness, which can arise from vegetation removal from only part of the river channel, and the temporal variations in vegetation growth. Engineers and managers need to be able to assess the effect of vegetation growth and its cutting and reliable methods for analysing these impacts should be available. This paper outlines work undertaken at HR Wallingford which investigates the methods available for assessing the hydraulic performance of spatially rough channels and also showed how numerical modelling can provide valuable information regarding the timing of vegetation cutting.

Introduction
The importance of environmental features in channel design is generally accepted but their effect on hydraulic efficiency is often unquantified. HR Wallingford compiled techniques, from a literature review, for assessing hydraulic performance of environmental features, HR Wallingford (1988). It was accepted that the methods for analysis given were the best and most appropriate available at the time but there was a need for further work to be carried out in some areas. The hydraulic impact of spatial variations in roughness and the hydraulic impact of aquatic vegetation cutting were amongst the topics identified for further study.

Natural channels provide habitats for a rich variety of aquatic vegetation which is extremely important from an environmental and ecological point of view. These variations in habitat mean that it is rare to find a cross-section of a natural channel which has the same roughness along its entire perimeter. For example the channel banks may be vegetated and the bed free from vegetation.

From the hydraulics viewpoint vegetation growth results in spatial and temporal variations in roughness. The vegetation reduces the capacity of a channel and therefore has an impact on the water levels. Water levels within a river can be influenced by the spatial variations in bed roughness, which can arise as a result of vegetation removal from only part of the river channel, and the temporal variations in vegetation growth. It is generally recognised that there is a need to control the growth of aquatic vegetation or undertake a programme of cutting from a hydraulic viewpoint but the environmental and ecological impacts of the cutting are now being more widely considered.

Current vegetation cutting practices are mainly based on what has been done historically. It may be possible that the vegetation in a number of rivers is being over-cut or cut at an inappropriate time for the type of weed growing. It may equally be that there are rivers which need more careful management. The extent and timing of weed cutting should be based on a more scientific basis than is currently practised.

This paper outlines work undertaken at HR Wallingford which investigates the methods available for assessing the hydraulic performance of spatially rough channels and also showed how numerical modelling can provide valuable information regarding the timing of vegetation cutting.

Current methods available for calculating effect of spatial variations in roughness
A number of formulae are available to compute equivalent or composite roughness. Some of these formulae have been verified in the laboratory by flume experiments but very little has been done to validate them against natural stream data. The four most commonly used methods are those given by Horton (1933), Lotter (1933), Einstein and Banks (1950) and Krishnamurthy and Christensen (1972).

Each of these methods makes assumptions. Horton assumed that each part of the cross-section has the same mean velocity, which is at the same time equal to the mean velocity of the whole section. The validity of this assumption must be questioned as the velocity and the mean velocity are functions of the roughness and depth, and so the mean velocity of parts with different roughnesses and depths must be different.

Lotter assumed that the total discharge is equal to the sum of the discharges in all the sub-sections and that the bottom shear stress is constant along the wetted perimeter. The main problem with this assumption is that the interference between the slower moving flow over the rough bed and the flow where the bed is smoother increases head losses significantly, as energy is dissipated, so that the discharge calculated by this method will be an over-estimate of the true channel capacity.

Einstein and Banks investigated the question of composite roughness where more than one type

2nd International Conference on River Flood Hydraulics. Edited by W. R. White and J. Watts

of resistance element is present. The theory proposed was that the total friction can be expressed as a sum of the individual resistances. As with the method by Lotter, it has been explicitly assumed that, in the channel with the constant equivalent roughness coefficient, the bottom shear stress is constant along the wetted perimeter.

Krishnamurthy and Christensen derived a method for calculating the equivalent roughness of a composite channel by assuming that the whole cross-section is shallow, the hydraulic radius of each sub-section can be approximated by the vertical depth and the vertical velocity distribution in each sub-section follows a logarithmic law.

Recently methods have been developed to determine the roughness or the conveyance of a channel with spatial variations in roughness. The conventional method is to divide the channel into subsections and by applying the Manning formula calculate the discharge in each subsection. The sum of the discharges in each subsection is taken to be the total discharge through the section. This tends to overestimate the conveyance because it ignores energy losses due to friction between sub-sections.

Garbrecht and Brown (1991) state that the over estimation of conveyance is a function of the section shape and increases with the number of section elements used in the summation.

The Lateral Distribution Method (LDM) was developed following work on the flood channel facility at HR Wallingford, Wark et al (1990). The method is based on calculating the distribution of flow within the channel and the governing equation is derived from the general 2-D, shallow water equations. It is assumed that the flow is steady and uniform in the longitudinal direction and the water surface is horizontal across the channel. The equations can only be solved numerically and the numerical model requires details of the channel geometry, the bed roughness and the eddy viscosity. It is simple to incorporate variations in roughness and eddy viscosity in the method and is therefore useful in predicting conveyance in channels with spatial variations in roughness.

Experimental investigation of spatial variations in roughness

Experimental work to investigate the impact of spatial variations in roughness was performed in a 3 ft wide tilting flume. The gradient of the flume was set to minimize the impact of the tailwater and to prevent supercritical flow and therefore hydraulic jump forming at the upstream end. The flume was approximately 25 m long and the gradient was fixed at 0.000865, a gradient typical of a UK river.

A different percentage of the bed of the flume was covered with stones for each of the tests A to F undertaken. The layout of the bed roughness can be seen in Figure 1.

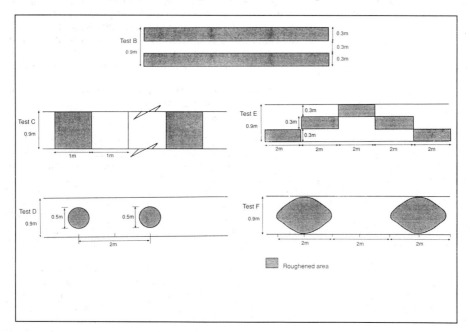

Figure 1   Layout of bed roughness

The figure shows that the roughness cover was distributed in different patterns to determine whether the shape as well as the percentage of the roughened area was an important factor in calculating an overall roughness value. The details of the experimental procedures can be found in a published report, HR Wallingford (1993b)

Comparison of measured and calculated values of roughness

Comparison of the measured Mannings 'n' values, from test series A to F, with calculated values from Lotter, Horton, Einstein and Banks and Krishnamurthy and Christensen gave results which are plotted in Figure 2. The results are for the same discharge to ensure that consistency is maintained.

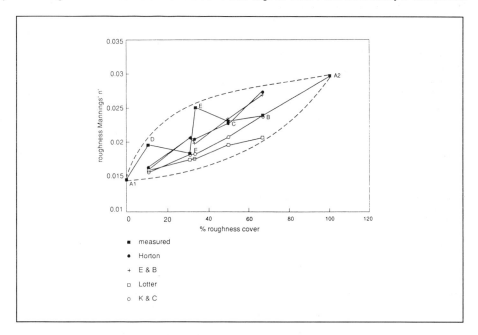

Figure 2   **The variation of Manning's n with percentage roughness cover: calculated and measured values**

In practice, the relationship between the Mannings n value of roughness and the percentage roughness cover is not linear which can be seen from the plot of the measured values in Figure 2. The values of overall roughness as calculated by Horton, Lotter, Einstein and Banks, and Krishnamurthy and Christensen do not always show good agreement with the measured values. If the roughened area has a relatively streamlined shape, however, as in tests B and F the values of Mannings n calculated by Krishnamurthy and Christensen appear to be close to the measured values.

It appears from these results that it is not just the percentage cover of each type of roughness that is important but that the shape of any form of bed roughness has an impact on the overall Mannings n. For a streamlined shape the Mannings n could be predicted quite accurately from the equation given by Lotter or by Krishnamurthy and Christensen equation. For a shape that is not streamlined or is more haphazard in form eg test series E, the formulae for predicting Mannings n tend to underestimate the value. This observation is demonstrated by comparing the results from tests E and F. The percentage roughness cover for tests E and F are very similar although the arrangements were different with the test F having a more streamlined shape. The Mannings n roughness value for tests E is however 17% higher than that for test F.

At the boundaries between the smooth and rough bed areas there is an interaction between the slower moving flow in the rough area and the faster flow in the smooth over the smooth bed. If there are many boundaries then the effects of this interaction will be greater. The bed layout for test E shows a large number of boundaries between the rough and smooth areas and the measured value of roughness for tests E is much greater than any of the calculated values, similarly test D, with a low % roughness cover shows a surprisingly high measured Mannings n value.

An envelope can be placed around the experimental results showing an upper and a lower bound for any particular roughness cover, Figure 2. If the roughened areas were streamlined in shape, the Mannings n value would come closer to the lower bound. If the shape was not streamlined or if there were many boundaries between the rough and smooth areas, the upper bound value would be more appropriate.

It can be seen from these tests, therefore, that there is not a unique relationship between Mannings n and any particular percentage roughness cover. For any selected percentage cover of roughness there could be several different values of Mannings n depending on the particular layout of the roughened areas.

Comparison of measured and calculated values of conveyance

The traditional method for calculating the conveyance of a cross-section with variations in roughness across the section divides the section into m sub-sections and calculates the conveyance of each sub-section and then adds these together to get the overall conveyance. This method tends to over-estimate the conveyance as the interactions between the sub-sections are not taken into account.

There are other methods available for calculating the conveyance of a section with spatial variations in roughness. One of these, Garbrecht and Brown (1991) is a hand calculation method whilst another is a computational method, lateral distribution method, Wark et al (1991).

Applying these methods, the lateral distribution method and the Garbrecht and Brown method, in turn to each of the tests B to F demonstrates that these methods could be adopted to estimate the conveyance more accurately than the current summation method. Table 1 shows the measured values of conveyance for each test and the calculated values of conveyance.

Table 1   Comparison of measured and calculated conveyance

Test	K_{meas}	ΣK	K_{calc} (G & B)	K_{calc} (ldm)
B1A	1.54	1.93	1.57	1.6
B2	1.08	1.21	1.03	1.07
B3	1.99	2.20	1.73	1.96
B4	2.23	2.48	1.90	1.78
B5	2.35	2.57	1.96	2.02
B6	2.29	2.86	2.15	2.14
C1	1.51	1.89	1.56	1.82
C2	1.37	1.75	1.46	1.54
C3	1.16	1.26	1.08	1.13
C5	2.07	2.54	2.00	2.01
C6	2.68	2.92	2.21	2.46
E1	1.4	2.02	1.67	1.8
E3	2.13	3.00	2.27	2.6
F1	0.93	1.38	1.17	1.51
F2	2.14	2.21	1.79	1.78
F3	2.02	2.02	1.66	2.15
F4	2.55	2.55	2.08	2.75

For each of the test series A-F performed, the sum of conveyances of the section elements $\Sigma_{i=1}^{m}$ K_i over a section, divided into m subsections, was compared with the measured value of conveyance.

Applying a linear regression to the calculated conveyance data and measured conveyance gives a relationship of $K_{calc} = 1.16K_{meas}$ and a correlation coefficient of 0.84,which indicates that on average the calculated conveyance was 16% higher than the measured conveyance.

Garbrecht and Brown (1991) suggest calculating the discrepancy E between the summed value of conveyances of the section elements $\sum_{i=1}^{m} K_i$ and the total conveyance for the undivided section. A graphical comparison is made of the relative discrepancy in conveyance, RE, to the ratio of the top width and maximum depth. The graph is drawn for a number of different shapes of channel. By this method the calculated, summed value of conveyance can be adjusted and the relationship between the calculated and measured conveyance is $K_{calc} = 0.91K_{meas}$ with a correlation of 0.77. It was noted that the in the tests where the width/depth ratio was larger (>5.0) ie at lower flows and small depths, B1, C3, E1 and F1, the values calculated by Garbrecht and Brown were more accurate suggesting that this method may be more applicable to channels with a smaller width/depth ratio.

The lateral distribution method was used to calculate conveyance and was compared with the measured values of conveyance from test series B to F. The relationship between measured and calculated conveyance in this instance was $K_{calc} = 1.005 K_{meas}$ with a correlation coefficient of 0.60. This indicates that on average the lateral distribution method gives calculated values of conveyance very close to those measured but the scatter on the points is quite large.

Timing of vegetation cutting
The major growth of aquatic weed occurs during the summer months when the vegetation can become very dense and severely restrict the conveyance of the channel. It is clear that there is a strong link between the roughness or conveyance of a channel and the growth of vegetation during the spring and summer months. A relationship between the plant cover and/or biomass of the vegetation and the roughness coefficient Manning's 'n' is needed to identify accurately the impact of vegetation growth on the hydraulic performance of the channel. There are a number of formulae which have been developed relating biomass and/or area cover to roughness coefficient and these have usually been based on or verified for one type of plant based on field data. The equations available are mostly verified for one type of plant based on field data collected over a number of years and it is unknown whether they can successfully be applied to other plant types which may have a different growth pattern.

Work undertaken by HR Wallingford, funded by the Ministry of Agriculture, Fisheries and Food (MAFF), HR Wallingford (1993a) on the Candover Brook in Hampshire supports the conclusion of other literature, Larsen et al (1990) and Pepper (1978), that the resistance offered by vegetation is inversely proportional to the product of the velocity and the hydraulic radius (VR). The equation which was developed from an earlier study, HR Wallingford (1992) gives the retardance coefficient n as:

$$n = 0.0337 + 0.0239\left(\frac{K}{VR}\right)$$

where K = vegetation surface area ratio
  V = velocity (m/s)
  R = hydraulic radius (m)
and 0.0337 is the retardance coefficient of the channel without vegetation.

From the results of this work undertaken at the Candover Brook site, HR Wallingford carried out a series of numerical modelling tests using a backwater programme to look at the impact of cutting vegetation at a range of times during the spring and summer. The modelling exercise was undertaken to demonstrate the useful information which can be supplied to river maintenance managers regarding the extent and timing of vegetation cutting.

Modelling temporal variations in aquatic vegetation
The details of the modelling of the Candover Brook site and the data used are published in HR Wallingford (1993a). Modelling tests were undertaken to determine the hydraulic effect of cutting the weeds in April, May, June, July or August or any combination of these. It was assumed that the weed would be cut back to its winter level of approximately 3% surface area cover and that the weed would grow back at its original rate.

There is some evidence from the literature that weed cutting will stimulate growth and that the growth will be synchronized. There is no quantitative data available to qualify this statement , however by cutting the vegetation during early summer, when the growth is greatest, it is thought that this could cause the peak of vegetation cover to be double the peak had the weed been left uncut. Further model

443

tests assumed that following cuts in May, June or July, the cover of vegetation in the following months would be double the percentage cover of vegetation in the following month if the weed had been left uncut.

A further series of model runs were performed with a steady maximum discharge in each month, instead of the average discharge previously used, to determine the effects of weeds on high water levels especially during the summer months.

Results of modelling programme

The effect on the water level at the upstream end of the reach due to the unlimited growth of aquatic vegetation showed that in the middle of the summer, at the peak of the vegetation growth, the water level for an average summer discharge would be greater than the water level in February for an average February discharge. This rise in water level during the summer months is due to the vegetation cover. In July, comparing the situation with aquatic vegetation in the Candover Brook to the situation with no weed, there would be a 40% rise in water depth for a 20% rise in surface area weed cover.

The impact on the water level, for average monthly discharges, at the upstream section, with no cutting and following cutting of vegetation in April, May, June or July was determined from the modelling. If it is assumed that the weed would grow back at its original rate after cutting, then the results show that the cutting would reduce the water levels in comparison to an uncut situation. If an early cut is undertaken in April or May then by July and August the weed growth would again be causing high water levels approaching the water levels in the uncut situation. Weed may need to be cut more than once to maintain an acceptable situation. If the weed was cut once in June or July the water levels would remain high during April and May. Figure 3 demonstrates these results.

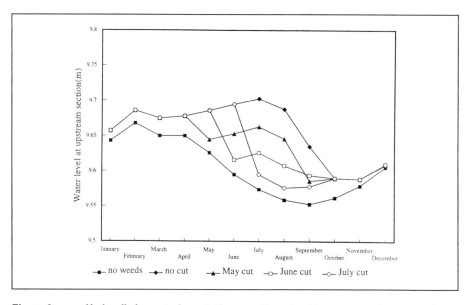

Figure 3   Hydraulic impact of vegetation growth and cutting: re-growth rate as original

If we assume that weed cutting stimulates growth, the impact on the water levels at the upstream section predicted from the model test runs are shown in Figure 4. These results are based on the assumption that the weed will grow to cover twice the percentage surface area at the peak of growth that it would have occupied if it had not been cut. Cutting in May would cause a small drop in water level during that month but there would be large increases in the water levels in the following months, June and July compared with the unmanaged situation. A similar situation would occur if cutting was done in June, with the impact only being beneficial in the month of cutting and in the subsequent months the water levels would be higher than if the weed had been left uncut. Cutting later in the growing season, say in July, when the weed cover is at its peak gives a reduction in water level in July and as the weed is not in its major growth period, the weed cutting is not likely to stimulate growth so the water levels in the subsequent months of August and September will remain similar to those calculated when the weed was left uncut. It can be seen that if we assume that weed cutting stimulates re-growth then any cutting early in the season is only beneficial during the month of cutting and the effect on water levels in subsequent months is worse than if the weed had been left uncut. It may be more beneficial in some circumstances not to cut the vegetation.

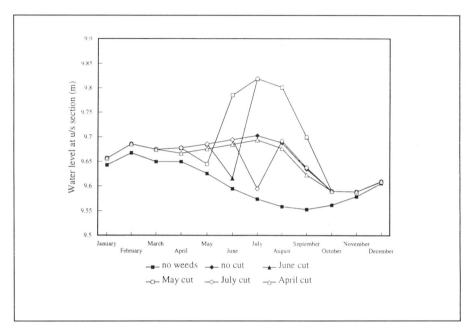

Figure 4   Hydraulic impact of vegetation growth and cutting: re-growth to twice original peak

One of the major concerns of a maintenance manager is the effect of the vegetation during a flood situation. The effect on the upstream water level due to the growth of vegetation and maximum monthly discharges is shown in Figure 5. It is assumed that the vegetation would re-grow after cutting, at the original rate of growth.

The effect on the water levels assuming weed growth and no cutting is most dramatic in July and August when levels go well above the levels for a flood in the winter months. These levels represent the worst case in a summer flood where discharges are high and weed growth is at its peak. The hydraulic impact of maximum flows during July and August could be reduced by cutting the weed, assuming that the re-growth is at its original rate. A cut during May would have most impact during that month but as the weed re-grows the water levels in the subsequent months of June and July would begin to approach the water levels in the un-managed situation.

If vegetation is cut every month during the summer then hydraulic impact of weed could be drastically reduced. Some rivers are indeed maintained in this manner but it is not necessarily the most effective, economic, ecological or environmental way of managing the river channel.

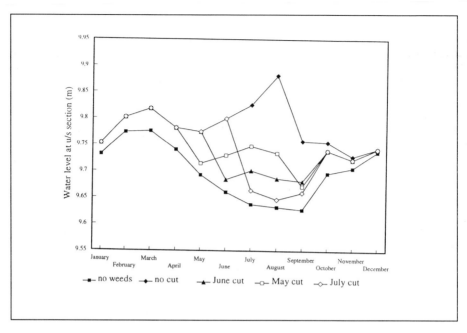

Figure 5   **Hydraulic impact of vegetation growth and cutting: re-growth at original rate and maximum monthly discharges**

Conclusions

Of the traditional, hand calculation methods available for calculating composite roughness values, those developed by Lotter (1933) and Krishnamurthy and Christensen (1972) appear to give the most accurate results. There are still some problems, however, with even the best of these methods. The shape of any form of bed roughness as well as the percentage cover has an impact on the overall Mannings n value.

There is not a unique value of Mannings n for a particular value of percentage roughness cover. The value of Mannings n is dependent on the percentage roughness cover and the arrangement or plan shape of the roughness. The value of Mannings n may fall between an upper or lower band at any particular percentage roughness cover: if the roughened areas were streamlined in shape , the Mannings n would come closer to the lower bound; if the shape was not streamlined, the upper bound value would be more appropriate.

The traditional method for calculating conveyance has been to divide the section into sub-sections where the roughness changes and to sum the conveyances of each sub-section. This tends to overestimate the conveyance as the interactions between the sub-sections are not taken into account. If engineers are required to calculate the overall conveyance of a channel with spatial variations in roughness more accurate calculation procedures are required. If a computational method is appropriate, the numerical method given by Wark et al (1990), the lateral distribution method (LDM) is recommended. The hand calculation method recommended by Garbrecht and Brown (1991) shows an improvement in calculated conveyance values over the traditional summation method.

The engineer now has a recommended method for calculating the overall roughness of a channel which has spatial variations in bed roughness but also requires advice regarding the temporal variations.

Using an equation developed by HR Wallingford to determine the roughness due to vegetation cover and a simple numerical backwater model, the effects on water levels of cutting or not cutting vegetation can be estimated. These estimations are based on assumptions regarding the rate of weed growth, re-growth after cutting and decay over a season.

Results of using this technique for a small river in Hampshire show that in the case of average flows and assuming that the cutting stimulates the weed growth the cutting of vegetation could cause the water levels to be higher in the month after cutting than if no cutting had taken place. We may therefore conclude that cutting may only have an effect for a short time and if cutting stimulates the re-growth of vegetation it can make things a great deal worse in subsequent months. It may be better in some circumstances not to cut the vegetation.

From a hydraulic viewpoint cutting the vegetation every month could reduce the possibility of summer flooding but this is not necessarily the most effective, economic, ecological or environmental way of managing the river channel. The technique described here may be useful to engineers and maintenance managers, uncertain about the times and frequency of vegetation maintenance.

Acknowledgements
The work described in this paper was undertaken with funding from the Ministry of Agriculture, Fisheries and Food and their support throughout the project is gratefully acknowledged.

References

Einstein HA and Banks RB (1950). Fluid resistance of composite roughness. Transactions American Geophysical Union, Vol 31, No 4, pp 606-610

Garbrecht J and Brown GO (1991). calculation of total conveyance in natural channels. Journal of Hydraulic Engineering Vol 117 No 6 pp 788-798

Horton RE (1933). Separate roughness coefficients for channel bottom and sides, Engineering News-Record, Vol 111. No 22. pp 652-653.

HR Wallingford (1993a). Modelling the hydraulic impact of vegetation in river channels. Report SR 346, March 1993.

HR Wallingford (1993b). Spatial variations of in-bank hydraulic roughness in channels. Report SR 357, April 1993.

HR Wallingford (1992). The hydraulic roughness of vegetated channels. Report No SR 305, March 1992.

HR Wallingford (1988). Assessing the hydraulic performance of environmentally acceptable channels. Report No Ex 1799, Sept 1988.

Krishnamurthy M and Christensen BA (1972). Equivalent roughness for shallow channels. Journal of hydraulics division ASCE. Vol 98. HY12 pp 2257-2262.

Larsen T, Frier J, and Vestergaard K (1990). Discharge/stage relations in vegetated Danish streams. International Conference on River Flood Hydraulics, Paper F1, September 1990, John Wiley & Sons Ltd.

Lotter GK, (1933). Considerations on hydraulic design of channels with different roughness of walls. Transactions All-Union Scientific Research Institute of Hydraulic Engineering, Leningrad, Vol 9. pp 238-241.

Pepper AT (1970). Investigation of vegetation and bend flow retardation of a stretch of the River Ousel. National College of Agricultural Engineering, 1949, Vol30 pp184-189.

Wark JB, Slade JE, Ramsbottom DM, 1991. Flood discharge assessment by the lateral distribution method. HR Wallingford Report SR 277.

Wark JB, Samuels PG, Ervine DA, 1990. A practical method of estimating velocity and discharge in compound channels. International conference on River Flood Hydraulics, Wallingford, England. 17-20th September 1990.

POWER LAW FOR VELOCITY PROFILES
IN OPEN-CHANNEL FLOOD FLOWS

TU HAIZHOU AND NOBUYUKI TAMAI
Dept. of Civil Engrg., Univ. of Tokyo, Tokyo 113, Japan

SUMMARY

Detailed measurements of velocity profiles were previously conducted in open-channel steady flows, as well as in flood (unsteady) flows, which were simulated by a series of hydrographs in a laboratory flume. The measured velocity profiles, along with some from the literature, are analyzed in the present paper using the power law, and their exponents calculated. Existing theory, though gives good prediction for the power-law exponent of the velocity profiles in steady flows, is found to overestimate it for the velocity profiles in flood flows. A new theoretical expression for the power-law exponent is derived in this paper, which renders good results for velocity profiles in unsteady as well as steady flows.

1. INTRODUCTION

Velocity profiles in boundary-layer flow, pipe flow and in open-channel flow may be expressed by the logarithmic law or a power low. While log-law is considered as semi-theoretic, power law is believed to be wholly empirical and "out of an old assumption" (Hinze [4], p.624), although it has been widely used. Hinze [4] and many others have employed the power law in their boundary-layer studies, and found that it describes very well the measured velocity profiles. Using a power law, Toffaleti [12] and Karim and Kennedy [6] investigated sediment-transport problems. And it was shown that the velocity profiles in wavy turbulent pipe flows (Hsu and Kennedy [5]) also follow the power law. Zimmerman and Kennedy [15] employed the power law to free-surface flow in wide rectangular channels. Recently, Chen [1] tried to derive general power-law formuas, for hydraulically smooth flows and for fully rough flows. Based on this, he [2] further developed theoretically the momentum- and energy- coefficients for circular pipes and wide open channels.

It seems that there are several reasons for the wide use of the power law. First of all, compared with the more general power-law velocity profile, the logarithmic profile is but a special case (Rouse [9], p.348-350). Secondly, power law does not display the troublesome near-bed singularity that detracts severely from the logarithmic relations. In fact, both Schlichting [10] (in his Figure 20.3) and Hinze [4] (his Figure 7-53) show that the power law describes better than the log-law the pipe-flow data obtained by Ni-

2nd International Conference on River Flood Hydraulics. Edited by W. R. White and J. Watts
© 1994 HR Wallingford Ltd. Published by John Wiley & Sons Ltd

kuradse and by Laufer, respectively. Moreover, compared with power law which has one unknown exponent, log-law involves several "universal constants" that are not universal (Tu [13], Ch.2), particularly in unsteady flow where they are shown to vary with the longitudinal pressure gradient (Tu and Graf [14]).

Needless to say, it is interesting to examine velocity profiles from unsteady flow, in light of the power law, to compare these profiles with the ones from steady flow and evaluate their respective power-law exponents.

In this paper, we shall first analyze the velocity profiles obtained in steady and flood (unsteady) flows and calculate the corresponding power-law exponents. Subsequently, the thus obtained results will be checked with existing theory and, if there is any problem, we shall try to improve it.

2. DATA PRESENTATION

The power law can be written in its familiar form in the following as:

$$u = u_{max} \left(\frac{y}{D}\right)^{1/m} \qquad \text{or} \qquad \frac{u}{V} = \left(\frac{m+1}{m}\right) \left(\frac{y}{D}\right)^{1/m} \qquad (1)$$

where the point velocity, u, is measured at the water height, y; and the maximum velocity, u_{max}, is supposed to appear at the water surface (where $y = D$); V, the depth-averaged velocity; m is the power law's inverse exponent, which in the following will be refered as the "power-law exponent", or simply the "exponent".

Data used in the present analysis include some velocity profiles from MacQuivey's report [8] as well as those from Tu's dissertation [13]. Brief information about these data is given in the following.

2.1. MacQuivey's data (steady flow)

In the early seventies, MacQuivey [8] conducted a series of turbulence measurements in natural rivers, conveyance channels as well as in laboratory flumes. These data are of high quality and very well documented. Here we select arbitrarily 6 velocity profiles from his data set, three being collected in a 2-foot-wide flume and the remaining three measured in a 4-foot-wide flume (see Table I). All the mean velocity profiles were measured with a small Pitot tube, of which the diameter was 1/8 inch.

The 2-foot-wide flume was a recirculating, tilting one, being 60 feet long and 2.5 feet deep. The side walls were made of 0.5-inch Lucite, and the floor was made of 0.25-inch stainless-steel plate, which in turn was covered by wooden blocks. The velocity profiles (R31, R35 and R37 in Table I) were measured 40 feet downstream from the headbox, where the flow was fully developed.

On the other hand, the 4-foot-wide flume, also a tilting one, was 120 feet long and 2 feet deep. The interior was surfaced with plywood coated with fiber glass, except for a 24-foot section of the left sidewall which was of Lucite. There were several set of experiments in the flume, with the floor being covered by different roughness. For the three velocity profiles analyzed here, these roughness were (see Table I): R41 corresponds to the 3/4-in rocks, R45 to the ones of 1.5 inch; and R47 was measured over an artificial riverbed, which was covered with rocks of 1.5 inch, and with 4- to 6-inch rocks placed 6 to 8 inches apart among the 1.5-in rocks.

2.2. Tu's data (steady and unsteady flows)

The details of the steady and unsteady flow experiments are described by Tu [13], but are briefly described in the following.

The experiments, both for steady and unsteady (flood) flows, were conducted in a tilting flume, which was 16.8m long, 0.6m wide and 0.8m deep, with glass side walls and a smooth steel floor being covered with two types of gravels. With the gravels tightly packed on the bed, seepage flow in all the experiments was considered negligible. Three micropropellers, each with a diameter of 1.5cm, were used to measure the point velocities at three sections (the first section was 12.4m downstream from the entrance, assuring thus fully developed flow), while the instantaneous water depth at each section was measured with a limnimeter. Both the micropropellers and the limnimeters were cleaned and calibrated when necessary. The displacements of the micropropellers were controlled automatically by a microcomputer.

In steady-flow experiments, the measuring arrangement was as the following: near the bottom the point velocities were measured every 2mm at 5 points; then measured every 5mm at another 5 points; from there up to the water surface the velocities were measured every 10mm. The sampling number at each point was 1200, with a frequency of 20 Hz. The data for the present analysis are listed in Table II.

For unsteady-flow measurements, bearing on mind the characteristics of natural floods which were examined beforehand, thirteen hydrographs were passed in the same gravel-bed flume as described above. The micropropellers and the limnimeters were installed at the same sections. The micropropeller displacement was as follows: near the bottom the point velocities were measured every 2mm at 5 points; then measured every 5mm at another 5 points; from there on till the water surface the velocities were measured every 10mm. There were usually 23 to 26 measuring points for each velocity profile. The data analyzed here are given in Table III.

2.3. Exponent in the power law

In all, 12 velocity profiles were selected from MacQuivey's and Tu's steady flow measurements, and 26 profiles were from Tu's unsteady flow experiments. These data cover a relatively wide range of flow conditions, as can be seen in Tables I to III, where: "bed" refers to the bed roughness; d_s, the roughness height; "width", the flume width; D, the total water depth; f, the Darcy-Weissbach friction coefficient. The other symbols are the same as defined above.

Several sample velocity profiles are shown in dimensionless form in Figures 1 to 3, with u/u_* versus y/d_s in semi-log scale. Note that in unsteady flow (see Figure 3) there are two velocity profiles corresponding to a certain water depth (D), one from the rising stage and the other from the falling stage, respectively. It is seen that (for more details see Tu and Graf [14]: 1) at the same water height, y, the point velocity in the rising branch is generally larger than the one in the falling branch; 2) this difference of the point velocities between the rising and the falling stage gets larger on approaching the water surface; 3) this difference of the point velocities becomes smaller with increasing water depth (i.e., on approaching the peak of the hydrograph). Also to be noted is that similar observations were reported by Suszka [11] and Grishanin [3].

One way to calculate the power-law exponent, as can be seen from the second expression in equation 1, is to plot the velocity profiles in dimensionless form, with u/V versus y/D (Figures 4 to 6), and use least-square method to the data points. This was done, and the obtained power-law exponent, m, are listed in Tables I to III.

Table I. Data from MacQuivey [8]; steady flow

MacQuivey (1973)	bed	d_s (cm)	width (cm)	D (cm)	V (cm/s)	$\sqrt{\dfrac{8}{f}}$	u_* (cm/s)	Π	m
R31	block	0.32	61	12.6	30.9	10.14	3.0	0.10	4.3
R35	block	1.27	61	12.6	53.3	6.65	8.1	0.00	3.4
R37	block	2.86	61	12.7	31.4	4.83	6.5	0.05	2.3
R41	rock	1.91	122	28.4	25.9	10.50	2.5	0.45	2.9
R45	rock	3.81	122	14.3	21.9	10.40	2.1	0.21	3.3
R47	riverbed	3.8-15.2	122	16.1	23.8	7.80	3.0	0.00	3.4

Table II. Data from Tu [13]; steady flow (gravel bed)

Tu (1991)	d_s (cm)	width (cm)	D (cm)	V (cm/s)	$\sqrt{\dfrac{8}{f}}$	u_* (cm/s)	Π	m
ST233	1.35	60	11.9	59.1	8.00	7.4	0.10	3.1
ST2101	1.35	60	12.8	74.7	7.30	10.2	0.20	2.4
ST243	1.35	60	14.5	81.1	8.40	9.6	0.25	2.9
ST313	2.30	60	14.2	46.3	6.90	6.7	0.11	2.6
ST3102	2.30	60	9.1	84.7	7.60	11.2	0.08	3.2
ST392	2.30	60	17.0	115.1	9.70	11.9	0.23	2.9

Table III. Data from Tu [13]; unsteady flow
(gravel bed, d_s = 1.35cm; width = 60cm)

t (s)	D (cm)	V (cm/s)	$\sqrt{\dfrac{8}{f}}$	u_* (cm/s)	Π	m
hydrograph	NS1(1)					
21	12.2	60.6	8.30	7.3	0.18	2.9
41	20.1	90.5	11.30	8.0	0.25	3.3
61	20.7	88.9	14.80	6.0	0.55	3.1
81	18.7	78.2	13.70	5.7	0.31	3.5
101	15.5	62.8	15.70	4.0	0.72	4.2
27	14.6	69.1	8.64	8.0	0.30	3.1
31	16.3	74.4	8.96	8.3	0.00	3.1
37	18.9	84.3	10.04	8.4	0.30	3.2
43	20.5	93.2	12.10	7.7	0.24	3.5
105	14.6	59.1	15.55	3.8	0.72	3.2
95	16.3	67.9	14.76	4.6	0.41	3.7
79	18.9	79.2	13.66	5.8	0.44	3.6
59	20.5	89.2	14.62	6.1	0.47	3.3
hydrograph	NS1(2)					
41	14.6	65.2	9.06	7.2	0.26	2.6
81	21.4	95.8	13.88	6.9	0.31	2.9
121	20.1	89.2	15.12	5.9	0.72	3.1
161	17.5	75.5	13.98	5.4	0.41	3.1
201	13.6	54.9	13.07	4.2	0.41	2.7
33	12.6	60.7	8.43	7.2	0.00	2.6
45	15.5	71.2	10.03	7.1	0.30	2.7
55	17.8	79.3	11.33	7.0	0.30	3.0
71	20.4	91.8	13.30	6.9	0.53	3.0
211	12.6	60.7	8.43	7.2	0.00	2.6
185	15.5	63.8	12.27	5.2	0.41	2.9
155	17.8	77.4	14.33	5.4	0.41	3.1
115	20.4	89.0	14.59	6.1	0.65	3.1

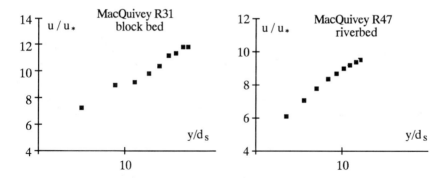

Figure 1. Velocity profiles in steady flow (from MacQuivey [8])
with u/u_* versus y/d_s

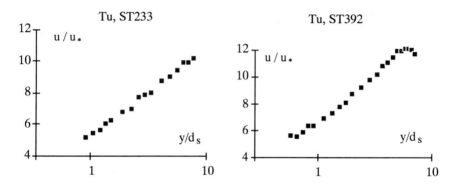

Figure 2. Velocity profiles in steady flow (from Tu [13])
with u/u_* versus y/d_s

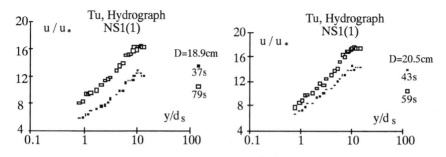

Figure 3. Velocity profiles in unsteady flow (from Tu [13])
with u/u_* versus y/d_s

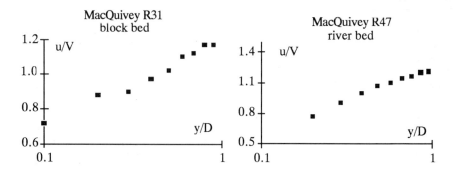

Figure 4. Velocity profiles in steady flow (from MacQuivey [8])
with u/V versus y/D

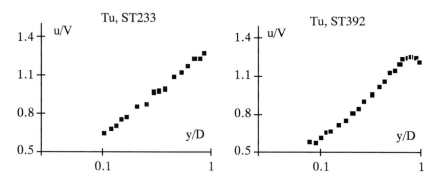

Figure 5. Velocity profiles in steady flow (from Tu [13])
with u/V versus y/D

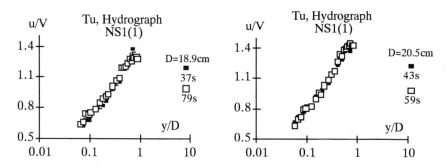

Figure 6. Velocity profiles in unsteady flow (from Tu [13])
with u/V versus y/D

3. DATA ANALYSIS

From the power-law exponent as summarized in Tables I to III, we see that it varies widely, as noted by Hinze [4] (p.630 and p.723). According to Hinze [4] (p.630), Clauser concluded that no universal value could be assigned to the power-law exponent, since it may vary "from 3 to 10 for the various velocity distributions considered". From Nikuradse's measurements in smooth pipes (Hinze [4], p.723), one has m = 6-10, with m being function of the Reynolds number. For rough pipes m is smaller, being 4 to 5. In alluvial river flows, m is around 6 (see for example, Toffaleti [12] and Li et al.[7]).

Thus the first observation from the data analyzed above is: in rough open-channel flows, the power-law exponent, m, varies around 3, being comparable with that obtained in rough pipe flows. Further, the velocity gradient can be derived from equation 1, as:

$$\frac{\partial u}{\partial y} = \frac{u_{max}}{m} \frac{D}{y} \left(\frac{y}{D}\right)^{1/m} \tag{2}$$

which indicates that the smaller the power-law exponent, the larger would be the velocity gradient. Hence, the above observation means that the velocity gradients for the velocity profiles measured in flow over large roughness, particularly near the bottom, are larger than those in flows over smooth bed.

Next, we shall check the m-values listed in Tables I to III with existing theory in the literature. An expression for the power-law exponent was derived theoretically by Zimmermann and Kennedy [15] and several researchers before them, based on the power law (equation 1), and the following logarithmic law:

$$\frac{u - u_{max}}{u_*} = \frac{1}{\kappa} \ln\frac{y}{D} \tag{3}$$

where u_* is the friction velocity; κ=0.41, the Karman constant. The final expression for the power-law exponent was given by Zimmermann and Kennedy [15] as:

$$m = \kappa \sqrt{\frac{8}{f}} \tag{4}$$

In Figure 7 the power-law exponent obtained directly from the velocity profiles are compared with those calculated with equation 4. While predicting reasonably well for the velocity profiles in steady flow, equation 4 overestimates the power-law exponent for the velocity profiles measured in unsteady flow.

Since equation 4 overestimates the power-law exponent for unsteady flow, it needs some improvement. This can be done as in the following.

Early in 1956, after examining data obtained in boundary-layer flows, Coles found that the following equation should be used, instead of equation 3, to describe the velocity profiles:

$$\frac{u - u_{max}}{u_*} = \frac{1}{\kappa} \ln\frac{y}{D} - \frac{2\Pi}{\kappa} \cos^2\left(\frac{\pi}{2} \frac{y}{D}\right) \tag{5}$$

where π = 3.14, and Π is the so-called wake-strength parameter, which varies with the longitudinal pressure gradient and is about 0.55 in zero pressure-gradient boundary-layer flows. Tu and Graf [14] found from their unsteady-flow investigations that the wake-strength parameter becomes more pronounced in decelerating flow compared with the one in accelerating flow.

A new expression for the power-law exponent can be derived using equations 1 and 5. Integrating equation 1 from the bottom to the water surface, and division by the total water depth, D, one has the depth-averaged mean velocity:

$$V = \frac{m}{m+1} u_{\max} \tag{6}$$

Subsequently, integrating equation 5 from the bottom to the water surface, and division by the total water depth, one has:

$$\frac{V - u_{\max}}{u_*} = -\frac{1}{\kappa} - \frac{\Pi}{\kappa} \tag{7}$$

After some simple mathematical manipulations, the depth-averaged mean velocity can be derived from equation 7, as:

$$V = (1 - \frac{1+\Pi}{\kappa} \frac{m}{m+1} \sqrt{\frac{1}{f}}) u_{\max} \tag{8}$$

From equations 6 and 8, the new expression for the power-law exponent can be readily deduced as:

$$m = \frac{\kappa}{1+\Pi} \sqrt{\frac{8}{f}} \tag{9}$$

Equation 9 indicates that, with stronger wake (larger Π-value), one has smaller m-value, thus larger velocity gradient (as discussed above). Note also that equation 9 reduces to equation 4 if one assumes that no wake exists in the velocity profile under consideration, which would mean that instead of equation 5, equation 3 is accurate enough for describing the velocity profiles.

With equation 9, the power-law exponent was recalculated for the velocity profiles and plotted in Figure 8. The figure shows reasonable agreement between the measured power-law exponents and the predicted ones. In the above, the Π-values in equation 9 were directly obtained from the velocity profiles. In practice the velocity profile is unknown, so we need to determine in the first place the Π-value from known hydraulic parameters. For the unsteady flow velocity profiles investigated by Tu and Graf [14], there was an empirical relation:

$$\Pi = 1.02 \beta + 0.46 \tag{10}$$

where β is a dimensionless parameter representing the flow unsteadiness. This parameter was obtained by Tu and Graf [14], as:

$$\beta = K \left(-\frac{D}{V^2} \frac{dV}{dt} \right) \tag{11}$$

where K is a coefficient. For negative β-values, the flow is an accelerating one and for positive β-values, the flow is a decelerating one. Plotted versus β (not shown here), the Π-values from the data set in Tu [13] (in all 273 velocity profiles) compared rather well with those reported in the literature for different types of flows. This indirectly confirms that β is indeed an important parameter.

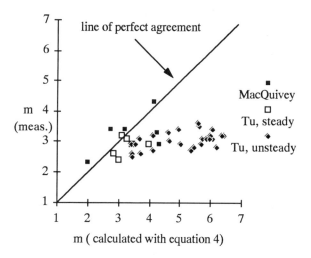

Figure 7. Power-law exponent (in equation 1) obtained from the velocity profiles and the ones predicted by existing theory (equation 4)

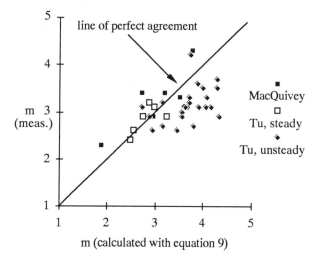

Figure 8. Power-law exponent (in equation 1) obtained from the velocity profiles and the ones predicted by the new theory (equation 9)

457

4. CONCLUSIONS

Velocity profiles measured in steady flows as well as in flood flows follow power law (equation 1). The power-law exponent obtained from the velocity profiles in steady rough flows are in reasonable agreement with the ones predicted by existing theory (equation 4). Smaller than those from plain river flows, they are comparable with those from rough pipe flows as reported in the literature. For the velocity profiles measured in flood flows, existing theory overestimates the power-law exponent (see Figure 7). A new theoretical expression is derived in this paper (equation 9), which gives good results for the velocity profiles in both steady and unsteady (flood) flows (Figure 8).

REFERENCES

1. C.L. Chen, 'Unified Theory on Power Laws for Flow Resistance', Proc. Am. Soc. Civ. Engrs, *J.Hydraulic Engrg.*, Vol.117, No.HY3, 1991.
2. C.L. Chen, 'Momentum and Energy Coefficients Based on Power-Law Velocity Profile', Proc. Am. Soc. Civ. Engrs, *J.Hydraulic Engrg.*, Vol.117, No.HY3, 1991.
3. K Grishanin, *Dynamika Ruslobich Potokob* (Dynamics of Alluvial Flow), Hydrometeoizat, Leningrad (in Russian), 1979.
4. J.O. Hinze, *Turbulence,* 2nd edn, McGraw-Hill Book Co., New York, 1975.
5. S.T. Hsu and J. F.Kennedy, 'Turbulent Flow in Wavy Pipes', *J. of Fluid Mech.*, 47(3), pp.481-502, 1971.
6. M. F. Karim and J. F. Kennedy, 'Velocity and Sediment-Concentration Profiles in River Flows', Proc. Am. Soc. Civ. Engrs, *J.Hydraulic Engrg.*, Vol.113, No.HY2, 1987.
7. Z. Li, Y. Chen and Y. Zhao, 'Laboratory Investigation on Drag and Lift Forces Acting on Bed Spheres', *Proceedings of the 2nd International Symposium on River Sedimentation*, Nanjing, China, pp.330-343, 1983.
8. R.S. MacQuivey, 'Summary of turbulent data from rivers, conveyance channels, and laboratory flumes', *U.S.Geological Survey Professional Paper 802-B* , 1973.
9. H. Rouse, *Advanced Mechanics of Fluids*, John Wiley & Sons, New York, 1959.
10. H. Schlichting, *Boundary-Layer Theory*, 7th edn, McGraw-Hill Book Co., New York, 1979.
11. L. Suszka, 'Sediment Transport at Steady and Unsteady Flow; A Laboratory Study', *Doctoral dissertation No.704*, Laboratoire de Recherches Hydrauliques, Ecole Polytechnique Fédérale, Lausanne, Switzerland, 1987.
12. F. B. Toffaleti, 'Definite computations of sand discharge in rivers', Proc. Am. Soc. Civ. Engrs, *J.Hydraulic Div.*, Vol.95, No.HY1, 1969.
13. H. Tu, 'Velocity distribution in unsteady flow over gravel beds', *Doctoral dissertation No.911*, Laboratoire de Recherches Hydrauliques, Ecole Polytechnique Fédérale, Lausanne, Switzerland, 1991.
14. H. Tu and W. H. Graf, 'Velocity distribution in unsteady open-channel flow over gravel beds', *J. Hydroscience and Hydraulic Engineering*, JSCE, Vol.10, No.1, pp.11-25, 1992.
15. C. Zimmermann and J. F. Kennedy, 'Transverse bed slopes in curved alluvial streams', Proc. Am. Soc. Civ. Engrs, *J.Hydraulic Div.*, Vol.104, No.HY1, 1978.

2nd International Conference on
RIVER FLOOD HYDRAULICS
22–25 March 1994: York, England

LARGE FLOW STRUCTURES IN MEANDERING
COMPOUND CHANNELS

D. A. Ervine **(University of Glasgow)**
R. J. Sellin **(University of Bristol)**
B. B. Willetts (University of Aberdeen)

SUMMARY

The theme of this paper is the complexity of three-dimensional mixing which occurs in meandering compound flows, when a curved main channel flow interacts with a nominally straight flood plain flow. The data have been collected from the large scale SERC Flood Channel Facility located at H.R. Wallingford, and relate to the Series B programme from 1989-91. The paper investigates streamwise and transverse velocity components, variations in water surface levels, pressure gradient driven secondary cells, and describes the results of a flow visualisation study designed to highlight key features of the flow.

INTRODUCTION

For many years research into compound channels, river/floodplain interactions and two-stage channel design has concentrated on modelling highly idealised cases of a straight main channel with straight parallel floodplains adjacent to the main channel. In many respects this work has been valuable in enhancing understanding of the turbulent shear interaction at the floodplain - main channel junction, clarifying the role of secondary currents in the same region, boundary shear stress distribution, and more particularly, in the proving of turbulence models over the range from zero-equation models Ref. [1], to Reynolds stress models, Ref. [2]. In a similar vein, discharge assessment in such idealised geometries has been quantified by Ackers and outlined in Ref. [3].

In reality, most rivers and two-stage channels are sinuous or meandering with the main channel slope and direction different from the floodplain or valley slope. This is the natural river morphology, as opposed to man-made creations involving straightening and widening over recent decades. Thus meandering river flooding and meandering

2nd International Conference on River Flood Hydraulics. Edited by W. R. White and J. Watts
© 1994 HR Wallingford Ltd. Published by John Wiley & Sons Ltd

two-stage channels are a natural progression of study following the straight, parallel cases, and present much more complex flow patterns, interactions and exchanges between main channel and floodplain.

The questions posed in this paper therefore are concerned with identifying flow structures in meandering compound flows and indicating the way forward in modelling such flows in a meaningful way given the complexity of the three-dimensional flow structures involved.

TEST PROGRAMME

The results presented in this paper stem directly from large scale experiments carried out in the SERC Flood Channel Facility (FCF) located at H.R. Wallingford. The meandering compound channel programme was carried out between 1989-91 and involved a collaborative programme between Bristol, Aberdeen and Glasgow Universities, with substantial other input from Birmingham and Sheffield Universities.

The flume itself is 56m long and 10m wide, carrying discharge in excess of 1 m³/s, with the longitudinal floodplain slope varying from 0.996×10^{-3} for the lower sinuosity geometry to 1.021×10^{-3} for the higher sinuosity geometry.

- The main channel sinuosity was tested at 1.374 as shown in Fig.1 and 2.034 as shown in Fig.2. The main measurement cross-sections are shown in these Figures, at least in the region of the main channel.

- The flow depth was varied in the range 50mm $< H < 300$mm with the three main overbank flow depths tested being H = 165mm, 200mm and 250mm, corresponding to relative depth ratios of 0.09, 0.25 and 0.4.

- The main channel cross-sectional shape was tested for the trapezoidal case with top width 1.2m and 45° sloping walls, but later tested with a "natural" cross-section based on data from 17 river channels.

- The flood-plain was tested for a range of roughnesses, from fully smooth to the case of fully rough, using vertical circular rods as roughening elements. The lateral flood plain slope was zero in all cases.

- Measurements were made of stage, discharge, two components of velocity, boundary shear stress, turbulent shear stress, detailed water surface levels and detailed flow visualisation tests.

- Further details of results from this programme can be obtained in Refs. [4], [5], [6], [7], [8], [9], and [10].

VELOCITY MEASURMENTS IN THE FLOOD CHANNEL FACILITY

Detailed velocity measurements were made in the FCF at selected cross-sections. The local flow direction in the horizontal plane was first measured using a balanced vane and the velocity magnitude later using a miniature propeller current meter. The current meter was mounted so that it could be automatically rotated to align with the local vector using the stored angle value measured by the vane.

As is shown in Figure 1 sections 01 to 05 are positioned around the inner channel bend and sections 06 to 11 in the straight channel cross-over region. Detailed velocity measurements were made from bed to water surface within the inner channel, and also over a marginal strip extending 300mm onto the floodplain at either side. The following discussion is limited to measurements taken with the low sinuosity channel geometry. However, measurements were also made for a higher sinuosity geometry not analysed here. In addition velocities were also measured on the floodplain areas lying outside the marginal strip referred to above, at a lower density of points.

Since full information is available for these velocity vectors in the horizontal plane (only very limited vertical velocity data was obtained, using an LDA system) it is possible to display this in perpendicular component form. Local reference directions are used in all cases and are defined by the alignment of the individual measurement section (see Fig.1). The longitudinal velocity component is defined as being perpendicular to the section line, and the transverse velocity component as being parallel to it.

Velocity traverses were carried out for all the 11 sections defined in Fig.1 at one in-bank depth (140mm) and three overbank depths (165, 200, 250mm) corresponding to relative depth (H-h)/H values of 0.09, 0.25 and 0.40.

Figure 3(a) shows contour plots of the **longitudinal** velocity values in the crossover region for a relative depth of 0.09, a relatively shallow flow over the floodplain . Other flow conditions are:- sinuosity 1.38: "natural" cross-section; smooth floodplain. Figure 3(b) shows the inferred secondary flow cell organisation constructed from the corresponding **transverse** velocity components for the same flow region.

It has been shown that the secondary flow organisation is very sensitive to the relative depth value. This is borne out in straight two-stage channels by Ackers Ref. [3] who demonstrated that the relative depth had a large effect on cross-boundary fluid shear **resistance** (due to the momentum exchange process). Of course in meandering two-stage channels the secondary flow system is driven by primary rather than secondary effects so that the flow coming off the floodplain would be expected to play an important role in the mechanics of the flow.

Figure 4(a) shows the distribution of **transverse** velocities in the bend region while Figure 4(b) shows this for the cross-over region, both for relative depth values of 0.25. By comparing the size of the principal secondary cells in Figures 3(a) and 3(b) it can immediately be seen how much stronger this feature is in the deeper flow.

It can be seen in Figure 3(a) how the surface cross-flow current switches direction at this depth as the sections move around the bend. The rotational sense of the principal secondary flow/cell is reversed at around section 04 and the transverse velocity profiles demonstrate very well how this comes about. Note that a smaller clockwise cell tries to get established in the outer corner under the main cell but this finally vanishes as the inner corner cell gathers momentum from the flow coming off the floodplain (sections 05 to 11).

At the bend apex (Section 03) the secondary cell rotates in the opposite direction to inbank flows. The strength of these transverse cells typically reaches values between 20-30% relative to the streamwise velocity component..

Surface levels and flow patterns

For each of three overbank flow depths and for each of the two channel geometries, water surface levels were measured over one meander wavelength and the whole flume width. Measurements were made using a Churchill conductivity probe moving in a plane parallel to the floodplain slope. The probe was calibrated before and after each series of measurements so that changes of conductivity associated with temperature, with ionic concentration, and with probe cleanliness could be compensated for. The compensation assumed that any change occurred at constant rate. A second purpose of the twice per session checks was to reset the datum level of the probe relative to the known water depth at one point monitored by still-well and micrometer point gauge.

Water level measurements were made for both mortar smooth and roughened floodplains but the following discussion will be confined to the smooth floodplain case. For this case, the level measurement locations in plan are indicated in Fig. 5(a) and 5(b) for the channel sinuosities of 1.37, and 2.04 respectively. Surface level was observed with floodplain depths of 15mm, 50mm and 100mm (total nominal depths above the deepest parts of the channel of 165mm, 200mm and 250mm). At floodplain depths of approximately 15mm the Churchill probe could only be used above the main channel, and floodplain measurement sites were eliminated from the programme. At each site, levels were recorded for 36 seconds at half second intervals: the accepted level was the mean of these readings after adjustment for conductivity drift and for the structural deflection out-of-plane of the support structure.

Fig.6 shows contours of water surface level produced from spot levels obtained in this way at nominal total depth 200mm in systems with channels of each sinuosity and with the quasi-natural channel bed topography in each case. It will be noted that the highest point in each half wavelength occurs over the main channel just downstream of each bend and the lowest point on the floodplain in roughly the same angular position relative to the bend. The level difference is approximately 6mm in each case corresponding to a static pressure difference of roughly 60 Pascals over a plan distance of about one metre. Another area in which surface level is high lies outside each bend apex. Fig. 7 indicates these three zones in sketch form.

In terms of elementary notions of energy and momentum exchange, and in the notation of Fig.7, areas 1 and 2 might be associated with the deceleration of floodplain water expanding into the greater depth of the main channel and the acceleration of water escaping from the channel onto the downstream floodplain. The elevated surface in area 3 appears to be associated with a modicum of flow curvature in the water negotiating the channel bend under the flood-flow.

The observations of vertical velocity which would have made possible a rigorous examination (and numerical modelling) of these energy and moment exchange postulations are not available. However, some rough checks on the mutual consistency of the pressure and velocity fields can be made using flow visualisations with more boldness than the data perhaps warrant.

Dye was injected at systematically selected points (both in plan and depth). The most information section of a very large information bank concerns the movement of dye injected at various points in the cross-section at the bend apex. Dye traces are shown in Fig. 8 for flow in the natural channel of sinuosity 1.37 at nominal floodplain depth 50mm. The positions of injection points are indicated in an insert (Fig.8). Fig.7 shows the path of the centre-line of some of these traces, ignoring dispersion.

Among several interesting points to emerge from the examination of the level information of Fig.7 in conjunction with the dye plume geometry also shown are the following:-

- Water in the main channel itself does undergo some direction change: the implied lateral acceleration is consistent with the pressure of gradient of zone 3.

- However, the flow curvature does not match that of the channel banks and a large proportion of the flow passing through the channel cross-section at the bend apex escapes onto the floodplain before the tangent point at the end of the bend. In doing so it exhibits considerable vertical translation.

- The evacuation of this water from the main channel, associated with the reversed secondary current which is noted elsewhere, accentuates the divergence of flow as water from the floodplain is drawn into the channel. This divergence implies reduced kinetic energy and thus increased depth in the vicinity of area 1.

- Clearly the adverse pressure gradient approaching that area increases the tendency for channel flow lines to straighten in plan and for water to escape.

- The escaping water accelerates upon entering the floodplain and the depth (or water surface level) is locally reduced.

CONCLUSIONS

The discussion above highlights the complexity of a curved main channel flow interacting with a straight floodplain flow, producing decelerations, accelerations, transverse pressure gradients, bend secondary cells in the opposite rotation to inbank flows, intense cross-over region mixing, vigorous expulsion of main channel water downstream of each bend apex and plunging of the floodplain flow into the main channel.

The next step concerns the numerical modelling of such flows. At one end of the spectrum there are one-dimensional models which do not pick-up any of the flow features mentioned, but when used in conjunction with the James and Wark approach Ref. [8], offer good estimates of stage/discharge for meandering compound channels.

At the other end of the spectrum are three-dimensional turbulence models Ref. [2] which may reveal many of the fine and coarse flow features described above but cannot realistically be used over an entire river catchment, because of the grid spacing and volume of input data which would be required. The immediate solution is to use 1-D models for global features and 3-D turbulence models for very localised features.

ACKNOWLEDGEMENTS

The authors acknowledge the financial assistance of SERC and H.R. Wallingford in making this work possible. The efforts of the Research Assistants, Manuel Lorena, Rosemary Greenhill and Richard Hardwick were greatly appreciated, as was the technical input from Mary Johnston (H. R. Ltd.). Thanks also to the input from Dr. Knight (Birmingham) and Dr. Guymer (Sheffield).

REFERENCES

[1]   Wark, J.B., Samuels, P. and Ervine, D.A. "A practical method of estimating velocity and discharge in compound channels". Proc. Int. Conf. on River Flood Hydraulics, Wallingford, Sept. 1990, 163-172. (Ed. W.R. White, John Wiley & Son.)

[2]   Cokljat, D.P. "Turbulence models for non-circular ducts and channels". Ph.D. thesis, City University, London, March 1993.

[3]   Ackers, P. "Hydraulic design of two-stage channels". Proc. ICE Water, Maritime and Energy, 1992, 96, Dec, 247-257.

[4]   Sellin, R.H.J., Ervine, D.A. and Willetts, B.B. "Behaviour of meandering two-stage channels". Proc. ICE, Water, Maritime and Energy, 1993, 101, June, 99-111.

[5]   Ervine, D.A., Willetts, B.B., Sellin R.H.J., and Lorena, M. "Factors affecting conveyance in meandering compound flows". Proc. ASCE. Journ. of Hyd. Div. (accepted for publication).

[6]   Greenhill, R.K. and Sellin, R.H.J. "Development of a simple method to predict discharges in compound meandering channels". Proc. ICE., Water Maritime and Energy, 1993, 101, March, 37-44.

[7]   Willetts, B.B. and Hardwick, R.I. "Stage dependency for overbank flow in meandering channels". Proc. ICE., Water, Maritime and Energy, 1993, 101. March, 45-54.

[8]   James, C. and Wark, J.B.   "Hydraulics manual for meandering compound channels". Report EX2606, H.R. Wallingford, June 1992.

[9]   Knight, D.W. et al.   "Boundary shear in meandering channels".   Proc. Int. Symp. on Hydraulic Research in Nature and Laboratory Wuhan, China, Nov, 1992.

[10]   Lorena, M., and Ervine, D.A.   "Conveyance of meandering compound channels".   2nd Int. Conf. on Hydraulic and Environmental Modelling (eds. Falconer, R.A. et al) University of Bradford, Sept, 1992, 27-41.

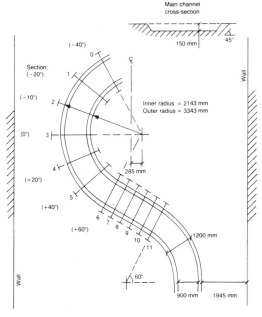

FIG 1.   PLAN   DETAILS   OF
         LOWER   SINUOSITY
         CHANNEL

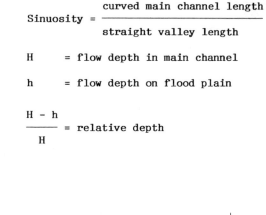

$$\text{Sinuosity} = \frac{\text{curved main channel length}}{\text{straight valley length}}$$

H   = flow depth in main channel

h   = flow depth on flood plain

$$\frac{H - h}{H} = \text{relative depth}$$

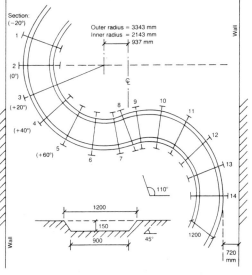

FIG 2.   PLAN   DETAILS   OF
         HIGHER SINUOSITY
         CHANNEL

465

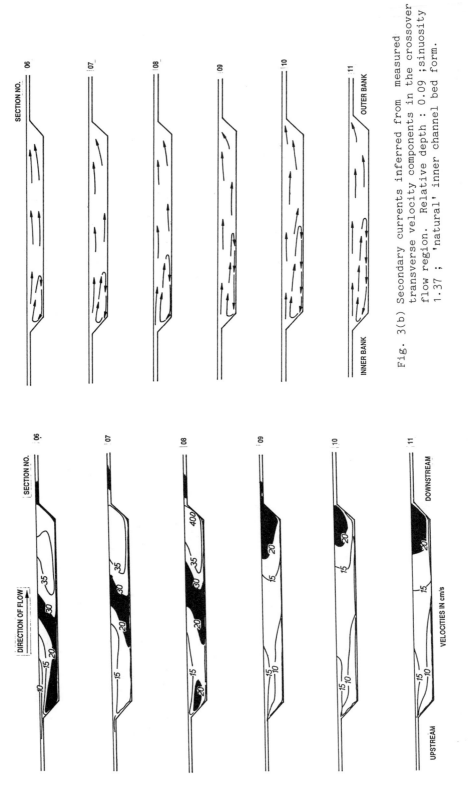

Fig. 3(b) Secondary currents inferred from measured transverse velocity components in the crossover flow region. Relative depth : 0.09 ;sinuosity 1.37 ; 'natural' inner channel bed form.

Fig. 3(a) Distribution of longitudinal velocity component in the deep channel at the crossover(sections 06-11).

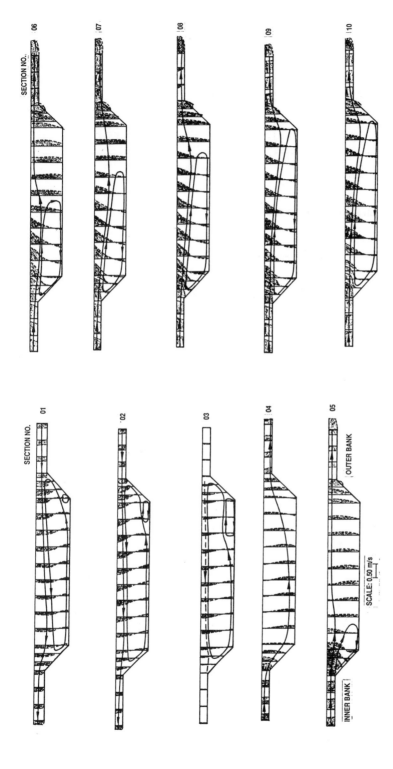

Fig.4. Distribution of transverse velocities in the deeper channel for relative depth 0.25, sinuosity 1.37, and trapezoidal cross-section.

(a) Sections 01-05 at bend region (above)
(b) Sections 06-11 at cross over region (opposite)

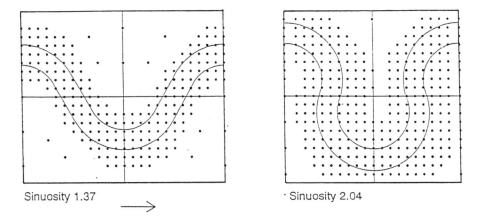

Sinuosity 1.37 ⟶   · Sinuosity 2.04

Fig. 5   Location in plan of level measurements.

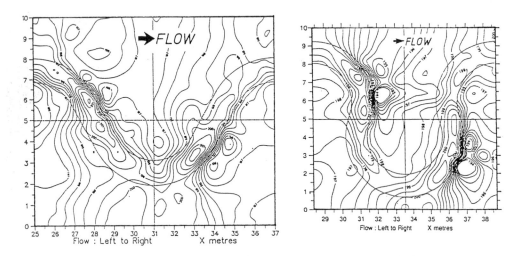

Fig. 6   Contours of water surface elevation.   Natural inner channel: nominal
floodplain depth 50mm.

(a) sinuosity 1.37, (b) sinuosity 2.04

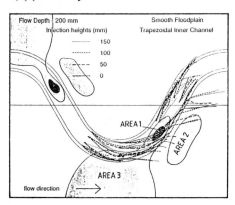

Fig. 7   Identification of prominent zones of high and low surface level. The centre-
lines of plumes of injected dye are also shown. Similar zones of surface level in
similar positions can be seen at sinuosity 2.04.

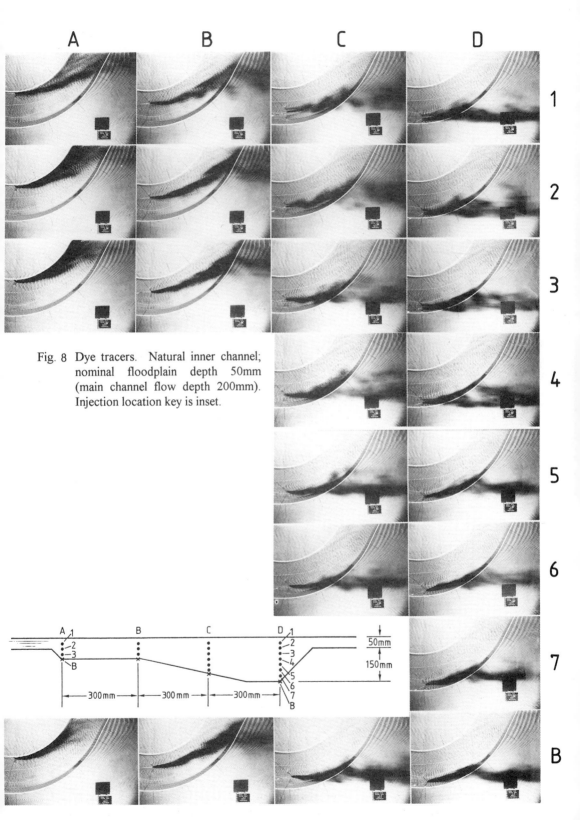

Fig. 8 Dye tracers. Natural inner channel; nominal floodplain depth 50mm (main channel flow depth 200mm). Injection location key is inset.

469

Chapter Ten

Environmental Aspects

MANAGEMENT OF FENLAND DITCHES FOR ENHANCEMENT OF WILDLIFE HABITATS

S R Runham   ADAS Arthur Rickwood Research Centre, Mepal, Ely, Cambs CB6 2BA

S C Rose   ADAS Soil and Water Research Centre, Anstey Hall, Maris Lane, Trumpington, Cambridge, CB2 2LF

T P Milsom   Central Science Laboratory, MAFF, Worplesdon, Guildford, Surrey GU3 3LQ

A Sherwood   ADAS Land and Environment, Brooklands Avenue, Cambridge CB2 2DR

ABSTRACT

The extensive network of inter-connecting watercourses in the fens of East Anglia is managed primarily to control flooding which in turn protects a valuable farming industry. Modified maintenance of farm ditches could encourage the development of a more valuable wetland habitat for fenland wildlife without compromising this primary function.

Whilst main drainage channels, managed by the Internal Drainage Boards, tend to be routinely cleared of vegetation, management of farm ditches is less well-structured, and varies between holdings. A better understanding of the effects of vegetation clearance on wetland communities, and a more co-ordinated approach to ditch management both on individual farms and between holdings, could improve the biodiversity of wetland habitats and safety of rare species, whilst ensuring efficient drainage. An experiment from 1989 to 1992, funded by the Ministry of Agriculture, Fisheries and Food (MAFF) at ADAS Arthur Rickwood Research Centre, studied the effects of ditch management techniques on aquatic and terrestrial plant communities associated with fenland ditches. Data from this experiment, described in this paper, are related to commercial ditch and main drainage channel management. Reference is also made to a more comprehensive ditch management project which started in 1992 and involves the co-operation of local landowners.

INTRODUCTION

The peat or 'black' Fens were formerly one of the largest wetlands in western Europe. However, they have been progressively drained since the 17th Century and now comprise one of the most intensively managed agricultural areas in Britain (Godwin, 1978; Darby, 1983). The agricultural dividend has been considerable because the peaty soils are very fertile and allow a wide range of crops to be grown (Seale, 1975).

Apart from the Washlands, which have been retained to regulate flooding (Thomas et al., 1980), and the few remaining fragments of the original Fens, as at Wicken and Woodwalton, the largest area of wetland habitat in the peat Fens survives in the drainage ditches. The extensive network of ditches offers potential for enhancement of wetland flora and fauna.

Recent surveys of fenland drains and ditches (Haslam, 1978; Critchley, 1987 and Anon., 1989) have shown the diversity of species in main drains and farm ditches. In one 100 m section of Internal Drainage Board (IDB) main drain there were 22 aquatic plant species (Critchley, 1987). Conservation consultants advise landowners to have regard for these valuable wetland habitats, whilst taking into account the need for efficient field drainage and arable farming. The maintenance of the drains by the IDB is well structured to reduce the risk of flooding. This may comprise mowing the banks once a year and removal of aquatic plant debris (slubbing) on a four- year cycle. Re-cutting of the banks is undertaken when required, usually as a result of erosion by flowing water. A main problem weed is common reed *Phragmites australis* which has rhizomes that spread unnoticed across the channel bed causing blockage and siltation before the plant stems become erect and visible above water. Regular weed cutting by boat is practised and, in an emergency, chemical weed control may be adopted. However, neither method removes the bulk of the weed and the sediment.

The management of private ditches is often unstructured, and some are neglected. Mowing and slubbing operations are irregular, but often long continuous sections are treated at the same time. Management decisions have been based on the risk associated with overgrown vegetation giving rise to sluggish drainage and waterlogged fields. The timeliness of clearance operations is more critical in lower-lying regions of the catchment area. At ADAS Arthur Rickwood, situated in one of the lowest lying parts of the Sutton and Mepal IDB catchment area, the aim has been to mow the banks of the ditches every year and to slub plant debris every four years to ensure efficient water discharge. In addition, ditches should routinely undergo an intensive cleaning operation to remove silt and plant debris which accumulates, reducing the ditch capacity. This procedure is an integral part of ditch maintenance in the Fens as elsewhere (Newbold et al., 1989).

Little is known about the effects of ditch management on flora and fauna on arable fenland ditches. In most cases, the exact effect of maintenance operations on the drainage function of the ditch is not known either.

The aim of the experiments based in the Mepal Fen area of Cambridgeshire is to provide a scientific basis for advice to landowners. An initial experiment (1989-1992), described in this paper, compared the effects of a range of timings of bank mowing on the flora of localised ditches with a view to enhancing their wildlife value, having regard for the need to maintain drainage efficiency. In 1992, this work was extended to larger sections of ditches belonging to several landowners. Brief reference is made to this experiment.

STUDY SITES

The initial experiment at ADAS Arthur Rickwood comprised two parallel ditches, each 200 m long, separated by 150 m (Fig. 1). Ditch 1 was 1 m. wide at water level, 4m. wide at the top and 2.5 m. deep. Ditch 2 was 2 m wide at water level, 4.5m. wide at the top and 2.2m. deep. Both ditches had been slubbed in 1987.

VEGETATION MANAGEMENT REGIMES

The bank mowing treatments were done either twice a year (October and March), once a year (October), once every two years (October) or left uncut for the duration of the experiment. The bank vegetation was closely trimmed to water level using a

Bomford 457 flail cutter. Each treatment plot was a 25 m long section of ditch. These were adjacent to other treatments along the same ditch. There were three replicates of the four bank mowing treatments; two on Ditch 1 and one on Ditch 2.

Field margins on either side of each ditch were rotavated frequently particularly during the summer months. This was done to separate the agricultural management from the experiment, for example, to minimise the risk of drift of either fertiliser or pesticides from normal farming operations onto the experimental sites.

HYDROLOGICAL ASSESSMENTS

Both ditches used in the initial experiment discharged within a relatively short distance to the main IDB drain. The source of water to both ditches was from other field ditches upstream and also from agricultural underdrainage systems outfalling directly into them. Continuous autographic water level recorders were installed in both ditches to monitor fluctuations in the water level at various locations in both ditches. It was considered that if the management regime of the ditch influenced the hydrological regime it would be apparent from both the general water levels in the ditch and the drawdown change from this level when the IDB pump was operated. In addition, a gauge board was installed in the middle of each treatment plot so that the ditch water depth at the time of each vegetation assessment could be noted. The water level fluctuations in the main IDB drain were recorded from October 1990 with the installation of a high range continuous water level recorder. This allowed changes in the IDB pumping regime throughout the year to be monitored and related to the hydraulic performance of the experimental ditches.

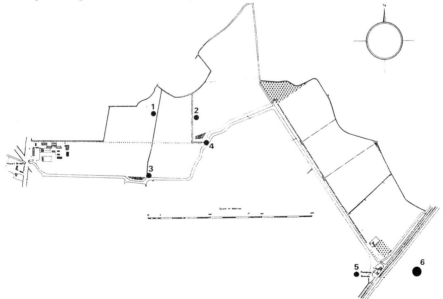

Fig. 1. Northern fields at ADAS Arthur Rickwood showing location of experimental ditches
Key: 1 & 2 = ditches, 3 & 4 = outfalls to main IDB drain, 5 = pumping station, 6 = Ouse Washes SSSI

As nutrient levels could have a significant impact on aquatic species, water samples for nitrate-N determination were taken routinely from both ditches between 1990 and 1992. In addition, spot samples from individual field drains outfalling into the ditches were taken whenever possible during the routine sampling regime.

VEGETATION ASSESSMENTS

Aquatic plant species were recorded as either 'present' or 'absent' in each of ten 2 m sub-sections of the central 20 m of each bank mowing treatment plot. Both sides of the ditches were examined at each assessment. These records were taken at monthly intervals from April to September inclusive in each year. Records were taken during 1989 prior to the commencement of the first mowing treatment in October 1989.

Terrestrial dicotyledonous plant species were recorded on both banks once a year in late summer using the same technique as for the aquatic plants.

RESULTS

Water levels

The water levels in both ditches responded to the pumping cycles in the main IDB drain (data not presented here). Ditch 2 showed a greater range of variation due to being closer to the main drain.

Over the experimental period the seasonal pumping regimes on the main IDB drain changed from year to year according to prevailing hydrological and climatic conditions. They were also affected by design changes at the local pumping station in 1990. Following the drought conditions in summer 1990, when most of the field ditch network went dry, the IDB reduced the amount of pumping in the early spring months and installed sluice boards in the main IDB drain to retain water in the ditch system during the summer months, primarily for irrigation purposes. Due to this policy, the ditches did not dry out during the drought in 1991. This was beneficial to both agriculture and aquatic plant species in the ditches. The level to which the main IDB drain has been pumped during the winter months has also been changed over the experimental period and this has had a profound effect on the water level fluctuations recorded in the experimental ditches. When the main IDB drain level was controlled to a level which was below the base level of the culverts through which the two experimental ditches discharged into it, then the ditch levels only fluctuated due to inflow from upstream and not to pumping cycles; this situation occurred for 3 months during the winter of 1991/92.

In both farm ditches, the range of water level variation declined quite markedly with increased distance from the main IDB drain. During the spring 1991 pumping period, this decline was 30% over a distance of 170 m in Ditch 1 and 30% over a distance of 70 m in Ditch 2. The increased hydraulic roughness associated with the differential vegetation growth in each of the management treatments also contributed to this decline. With the experimental design used it proved very difficult to assess the impact of any one treatment on the hydraulic performance of the ditch sections, because one treatment could affect water levels in the upstream sections.

Water quality

Water samples taken from the ditches always showed the highest concentration of nitrate-N during the March to April pumping period, following fertiliser applications to the surrounding agricultural land. In spring 1991, concentrations reached 13 mg/l for both ditches and in spring 1992, the peak concentration was 10 mg/l. Nitrate-N concentrations recorded in water flowing out of individual field underdrainage pipes into the Ditch 2 were up to 17 mg/l, which contributed to the slight increase in concentrations observed in the downstream samples taken from that ditch.

During the summer months, when the ditch water levels were generally higher due to retention of water for irrigation, and the water stationary for long periods of time, the nitrate-N concentrations fell rapidly to below 1 mg/l. From this time until the following spring period, the concentrations rarely rose above 2 mg/l, even during the autumn when the land would have been cultivated and bare prior to the establishment of the following crop.

Aquatic vegetation

When assessed in 1989, prior to the start of the mowing treatments, the distribution patterns of aquatic plant species differed between the two ditches. The diversity of emergent species tended to be greater in Ditch 1: two species, the common reed *P. australis* and branched burr-reed *Sparganium erectum* were widespread in Ditch 1 but absent in Ditch 2. Floating and submerged species tended to be more abundant in Ditch 2.

The aquatic flora of the ditches changed with time. Some floating and submerged species such as water starworts *Callitriche spp* and pondweeds *Potamogeton spp* disappeared when the ditches dried out temporarily during 1989/90 and in August 1990 (Sherwood and Harris, 1991). None of these species re-appeared during the rest of the experiment. Some species may have been affected adversely be competition from emergent species such as sweet grass *Glyceria fluitans* or common reed *P. australis*.

The abundance of the emergent aquatic species also changed. Two examples, which relate to typical fenland species, are given here (Fig. 2).

The greater reedmace *Typha latifolia* increased in some plots and decreased in others but the trends in abundance did not appear to be correlated with mowing frequency. In contrast, the abundance of sweet grass *G. fluitans* was affected by altering the mowing interval. It decreased in uncut plots but remained unchanged or varied independently in the other plots. The difference was statistically significant.

The growth of common reed *P. australis*, but not its abundance, was affected by mowing frequency. Observations and photographic records of the plots indicated that frequent (twice yearly) mowing encouraged more vigorous and dense growth of the common reed than in adjacent plots left uncut.

Overall, there appeared to be a greater effect of the bank mowing treatments in the narrower Ditch 1 than the wider Ditch 2.

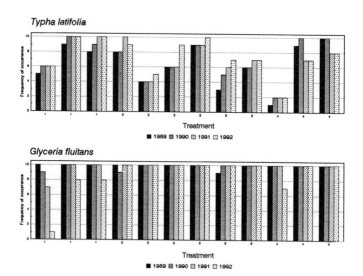

Fig. 2. Changes in abundance of two emergent aquatic plant species in relation to four mowing treatments with three replicates.

Key: 1 = uncut, 2 = cut twice per year in March & October, 3 = cut annually in October. 4 = cut once every two years in October.

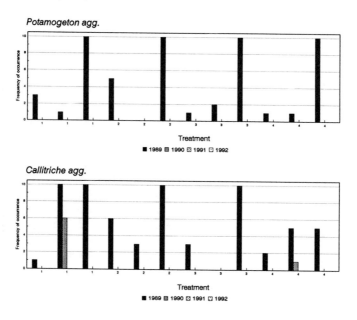

Fig. 3. Changes in abundance of two groups of submerged/floating aquatic plants in two fenland ditches by mowing treatment.

Key: 1 = uncut, 2 = cut twice per year in March & October, 3 = cut annually in October. 4 = cut once every two years in October.

Bank vegetation

Fifty nine species of terrestrial dicotyledons were recorded on the ditch banks during the experiment. Most common were arable weeds. Only 33 (56%) of the 59 species were present throughout the experimental period. Seven species were lost and 19 attempted to colonise (Table 1). However, many of these colonisation attempts failed. Overall, the number of species increased between 1989 and 1991, but this trend was reversed in 1992. The trends in numbers of species suggest that the balance between the rates of colonisation and extinction varied between treatment plots, but the net rate of colonisation did not differ significantly between treatments or blocks.

The banks became dominated by tall grass species especially by 1992, which was a wetter season than the previous ones. These grasses have 'smothered' out many of the less competitive species.

Table 1. Number of plots colonised by terrestrial plant species during experiment

	1989	1990	1991	1992
Aethusa cynapium				
Epilobium palustre	-	1	-	-
Malva sylvestris	-	1	-	-
Papaver lecoqii	-	4	6	-
Equisetum arvense	-	1	1	-
Chenopodium polyspermum	-	1	-	3
Veronica arvensis	-	5	9	8
Erysimum cheiranthoides	-	-	1	-
Pisum sativum				
Urtica urens	-	-	1	-
Vicia faba	-	-	1	-
Polygonum amphibium	-	-	1	-
Veronica agrestis	-	-	3	-
Rumex obtusifolius	-	-	1	1
Veronica hederifolia	-	-	1	1
Tragopogon sp.	-	-	1	2
Euphorbia helioscopia	-	-	2	2
Polygonum lapathifolium	-	-	2	2
Rumex acetosa	-	-	-	2

DISCUSSION

Flooding during the 1992/93 winter and spring re-emphasised the need to maintain ditch capacity and efficiency, which would be reduced if growth were not regulated.

Overall, though, throughout the experiment the conveyance of water through the ditches to the main IDB drain was never severely inhibited by plant growth.

However, particularly heavy rainfall leading to flood risk conditions did not occur until the end of the experimental period. Restricted water movement could potentially manifest itself if plant debris from bankside mowing or natural degradation processes, is allowed to build up on the ditch bed over a longer period than the duration of this initial experiment. The ditch could become clogged, especially just upstream of culverts where this debris will accumulate. Field underdrainage outfalls would become submerged for long periods and, ultimately, crops could be affected by waterlogging or inundation. Regular clearance of this accumulated debris is likely to be required to remove this potential problem.

Water availability greatly influenced the floating plant species community which proved dynamic during the experiment. These species were capable of surviving disturbance, and proliferated following ditch cleaning operations undertaken before the experiment started. However, they were not capable of surviving drought, disappearing in the summer of 1990 in the dried ditches and not returning during the rest of the experiment. In contrast, the emergent and semi-emergent plant species remained relatively stable during the experiment and throughout dry periods.

Competition between plants may have caused loss of some species whereby vigorous "dominant" species swamped or possibly excluded light to other species.

Data from this initial experiment appear to show that mowing, as practised by the technique described, had no effect on submerged or floating aquatic plant species in the wider Ditch 2, but perhaps an indirect effect in Ditch 1. Mowing also had little discernible effect on most emergent species in the ditch plant communities but again, there were differences in response between the wide and narrow ditches. However, the emergent species common reed *Phragmites australis* grew more densely with frequent mowing; this result is in agreement with those obtained elsewhere (Haslam, 1968; Cowie et al. 1992). The benefits to wildlife from promoting the growth of *P. australis* can be considerable because reed fringes are often the only nesting habitat for birds in ditches; they are also valuable for gamebird cover.

Against this, is the concern by fenland farmers and IDB managers that vigorous plants such as common reed can quickly reduce the capacity of a drain or ditch. It may be that reeds can be allowed to proliferate in ditches categorised as "less important" for rapid water run-off. Allowing reeds to grow along one side only of a responsive ditch may offer another alternative solution. Growth of common reed and other vigorous plants is much more likely to be influenced by ditch cleaning or 'slubbing', where aquatic plants are positively removed from the ditch, than by mowing. Overall, the optimum management regime for enhancement of a wildlife habitat may depend on the plants in the ditch, or width of the ditch, and on the desire to encourage the proliferation of certain species.

Data and experience gained from the initial experiment are showing some indications of the complex relationships between water availability and conveyance in fenland ditches and their associated plant communities. This information is limited by both the small size of this experiment and its short duration.

In 1992, a more comprehensive experiment was started with the aim to manipulate larger sections of ditches belonging to several landowners in the Mepal Fen area of Cambridgeshire. The ditches have already been categorised into those which respond rapidly to changes in the water tables in nearby main drains affected by the IDB pump, and those which respond slowly or not at all. In addition, distance of the plot from the main drain has been used as a criterion for selection. This factor is expected to influence the rate of recovery from management operations by affecting the availability of aquatic species for replenishment of the habitat. Water level changes caused by the IDB pump action will be monitored, to determine the influence of vegetation management regimes on the water conveyance and drainage function of the ditches. A section of each experimental ditch has been 'slubbed' to remove plant debris along one side only. Replenishment of the ditch aquatic plant species will be assessed following the mowing operations.

The effects of ditch maintenance, and location of the ditch within the catchment itself, on the preservation of these species should be better understood at the end of the period of study.

This will lead to reliable advice for landowners for management for wildlife without increasing the risk of flooding. Conservation consultants, landowners and drainage engineers can then work towards a co-ordinated approach to management of fenland ditches.

ACKNOWLEDGEMENTS

The work was funded by Land Use, Conservation and Countryside Group, MAFF. The contributions of Donald Ashmore, Jackie Town and Peter Nixon of ADAS Arthur Rickwood Research Centre, Graham Harris of ADAS Soil and Water Research Centre, Nigel Critchley of ADAS Newcastle and both Kevin Hand and John Crowe, formerly of ADAS are acknowledged.

REFERENCES

Anon. (1989). Report on the Conservation Value of Dykes and Ditches in Cambridgeshire. Report commissioned by Cambs County Council, Shire Hall, Castle Hill, Cambridge.

Cowie, N. R., Sutherland, W. J., Ditlhogo, M. K. M. and James, R. (1992). The effects of conservation management of reed beds. II. The flora and litter disappearance. Journal of Applied Ecology, 29, 277-284.

Critchley, J. N. R.(1987). Arthur Rickwood EHF - The Wildlife Resource: an evaluation and recommendations for management. Unpublished Report. ADAS Cambridge.

Darby, H. C. (1983). The Changing Fenland. Cambridge University Press, Cambridge.

Godwin, H. (1978). Fenland: Its Ancient Past and Uncertain Future. Cambridge University Press, Cambridge.

Haslam, S. M. (1968). The biology of reed (*Phragmites communis*) in relation to its control. In: Proceedings of the 9th British Weed Control Conference, 392-397.

Haslam, S. M. (1978). River plants. Cambridge University Press.

Newbold, C., Honnor, J. and Buckley, K. (1989). Nature Conservation and the Management of Drainage Channels. Published by the Nature Conservancy Council in conjunction with the Association of Drainage Authorities, Peterborough.

Seale, R. S. (1975). Soils of the Ely District. Memoirs of the Soil Survey of Great Britain, England and Wales: Sheet 173. The Soil Survey, Rothamsted Experimental Station, Harpenden.

Sherwood, A. and Harris, G. L. (1991). The Management of Ditches in Arable Fenland for Drainage and Wildlife. Unpublished Report. Ministry of Agriculture, Fisheries and Food, Cambridge.

Thomas, G. J., Allen, D. A. and Grose, M. P. B. (1980). Aquatic plants at the Ouse Washes in 1978. Nature in Cambridgeshire, 23, 29-39.

PAPER 42

2nd International Conference on
RIVER FLOOD HYDRAULICS
22–25 March 1994: York, England

Rehabilitation of an Urban River

Heinrich Patt
University of the Federal Armed Forces Munich
Werner-Heisenberg-Weg 39, D-85577 Neubiberg, Germany

I. INTRODUCTION

The preservation of nature for future generations and concern for the health of the populations were the main reasons why the Parliament of the Federal Republic of Germany has brought in legislation to reduce the steadily increasing burden on nature.

In 1976 the (federal nature preservation law) "Bundesnaturschutz-gesetz" was passed by Parliament and step by step completed by individual laws and regulations in all German states (Länder). These laws, which prescribe the conservation and restoration of nature, are now the legal basis for every water related project.

The growing ecological consciousness of the population, the significant improvement of water quality in the last decade and last not but least the financial support programs of the goverment enabled the restoration of certain sections of channelled waters thus improving their aesthetic and ecological structures. Under urban conditions very often flood security and the required space are the limiting factors for many river restorations.

The extensive preliminary work depends on the very different starting conditions that exist in practice. For these reasons this short contribution cannot be a detailed summary that is valid for every type of rehabilitation. In practice the planning staff has to include experts on biology, ecology and landscape. The early participation of nature conservation bodies, fishermen, owners of the river bank areas etc. is advisable to avoid protests on important elements of the study at the end of the planning process.

As an example of rehabilitation of a river under urban conditions, the small domain of hydraulic investigation which was carried out for the river "Roter Main" in the district "Oberfranken" in Northern Bavaria will be presented.

2nd International Conference on River Flood Hydraulics. Edited by W. R. White and J. Watts
© 1994 HR Wallingford Ltd. Published by John Wiley & Sons Ltd

II. PRACTICAL APPROACH

A great deal of information about a river system and its corridor is necessary to decide whether a river rehabilitation is appropriate. Nearly every regional authority has its own guide lines which describe the preliminary work which has to be done for the feasibility study. These rules vary from the different methods of describing the watercourses in respect to hydrology, morphology and ecology, up to a detailed presentation of flora and fauna. In addition legal aspects, water rights and ownerships of watercourses must be taken into account.

The main goal of a rehabilitation must always be the restoration of the typical, natural flow situation as far as possible. The most important criteria that have always to be fulfilled for that reason, and without which a rehabilitation is not meaningful, are an adequate water quality and enough space for lateral movements of the waters. Figure 1 shows the so-called "Leitbild" concept that can be used as a general guide line for rehabilitation projects (Kern, 1991).

Fig. 1: The "Leitbild" concept and further steps to the final design of a rehabilitation project (Kern, 1991)

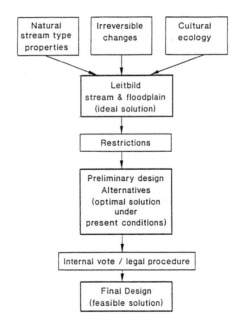

The results of the feasibility study can be used for a first assessment of the status quo of a river reach and the kind of procedure that must be taken as a basis (preservation, mitigation, restoration or do-nothing).

If the basic demands for a rehabilitation are fulfilled, a more intensive data collection must be started (natural stream type properties, irreversible changes, cultural development, ecology of water and banks etc). This includes also land-use, flood plain habitats, channel morphology, hydrological and hydraulic data as well as chemical investigations (Ministry of Environment Baden-Württemberg, 1992).

Striving for the ideal solution (the untouched waters of the same region; the "Leitbild"), all these considerations and investigations lead to the final project design (Fig. 1).

III. EXAMPLE OF A REHABILITATION

In the sixties the "Roter Main" river in the famous "Wagner-City" of Bayreuth was channelled to protect the town against floods. Simultaneously a nearly 200 m portion of the channel was covered to provide parking space for the numerous visitors to the town.

During the flood periods the whole cross-section is more or less filled (the present bankfull return period event is a 20-year flood with 120 m^3/s), while during the long low water periods (mean discharge 2,6 m^3/s) the "Roter Main" is only a small brook in an ugly concrete channel (Fig. 2). Upstream the city the river is forced into a straight bed with concrete primary channel confined between levees (Fig. 3).

The covered part of the river can be classified as a completely degraded river without any realistic possibility of restoration (parking space and public traffic areas are on top - see Fig. 2 in the background -). In the sections with vertical concrete walls, which are not covered, a few changes that improve the view of the river seemed to be feasible.

Outside of these sections the appearance of the "Roter Main" can be mitigated by rehabilitation. The situation in Bayreuth is typical for the very limited space which often prevails in the center of a town.

A further problem is a flow rate reduction in the investigation area through a by-pass that has to be preserved because of the existing legal situation. In times of medium water discharge this intake reduces the flowing rate in the main channel up to 70 percent. Particularly in low water periods in the summer months (discharge in the main channel only 110 l/s), this factor is unsatisfactory for the rehabilitation and undoubtedly must be the object of further consideration and investigation.

Fig. 2:Actual situation in Bayreuth during the low water periods
        (section with vertical concrete walls and the flow limi-
        ting bridge in the background)

Fig. 3:Actual situation in Bayreuth (Straight section of the con-
        crete mean water bed with enough space for embayments and
        lateral movements of the river)

IV. Physical Model

A physical model (scale 1 : 30) was built to estimate the channel efficiency and to verify the different rehabilitation solutions, which were proposed for the "Roter Main" by the water management authorities in a preliminary study.

In the sections with vertical concrete walls and paved bed, movable weirs and sills were installed to maintain an adequate water depth in low water periods. In the regimes upstream and downstream of this area the straight primary channel was replaced by a meandering channel, whose water surface was influenced through numerous groynes, islands and other formations that usually exist in natural rivers.

By raising the levees the maximum channel efficiency could be increased to be 165 m^3/s. The limiting section was the covered part of the channel in connection with a bridge that was located 200 metres downstream.

The construction height of this bridge is very low with a pier in the middle of the flow cross-section. For a later test run the influence of this bridge on the flow was eliminated by increasing its height and removing the pier. This increased the maximum discharge in the channel up to 175 m^3/s.

The variant with sills was not further taken into account, because it reduced the channel flow to 156 m^3/s.

An increasing friction factor of the natural channel generally produces a reduction of the channel efficiency. In Bayreuth this can be compensated through embayments, which are placed in some locations. The minimum channel width, that has to be observed when the river bed is naturally formed, was determined in the physical model. The present channel width (mean width 60 m) has to be broadened by about 10 % to compensate the increased roughness.

The resulting floodplains can be naturally formed in many ways. A free formation of the sinuosity ought to be tolerated as long as it does not influence the channel efficiency, the security of the levees or the foundation of piers and walls.

Fig. 4a shows the situation outside of the centre before and Fig. 4b the naturally formed mean water bed after rehabilitation. This section corresponds to Fig. 3.

Additionally the whole project is influenced by some sewer outfalls from the municipal sewerage system (corresponding retention tanks are under construction) and the high suspended load of the "Roter Main", that has to be reduced by a river settling basin to avoid deposition at undesired locations downstream.

Fig. 4: Rehabilitation of the mean water bed outside of the city of Bayreuth (physical model scale 1 : 30)

Mean water bed

a: original situation   b: after rehabilitation

V. CONCLUSION

The whole development of a river in Germany - from the expensive "improvements" in the sixties to the even more expensive rehabilitation in the nineties - are a part of the history of river engineering in industrial countries.

The experiences with river rehabilitations that were obtained over the past ten years, show that in many cases the difficult way combining the "hydraulically necessary" and the "ecologically meaningful" can actually be achieved in many cases.

VI. REFERENCES

Kern, K., Rehabilitation of Streams in South-West Germany, in "River Conservation and Management", Ed.: P.J. Boon, P. Calow, G.E. Petts, Wiley & Sons, Chichester, 1991.

Ministry of Environment Baden-Württemberg, Handbuch Wasserbau - Naturnahe Umgestaltung von Fließgewässern, Heft 2, Stuttgart, 1992.

Naimann, R.J., Lonzarich, D.G., Beechie, T.J., Ralph, S.C., General Principles of Classification and the Assessment of Conservation Potential in Rivers, in "River Conservation and Management", Ed.: P.J. Boon, P. Calow, G.E. Petts, Wiley & Sons, Chichester, 1991.

RIVER MAINTENANCE EVALUATION

J. Morris, D. C. Sutherland and J A L Dunderdale

BACKGROUND

Rivers serve a variety of interests including those of water supply, drainage, environmental quality, and recreation. One of the main functions of managed rivers is to dispose of surplus water from urban and rural areas. In the case of rural areas this drainage function relates to the control, within acceptable limits, of flooding and water table levels on riparian, mainly agricultural land.

The purpose of river maintenance is to sustain a particular standard of drainage service. In the case of agricultural land, there are, therefore, no extra benefits to be set against maintenance costs, but rather the avoidance of losses which would be associated with a decline in agricultural productivity due to a deterioration in drainage standards.

During the mid 1980s, Severn Trent region of National Rivers Authority (NRA) (and its predecessor Severn Trent Water Authority (STWA)) began to apply objective management criteria to the appraisal of its river maintenance programmes. In January 1989, NRA commissioned Silsoe College to undertake an evaluation of river maintenance activities on selected sites with Severn Trent region. This paper reports on this research.

STUDY AIM

The broad aim of the study, (Morris and Sutherland, 1993), was to develop and verify a database and methodology for the appraisal of river maintenance in rural, mainly agricultural catchments. In this respect the concern of the study was more with methods of appraisal than the evaluation of particular maintenance schemes.

STUDY APPROACH AND METHODS

Overview

The principal maintenance operations involve dredging and/or desilting, weed cutting and clearance, tree and bush maintenance, bank and flood bank protection and grass cutting, debris and obstruction removal, and repair of structures.

These river maintenance activities affect levels of service to riparian land users through the impact on channel dimension and roughness. Maintenance influences the relationship between flows and levels in the river and drainage system. In this way, maintenance affects the ability of the river to retain flows of a given magnitude, and thereby the risk of flooding. Similarly, maintenance affects water levels in the river and tributary ditch system and the outfall for field drainage, whether by natural movement of water through soils or assisted by underground pipes. Maintenance also affects environmental qualities, either

---

directly through its impact on conditions within the channel, or indirectly through its impact on soil water regimes in the adjacent floodplain. Figure 1 summarises the variables and relationships considered in the assessment of maintenance benefits. Resultant changes in drainage status due to river maintenance interact with farming systems to determine agricultural productivity benefits. Maintenance appraisal compares maintenance costs and benefits taking into account environmental factors.

The impact of river maintenance was assessed by comparing "with" and "without" maintenance conditions in the watercourse, and the effects on land-use, land users and environmental features in the floodplain. Site monitoring, farmer interview and review of research literature were used to assess: the effect of maintenance on river channel conditions; the effect of the latter on flood risk and watertable heights in the floodplain; the link between these drainage conditions and agricultural productivity; and, in the case of major maintenance activities such as desilting, the likely longevity of the works. These methods enabled the study findings to be extrapolated beyond the period of study and to provide databases and routines for maintenance programming and prioritisation.

Flood Risk

With respect to the influence of channel maintenance on flooding, channel dimensions were taken and estimates of channel friction made for with and without maintenance. Figure 2 shows an example of the effect of maintenance on channel capacity, performance and flood return period in the River Sence, Leicestershire. These data were combined with flow data to estimate flood risk associated with different maintenance standards.

Watertable Levels and Drainage Status

A model, developed at Silsoe College, (Youngs et al, 1989), was used to determine the influence of river and ditch water levels, and hence river maintenance, on field drainage conditions, taking into account local rainfall, evapotranspiration, soil type and the intensity of artificial field drainage. The information required by the model is detailed in Figure 3. The model predicts watertable depth, (Figure 3), in the surrounding floodplain against time for given weather conditions. These watertable heights are then compared with those required for crop growth and trafficability of soils.

Recognising that the impact of river maintenance is likely to vary according to the frequency of rainfall and river flows, the model was used to show the effect of different standards of maintenance on water table heights for different weather conditions. For this purpose, historical rainfall data was used to classify and determine the relative frequency of wet, mean and dry years.

Agricultural Impacts

With respect to drainage standards for agriculture, a review of literature revealed that watertable levels at or greater than 0.5m depth do not impede yields or farming practice. Water tables between 0.3m and 0.5m from the surface can depress yields and limit field access by machines and animals. Watertables persistently within 0.3m of the surface, however, lead to severe restrictions on land use. These agricultural drainage categories were labelled "good", "bad" and "very bad", respectively. Drainage status was then defined in terms of the proportion of the time that the watertable lay within these critical boundaries. A season with 80% of weeks with water tables deeper than 0.5m was described as one of good drainage status. A season with at least 50% of weeks with water tables deeper than 0.3m was described as one of bad drainage, a season with at least 50% of weeks with water tables within 0.3m of the surface was described as one of very bad drainage. From a land-use viewpoint, the main concern in Britain is with field drainage status during the spring and autumn periods, especially as this influences the timeliness of field operations.

Information was derived from the farm survey and the literature to compile farming productivity scenarios which described the input-output relationships and resultant financial performance of land use and farming practice under the categories of drainage status previously described, (Hess and Morris, 1985, Hess et al, 1989). The estimates of benefits associated with the different productivity classes were used to determine the benefits attributable to the maintenance of standards of drainage service, and thereby, the benefits of river maintenance. For instance, if a good drainage status on a particular land use generates a benefit of £460/ha/year and a bad drainage status generates a benefit of £340/ha/year, the net benefit of river maintenance which prevents a decline from good to bad drainage conditions is £120/ha/year.

Using the methods described above, the drainage status and related benefits of land in the benefit areas of schemes were estimated for wet, mean and dry rainfall conditions and for with and without river maintenance. The benefits of maintenance were thereby identified by the change, if any, in drainage status for given climatic conditions. Drawing on historical weather data, the benefits were then weighted by the relative frequency of the three types of weather conditions to derive an average, expected annual benefit.

A similar approach was adopted to estimate the benefits of flood alleviation associated with a change in maintenance standards. Estimates were derived of the cost of single or multiple flood events occurring on given land use (and productivity class) at different times of year and the change in flood risk associated with channel maintenance. For example, if deteriorating maintenance standards result in a decrease in the interval between floods of, say, 3 to 2 years for which the average annual costs of damage are £9/ha and £6/ha respectively, the flood alleviation benefits attributable to maintenance is £3/ha over the area of flood risk.

The benefits of flood alleviation were added to the benefits of drainage status (weighted by the probability of types of weather year) to determine total benefits attributable to maintenance. These benefits were aggregated within the benefit area of a scheme and set against the cost of providing the maintenance service to determine the overall value-added. The discounting procedure was used for this purpose.

Environmental Impacts

Since the late 1980s, increasing emphasis has been placed on the protection of environmental features as part of maintenance schemes. To enable the impact of river maintenance on the environment to be determined, river corridor surveys using the Nature Conservancy Council, (NCC, now English Nature), survey methodology were completed for each 500 m section of the study reach before and after maintenance.

This method concentrates on the river and immediate corridor of adjacent land, (50 m either side of the banks). Any areas of land which would benefit from the proposed maintenance work were also surveyed. This standard format for the river corridor surveys enables a concise picture of the river to be recorded which can be easily interpreted. Survey cards were completed for each 500 m reach; all records being made for the river itself, bank features/vegetation and adjacent habitats. Bank profiles and characteristics, bed substrates, in channel/bank and adjacent vegetation and river habitat information such as location of pools, weirs and protruding rocks were detailed.

Maintenance related actions which aim to protect or enhance environmental features such as bankside preservation or shoal creation may affect the processes of sedimentation and erosion and therefore the hydraulic performance of the channel. This is being investigated in collaboration with Hydraulics Research Ltd.

Information regarding non agricultural features and interests such as angling and water sports is collected from interested parties and various sources, including farmers within the benefit area.

ANALYSIS AND RESULTS

The above methods were developed and applied in the context of six river sites located within the Severn Trent region. These sites, chosen from a list of 23 possible sites, were selected for study using the criteria of river characteristics, floodplain features and type of maintenance operations.

The study sites covered a variety of river and flood plain types. They ranged from 3 to 30 cumecs mean annual flow, with flood plains which varied in width, shape and slope. Soils were mostly alluvial, silty or sandy clays on mainly grade 3, and to a lesser extent, grade 2 agricultural land. The average reach studied was about 4 km, with a benefit area of about 120 ha.

With respect to farm type and land use, the benefit areas accommodated a range of farm types, reflecting locally dominant farming systems: arable in the east, livestock in the west. Average farm size was 103 ha, with an average of about 20% of their total areas lying within the benefit area of a scheme. Forty-four per cent of land was down to continuous grass, 38% was continuous arable, and the remaining 18% involved grass/arable rotations.

Maintenance activities included desilting, weed cutting and tree and bush work. The cost of works range from about £600/km (£21/ha of benefit) for annual weed cutting to over £11,000/km (£372/ha of benefit) for a 15 year desilting operation. Obtaining reliable cost estimates of work carried out was not always easy, either because costs were insufficiently segregated between different activities, or because costs were based on predicted works at standard rates rather than on actual works at actual costs. Cost were higher where environmental protection or enhancement works were also carried out within the maintenance programme.

River engineers responsible for managing the maintenance function were interviewed regarding management practices. Most maintenance work was part of a routine programme which followed river inspection in order to confirm the need to do work. All of the work examined was justified in terms of land drainage and flood alleviation. Custom and practice were given as the main criteria for determining maintenance frequency, standards and methods. Maintenance schemes increasingly incorporated conservation protection and enhancement measures. Landowners were always contacted before commencement of works, but, in most cases there was no post operation follow-up.

With respect to the effect of river maintenance on flood risk and field drainage status, farmers reported that maintenance was associated with lower flood risk: maintenance prevented flooding on 10% of the area, and reduced its incidence on a further 17% of the total area. These estimates accorded well with the results of hydraulic modelling.

Analysis showed that the estimates of drainage status obtained by farmer interview and by groundwater modelling were closely related. In a mean rainfall year, the percentages of the combined benefit areas classified as good, bad and very bad drainage were 45%, 36% and 19% respectively in the absence of maintenance. With maintenance, these percentages were 55%, 35% and 10% respectively. By comparison, in wet years, drainage status was generally poorer and maintenance had a greater beneficial effect. The study observed that the sensitivity of drainage status to river maintenance is influenced by the presence or absence of field drainage or intensive ditch systems, the hydraulic conductivity and drainable porosity of soils, and the degree to which river and ditch levels change as a consequence of doing, or not doing, maintenance.

The benefits of maintenance were aggregated at scheme level and set against the costs of carrying out the works in order to determine the economic value of maintenance activities. Annual benefits per hectare varied considerably amongst schemes from about £4 to £30, reflecting the standard of service provided and the sensitivity of farming to such provision. Generally, the more intensive was the land use, the better was the standard of field drainage (either due to light soils or piped underdrainage), and the greater was the sensitivity to standards of river maintenance.

Maintenance benefits exceeded maintenance costs at the Treasury's 6% test discount rate on four of the six sites that were studied. Of the other two schemes, one was prejudiced by higher than anticipated costs, and the other by very low benefits. This analysis requires cautious interpretation, not least because the analysis looked at selected reaches of river in isolation of the larger catchment, and within the time frame of the study, it was not possible to assess the long term consequences for the river, and related levels of service, of not carrying out the maintenance works.

With respect to the environmental impact of river works, maintenance did not appear to result in negative, long term, irreversible changes in the river environment. In some cases, maintenance works were accompanied by environmental enhancement activities, such as berm creation and tree planting.

CONCLUSIONS AND RECOMMENDATIONS

The study concluded that it was possible to formulate guidelines for the objective appraisal of river maintenance works in rural areas. The main components of appraisal for which data and assessment methods are required are those which relate to the maintenance activity, the physical and hydrological characteristics of the river and floodplain, land use and farming systems, and environmental qualities.

The study developed new methods for maintenance appraisal which provide the basis for practical guidelines for assisting the management of the river maintenance function. Recommendations were made regarding the practical application of the methods developed and the need for further research. It recommended:

> - action to test the practical application of the appraisal methods in the Severn Trent region of NRA;

> - extension of the study in order to further refine the appraisal methods and apply them in other regions of the NRA;

> - further research in order to determine the long term implications of not carrying out maintenance work, either for commercial farming or environmental interests;

> - a detailed assessment of the environmental impacts of river maintenance in order to identify, and incorporate into river maintenance, appropriate environmental enhancement and protection measures.

Some of these recommendations are currently being acted upon and the study has been extended to cover 12 additional rivers in five NRA Regions.

REFERENCES

Hess, T.M., and Morris, J., (1985): *A Computer Model for Agricultural Land Drainage Scheme Appraisal*, MAFF Conference of River Engineers, Cranfield, 16 - 18 July, 1985.

Hess, T.M., Leeds-Harrison, P.B., and Morris, J., (1989): *The Evaluation of River Maintenance in Agricultural Areas*, Proceedings of the Eleventh International Congress on

Agricultural Engineering, Dublin, 4 - 8 September, 1989, in *Agricultural Engineering*, 501 - 507.

Morris, J., and Sutherland, D.C., (1993): *The Evaluation of River Maintenance*, Report to the NRA.

Youngs, E., Leeds-Harrison, P.B., and Chapman, J.M., (1989): *Modelling Water Table Movement in Flat Low-lying Lands*, in Hydrological Processes, 3, 301 - 315.

River Maintenance Benefit Assessment - Variables and Relationships

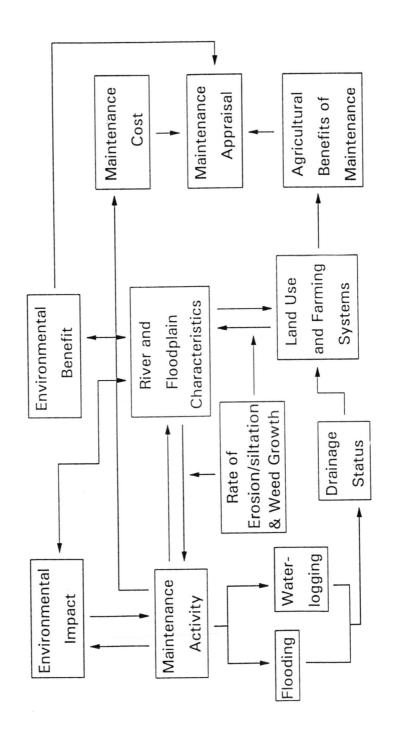

Figure 1

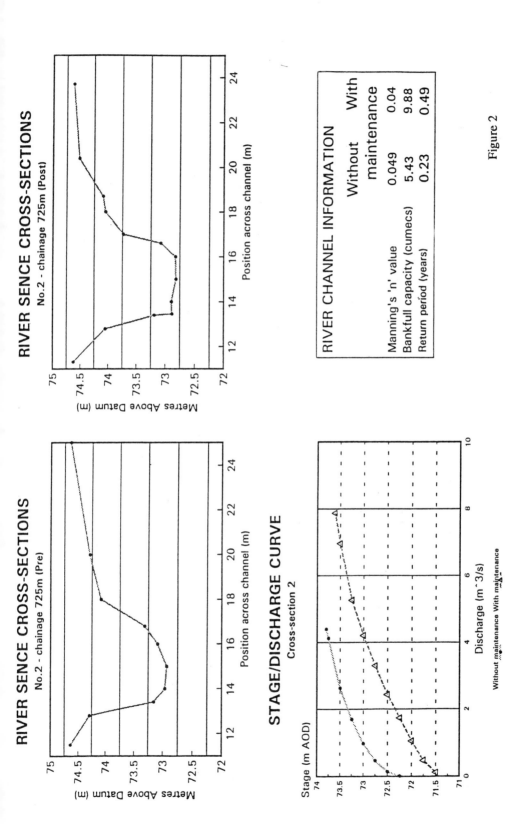

Figure 2

499

Figure 3 Watertable Model

Listed below is the data required for each block of land:-   The same rainfall and evapotranspiration data are used for all land within the same scheme. The output from the model is in the form of a graph showing watertable depths throughout each month of the year. Weather data can also be shown on the same graph, as in the example below.

Data required:-   Ditch spacing (m)
Depth to impermeable layer (m)
Geometrical factor for ditch system
Initial watertable depth (m)
Hydraulic conductivity of topsoil (m/day)
Hydraulic conductivity of subsoil (m/day)
Soil boundary depth (m)
Topsoil specific yield (m/m)
Subsoil specific yield (m/m)
Unsaturated hydraulic conductivity exponent
Surface elevation (m AOD)
Ditch base elevation (river bed level) (m AOD)
Set ditch base water levels?   1 = yes, 0 = no
Is there irrigation?   1 = yes, 0 = no
Draw ditch water levels? 1 = yes, 0 = no

Example output from watertable model:-

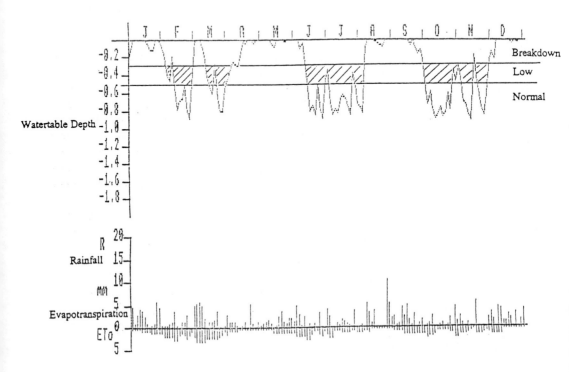

A STUDY ON THE ENVIRONMENTAL EFFECTS OF 20 JUNE 1990 FLOOD
IN TRABZON AND ITS NEIGHBORHOOD, TURKEY

ÜÇÜNCÜ, O.[*],   ÖNSOY, H.[*],   YÜKSEK, Ö.[*]

ABSTRACT

The great flood which took place in Trabzon Province and its
neighborhood on 20 June 1990 caused death of 47 people and great
damages to properties. Although it is impossible to prevent the
floods from occuring, we can do something to minimize the
damages. Since the streams are very steep and the annual
precipitation is very high in the region, it is highly probable
for such great floods to be occur. So, it is necessary to draw a
lesson from this flood and to be ready to decrease any possible
damages both to life and to properties.

One of the greatest reasons for being so great damages was
psychological which has given rise to the people and state to be
caught unprepared about a possible flood. Most of civil and
official people have seemed to forget the fact that a great flood
is possible at any time. As a result of this indifference,
private and official institutions have inexcusably interfered to
the natural situation of river beds and riverbanks. The cross
sections of rivers were lessened by river improvement and highway
construction activities; so, the conveyance capacities of the
rivers were reduced, the flood water overflowed on the vicinity
areas and caused serious damages. In addition, some mistakes have
been made in bridge designing and the flood water could not pass
under the bridges and overflowed.

In this study, various measures that can be taken against
flood damages are discussed, the effectiveness and costs of these
measures are discussed.

* Ass.Prof.Dr., Blacksea Tech.Univ.Civil Eng.Dept. Trabzon TURKEY

2nd International Conference on River Flood Hydraulics. Edited by W. R. White and J. Watts
© 1994 HR Wallingford Ltd. Published by John Wiley & Sons Ltd

1. INTRODUCTION

As a result of breaking of ecological balance among flora, soil and climate; especially in the last decades, natural disasters , such as landslides and floods, have taken place very often. The damages of these disasters both to human life and properties have amounted to great values. By taking some technical and legal measures, it is possible to prevent, or, at least to minimize, landslides. Although it is impossible to prevent floods from taking place, people can do something to minimize their damages.

The great flood which took place in Trabzon Province and its neighborhood on 20 June 1990 caused death of 47 people and great damages to properties. Several factors have affected to occur such great damages.

In this study, the magnitude and region of the flood are introduced; the damages due to the flood and possible measures are evaluated.

2. FLOOD REGION

2.1. Location

The area in which a great flood occured on 20 July 1990 is located in Eastern Black Sea Basin of Turkey (see figure 1). The basin is located between 40°15' to 41°34' north latitudes and between 36°43' to 41°35' east longitudes. The basin, in which floods were observed very often, is surrounded by Eastern Black Sea Mountains. The basin is split by valleys reached from the sea into south zones. There are a lot of steep rivers in the basin.

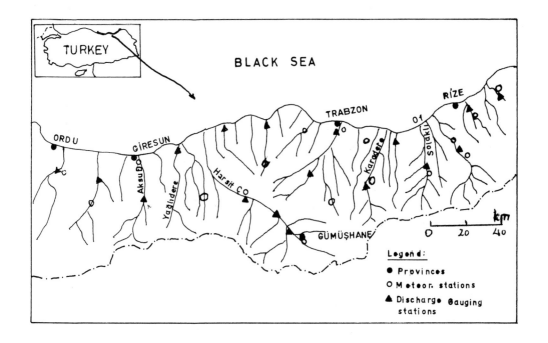

Figure 1. Location Map of the Flood Region

2.2. Meteorology

The basin is the most rainy basin in Turkey. Annual rainfall and mean temperature go down from the sea (north) to the mountainous zone (south). For example, in Rize Province, located at coast, the annual rainfall height is 2329 mm, but in Dağbaşı, a town 30 km far from coast, this value downs to 715 mm. The mean annual rainfall height of the basin is 1000 to 1200 mm (1).

2.3. Geology and Morphology

The strati of the region are generally made of impermeable or semipermeable volcanic rocks. These strati prevent the rainfall from percolation and force the flow to be surface runoff.

In the studied zone, since there are great differences among the discharges of a river gauged within a year, it was concluded that, the nourishment of the rivers by grounwater is rather limited and that surface runoff reachs to its maximum values during the rainy and snow melt seasons.

The steep slopes cover great areas in the region and this gives rise to increase of surface runoff velocities (2).

2.4. Flora

Since the basin is the most rainy region of Turkey, the north slopes of the region have a green flora. But, in the southern zones, in which the rainfall height is less, this flora tranformed into meadow.

The basin is rich in forestry. Pine, fir, beech, spruce, oak, hornbeam, elm, chestnut and alder are the most prevalent trees.

3. ESTIMATION OF THE MAGNITUDE OF THE FLOOD

3.1. Rainfall Analysis

Annual average (R_{av}) and daily maximum (R_{max}) rainfall height values (in mm) and observation years of the maximum values for the flood region stations are given in table 1. In this table, the rainfall values gauged on 19 and 20 June 1990 and their total values (R_{19}, R_{20} and R_t) are also presented.

Although the daily maximum rainfall values are generally greater than the total values, their observation years are rather scattered and they are only regional values. But, the total values represent a great zone of the basin.

504

Table 1. The Gauged Rainfall Values

Station	R_{av}	R_{max}	Year	R_{19}	R_{20}	R_t
Şebinkarahisar	575	100	1986	27.9	19.1	47.0
Bulancak	1119	144	1962	10.9	21.3	32.2
Giresun	1297	180	1949	13.7	24.1	37.8
Keşap	1446	136	1959	21.1	45.9	67.0
Tirebolu	1670	241	1977	6.4	81.4	87.8
Doğankent	1270	226	1965	24.8	138.4	163.2
Kürtün	616	71	1980	20.6	138.7	159.3
Gümüşhane	445	60	1936	16.2	51.7	67.9
Vakfıkebir	1238	171	1974	2.1	112.1	114.2
Tonya	1003	56	1987	27.4	127.8	155.2
Maçka	686	78	1952	18.4	38.5	56.9
Akçaabat	656	86	1953	5.4	16.2	21.6
Trabzon	802	107	1971	14.4	38.5	56.9
Arsin	937	101	1965	19.6	43.4	63.0
Dağbaşı	715	72	1970	17.0	30.1	47.1
Araklı	1096	86	1984	18.2	32.9	51.1
Şiran	511	47	1958	21.5	26.0	47.5
Kale	428	43	1958	9.0	36.0	45.0
Köse	361	31	1974	15.1	15.7	30.8
Aydıntepe	436	37	1975	23.7	3.9	27.6
Kelkit	352	47	1987	13.7	12.6	26.3
Çamoluk	511	36	1975	20.9	24.9	45.8
Güzelyayla	1250	48	1982	22.0	62.4	84.4
Sınır	750	50	1987	1.6	118.3	119.9
Tamdere	1700	101	1987	0.0	48.3	48.3

Isoheytal map for total rainfall values is given in figure 2.

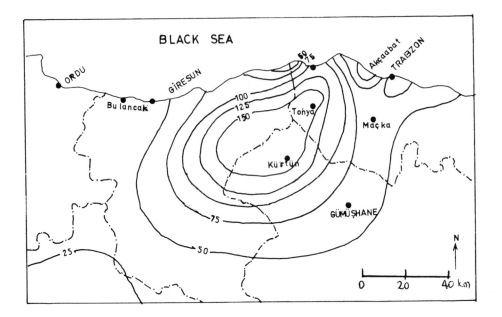

Figure 2. Isoheytal Map for Total Rainfall

From the table 1 and figure 2, it is obvious that, the rainfall rained on 19 and 20 June 1990 in the region is an extreme event for Eastern Black Sea Basin.

3.2. Flood Frequency Analysis

In the region, 9 out of the 13 discharge gauging stations were destroyed by the flood and because of the variation at the stream beds during the flood, right gauging could not be achieved at the other 4 stations.

Because of the heterogeneous rainfall distribution in the

506

region, peak discharges and their return periods at each station are calculated seperately. Since the discharges could not be gauged, the peak discharges during the flood were indirectly calculated by three methods as follows (3):

a. By using the flood marks at the gauging stations, the flood sections are estimated and, by means of some empirical methods, the peak discharges are estimated.

b. By means of the flood marks, the gauge levels are estimated, the rating curves of the stations are extended and the peak discharges are estimated.

c. By using the physical properties of the rivers and isoheytal maps, the rainfalls which affected the flood are determined. Since enough rainfall had rained before the flood, infiltration through soil and the other surface losses are considered to be minimum; thus, assuming that 95 percent of the rainfall was transformed into runoff, the peak discharges are estimated.

The estimated values of each gauging station are presented in table 2 as Q_a, Q_b and Q_c, respectively. By using the annual peak discharge data of each station (one maximum value for every year at each station) and assuming that these data is distributed according to Extrem Value I (Gumbel) Distribution (4), for every station, a point analysis is used and the return periods of 20 June 1990 floods (in years) are estimated. These values are given in table 2 as T_a, T_b and T_c, respectively. In this table, the basin areas (km^2) and maximum discharges gauged before 20 june 1990 are also presented as A and Q_{max}, respectively.

As can be seen from table 2, the return periods of the 20 June 1990 flood vary from 50 to 10 000 years. But, it is evident that, since the observation periods of the stations are very short, the return period estimations greater than 100 years may be wrong.

Taking into consideration the above considerations, it can be said that, the flood took place in Trabzon and neighborhood region on 20 June 1990 is an extreme value of which return period is at least 50 years and the flood have affected a great area in the region.

Table 2. Discharges of The Flood Region

Station	A	Q_{max}	Q_a	Q_b	Q_c	T_a	T_b	T_c
Ormanüstü	151	23	—	—	251	—	—	500
Altındere	267	29	157	—	151	50	—	50
Galyandere	126	25	157	135	148	500	500	500
Esiroğlu	732	80	647	610	578	10000	10000	10000
Helvacı	249	29	350	—	348	10000	—	10000
Bahadırlı	219	155	—	—	246	—	—	1000
Cücenköprü	167	130	276	280	246	10000	10000	10000
Torul	1903	320	700	700	659	500	500	500
Eymür	3011	360	2457	—	2024	10000	—	10000
Kürtün	2686	731	2016	—	1813	10000	—	10000
Hasanşeyh	258	60	333	345	—	10000	10000	—
Sınırköy	293	56	—	250	—	—	500	—
Tuğlacık	344	—	—	300	359	—	1000	1000
Hacıbeşir	29	—	—	—	40	—	—	50
Derecik	121	—	—	—	194	—	—	500
Kireçhane	18	—	—	—	28	—	—	50
Çarşıbaşı	80	—	—	—	117	—	—	500
Kirazlık	77	—	—	—	113	—	—	500

4. FACTORS AFFECTED THE FLOOD DAMAGES AND POSSIBLE MEASURES

4.1. Hydrological Factors

The rainfall and runoff values of old years have of vital importance in designing hydraulic structures such as bridges, culverts and urban drainage channels. In Eastern Black Sea Basin, however, the gauging network is not enough both in quantity and in quality. At most of the gauging stations, the observation periods are too short to be considered for a statistical analysis. Thus, in designing the hydraulic structures, the used data were far from the actual situation, which results in insufficiency of the functions of these structures during a great flood. In order to solve this problem, it is necessary to establish a gauging network which is sufficient in quality, quantity and distribution in the region.

4.2. Psychological Factors

Two great floods which took place in 1929 and 1959 in Eastern Black Sea Basin seemed to be forgotten by people and state; so, a possibility of another great flood might be taken place could not be remembered. As a result of this indifference, private and official institutions have inexcusably interfered to the natural situation of river beds and riverbanks. The river beds were narrowed by several structures and the rivers have been forced to flow within some 'artifically narrowed' sections. Although some small damages, such as inundation and landslide of highways, had occured during small floods, nobody was able to draw lessons from these events. Nobody tried make a solution to this question:

"What can we do in case of a great flood?" Similar mistakes were done at urban rainfall drainage channels. The great flood has exposed that these mistakes can not be excused.

4.3. Socio-Economical Factors

Despite the fact that the economical life of the residents of the region depends primarily on agriculture, the areas suitable for agriculture are rather scarce and expensive. Therefore, the people have been forced to get some areas on the alluvial soils within the river beds and riverbanks. In addition, for the similar reasons, the people have established great housing and industrial facilities near or within the river zones.

4.4. Technical Factors:

18 bridges have been destroyed in the flood. The reasons for such a great destruction were: Designing mistakes (wrong site and bearing system selection), construction mistakes, usage, maintenance and repairing mistakes. Most of these bridges were designed according to some typical projects and it was not investigated whether or not these projects were proper for the region. It is necessary to study on this matter (5).

Rainfall drainage channels were also seriously destroyed by the flood. In addition to the insufficient sectional areas, because of the insufficient maintenance and repairing, these channels have been stopped up and caused inundation.

The flood also destroyed Trabzon Domestic Water Facilities in Değirmendere Basin. The main reasons for these damages were breaking of side wall of diversion weir and insufficient maintenance of wells.

In addition to the above factors, the ruining of forests also caused an increase in flood damages.

5. CONCLUSIONS AND RECOMMENDATIONS

a.   In   designing of hydraulic   structures,   sufficient hydrological data have of vital importance. Since there   are   not a proper rainfall and runoff gauging network in Eastern Black Sea Basin   of   Turkey, in which a great flood took place on   20   June 1990,   it   is very difficult to guess   the   magnitudes and return periods of floods.

b.   Despite the insufficient data, by means of some   indirect methods,   it   is estimated that the return period   of   the   flood took   place on 20 June 1990 would be at least 50 years. But,   it does   not mean that any flood can not occur within 50   years.   It should not be forgotten that, a great flood may take place at any time and location.

c.   It   must be put an end to the   illegal   and   uncontrolled building of houses and other facilities within or near the   river zones. The regulative activities on rivers, such as revetments to protect highways, should not narrow sectional areas and   decrease conveyance capacities of rivers.

d.   Modern technology should be used in designing of   bridges and urban rainfall drainage channels.

e.   Ruining of forests should be stopped and   forestry   areas should be increased.

REFERENCES

1. KULGA, Z.,"The Impact of Height and Intensity of Rainfall on Floods", Symposium of 20 June 1990 Flood, 22 to 24 November 1990, pages 1 to 17, Trabzon,Turkey (in Turkish).

2. CERiT, O., The Relations Between Flood in Trabzon and Geological, Morphological and Rainfall Properties", Symposium of 20 June 1990 Flood, 22 to 24 November 1990, pages 181 to 195, Trabzon, Turkey (in Turkish).

3. General Directorate of State Hydraulic Works (DSi), The Report on the Flood of Trabzon, Giresun and Gümüşhane Provinces and Neighborhood Flood, 1990, Trabzon, Turkey, (in Turkish).

4. YÜKSEK, ö., "A Proper Flood Prediction Method for Eastern Black Sea Basins", Ms. Thesis, Black Sea Technical University, 1986, Trabzon, Turkey (in Turkish).

5. DURMUŞ, A., "Natural Disasters and Bridges", Symposium of 20 June 1990 Flood, 22 to 24 November 1990, pages 247 to 259, Trabzon, Turkey (in Turkish).

2nd International Conference on
RIVER FLOOD HYDRAULICS
22–25 March 1994: York, England

Environmentally Led Engineering :

The Maidenhead Windsor and Eton Flood Alleviation Scheme

Author & Affiliation: H Clear Hill BSc (Hons) MIWEM MIEnvSc
Independent Consultant

22 Moreton Road
Aston Tirrold
Didcot
Oxon
OX11 9EW

Tel: 0235 850953

2nd International Conference on River Flood Hydraulics. Edited by W. R. White and J. Watts
© 1994 HR Wallingford Ltd. Published by John Wiley & Sons Ltd

1   INTRODUCTION

The National River Authority - Thames Region (NRA) has proposed a major scheme
on the middle River Thames to alleviate flooding in the towns of Maidenhead, Windsor
and Eton and surrounding areas. This scheme will involve the construction of a new
channel some 11.8 kilometres in length leaving the existing river upstream of Maidenhead and re-entering it downstream of Windsor. In addition to the main channel, the
scheme also requires the upgrading of a small channel through Maidenhead town centre,
and various minor embankments and flood walls to ensure scheme integrity and
consistent standards of protection. The elements of the scheme are shown in Figure 1
below.

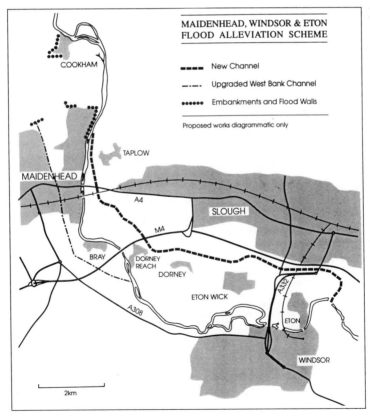

Figure 1

MAIDENHEAD, WINDSOR & ETON
FLOOD ALLEVIATION SCHEME

---- New Channel

-·-· Upgraded West Bank Channel

••••• Embankments and Flood Walls

Proposed works diagrammatic only

The new channel will have a capacity of 215 cumecs (cubic metres/second). Typically this might require a 45 metre top width on a trapezoidal channel. However, in places the proposed channel will be widened up to 150 metres for environmental enhancement reasons. Typical cross sections are shown in Figure 2 below.

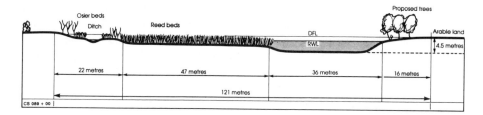

A: Widened channel with extensive reed beds and ossiers

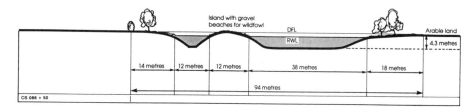

B: Channel with small islands

DFL - Design Flood Level   RWL - Retained Water Level

Figure 2

This channel will have to pass beneath the M4 motorway, three railways and numerous other roads and services. Some of the land through which it will pass is in agricultural use, but the channel will also pass through old sewage drying beds, a registered garden of historic interest and through the edge of Eton College's famous playing fields. There are also extensive areas of registered common land. Each of these areas raises different concerns.

The area in which the scheme is to be built is very sensitive in planning terms. All the land outside the towns is designated Metropolitan Green Belt carrying a general presumption against development except in certain very special circumstances. Almost the whole of the main channel is to be built through gravel bearing land. This is a particularly contentious aspect as commercial gravel extraction is very unpopular with local people and their elected councils. Hence, the NRA has had to justify its proposals in the face of a belief, in at least some quarters, that it is simply a backdoor means of allowing gravel digging.

The final scheme is the result of many years of work by the NRA (and its predecessor bodies) and specialist consultants. Engineering and environmental disciplines have worked closely throughout the design period to appraise numerous options for flood alleviation. There has been close liaison with local planning authorities, specialist interest groups and affected landowners and residents. After a lengthy period of deliberation at local level, the planning application for the scheme was eventually called in (by the Secretary of State for the Environment) for a public inquiry. This inquiry was held in late 1992. The Inspector's report was submitted to the Department of the Environment in June 1993 and a result is awaited.

2   THE ROLE OF THE NATIONAL RIVERS AUTHORITY IN FLOOD DEFENCE

Lord Crickhowell, Chairman of the National Rivers Authority, said in a speech at the inauguration of the NRA that "our first duty is to protect life and property from flooding".

The NRA was established by the Water Act 1989 and has statutory responsibilities for flood defence, water resources, pollution control, fisheries, recreation, conservation and certain navigations in England and Wales - including the River Thames. The NRA has a duty to supervise matters relating to flood defence. The Regional Flood Defence Committee (RFDC) is the statutory and executive body through which the NRA carries out its flood defence functions. Flood defence is financed by a levy now included within the Council Tax, and in certain circumstances by partial grant aid of specific schemes by the Ministry of Agriculture Fisheries and Food (MAFF).

A general environmental duty is placed on the NRA by Section 16 of the Water Resources Act 1991 which states that: "It shall be the duty of the Authority, in formulating or considering any proposal relating to any functions of the Authority ... so to exercise any power conferred on ... it with respect to the proposals as to further the conservation of flora, fauna and geological or physiographical features of special interest ..."

Under sub-section 2.2 of the 1991 Act, the NRA's duties extend, to such extent as it considers desirable, generally to promote:

a)   the conservation and enhancement of the natural beauty and amenity of interest and coastal waters and of land associated with such waters;

b)   the conservation of flora and fauna which are dependent on the aquatic environment;

c)   the use of such waters and land for recreational purposes.

Thus, the NRA has a duty in exercising its powers to achieve improvement in conservation terms consistent with other objectives such as flood defence. On the Maidenhead, Windsor and Eton Flood Alleviation Scheme this duty has been taken on board fully.

3   FLOODING IN THE MAIDENHEAD, WINDSOR AND ETON AREA

A very major flood occurred on the River Thames in March 1947 and this is commonly taken as a benchmark for comparison with other flood events. The peak flow in this event was 500 cumecs.

Flooding from the River Thames resulting in extensive damage to property in the area covered by this scheme has happened roughly twice a century. Smaller but still serious floods have happened much more often. Whilst there has been a gradual trend towards a reduction in the severity and frequency of major floods since the 1947 flood, detailed examination of the records has shown that there does not seem to have been any permanent change in the character of flooding on the river.

The NRA has established that in a repeat of the 1947 flood, some 4,800 domestic and 700 commercial properties will be at risk in the scheme area, with a further 1,500 - 2,500 houses having services or access interrupted. This would affect a total of 18,000 to 20,000 people.

Immediately after the 1947 flood, consideration was given to measures which could be taken to prevent a repeat of the damage and disruption caused. At that time it was considered impractical to provide a comprehensive alleviation scheme. However, by the early 1980s further investigations showed cost-effective options might exist and these eventually led to the present scheme proposals.

The scheme has a design capacity of 515 cumecs and is designed to protect the Maidenhead, Windsor and Eton area completely from a flood of slightly greater intensity than 1947 and all lesser floods also. It will of course also provide very considerable alleviation against larger floods.

4   THE HISTORY OF THE MAIDENHEAD WINDSOR AND ETON
FLOOD ALLEVIATION SCHEME

Consulting engineers (Lewin Fryer and Partners) submitted an Interim Report on the scheme in 1983. A number of options were taken forward and environmental and planning consultants (RPS Clouston) were appointed in 1985 to undertake a preliminary appraisal of the options for flood alleviation then under consideration.

Four broad options were considered in this process:

- major dredging and widening of the existing channel of the River Thames

- raising of flood walls and embankments along the river

- a new channel on the west bank of the river through Maidenhead

- the construction of a new channel on the east bank of the river.

(Provision of sufficient flood storage was demonstrated to be impractical early in the engineering studies and was not subjected to detailed environmental scrutiny).

Early in the evaluation process it was evident that provision of the required extra capacity solely through widening and deepening of the existing Thames channel would be unacceptable in environmental terms. In particular, the biological impact of such works would have been very detrimental.

Ten main options, combining elements of new channels, embankments and minor river works, were then subjected to detailed evaluation, and compared under the headings of economics, engineering, environmental impact and implementation. Arising from this work, an option based on the creation of a new east bank flood alleviation channel with subsidiary elements elsewhere was selected as offering the best balance of the factors evaluated.

More detailed evaluation of this option followed and the scheme was also extended from just Maidenhead (as originally envisaged) to also include Windsor and Eton. Throughout this period, many detailed refinements to the route of the channel, the scale of various elements and the construction strategy for the works were considered. Agreement in principle to carry out a scheme was given in January 1988. A further review of all options, including differing levels of protection, was then undertaken.

In March 1989 the Regional Land Drainage Committee (now replaced by the RFDC) decided to pursue an integrated Maidenhead, Windsor and Eton scheme. Work then concentrated on the preparation of a planning application and supporting Environmental Statement. These were submitted in January 1991.

The application was considered by the County Council's of Berkshire and Buckinghamshire - it was a 'county matter' due to the significant element of minerals extraction required as an integral part of the scheme. Very extensive discussions took place with the local authorities on details of the application and the environmental impacts of the scheme. Because of the complexity of the issues involved, the NRA agreed to extend the normal time limits for determination of the planning application. However, before a decision was actually reached, in February 1992 the whole scheme was 'called in' for a public inquiry.

5   CONSULTATIONS AND LIAISON

Throughout the development of this scheme there has been very detailed consultation and discussion with other interested parties. A series of liaison and advisory groups operated from early 1987 onwards meeting regularly to consider progress on the scheme. These groups were constituted as follows:

- Local Authority Advisory Group - officer representation of all affected county and district authorities

- Parish Council Advisory Group - parish council representatives plus local amenity groups

- Environmental Advisory Group - representatives of national and regional environmental, recreation and farming interests

- Internal Liaison Group - NRA officers including engineering, conservation and water quality specialists

In each case, members of the NRA's project team took part together with the engineering and environmental coordinators from the two lead consultants.

Later in the design process, as more detailed matters relating to the planning impacts and proposed construction method and long term management of the scheme became pertinent, other specialist groups met regularly to consider matters such as the minerals extraction strategy and legal aspects of scheme implementation. Specialist minerals consultants joined the project team, together with external solicitors to handle detailed matters relating to the planning applications and public inquiry.

The role of the engineering and environmental coordinators proved crucial in the refinement of the proposals leading to the final submitted scheme. Operating in regular day to day contact and ensuring a consistency of approach and regular feed back of information between all the many disciplines and different discussion forums, the coordinators sought to ensure that particular specialist interests did not compromise wider scheme objectives. This cooperative approach led to a highly innovative scheme which has received widespread support for the landscape enhancement, wildlife habitat creation and recreation provision which is proposed. All these features are to be included without in any way sacrificing the main object of the scheme which is, of course, the alleviation of flooding.

It was particularly pleasing to see the constructive way in which bodies with often widening different interests and opinions on the scheme approached these discussions. Whilst it is perhaps inevitable that not every issue was resolved to the absolute satisfaction of all parties, at the end of this process most of those who had taken part complimented the NRA on the way in which their views had at least been given a thorough airing. The reasoning for decisions was clear and therefore open to sensible debate. This approach proved useful to proper consideration of remaining points of ·difference at the eventual public inquiry into the scheme.

6   DESIGN PHILOSOPHY AND OBJECTIVES

In order to provide design guidance to the engineers, a very thorough information gathering and analysis exercise was required. This involved work by many disciplines. Because of the pattern of land ownership in the area and its diversity of use, this required some often complex research and field investigations. This process has many parallels in the techniques that are now being employed by the NRA in the preparation of detailed Catchment Management Plans.

The central design objectives, from an environmental viewpoint, were to design a scheme which would achieve its main purpose with minimal environmental impact and wherever possible to take opportunities for environmental enhancement. Key environmental benefits are listed in Table 1 below.

TABLE 1: KEY ENVIRONMENTAL BENEFITS -
         CONSERVATION/ LANDSCAPE

Net Habitat Creation

Woodland	31.0ha
Species Rich Grassland	23.5ha
Open Water	37.0ha
Marginal Wetland Habitats	24.0ha
Hedges	6.7km

The new channel is designed to look as much as possible like a river, constrained in very limited areas by engineered structures. The banks will be natural in appearance and the channel is designed to have small islands and low wetland areas. Extensive bankside planting, woodland, hedgerows and marginal wetlands are proposed. This will create very substantial new wildlife habitat in an area which is at present of generally low nature conservation interest. The following illustrations show examples of how the channel is designed to appear:

The new channel meanders through the countryside as a river. New planting integrates the channel with existing hedgerows and trees

Existing trees form a backcloth to the new channel

River edge parkland character

Figure 3

The scheme passes through an area surrounded by large urban centres but apart from the banks of the River Thames itself and a few key sites, offering limited recreational access. The proposals involve much more than the usual requirements for diversion of public rights of way and replacement of common land. There will also be very substantial provision of new public access including a channel side path along almost the whole length, much of it to cycleway or bridleway standard. Key recreation benefits are listed in Table 2 below.

TABLE 2 - KEY ENVIRONMENTAL BENEFITS - RECREATION

New Footpaths Created	4.8km
New Bridleways Created	2.3km
New Cycleways Created	2.5km
New Car Park Provision	70 spaces
New Angling Provision	Along much of 11.8km channel

There will also be more general access to an area that is at present contaminated with old sewage sludge but which will be comprehensively restored as part of the spoil disposal arrangements for the scheme.

7   ISSUES ADDRESSED AT THE PUBLIC INQUIRY

The Public Inquiry into the scheme in Autumn 1992 focused attention on 'relevant matters' identified in the call-in notice issued by the Secretary of State. These were the relationship of the proposals to relevant planning and minerals policies, the effects of the proposals on known archaeological features, the relationship of the scheme to proposed widening of the M4 motorway in the same area, and the effects of the proposals on the natural environment and wildlife. The benefit: cost ratio of the proposals was not identified as a 'relevant matter' in the call-in notice though it was raised on several occasions at the Inquiry. The detail of costs and benefits estimates inevitably varied throughout the development of the proposed scheme design, but the benefit: cost ratio has consistently been calculated to exceed unity. Environmental elements, such as alteration of channel profiles and landscape works, are an integral part of the scheme design that has been costed in these calculations. At March 1991 prices the scheme was estimated to have a total cost of £63.1 million including all pre-planning approval and feasibility costs as well as construction and implementation costs.

Subject to concerns on details, the NRA was supported at the inquiry by Berkshire County Council, the Royal Borough of Windsor and Maidenhead, and Slough Borough Council. This support was based on the 'whole package' of the scheme, including the environmental enhancements proposed in the NRA's design. Buckinghamshire County Council and South Buckinghamshire District Council resolved to oppose the scheme, as did several parish councils, action groups and individuals. The inquiry was originally programmed to run for sixteen weeks but in the event was completed in seven weeks. The NRA presented evidence on the history of the scheme, the justification for its proposals and details of engineering and environmental aspects of scheme design. This was subject to cross examination by those opposing the scheme. Counter evidence was placed before the Inspector, who was assisted in this case by an assistant inspector to cover specific matters on related legal orders, and a technical assessor on hydraulics.

Particular attention was paid at the inquiry to the likely condition of the channel in times of drought. Water levels in the new channel will be controlled by low weirs and sluices to maintain existing groundwater levels. A flow will be allowed in from the Thames, the size of which will be controlled to ensure the maximum benefit in the new channel whilst not threatening the biological integrity of the main river itself. The whole system will be regularly monitored, not least in relation to major water extractions which lie just downstream of the scheme area.

Much consideration was also given to the effects of the scheme on downstream flood levels. This had already been the subject of extensive modelling studies commissioned by the NRA and during the inquiry further work was undertaken. Some local people remain concerned on this point, but the main parties which had raised this issue, Berkshire County Council and the Royal Borough of Windsor and Maidenhead, expressed themselves satisfied that their concerns had been answered satisfactorily.

In June 1993 the Inspector's report was submitted to the Secretary of State for his final decision. If permission is granted, then the NRA hopes to complete construction within five years of construction commencing.

8   CONCLUSIONS

The Maidenhead Windsor and Eton Flood Alleviation Scheme will be the largest riverine flood scheme to have been undertaken in the UK. When complete it will provide a substantial degree of protection to many thousands of people and properties in a very densely developed area. The risk of disruption to services and communications affecting a much wider area will also be greatly reduced.

This will be achieved not at the sacrifice of environmental resources but rather through the creation of a new and valuable feature in itself. Through a very thorough and considered design process, with engineers and environmental interests working closely together, the Maidenhead, Windsor and Eton Flood Alleviation Scheme illustrates an innovative and creative approach. This will require compulsory purchase of land beyond that which would be needed for a 'basic' engineering scheme. However, bearing in mind its duties under the Water Resources Act to further and enhance conservation of natural beauty, the NRA has taken the line that this is fully justified. In the current climate of environmental awareness 'basic' engineering is no longer a viable option. Schemes such as this must embrace the wider concerns of environmentally led engineering.

Chapter Eleven

Morphology

Modelling morphological impact
of a flood control dam

Philippe BELLEUDY, LHF - Laboratoire d'hydraulique de
France, 6, rue de Lorraine, F-38130 Echirolles

Holger SCHÜTTRUMPF, Leichtweiss-Institut für Wasserbau,
Beethovenstr. 51a, 3300 Braunschweig, Germany.

Abstract

The paper presents a part of the knowledge acquired during
application of SEDICOUP mobile bed model to projects.

A particularly challenging application concerning the
study of the morphological impact of a flood control dam
is presented.

From this experience some questions are raised concerning
the validity and the limits of the model.

Introduction

SEDICOUP modelling system permits implicit and coupled
simulation of unsteady flow sediment transport and
sediment changes of river beds.

Its latest version is the result of nearly a decade of
modelling development efforts by Iowa Institute of
hydraulic research and by Laboratoire d'Hydraulique de
France with the support of the German Bundesanstalt für
Wasserbau.

A first application to a field situation was performed
through morphological study of reaches of Danube and Isar
Rivers.

This experience has been already reported [5], [6], [7].
The project was concerned with the calculation of long
term evolution of navigation conditions in the Danube
River due to forecast changes in sediment input from Isar
River, a Bavarian tributary of the Danube.

Quite different flow and sediment transport situations
were encountered for the second application of the
program. The objective was the study of the morphological
impact (short term, and long term) of the periodic
operation of a flood control dam whose construction is
planned on a French river.

1   SEDICOUP

Presentations and discussion of various aspects
(equations, numerical scheme, physical formulation) of
SEDICOUP one-dimensional modelling system have already
been done in previous papers: [1], [2], [3], [4], [6].

2nd International Conference on River Flood Hydraulics. Edited by W. R. White and J. Watts

Let us just recall the basic principles of the program which has been to suit the needs of non-equilibrium alluvial simulation under unsteady flow conditions:

- coupled resolution of all the processes which are under modelling;
- modelling of sorting and armoring situations with the breakdown of the solid phase into several sediment size classes and with the adoption of the mixing layer concept;
- make the distinction, when necessary between bedload transport and suspended load.

Additionally, the modularity of the program allows a rapid adaptation of the program to most of the specific requirements of a project. e.g. at the date this paper is written three sediment transport predictors are available: Van Rijn and Engelund-Hansen for total load, Meyer-Peter and Müller type for bedload (with several formulations for hiding factor/exposure coefficient).

2   Application

A dam is planned on a French river with the objective of flood control by limitation of flood discharge and temporary flooding of grassland area upstream the dam.

The 50 km reach of the river under concern is in the present situation (nearly natural conditions) in morphological equilibrium. However sediment transport is very active both in suspended and in bed-load modes. Rapid evolution of gravel bars is observed as well as formation of armored layers during certain periods in the minor bed.

Temporal changes of flow conditions upstream of the dam will cause deposition of transported material in the reservoir and also a deficit of sediment transport downstream of the structure (where limited but still important water discharges are maintained).

A modelling of the river has been done whose purpose is the study of the morphological impacts of the dam in a short term (during the flood and a few months later) and over several cycles of operation.

The 120-point model includes an automatic control gate whose discharge is adjusted according to predefined operation rules.

3   Questions

Our intention is to present here some of the questions raised by the application of SEDICOUP model to 'real' projects (as contrasted to numerical experiments or to reproducing laboratory experiments).

And among the many questions - not the ones concerning modelling choices (e.g. transport formula, sorting effects, transport mode) - are those which are related to the validity of this 1-d modelling.

These doubts had already arisen in the Danube study. They were even more strongly felt in the present application because of time scale effects (rapid changes in flow conditions) and variability of transport conditions: droughts and floods with dam, deposition/erosion problems.

3.1 Stabilization

Construction of a model for numerical simulation of sediment transport is identical to the construction of a model for fixed-bed numerical simulation (at least as concerns geometry and topology).

Cross-sections are entered as they were levelled, i.e. by (distance,elevation) pairs. We shall refer later to the talweg elevation which is the minimum elevation of the polyline.

These cross sections become computational points of the calculation grid. Each cross-section is supposed to be representative of flow and solid transport conditions within the computational reach. The longitudinal variability of the channel is partially taken into account by the spacing of the different points (average reach length = 470m). The so-called 'original model' is thus built and is ready for simulation.

Then a calculation is made from this 'original model' as initial bed conditions and from an initial steady flow line. The same low flow conditions are maintained during a one-year calculation. For such low flow conditions (100 m3/s, annual exceedence 200 days), solid transport in the river is very low.

Figure 1 displays the evolution of solid transport rate and of talweg elevation for selected points of the model during the calculation. A 'stabilization' process appears clearly during the first period of the calculation: the solid transport rate tends to an expected small equilibrium value but after some rearangement of the cross sections. Other characteristic variables of the cross-sections (e.g. the mixing layer granulometry) have the same behavior.

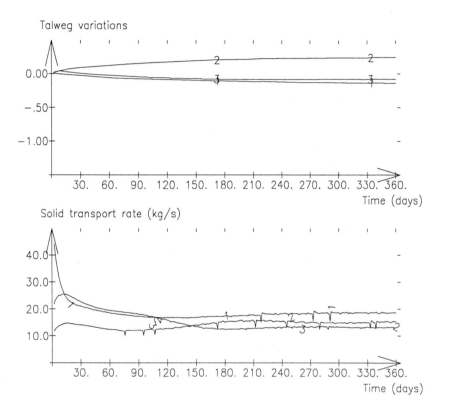

figure 1: talweg variations and solid transport rate during a 1 year long low flow stabilization

In order to eliminate the doubt concerning an influence of grading of sediment (building of an artificial armor coat on the bed surface), the same one year calculation from the original model has been reproduced but with hydrologic conditions corresponding to a real time series. A year without any important flood (1980) has been selected for this purpose.

Upstream limit hydrograph and evolution of talweg elevation for selected points of the model during the simulation is reported on figure 2. The same stabilization is observed after the first few months of the simulation.

After this first stage, the talweg elevation varies in
relation to flow conditions (periods of erosion and
periods of deposition). The global change of the river
morphology is then negligible on an average, as it is on
the real river.

A 10-year simulation (1981-1990) is conducted then on the
'stabilized model' which has been obtained at the end of
1980 simulation. Equilibrium of the river conditions is
still reproduced on an average. The same figure 2 displays
upstream discharge, and selected talweg and d50 evolution
as computed during this long term simulation.

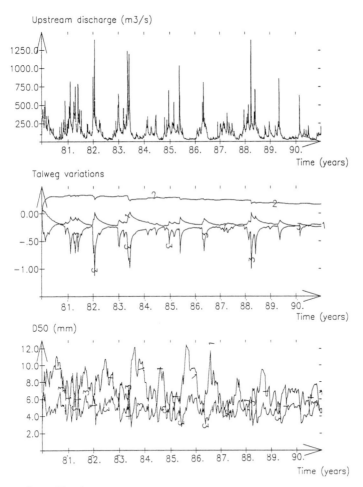

figure 2: discharge, talweg variations and mixing layer
characteristic diameter during stabilization (year 80) followed by a
10-year simulation.

Primary reaction of the modeller, and of the observer/client is then: "_ What I know the best is the geometrical description of the cross section. I introduced in the model the reality. Is the modelling really reliable when it begins with correcting the only piece of certainty ?"

The stabilization stage is a necessary running-in period for the model to bring river description in accordance to schematization of the modelling. We shall see in section 3.3 its implications for the specification of the data necessary for model construction.

The very simple assumptions which are made for the repartition of erosion/deposition within the cross-section make the talweg elevation only a reference elevation, whose variations must be considered by preference to its absolute value.

3.2 Composite channels

The cross-section is made of several sub-sections. SEDICOUP modelling gives the possibility for description of 5 different subsections (see figure 3).

The five subsections behave differently as regards sediment transport: (i) exchanges between bed material and transported sediment take place in the active bed, bed load transport is also limited to the active bed; (ii and iii) the left and right bank-groyne zones may exchange materials with active bed in form of source terms depending of bank physical characteristics; (iv and v) the flood plain may participate to flow conveyance but never changes its shape.

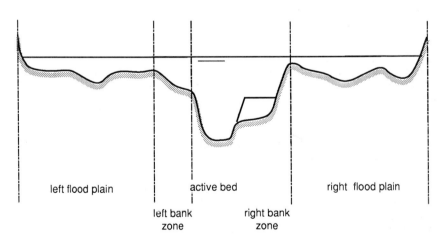

figure 3: description of a composite cross section

To what extent is 1-d modelling (assuming fluxes perpendicular to the cross section, average value for fluxes, single horizontal water level for the cross section) capable for modelling variability within the cross section and three directional effects due to longitudinal variability and curvature effects ?

This question already exists in 1-d hydraulic flow modelling (fixed bed). Different techniques are used for calculation of the conveyance and limitations of the modelling are in this case easier to define (may be only because enough experience has been accumulated by the modellers, and the 'consumer' is accustomed to the methodology and is aware of its limitations).

This question is renewed in mobile bed modelling:

Distinction of different flow and transport zones is clear for 'channelized' rivers (as the Danube). It is more difficult in the exemple which is decribed in section 2 because of the braided aspect of the active bed during low flow conditions and also because of the variety of flow conditions in the reservoir area.

Sub-questions arise then: How do the bed changes of the active bed (shape, braided active bed, transverse sorting) proceed? What is the average transport capacity (equilibrium) of the cross section? What is the amount of exchange of material with the bank zones?

Waiting for further refinements (necessarilly designed and calibrated for each particular application), very simple procedures have been introduced in SEDICOUP as an answer to these questions : integration of the transport capacity over the active bed, displacement without deformation of the active bed shape.

3.3 Construction and calibration of the model

This section focusses on part of data requirements for construction and calibration of such models, as they are connected to the questions which were mentioned in previous sections.

3.3.1 Construction of the model

Back to the reactions of the observer/client concerning 'runing-in' of the original model which was described in section 3.1:

After the initial defiance period, the question was then: "_ But why did you require such a complete and precise levelling of the cross-sections only to affirm then that it does not reproduce the reality of the modelling ?"

First answer: "_ Because this I did not know". Modelling sediment transport in such a sophisticated way (rapidly varying flow conditions, graded sediment, composite channels, etc.) is a new technology. Through the first applications, we discover its possibilities and its limitations.

Probably, the same study could be conducted with the same results with a very schematic description of the cross section (prismatic subsections). But even in that case, it is the modeller responsability to define these schematic cross-sections, from the real ones whose levelling is still necessary. The schematic cross section should reproduce not only the flow conveyance properties but also the transport capacity of the real cross-section.

A precise description of the cross-section profile avoids such a hazardous pre-processing of rough data which is equivalent to the stabilization stage of the model.

Finally, it seems that the period for levelling has some importance.Figure 2 (middle) shows the average stability of the 'reference level'/talweg elevation but its variations in time depending of hydrology conditions.

This is one more argument for the necessity of stabilization stage of the model because the condition of concomitance of the levelling was not respected (the amplitude of seasonal bed variations is for certain sections the same order of magnitude than the average adjustment of the bed elevation during the stabilization period).

3.3.2 Calibration of the model

Calibration of the model proceeds in two successive stages:

(i) Calibration of hydraulic parameters and of flow conditions (ie. of roughness coefficient and of singular head-losses). The usual methodology is used which combines calibration in steady flow conditions and calibration of the model during flood events.

(ii) Calibration of transport parameters:

The choice of the transport formula is made according to its domain of validity (grain size, shear conditions, transport mode). But most of the transport formulae have been initially set up in terms of simple grain size distributions, and quite often extended to sediment mixtures by using a characteristic diameter.

An extension of this initial use is made in SEDICOUP with the application of the selected transport formula separately for every grain size fraction. A necessary calibration of the parameters of the formula and of the hiding/exposure effects in grain mixtures is necessary.

The past evolution of the river is reproduced. This is particulary fruitful in case of non-equilibrium of the river.

For calibration of Danube/Isar model an estimate of the average annual rate of sediment transport along the model has been made by Bundesanstalt für Wasserbau [6]. This estimate has been made from yearly levelling of the cross-sections and from dredged quantities necessary to maintain navigation capacity of the River [5]. It was corroborated by local measurements of sediment transport (mainly bed-load) for a complete range of hydrologic conditions in three different cross-sections.

But reproduction of past evolution of the river gives only a very partial calibration of the sediment transport parameters in certain cases:

The application which is presented in section 2 of this paper is a good example: The river bed is 'stable' i.e. the flow conditions are unchanged on a yearly average (there is no variation of the elevation/discharge rating curves neither of the low flow long profile for the same discharge levelled with several years of time interval).

This apparent stability is reproduced easily in simple channels by the simulation if the flow capacity (i.e. the friction slope) for different stages is respected. In the case of composite cross sections the calibration of conveyance parameters for a good reproduction of flow (often for a limited number of discharges) does not imply that the calculation of solid transport capacity is well reproduced and sometimes stages 1 (flow) and 2 (sediment transport) of the calibration must be performed in a coupled way.

But reproduction of stability is not sufficient as it may be obtained with the same accuracy by very different magnitudes of transport rate. The solid transport capacity is uniform along the river. Anyway the transverse variations of the cross-sections and the evolution of the sand-bars denotes a great activity of the solid transport. This is of great importance as the purpose of the modelling is the simulation of the morphological evolution of the river after this equilibrium is broken.

Direct measurement of bed transport are then necessary in most cases, on a limited number of spot areas but as complete as is possible and taking into account the different transport modes and the grain size variety.

Last calibration index (in the present list) is grain sorting observations if they are possible. In the present case investigations had been conducted of the vertical distribution of the granulometry of the bed material in the active bed in very low flow conditions.

4   Validity of the modelling

Are the results reliable?

Not really so far as the precise evolution of a given cross-section is concerned.

But they give an estimate of the global changes of the river (in terms of river reaches). Also the results of simulations are reliable if we are interested in the comparison of different alternatives (e.g. the flood control discharge).

The degree of reliability of predictive modelling is also a function of the validity of the hypothesis, of the numerical methods, and of the efforts during construction stage and calibration stage of the models. A sensitivity analysis may be necessary to take account of scaterred field data (e.g. hydrological conditions in [7]).

references

[1] Holly, F.M.(1988), "CHARIMA and SEDICOUP codes for riverine mobile-bed simulation", 2nd. Seminar on Stream Sedimentation Models, Interagency Advisory Committee on Water Data, Denver, CO, 10-20 October.

[2] Holly, F.M., and Rahuel, J-L., (1989), "Riverine mobile-bed modelling under non-equilibrium conditions", HYDROCOMP 89, Dubrovnic, Yugosloavia, June.

[3] Holly, F.M., and Rahuel, J-L., (1990), "New numerical/physical framework for mobile bed modelling. Part 1 : Numerical and physical principles", Journal of Hydraulic Research, Vol. 28, N° 4.

[4] Holly, F.M., and Rahuel, J-L., (1990), "New numerical/physical framework for mobile bed modelling. Part 2 : Test application", Journal of Hydraulic Research, Vol. 28, N° 5.

[5] Söhngen, B., Kellermann, J., Loy, G.,(1992), "Modelling Danube and Isar Rivers Morphological evolution. Part 1: Measurements and formulation", 5th. Int. Symp.on River Sedimentation - Karlsruhe, Germany, 6-10 April.

[6] Belleudy, (1992), "Modelling Danube and Isar Rivers Morphological evolution. Part II : Comparison of Field Data with modeling Results", 5th. Int. Symp.on River Sedimentation - Karlsruhe, Germany, 6-10 April.

[7] Loy, Belleudy, Kellermann, Söhngen, B., (1992), "Modelling Danube and Isar Rivers Morphological evolution. Part III : Range of Uncertainty caused by Scattered Field Data with special Respect to Grain Sorting", 5th. Int. Symp.on River Sedimentation - Karlsruhe, Germany, 6-10 April.

2nd International Conference on
RIVER FLOOD HYDRAULICS
22–25 March 1994: York, England

AN ALTERNATIVE APPROACH FOR PREDICTION OF CHANNEL GEOMETRY IN ALLUVIUM

M. A. Matin[1], A. Nishat[1] and D.I.H Barr[2]

ABSTRACT

A functional approach for the prediction of channel geometry in alluvium is presented. This approach is based on the application of dimensional analysis of the salient variables that control the channel behaviour. The numerical coefficients of the relationship were obtained by analyzing a large number of data compiled from different sources. The analysis was based on the main channel schematisation in which it was assumed that the central channel section with horizontal bed was the active zone providing resistance to flow. The predictive capacity of the present approach was tested against independent set of data and found an excellent agreement. With the same set of data, results achieved were compared with those obtained from the Wallingford Optimal Method for prediction of channel regime geometry (White et al. 1982). Prior to making this comparison, it was necessary to rework the Wallingford Method. The applicability of Wallingford method was verified against available channel observations and it was found that the overall cross-section was relatively deeper and narrower compared to prototype situation. Usage of the authors' approach for prediction of channel geometry is simpler. It gives reasonable accuracy in the predicted results, when compared with field data. Predictions obtained by the authors' approach provide a suitable cross-sectional area and aspect ratio for long term stability.

INTRODUCTION

One of the focus of studies on channel geometry is to examine the different combination of controlling parameters that results in a stable condition. It is important that such combination of parameters are known to an engineer when he designs a new channel or plans to channelise a river. Channelisation of natural streams may be required for improvement of navigation and acceleration in the passage of floods, for which widening, deepening and straightening of the channel may be involved. Artificial channels may be constructed for irrigation or navigation projects. In these cases, the problem is to determine the combination of cross-sectional area, shape and slope of channel that will carry a given discharge of water and sediment load and remain in stable condition.

1/ Dept. of Water Resources Engg. BUET, Dhaka, Bangladesh.
2/ Dept. of Civil Engineering, University of Strathclyde, U.K.

2nd International Conference on River Flood Hydraulics. Edited by W. R. White and J. Watts

The study of stable alluvial channels in terms of cross-sectional geometry, slope and channel pattern has been a subject of considerable research over a century. Traditionally, an alluvial channel is considered to posses three degrees of freedom to adjust its cross-section for a given flow condition. These three degrees of freedom are in width, depth and slope. In recent years, investigators have agreed that these are all dependent variables in alluvial channel flow. Thus, there has been the necessity for atleast three equations to express these variables quantitatively. The problem appears more complex when one recognises the fact that sediment transport also affects the channel stability. For describing such effects, other variables such as sediment concentration and its median size are to be taken into consideration.

It is considered that the whole wetted perimeter of channel contributes to resistance. But which part of the perimeter play dominant role depends on various factors. These factors are the channel shape, the characteristics of bed and bank material and the location of bed form. The cross-sectional shape of a channel in equilibrium is approximately a trapezoidal section. Blench (1957, 1969) observed that the standard canal section was a trapezoidal with side slope 1/2:1, and with dunes of sand on the bed. He also observed that "sides were erodible-depositable, made of silt-clay loam and beautifully maintained so as to be apparently hydraulically smooth." Barr et al. (1980) put forward a similar view that river channels over straight reaches can be considered as trapezoidal section similar to that of a canal. A trapezoidal channel section may be schematised in to two distinct portions. These are main channel section and two side channels. Nishat (1980) analyzed a large volume of data to establish combination of various geometric parameters for stable alluvial channels based on main channel section. He postulated that the main channel approach might lead to a better basis of correlation, in comparison with whole channel basis. Based on this idea and with the application of echelon matrix (Barr 1985) procedure of dimensional analysis, Kaka(1986) and later Matin (1988) consolidated this work which led to development of an alternative approach for the prediction of channel geometry.

MAIN CHANNEL SCHEMATISATION

In the compilation of alluvial channel data, the observed values are usually given for discharge, mean depth of flow, water surface width and longitudinal slope. However for analysis of data on main channel basis, it is necessary to estimate the flow associated with the main section of the channel. Obviously there is a difference between the mean depth of main channel and the mean depth of flow. The mean depth of flow (H) and main channel depth (H') can be related by the following expression:

$$H = H' - (H^2 Z)/B \qquad \cdots \; \cdots \qquad (1)$$

Thus the values of main channel depth (H') can be calculated from given values of channel mean depth, water surface width (B) and side slope (Z). The average velocity of side channel sections can be assumed as 2/3 that of main channel velocity (Nishat, 1981). Thus the equation for main channel flow (Q_m) was obtained as:

$$Q_m = \frac{Q}{(A_s/A_m) * 0.67 + 1} \qquad \cdots \; \cdots \qquad (2)$$

Here, A_s is the total side channel area, A_m is the area of main channel sections and Q is the total discharge.

NON-DIMENSIONAL CORRELATION

A potential basis of correlation of alluvial channel data have been evolved (Matin 1988, Matin and Barr 1990) by applying the echelon matrix procedure (Barr 1985) of dimensional analysis. The correlation in terms of non-dimensional functional arrangement is as follows:

$$\left[\frac{B}{H}, \frac{Qg^2}{V_s^5}, \frac{Q_s g^2}{V_s^5}, \frac{V_s}{(gH)^{1/2}} \right] = 0 \qquad \cdots \; \cdots \qquad (3)$$

Here, Q_s is the sediment discharge and V_s is the fall velocity. Equation 3 can be rearranged as the following two alternative forms for convenient of analysis:

$$\left(\frac{B_m}{H}, \frac{Q_m g^2}{V_s^5}, \frac{V_s}{(gH)^{1/2}} \right) = 0 \qquad \cdots \; \cdots \qquad (4)$$

$$\left(\frac{Q_m g^2}{V_s^5}, \frac{V_s}{(gH)^{1/2}}, \frac{Q_s g^2}{V_s^5} \right) = 0 \qquad \cdots \; \cdots \qquad (5)$$

Here, the sediment discharge is calculated as $Q_s = 10^{-6} * C * Q_m/s$. Where s is the specific weight of sediment grains and C is the sediment concentration in PPM.

DATA USED FOR EVALUATION

Obviously, the establishment of a functional relationship would depend on analysis of a large volume of data. Table 1 summarises the data used in the present investigation. These data obtained from computerised data bank namely the Strathclyde laboratory data (Hossain 1985) and Brownlie data (Brownlie 1981) and data from many other sources covered a wide range of flow condition.

ESTABLISHMENT OF CHANNEL GEOMETRY RELATIONSHIPS

The resulting equational forms of the functional correlation relevant to Eq. 4 can be expressed as follows:

$$\frac{B_m}{H} = 10^{-(a_m/b_m)} \left(\frac{Q_m g^2}{V_s^5} \right)^{(1/b_m)} \qquad \dots \dots (6)$$

$$\text{where, } \begin{aligned} a_m &= 0.376 - 4.59 \log F_s & \dots (7) \\ b_m &= 0.768 - 0.048 \log F_s & \dots (8) \\ F_s &= V_s/(gH)^{1/2} \end{aligned}$$

Again, the non-dimensional functional equation (Eq. 5) can be deduced as the following form:

$$\frac{Q_m g^2}{V_s^5} = 10^{-c_m} \left(\frac{Q_s g^2}{V_s^5} \right)^{d_m} \qquad \dots \dots (9)$$

$$\text{where, } \begin{aligned} c_m &= 1.404 - 2.488 \log F_s & \dots (10) \\ d_m &= 0.589 - 0.058 \log F_s & \dots (11) \end{aligned}$$

Thus, knowing the input variables Q, Q_s, V_s, the solution of these equations(Eqs. 9 to 11) will give the values of fall velocity Froude number and then depth H. The channel breadth B is obtained from Eq.6.

COMPUTATIONAL PROCEDURE

The basic input variables are the discharge Q, the sediment median size (D_{50}), the sediment concentration (C). All these variables should be in SI units. Other input data are the kinematic viscosity (υ) for calculation of fall velocity and the channel side slope (Z). The channel side slope is calculated using the Smith (1974) relationship. The calculation of channel width and depth are carried out as follows: First an assumption has to be made that the discharge within the main channel is equal to the actual discharge. Then the initial values of fall

TABLE 1. Summary of the basic data sets used for the investigation.
(Source: Matin 1988)

Source Description	No. of Data sets used	Discharge (m^3s^{-1})	Sediment concentration (ppm)	Slope x 1000	Sediment median size (mm)
Strathclyde lab.	223	0.0005-0.015	525.0-9250.0	1.000-32.00	0.150-0.300
R. Raju et al	5	0.018-0.015	150.0-2425.0	0.750-2.830	0.27
Ackers	24	0.028-0.151	10.0-476.0	0.410-9.200	0.150-0.200
Ikeda	3	0.008-0.010	57.0-121.0	1.810-2.020	1.30
Simons Bender	7	4.14-29.19	52.0-447.0	0.058-0.330	0.096-0.715
Up Canals	28	0.42-281.9	58.0-2010.0	0.102-0.434	0.110-0.410
CBIP (India)	18	1.15-242.0	670.0-1518.9	0.700-0.100	0.051-0.820
CHOP	30	27.52-427.57	115.7-1316.9	0.051-0.254	0.090-0.311
NEDECO	93	28.90-3089.90	8.3-2000.5	0.015-0.620	0.100-1.300
ACOP Canals	275	29.47-297.15	5.0-1007.0	0.045-0.150	0.090-0.360
Atchafalaya River	40	2044.40-14186.30	12.5-567.0	0.020-0.504	0.105-0.303
Colorado River	68	77.53-408.35	18.0-572.0	0.030-0.304	0.160-0.695
Leopold's Data	37	83.33-454.30	49.0-516.0	0.053-0.346	0.140-0.443
Middle Loup	27	9.03-13.61	437.8-2269.2	0.920-1.570	0.270-0.430
Mississippi river	65	1885.84-28825.67	7.4-329.1	0.020-0.133	0.173-1.129
Mountain Creek	19	0.07-15.10	40.8-686.0	1.370-1.790	0.200-0.899
Niobrara River	20	5.91-16.05	391.9-2089.0	1.136-1.780	0.218-0.359
Red River	21	190.28-1537.58	7.9-499.0	0.060-0.082	0.094-0.217
Snake River	9	971.24-3511.18	3.8-25.0	0.245-1.210	0.051-0.640

velocity Froude number, width and depth of the main channel are calculated by using the equations 6 to 11. Values of width and depth obtained correspond to main channel section. Now the continuity of flow should be checked for these values of channel dimensions. For continuity check, the initially assumed value of main channel discharge to be replaced by that of calculated discharge value. This process is repeated until Q_m/Q_{mc} tends to unity. Here Q_{mc} is the calculated main channel discharge. Finally the predicted depth and breadth should be adjusted for the equivalent trapezoidal section by using the following relations:

$$H = H' - \frac{H^2 Z}{B_m + 2H'Z}$$

$$B_m = (B_m + 2H'Z) H'/H$$

DEGREE OF COMPLIANCE OF FUNCTIONAL PROCEDURE

The geometry of alluvial channels as predicted from the authors approach was tested against wide range of channel data as summarised in Table 1. The degree of compliance was tested by comparing the values of predicted geometry variables with those of observed variables. Results of the prediction are shown in Fig.1 for breadth and in Fig.2 for depth. These figures indicate a reasonable agreement between observed and predicted values.

WALLINGFORD OPTIMAL METHOD

White et al. (1981, 1982) have suggested an approach to the prediction of alluvial channel geometry. They considered six variables for describing the river regime. These are: the average velocity, average depth , slope, discharge, sediment concentration, and width. For the purpose of relating these variables, use of three equations had been proposed. These are i) Ackers and White sediment transport formula (1973) ii) White, Paris and Bettess resistance formula (1980) and iii) a equation for optimization. A fourth link was provided by the continuity relationship.

The primary reason of examining the Wallingford method was to make a comparative assessment with the authors' approach in terms of predictive function against available alluvial channel data. Prior to make any comparison, it was found necessary to devise a simplified alternative solution procedure of the Wallingford method. Flow diagram showing this alternative solution routes is given in Fig.3. The efficacy of this procedure has been tested (Matin 1988) against the tabulated results of White et al. (1981) and against the actual channel data used by White et al. A typical result obtained from minimisation of slope is shown in Fig.4.

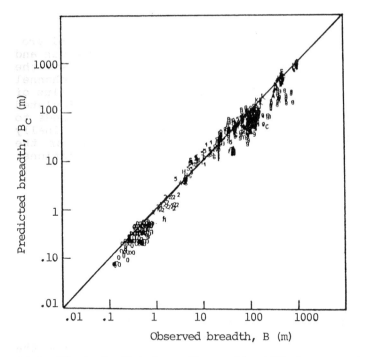

Fig.1: Predicted vs. Observed breadth for suggested
alternative approach (main channel basis)

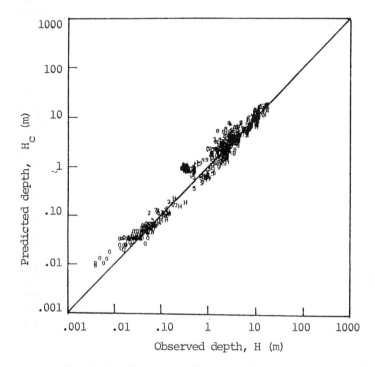

Fig.2: Predicted vs. Observed depth for suggested
alternative approach (main channel basis)

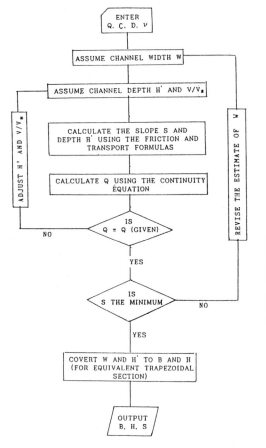

Fig.3: Flow diagram showing major steps of calculation (for the minimisation of slope)

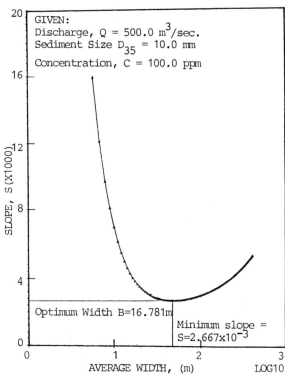

Fig.4: Slope against the width for minimisation of slope.

VERIFICATION USING FIELD DATA

Data used for the initial assessment includes the same data that were utilized in the formulation of various geometry relationships. However verification of the degree of compliance of the relationships against independent data is necessary. In particular it is most desirable to utilize field data for such verification. This is because it is to such circumstances that the practical design application has to be made.

In recent time, a notable effort has been by Mahmood et al. (1987) who have assembled observations from large sand bed channel of link and irrigation canal systems of Pakistan in order to verify the existing theories and relationships for design of stable channels. This data base is referred here as Washington data. The characteristics of the Washington data are summarised as follows:

Q (m^3/s)	B (m)	H (m)	S$(*10^3)$	D_{50} (mm)	C(PPM)
0.30 – 617.28	2.224 – 157.58	0.306 – 4.437	0.013 – 0.337	0.063 – 0.49	5.0 – 2233.0

A total of 486 sets data from Washington file were used for further performance test. The results of the degree of compliance against the Washington data are shown in Fig.5 and Fig.6 for authors' approach and in Fig.7 and Fig.8 for the Wallingford approach. Percentage of data coverage in selected discrepancy ratio bands of 0.833 to 1.20 and 0.714 to 1.40 are calculated for making comparison of the results of width and depth prediction obtained from these two approaches. Regarding the capacity of predicting channel breadth, it is found that the authors' approach have a complience of 38 % within the range 0.833-1.20, while the Wallingford method complies with 2.91 % data. For depth prediction, with the range of discrepancy ratio between 0.833 to 1.20 about 37% data is in agreeement for the authors approach. With Wallingford approach the agreement for same range is only for 2.5 % of data. From these results, it may be said that the prediction obtained by the authors' approach show satisfactory performance in predicting channel breadth and depth.

DISCUSSION

There is benefit to be achieved by applying dimensional analysis in problems related to study of the alluvial channels behaviour. However dimensional analysis must be carried out in conjunction with the physical understanding of the process involved. Together with the physical arguments, the application of dimensional analysis provide towards formulation of reliable basis of correlation between pertinent parameters. In authors findings it demonstrate that the shape factor (B/H) of an alluvial channel is a function of non-dimensional discharge (Qg^2/V_s^5) and the fall velocity Froude number $V_s/(gH)^{1/2}$. The role of sediment fall velocity Froude number is also significant that quantifies interrelationship between the fall velocity and the depth.

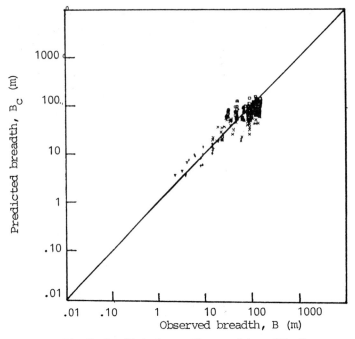

Fig.5: Predicted vs. Observed breadth for suggested
alternative approach against the Washington data.

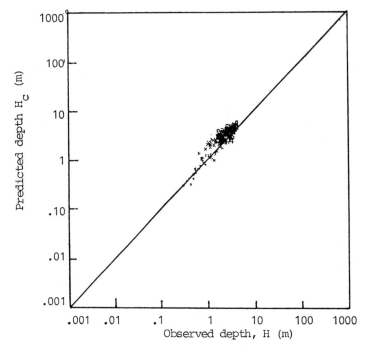

Fig.6: Predicted vs. Observed depth for suggested
alternative approach against the Washington data.

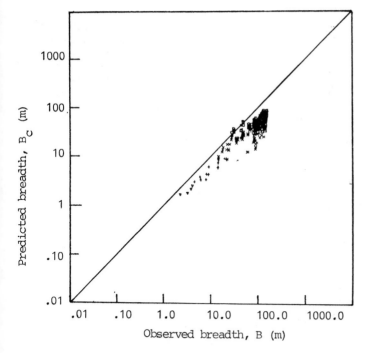

SYM.	DATA REFERENCE
Δ	$0.010 < Q < 0.100$
∇	$0.100 < Q < 1.000$
+	$1.000 < Q < 10.00$
x	$10.00 < Q < 100.0$
□	$100.0 < Q < 1000.$

Fig.7: Predicted vs. Observed breadth for the
Wallingford method against the Washington data.

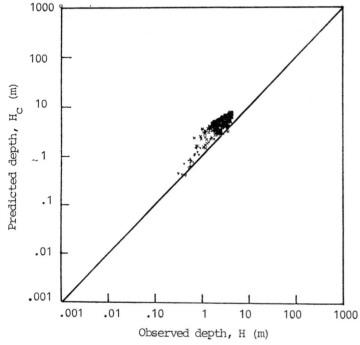

SYM.	DATA REFERENCE
Δ	$0.010 < Q < 0.100$
∇	$0.100 < Q < 1.000$
+	$1.000 < Q < 10.00$
x	$10.00 < Q < 100.0$
□	$100.0 < Q < 1000.$

Fig.8: Predicted vs. Observed depth for the Wallingford
method against the Washington data.

547

A functional procedure has been suggested for the purpose of channel geometry prediction. The input variables adopted are the water discharge, the sediment size, the sediment concentration. The channel longitudinal slope may be considered as dependent variable and can be calculated from the discharge values (Nishat 1981, Matin 1988). On testing the applicability and efficacy of authors' approach, it has been found that this can be applied successfully over a wide range of channel sizes.

The Wallingford approach is based of the extremal hypothesis which states that a stable channel section maximises the sediment transport capacity or minimises the slope. Together with this hypothesis, sediment transport and resistance equations developed at Hydraulic Research have been utilised. These equations are however empirical and based on non-dimensional transport and resistance parameters as established from comprehensive flume investigations. As reported by White et al.(1982), the solution of the relationships for prediction of channel geometry is complex and highly implicit nature. Therefore a simplified procedure of the method has been worked out by the authors. The major steps of the computation are shown in Fig.3. This procedure is regarded as an alternative to the original system developed by White et al. (1982). It is found that the results obtained from this procedure provide almost full agreement (Matin 1988) with the tabular results given by White et al. (1981). Thus, for use in design, the present solution procedure can be adopted to deal with any set of input data within the scope of the system. The applicability of Wallingford method has been tested against the available Washington data data (Mahmood et al. 1987). From this verification it is observed that the channel breadth is under-predicted and depth is over predicted. The overall predicted cross-sections is found to be relatively deeper than those obtained in field conditions. It may be noted here that recently the original sediment transport equation (Ackers and White 1973) have been revised and updated (Ackers 1991).

CONCLUDING REMARKS

It is argued that the usage of proposed approach for the prediction of channel geometry is simple. It gives reasonable accuracy in the predicted results, when compared with prototype data. Predictions obtained from this system lead to a suitable cross-sectional area and shape factor for long term stability. For use in design work, the proposed approach can be adopted for determination of suitable dimensions of channel for water development projects.

REFERENCES

ACKERS, P (1991): The Ackers-White sediment transport function for open channel Flow: A review and Update. Newsletter, Hydraulic Research , Wallingford, July.

ACKERS P and WHITE W.R (1973): Sediment transport:- new approach and analysis. Proc. ASCE, Vol. 99, No. HY11, November, 1973, 2041-2060.

BARR D.I. H, ALAM M.K.and NISHAT A. (1980): A contribution to regime theory relating principally to channel geometry. Proc. ICE. Part 2. Vol.69. 651-670

BARR D.I.H. (1985): Matrix Procedures for dimensional analysis. Int. Jour of Math. Education and Sci. Tech., vol. 16, No. 5, 1985, 629-644.

BROWNLIE W.R. (1981): Compilation of alluvial channel data - Laboratory and Field. W.M. Keck Laboratory of Hydraulics Water Resources Report No. KH-R-43B. California Inst. of Technology, November 1981.

BLENCH T. (1957): Regime behaviour of canals and rivers, Butterworth, London

BLENCH T. (1969): Mobile bed fluviology. The University of Alberta Press. Edmonton, Canada

HOSSAIN M.M. (1984): Development of a sediment transport equation Ph.D. thesis, Dept. of Civil Engineering, University of strathclyde, Glasgow.

KAKA N. M. (1986): Hydraulic geometry and sediment transportation of alluvial channels. Ph.D thesis, Dept. of Civil Engineering, University of Strathclyde, Glasgow.

MAHMOOD et alia. (1987): ACOP canals equilibrium runs computerised data base. Int. Water Resources Inst., The George Washington University. Report No. IWRI-87-4 November, 1987, 157-273.

MATIN M.A. (1988): The geometry of alluvial channels. Ph.D. thesis. Dept. of Civil Engineering, University of Strathclyde. Glasgow, December 1988.

MATIN M.A and BARR D.I.H (1990): The prediction of channel geometry in alluvium. Proc. of seminar on 'Technology for sustainable development' AIT-BUET programme, BUET, Dhaka, August 1990, 166-194.

NISHAT A. (1981): A study of alluvial channels in regime. Ph.D. thesis, Dept. of Civil Engineering, University of Strathclyde, Glasgow, 1981.

SMITH K.V.H (1974): Comparison of prediction techniques with records of observations on the lower Chenab canal system. Univ. of Southumpton, CE/5/74

WHITE W.R. PARIS E. and BETTESS R. (1980): The frictional characteristics of alluvial streams- a new approach. Proc. ICE,Part 2 sept. 1980, 737-750.

WHITE W.R. PARIS E. and BETTESS R. (1981): Tables for the design of stable alluvial channels. Hydraulic Research Station. Wallingford, Report No. IT 208.

WHITE W.R., BETTESS R. and PARIS E. (1982): Analytical approach to river regime. Proc. ASCE, Vol. 108. No. HY10, 1179-1192.

Chapter Twelve

Flood Management— Indian Subcontinent

An Assessment of the Impacts of Dhaka City Flood Control Project

Muhammad Abdul Momin Khondaker
Jahir Uddin Chowdhury

Institute of Flood Control and Drainage Research (IFCDR)
Bangladesh University of Engineering and Technology (BUET)
Dhaka-1000

ABSTRACT

Assessment of the impacts of Dhaka City Flood Control Project has been made through extensive field inspections and public opinion survey in the constructed part and through mathematical model study in the proposed part of the project. There had been drainage congestion and waterlogging at several locations after the construction of the project. Most respondents in the survey consider that fear from flood related disaster has been removed, but the project does not provide economical opportunities and additional facility for communication. There would be significant hydraulic impacts in the proposed part after its implementation: during rainfall average flow rates in the channels would be reduced to 60-80%; during receding flow, average flowrates in the channels would increase to 114-143% and water levels in the water bodies would be depleted by 0.36 to 0.6m.

1. INTRODUCTION

Dhaka City, the capital of Bangladesh, is located in the flat region near to the confluence of three major international rivers, the Ganges, the Brahmaputra and the Meghna. The city is surrounded by distributaries of these major rivers. Flood water from surrounding rivers inundates the lowlying area of the city. During the monsoon of 1988, Dhaka city was subjected to catastrophic flood. Soon after this flood , the Government took a project to protect the city from overbank spills of surrounding rivers by constructing embankments. The storm water drainage channels of the city discharges to the rivers. The embankment obstructs the hydraulic links between the drainage systems and the rivers. This paper discusses some important impacts upon surface water environment of the city.

2. DHAKA CITY FLOOD CONTROL PROJECT

The Dhaka City Flood Control Project covers an area of 265 sq.km. and is divided into two phases as shown in Fig.1. Under the Phase-1 program, 68 km of embankments, 1 pump station and 7 regulators have been constructed in the existing urbanized part covering 147 sq.km.

2nd International Conference on River Flood Hydraulics. Edited by W. R. White and J. Watts

In the phase-2 program, construction of 65 km of embankments, 4 pump stations and 6 regulators has been proposed in the flood plain of the adjacent rivers covering 118 sq.km (JICA,1992). Major part of the phase-2 area is not urbanized, but the city is rapidly expanding into this area. The flood control and drainage schemes would be implemented in stages by dividing the area into 4 compartments.

3. SURFACE WATER SYSTEMS

The surface water systems of Dhaka City comprise of several depression storages (ponds, lakes, submerged lowlying lands) and they are linked to the surrounding rivers as shown in Fig.1. The city rainfall runoff is accumulated into the depressions and discharges to the surrounding rivers through the channels. There are more than 40 channels having catchment area varying from 6 to 40 sq.km. In a normal flood, average depth of water in the depressions vary from 1 to 2.5 m during monsoon (khondaker et al., 1992). Frequency analysis indicates that approximately 60% of the

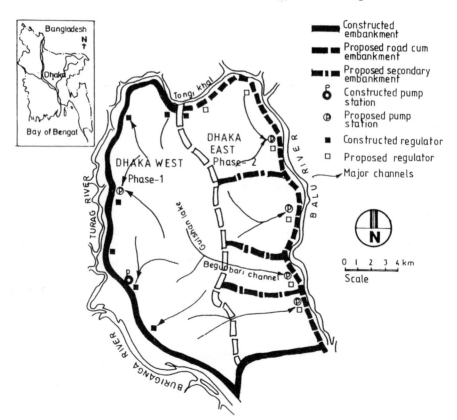

Fig.1: Dhaka City Flood Control Project

city area is under mean annual maximum flood level, and 75, 81, 87, and 90% of the area are subjected to flood at 10, 5, 2 and 1% exceedance probability respectively (Khondaker et al., 1992).

4. METHODOLOGY FOR IMPACT ASSESSMENT

The methodology has two parts. In the part one, assessment of occurred impacts of constructed part of the project has been made through field inspections and public opinion survey. In the part two, predictions of possible hydraulic impacts of the proposed part of the project has been made through mathematical model study.

Extensive field inspections were made to four locations adjacent to the embankment during the period September 1990 to August 1992. The four locations were selected based on landuse pattern: one agricultural area, one residential area, one residential and agricultural area, and one residential and industrial area. Public opinion survey was made through questioning to 325 inhabitants in these areas during November to December of 1991. The classification of respondents in terms of profession and age groups are given in Table 1.

Table 1 Number of respondents in the public opinion survey

Age (years) Profession	25-35	36-45	46-55	56-65	Total
Traders	22	56	34	21	133
Agricultural landowners	18	41	23	8	90
Fishermen	4	9	5	2	20
Employed persons	8	45	29	0	82
Total	52	151	91	31	325

Mathematical model consists of a rainfall-runoff submodel (McCuen, 1986) for a drainage catchment and a flow routing submodel (Chowdhury, 1986) for the channel. The water levels at the outlet of the catchment during a rainfall were measured and the model was calibrated against these water levels. Then model was verified against another set of observations. The impact assessment has been made by running the model for the 'with project' (WP) and 'without project' (WOP) conditions.

5. IMPACTS DURING PROJECT CONSTRUCTION

The implementation period of the phase-1 of the project was from 1989 to 1991. The drainage regulator were constructed after the construction of embankment. One pumping station was constructed at the end of 1992. Field observation of the project during the period of September 1990 to August 1992 and results from public opinion

survey during the period November to December of 1991 are briefly
discussed below.

5.1. Field Observation

The embankment has caused drainage congestion and waterlogging at
several locations. The consequences was so severe that the people
in one area cut the embankment in the first year of its
construction. Temporary pumping was made to remove drainage
congestion before the regulators have been. Even after construction
of regulators, drainage congestion and waterlogging occurred in
some areas. This is due to absent of link channels to the inlet of
the regulator and due to operational problems related to
regulators' gate openings at the time of heavy storm and high
waterlevels in the rivers.

5.2. Public Opinion Survey

Every respondent was asked a total of 20 questions as per printed
proforma. A brief summary of results from important questions is
given in tables 2 and 3. Most of the respondents are of the opinion
that the project has removed the fear from flood related disasters.
However there are significant concerns for the drainage congestion
and waterlogging created by the embankment. A significant number of
respondents does not consider that the project is helpful for
economic activities. They also do not consider that the embankment
has provided additional facility for communication. These aspects
should be given due attention during the design stage at phase-2
part of the project.

Table 2 Public opinion regarding the impacts of the project

Question	Reaction in terms of % total respondents		
	Yes	No	Do not know
Do you feel free from the fear of flood related disaster ?	71	20	9
Has drainage congestion and waterlogging caused harm to public health ?	47	38	15
Do you use embankments for communication ?	50	38	12
Has trade activities via boat communication declined ?	52	37	11
Has economic opportunities increased ?	50	40	10

The employed persons and traders seem to be the most happy with
the project as indicated by Table 3. This is perhaps due to
increase in employment opportunities created by the project. As
expected the fishermen are the worst sufferer. Among the four age
groups, the youngest group are unhappy about the performance of the

project. The youngest group are also seemed to be the most
sensitive to environmental consequences of the project.

Table 3 Variation in public opinion regarding the project performance

Question	Percent of respondents who replied ' yes'		
	Profession		Age group
Has the project been beneficial to the area ?	Traders : 41 Agricultural landowners: 33 Fishermen : 5 Employed persons : 76		25-35: 29 36-45: 48 46-55: 55 56-65: 26
Has the project caused significant adverse impact to the area ?	Traders : 24 Agricultural landowners: 44 Fishermen : 90 Employed persons : 18		25-35: 57 36-45: 26 46-55: 11 56-65: 26

6. PREDICTION OF HYDRAULIC IMPACTS IN THE PROPOSED PART

6.1 Flow Characteristics During Rainfall

In the 'without project' condition the outlet of the channels fall
into the surrounding rivers. So the design 100-yr flood water level
in the rivers has been used as the outlet boundary condition of the
channels. In the 'with project' condition the rainfall runoff would
be disposed off by pumping. So proposed pump discharges in the
project are used as the outlet boundary conditions here. The
predicted effect as shown in typical figure 2(a) indicates that the
flow rates in the channels would be reduced if the project is
implemented. In the 'without project' condition the maximum and
average flow rates in the channels during the rainfall (proposed
for pump discharge estimation) are computed as 112 to 138 m^3/s and
59 to 73 m^3/s respectively. These would be reduced to 72 to 88 m^3/s
and 44 to 51 m^3/s respectively. The rate of pumping is less than the
rate of inflow in the retarding basins of pump stations which
results in high water level at downstream with respect to upstream
of the channels and thus causes less head difference to flow.
Consequently the water levels in the lakes and other water storage
areas would rise as shown in typical figure 2(b). This figure also
shows that the water level would be reduced by 3.86m with respect
to 100-yr flood level if the project is implemented and thus the
city would be protected from river flood.

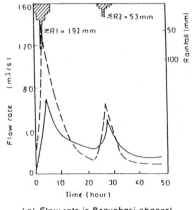

(a) Flow rate in Begunbari channel

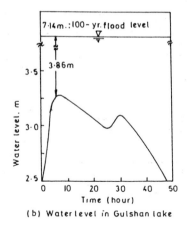

(b) Water level in Gulshan lake

Fig.2: Effect of the Proposed Project Upon Flow Characteristics
During Rainfall

6.2. Flow Characteristics During Receding Flow

In both 'without project' and 'with project' conditions the outlet
boundary of the channels in the model have been kept as the
surrounding river water levels during post-monsoon period. In the
'without project' condition the existing water storage areas and in
the 'with project' condition the proposed water storage areas have
been input in the model. The predicted effects as shown in the
typical figures 3 (a) and (b) indicate that the channels would
have higher flow rates which would result in quick depletion in
water level in the water bodies. Due to reduction in water storage
areas and flow of confined water through confined water ways after
the project, such effects would result. The average flow rates in
the channels in the 'without project' conditions are estimated as
0.72 to 1.0 m^3/s. These would increase to 1.01 to 1.33 m^3/s. The
reduction in water level in the lakes and other water storage areas
at the end of the post-monsoon are predicted as 0.36 to 0.60 m.

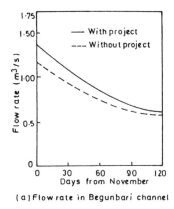

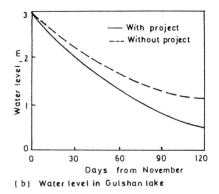

(a) Flow rate in Begunbari channel

(b) Water level in Gulshan lake

Fig 3 **Effect** of the Proposed Project Upon Receding Flow Characteristics.

7. CONCLUSION

There had been severe drainage congestion and waterlogging at several locations after the construction of flood protection embankment. These undesirable consequences occurred because the regulators and link channels have been constructed long after the construction of embankment. Long implementation period of the project has caused increase in severity of consequences. However, most the people questioned during the survey consider that the project has removed the fear of hazards related to river floods.

Mathematical model studies in the proposed part of the project predict that during rainfall in the monsoon the average flow rates in the drainage channels would be smaller in comparison to the 'without project' condition. The recession of the flow in the water bodies and channels during post-monsoon period would be quicker in the 'with project' condition. Revision of the proposed flood control and drainage schemes to preserve more surface water storage areas to reduce hydraulic consequences should be considered.

ACKNOWLEDGEMENT

The authors thank the IFCDR for approving the research study and the United Nations Centre for Regional Development (UNCRD), Nagoya, Japan for financial assistantship for this study.

REFERENCES
Khondaker, M.A.M. and Chowdhury, J.U. (1992), Effect of Dhaka City Flood Protection Embankment Upon Surface water Drainage Systems and Environment, IFCDR, BUET, Dhaka.

JICA (1992), Feasibility Study on Greater Dhaka Protection Project of FAP-8A, Main Report, Flood Plan Coordination Organization, Dhaka.

Mc Cuen, R.H and Snyder, W.M. (1986), Hydrological Modelling Statistical Methods and Applications, Ch.8, Prentice-Hall, New Jersey.

Chowdhury, J.U. (1986), An Implicit Numerical Model of Unsteady Flow in River Network, Report No. Ro1/86, IFCDR,BUET.

A RISK METHODOLOGY FOR DETERMINING AN APPROPRIATE SET-BACK DISTANCE
FOR A FLOOD EMBANKMENT ON THE RIGHT BANK
OF THE BRAHMAPUTRA RIVER

A P G Russell, Director, Sir William Halcrow & Partners Ltd
P H von Lany, Principal Engineer, Sir William Halcrow & Partners Ltd

THE PROBLEM

The extent of flood alleviation provided by an embankment depends on its alignment. The nearer the embankment is to the river the greater will be the area protected from flooding by it, but the higher will be the likelihood that the embankment can be breached as a consequence of river bank erosion. The likelihood of breaching can be reduced by realigning the embankment further away from the river, but this exposes more land, between the embankment and the river, to flooding. In the absence of river training works to secure the bank-line, there is a tradeoff between the level of security achieved against breaching and the extent of flood alleviation provided by the embankment. This needs to be taken into account in devising a risk management strategy.

FLOODING ALONG THE BRAHMAPUTRA

The Brahmaputra River in Bangladesh underwent a major avulsion at the end of the 18th century and initially displayed a predominantly meandering form in its new course. Since the first reliable map was published by Wilcox in 1830 (source: India Office Map Room, London), the river has become steadily more braided and its overall width has increased, while at the same time large islands have developed, with their tops at much the same elevation as the flood plain. These islands, locally known as <u>chars</u>, undergo continual change in size as the anabranches change their planforms and increase and decrease in dominance, sometimes becoming attached to the bank and blending into the flood plain. This makes it difficult to define the bank line at any time and complicates the quantification of the rate of bank line change. This effect is more pronounced on the left bank than on the right, a feature associated with the fact that the right bank is experiencing net erosion whereas the left bank is closer to a state of dynamic equilibrium between erosion and accretion (Coleman, 1969, Thorne et al, 1993).

As the river enters Bangladesh it undergoes an important morphological change, probably linked to its more unstable phase; upstream the general fall of the land is towards the river and there are a number of major tributaries joining the main channel. The last of these tributaries is the Teesta and downstream of this point the pattern is one of distributaries, with the Old Brahmaputra course on the left bank being the best defined (Figure 1). Up to the confluence with the Ganges River only one river flows into the Brahmaputra, the Hurasagar or Balal River which rises in the northwest and drains the right bank flood plain.

The form of this macro drainage pattern is of great significance with regard to flood control. As snowmelt in the Himalayas causes the level of the main river to rise in April, the distributaries convey this water into the flood plain area, resulting in inundation of the land considerably earlier than

---

2nd International Conference on River Flood Hydraulics. Edited by W. R. White and J. Watts
© 1994 HR Wallingford Ltd. Published by John Wiley & Sons Ltd

experienced in those areas dominated by rivers fed by local rainfall. Moreover, the regional rivers tend to rise and fall within a timescale of a few days, in response to storms in their catchment areas, whereas those areas influenced by the main river remain inundated to a considerable depth for several weeks at a time. Flow velocities are relatively high and the ratio of sandy sediment to silt is substantially higher than in the regional rivers (Halcrow et al, 1993). Sudden inundation from the main river through breaching of the flood embankment is thus much more damaging to arable crop production than that from the regional rivers.

THE BRAHMAPUTRA RIGHT EMBANKMENT

In the early 1960's it was concluded that the control of flooding from the Brahmaputra River would provide a substantial net benefit to the productive soils of the right bank flood plain, which in origin are associated with the silt laden regional rivers rather than coarser grained material carried by the Brahmaputra river. Consequently, a flood embankment, known as the Brahmaputra Right Embankment (BRE), was constructed during the period 1957 to 1968 along most of the length of the river up to the Teesta confluence, and for some distance along the Teesta itself. Gated control structures were incorporated in the BRE to permit the regulated release of water into the distributaries and the drainage of any ponded water back into the Brahmaputra as levels fell following the flood flows. This embankment was set back between 1.5 and 2.0km from the main river bank and for the first decade following its construction provided freedom from the prolonged deep river flooding that had previously been a major constraint on agricultural production. Its efficacy was quickly reflected in the changing cropping pattern in the protected area, with higher yielding rice varieties being introduced and flood tolerant crops being phased out (Brammer, 1990).

It soon transpired that the set back distance provided would not safeguard the embankment from attack from the river for as long as had been expected. By the 1980's parts of the BRE were being intermittently breached as a direct consequence of river bank erosion (Figure 2) and today almost 90km of embankment, or approaching 50% of the length of the main BRE, is within 500m of the river bank. It is anticipated that in the absence of major investment in bank stabilisation works, within the coming 5 to 6 years, most, if not all, of this 90km of embankment will either have been destroyed by bank erosion or will be in imminent danger and will have to be reconstructed further back from the river bank.

Bank stabilisation works have been designed for limited lengths of the river, where there are sound economic arguments for this, and arrangements are in progress for the letting of international contracts for their construction. But, the lead time is such that works will not be effective at best until 1995. Despite the fact that the government, in response to strong lobbying from the riparian farmers, is publicly committed to a strategy of bank stabilisation in preference to planned realignment of the embankment, it will be a very costly undertaking and the procurement of financing for further bank stabilisation will itself take time. It must therefore be anticipated that in the meantime the realignment of considerable lengths of the BRE more than once will be necessary to maintain an acceptable level of flood alleviation.

The question inevitably arises as to whether the maintenance of the flood protection is indeed in the national and the regional interest. In common with many studies at the time, no thorough evaluation of the negative impact in terms of fisheries and other sociological factors was undertaken and it is not possible retrospectively to quantify them. After the passage of 20 years the new physical regime has become established and the socio-economic conditions have become adapted to these conditions. Any lowering of the standard of flood control will result in a significant drop in agricultural production and with it rural employment. There is no firm evidence that there would be any significant improvement in 'capture' fisheries that could begin to compensate for this. So in this case the abandonment of the flood embankment cannot be considered as either a socially acceptable or an economically viable alternative (Halcrow et al, 1993).

RIVER BANK EROSION

In order properly to understand the problems facing those responsible for deciding on the timing of realignment of a section of embankment and for selecting its setback distance, it is first necessary to develop insight into river bank erosion. The timescale of the realignment problem is 5 to 10 years from problem identification to re-construction, over which period an indication of future erosion rates, and their duration, is required.

The right bank of the Brahmaputra has over the past 30 years been experiencing a net erosion which on average has been between 50 and 100m/yr. This has not been uniform and some reaches have seen relatively little erosion while others have been through alternating periods of erosion and accretion.

Bank erosion is closely linked to the growth and decay of the major chars and the movement of the lesser sandbars that are inundated when the river is bankfull; lesser in this context is a relative term as these sandbars are typically of the order of 3km long and 1km wide. Both these processes are stochastic by nature being influenced not only by the hydrological pattern in any one year but also by the annual sequence of high and low monsoon river flows. There is some evidence that the high flows in 1988 resulted in above average bank erosion during the succeeding two years and a below average erosion rate since then. The complexity of the physical processes involved and their sensitivity to boundary conditions means that erosion prediction even in the short-term can only be indicative (Enggrob and von Lany, 1994). Over longer periods it may be possible to detect trends and patterns that could form the basis for a more general forecast.

Bank erosion is typically associated with the concave face of anabranch bends and in general increases in severity as the bend radius decreases until a cutoff occurs. Unlike in meandering rivers, bends in a braided river tend to be transitory as the braid pattern changes from year to year, and bends will normally be overtaken by such changes before a cutoff has time to take place. Very rapid erosion, which may exceed 600m/yr over a period of two or three years is dramatic and difficult to predict but it is relatively rare. The most commonly experienced erosion rate is in the range of 120 to 150m/yr. The high 1988 flows appear to have caused the formation of an unusually large number of the more aggressive bends, distributed notably evenly down the length of the river and corresponding to the island pattern, and this has tended to distort the popular perception of the erosion pattern and its severity. Attempting to predict rates of erosion by concentrating on the characteristics of bends, as one might do for a meandering river, is thus unlikely to produce much of practical value (Halcrow et al, 1993).

As part of the Riverbank Erosion Impact Study (Jahangirnagar University and the University of Manitoba), some work was carried out on trying to devise a means of predicting river bank erosion. Promising results are reported to have been obtained using a transfer function noise model operating on a short-term time series analysis of historic bank-line movement (Elahi and Rogge, 1990). The detailed results from this work were not available at the time the work described in this paper was being carried out.

EROSION RATES

It has been possible to establish useful relationships for the probability of occurrence of different rates of erosion on an annual basis by measuring bank movement at regular intervals down the river from rectified Landsat satellite imagery covering the period 1973 to 1992 (Halcrow et al, 1993). The measurements were analysed for each of the four reaches, defined on the basis of morphological and erosion characteristics, shown in Figure 1. An example of a cumulative frequency plot of erosion rates for one reach (Reach 3) is shown in Figure 3. A disaggregated form of this plot, showing the distribution of erosion rates during different periods within the overall period 1973 to 1992, is shown in Figure 4. This illustrates the variability in erosion rates with time.

It needs to be emphasised that the erosion rates shown in Figure 3 are average values applicable only to lengths of the river that are experiencing erosion. They cannot be used to predict the probability of occurrence of a particular rate of erosion at a specific location in any one year since this will be influenced by the recent history of erosion locally. For example, if a reach has a recent history of several years of low erosion or accretion and is currently experiencing a higher rate of erosion then this is more likely to persist in that reach for several years than in a similar reach which has a recent history of active erosion.

Figures 5 and 6 show the cumulative frequency distribution of different durations of active erosion and accretion respectively, for various levels of severity, based on analysis of the 1973 to 1992 data. Figure 5, for example, can be interpreted as follows: if, say, rapid erosion has been taking place over a period of 4 years then there is a less than 20% chance that the same rate will persist beyond the fourth year. In order then to decide whether a higher or a lower rate of erosion will follow, the particular reach in question needs to be assessed in terms of recent variations in the braid pattern of the reach paying particular attention to changes in char planforms, as well as the relative size, curvature, and alignment of the near-bank anabranch (Halcrow et al, 1993). The average probability distributions shown in Figure 3 can thus be modified to reflect these reach-specific observations, although with the limited data at present available the procedure for doing this is somewhat subjective.

THE TRADE-OFF

There is a spectrum of perception as to the value of the BRE and the most appropriate strategy for ensuring its continued functioning at a high level of reliability (Halcrow et al, 1993). There are three main groups of rural population directly and indirectly affected by realignment of the embankment. These are in addition to those responsible within the government for planning, designing, and implementing embankment realignment, who constitute a fourth interest group. Other interested parties include the potential providers of finance, those responsible for providing support to the population displaced by bank erosion, and those concerned with the improvements in the fisheries sector.

Of the three principal groups within the rural population, the first is composed of those involved in agriculture related activities within the zone of influence of the distributary and regional rivers. They benefit from the flood control but do not stand to lose any land from bank erosion and BRE realignment. Most will not suffer direct damage to crop, property or land in the event of a breach but will experience a drop in crop yield due to prolonged inundation. If this risk is perceived to be chronic they will respond by changes to their cropping pattern.

The second group consists of those in close proximity to the BRE on the landward side but sufficiently far away as to be at no risk of either losing their land or of finding themselves on the wrong side of a realigned length of embankment. They are vulnerable in the event of a breach in the BRE and will be generally in favour of an alignment strategy that minimises such a risk.

The third group is made up of those within a few hundred metres of the BRE on the landward side. They have the most to lose when the BRE is realigned, either through acquisition of their farm land for embankment construction or the loss of protection. The unfortunate group which is already on the river side of the embankment are only indirectly affected in that they may rely to some extent on employment in the protected area.

The first two groups will thus tend to favour an alignment that provides the maximum security while the third will seek the minimum practicable setback distance, river bank protection and the maximum possible postponement of the decision to realign.

The government officers responsible for the realignment are in an unenviable position. By setting the embankment further back they minimise the risk of breaching and maximise the period before the next realignment becomes necessary, with all its attendant problems. On the other hand they face strong and active lobbying from those who stand to lose flood protection: the further back the realignment, the more powerful becomes this lobby group. Higher up the government hierarchy, and further from direct contact with the affected parties, the preference may be for the solution that takes up the least amount of a scarce development budget. Since the greater the set-back distance the less frequent would be the need for reconstruction, they will favour the maximum set-back consistent with political considerations.

At present the timing and magnitude of a realignment is largely determined by local political considerations and as a consequence it is not uncommon for action to be postponed until the set-back becomes insufficient and a breach occurs. The damage due to unexpected flooding and deposition of sand caused by a breach can be significant.

A BASIS FOR DECISION MAKING

There are two key decision variables in this problem:

(a)   the set-back (SB)

(b)   the trigger distance (TR).

These variables are illustrated by sketches in Figures 7(a) and 7(b). The set-back is the distance between the (active) embankment and the river bank at the time of realignment. The larger this distance, the lower the recurrence of erosion breaches and subsequent realignments but the greater the area over which flood alleviation is lost. A lower bound value of SB is TR. The trigger distance is the distance between the embankment and the river bank at which the decision to realign is made. As TR increases realignments will take place well in advance of bankline retreat but at the possible cost of exposing a larger area to flooding. A acceptable lower bound value of TR depends both on the time that it would take to realign a length of embankment, and the prevailing erosion rate.

The optimal strategy for realignment is one which maximises the overall effectiveness of the flood embankment through selecting appropriate values for SB and TR. As a measure of effectiveness, the net present value (NPV) of each realignment strategy can be calculated, subject to meeting social and environmental requirements. Provided that appropriate provisions for fisheries interests are made in the design of the realigned embankment, these should have little impact on the realignment strategy. Those directly involved with the societal aspects of the problem will be concerned with the impact of the strategy on those who suddenly find themselves in a less favoured socio-economic group, the resettlement and redeployment of those who lose land and employment as a consequence of the realignment, and the possible social discord generated within the community. The quantification of these issues can be difficult and will certainly vary between observers.

A METHOD FOR ANALYSIS

The effect of erosion or accretion on the state of a given length of flood embankment over two successive flood periods is illustrated as a series of transitions in the following 'event-on-node' diagram. The concept of an 'event-on-node' diagram is described by Cooper and Chapman (2987).

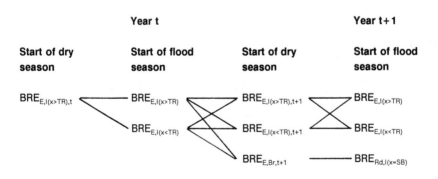

Year t		Year t+1	
Start of dry season	**Start of flood season**	**Start of dry season**	**Start of flood season**

Notes:
1. $BRE_{E,I}$ denotes an existing embankment intact
2. $BRE_{E,Br}$ denotes an existing embankment breached
3. $BRE_{Rd,I}$ denotes a realigned embankment intact - this becomes the new 'existing embankment intact'
4. x is the distance between the river bank and the embankment
5. SB is the set-back and TR is the trigger distance

The probability that the embankment will be breached as a consequence of river erosion at a particular location is a function of the rate of bankline retreat, the variability of this retreat rate (which may include accretion and erosion), and the distance between the river bank and the embankment. Once the embankment has been realigned, the focus of the analysis moves to the new embankment which takes over from the previous embankment, and breach probabilities then refer to the new embankment.

The following approach was used to evaluate the costs and benefits of embankment retirement in a probabilistic manner (Halcrow et al, 1993). The principal benefit of the flood embankment derives from the flood alleviation it provides. Thus, there is a dis-benefit (or cost) following embankment realignment further away from the river as flood protection is lost over the area exposed to the river. This will reduce the productivity and the value of the land. The loss of part of this land to erosion each year needs also to be taken into account. Other costs of realignment include land acquisition, disruption and relocation of affected people, and construction of the realigned embankment.

The principal benefit of realignment derives from reducing the frequency of embankment breaches due to river erosion, and hence the damage caused by them. To this can be added the indirect benefit of an enhanced level of confidence and agricultural production in response to the provision of a higher level of security against embankment breaches.

The benefits and costs of embankment realignment can be described in terms of 'expected' or probabilistic values by the following equations, which contain probabilities for the transitions depicted in the above 'event-on-node' diagram.

(1)   The 'expected' benefit of realignment, B_t^*, by avoiding breaching of the existing embankment in a given year, t, can be calculated as:

$$B_t^* = (p(BRE_{E,I(x>TR),t} \rightarrow BRE_{E,Br,t+1}) + p(BRE_{E,I(x<TR),t} \rightarrow BRE_{E,Br,t+1})).D_t$$

where $p(BRE_{E,I,t} \rightarrow BRE_{E,Br,t+1})$ is the probability that transitions resulting in breaching will occur in a given length of embankment in year t

D_t is the potential damage that would be caused by breaching of the existing embankment in year t

In this case the benefit is conditional on the probability that the existing embankment will breach in any one year. The equation can be expanded to include a term for possible breaching of the realigned embankment in the same year as its construction. This may be a possibility when a small set-back is overtaken by aggressive erosion, but if a sensible lower limit is placed on SB the significance of this term should be limited.

(2)   The 'expected' cost of embankment realignment in year t, C_t^*, can be calculated as follows:

$$C_t^* = (p(BRE_{E,I(x>TR),t} \to BRE_{E,I(x<TR),t+1}) + p(BRE_{E,I(x>TR),t} \to BRE_{E,Br,t+1})).C_t$$

where $p(BRE_{E,I,t} \to BRE_{E,I(x<TR),t+1}) + p(BRE_{E,I,t} \to BRE_{E,Br,t+1})$ refers to the probability of a breach or of a reduction in x to less than TR.

C$_t$ is the total cost of realigning a length of embankment in year t, taking into account that the realigned length of embankment may differ from the existing length for a given stretch of river

(3)   A term for the expected disbenefit from exposure to flooding following realignment, in any one year, (CF_t^*), needs to included in the benefit-cost analysis. Whether or not the disbenefit is incurred depends on the whether the embankment is realigned, which in turn depends on the probability of a breach or a reduction in x to less than TR. Using similar notation to that above, the 'expected' cost of flooding is therefore:

$$CF_t^* = (p(BRE_{E,I(x>TR),t} \to BRE_{E,I(x<TR),t+1}) + p(BRE_{E,I(x>TR),t} \to BRE_{E,Br,t+1})).(SB_R - TR_E - X_E).CF_t$$

where $p(BRE_{E,I,t} \to BRE_{E,I(x<TR),t+1}) + p(BRE_{E,I,t} \to BRE_{E,Br,t+1})$ is as defined above

SB$_R$ and TR$_E$ are the set-back for the realignment, and the trigger distance for the existing embankment, respectively.

X$_E$ is the land within the area (SB$_R$-TR$_E$) lost through erosion.

CF$_t$ is the disbenefit from exposure to flooding per unit width of flood plain along the length of embankment under consideration

(4)   The above terms can be combined as cost and benefit streams to calculate the net present value of embankment realignment as:

$$NPV = \sum_{t=0}^{t=n} \frac{(B_t^* - C_t^* - CF_t^*)}{(1+r)^t}$$

where   n is the time horizon over which the NPV is calculated

r is the annual discount rate for capital

DETERMINING AN OPTIMAL REALIGNMENT STRATEGY

The optimal realignment strategy can be described in terms of the most appropriate values for SB and TR for a length of embankment under threat from erosion, given the likely erosion rate at that site and the prevailing local socio-economic and environmental considerations.

An initial analysis was attempted using an event-tree to calculate the sequence of breach and realignment probabilities for a length of embankment. The event tree rapidly became complex because of the large number of potential outcomes and associated conditional probabilities, and was not taken further. A recursive model such as a Markov chain was considered as a means of capturing the repeated transitions implicit in the event-on-node diagram of 'erosion - realignment - erosion' or indeed, 'erosion - accretion - erosion', but the breach (ie. transition) probabilities are not constant with time. A Monte-Carlo simulation model was considered to help with the calculation, but the degree of detail of erosion data available, especially its variation with time, did not justify such an elaboration of the approach.

A more general method was therefore devised with the specific objective of investigating the sensitivity of the calculated NPV of realignment, under a given erosion rate, to various assumed values for the decision variables SB and TR. A computer spreadsheet was set-up incorporating the equations already outlined, with variables including the length of realignment, the erosion rate probability function, agricultural production values for the different extents of flood protection, and breach probability (Halcrow et al, 1993).

The following assumptions were made to reduce the complexity of the analysis:

(a)   By expressing TR and SB as proportional to the mean erosion rate, which is intuitively the case for longer-run average values, the problem of adjusting the erosion rate probability to take antecedent conditions into account was avoided.

(b)   It was (reasonably) assumed, for this level of analysis, that the shape of the cumulative frequency curve remains approximately the same irrespective of the mean erosion rate.

(c)   The irregularities in the present alignment of the BRE were ignored and it was taken to be effectively parallel to the river bank. The realignment of a length of the BRE will normally take place in a series of smaller phased realignments, each dealing with a particular focus of erosion. The actual length of embankment constructed will thus be greater than the simple length of the realigned section; this can be simply accounted for by means of a factor applied to the cost per length parallel to the river bank.

(d)   The average cost of realignment over a period was then taken to be linearly related to the set-back distance; thus if the set-back distance was doubled the average frequency of total realignment of that length of the BRE would be halved and consequently the average cost over a period of time would be halved. An arguable weakness in this approach is that it does not take into consideration the fact that with a greater set-back distance there will be some postponement of construction so that the present value of the work will be reduced. If this is taken into account there will be some weighting in favour of a greater set-back.

RESULTS

Selected examples of the results of the optimal realignment calculation at one site along the BRE are shown in Figures 8A and 8B. A set of graphs along the lines of these two figures were produced for each site, exploring the interaction of different values of SB and TR. Figure 8A shows the variation of the NPV of realignment with a SB for a TR of twice the mean annual erosion rate of 150m/yr. Figure 8B shows the variation of NPV with TR for SB equal to six times the annual erosion rate, a near optimal value for SB. This shows a best value of TR to be about four times the erosion rate.

The results show that when SB exceeds the mean erosion rate by a factor of about two, the incremental benefit from avoiding breach damage falls off rapidly. Thereafter, the tradeoff is principally one between the cost of realignment, which reduces asymptotically with SB, against the reduced productivity of the land exposed to flooding, which increases linearly with SB. The net present value of the realignment was found to peak weakly for SB greater than about six to eight times the mean annual erosion rate.

Since the value of breach damage was found to be high in relation to all other benefits and costs, the relationship between TR and the probability of an embankment breach becomes a significant factor when combined with low values of SB simply because the embankment is then vulnerable to attack for longer periods. A value for TR of the order of at least 1.5 times the mean expected erosion rate was found to provide a reasonable level of confidence that the embankment is not being excessively exposed to erosion.

CONCLUSIONS

This paper describes an approach to determining an appropriate set-back distance for a flood embankment on a river where bank erosion is a problem. It demonstrates the use of risk analysis in evaluating alternative realignment possibilities.

The primary objective of the analysis was to evaluate the relative importance of the set-back and trigger distance on different potential solutions in order to provide a reasoned basis for decision making. This provides a framework which can then allow less tangible factors describing social and environmental issues to be taken into consideration before finally selecting a realignment route. The insight gained through the process of analysis places the problem into perspective, thus improving the understanding of it and clearing the way for decisions to be taken in a more consistent manner than has hitherto been the case.

The results for the BRE at threat from erosion in 1991 showed that there is a wide range of near optimal values of set-back distance in excess of about six times the mean expected annual erosion rate with trigger distances in the region of two to five times the erosion rate. The analysis thus demonstrated that the value of realignment is relatively insensitive to small variations in set-back and trigger distance within its optimal range. Social and infrastructure factors will therefore more strongly determine the actual realignment route. The calculated values enable a corridor to be defined within which the best realigned route would lie, and confirmed that a planned sequence of realignments was a more cost effective strategy than a full realignment of the BRE by several kilometres.

ACKNOWLEDGEMENTS

The authors gratefully acknowledge the contribution made by the Bangladesh Water Development Board, Bangladesh University of Engineering and Technology, and other members of the Brahmaputra River Training Studies Team to the many topics related to this paper.

REFERENCES

Brammer, H (1990) Part 1 Floods in Bangladesh - Geographical background to the 1987-88 floods, Geographical Journal, Vol 156, Part 1; and Part 2 Floods in Bangladesh - Flood mitigation and environmental aspects, Geographical Journal, Vol 156, Part 2

Coleman, JM (1969) Brahmaputra River - Channel processes and sedimentation, Sedimentary Geology, Vol 3

Cooper, DF and Chapman, CB (1987) Risk analysis for large projects - Models, methods and cases, Wiley

Elahi, KM and Rogge, JR (1990) Riverbank erosion, flood and population displacement in Bangladesh, River bank Erosion Impact Study, Jahangirnagar University, Bangladesh

Enggrob, HG and von Lany, PH (1994) An application of 2-d mathematical modelling on the Brahmaputra River, Accepted for presentation at the 2nd International Conference on River Flood Hydraulics, York, England

Halcrow, DHI, EPC and DGI (1993) River Training Studies of the Brahmaputra River - Masterplan report, Bangladesh Water Development Board, Dhaka

Thorne, CRT, Russell, APG and Alam MK (1993) Platform pattern and channel evolution of the Brahmaputra River in Bangladesh, Braided Rivers, eds C Bristow and J Best, Geological Society

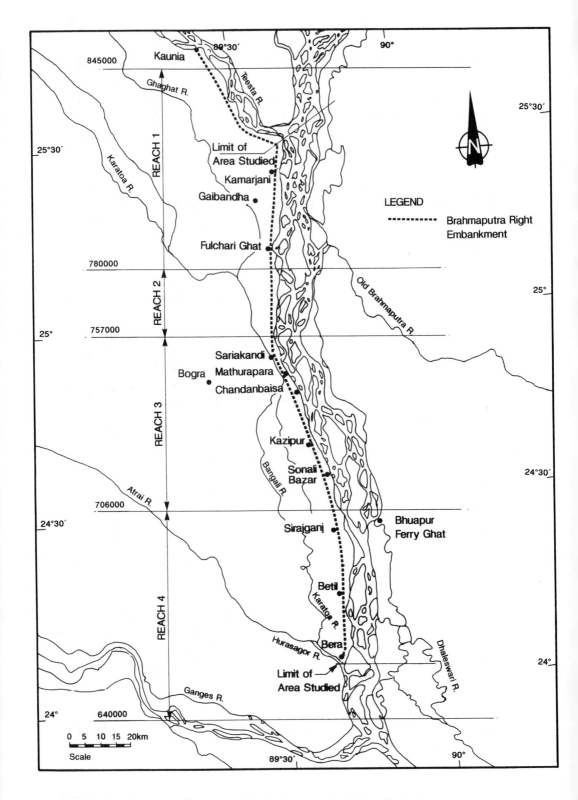

Figure 1: River Brahmaputra in Bangladesh

572

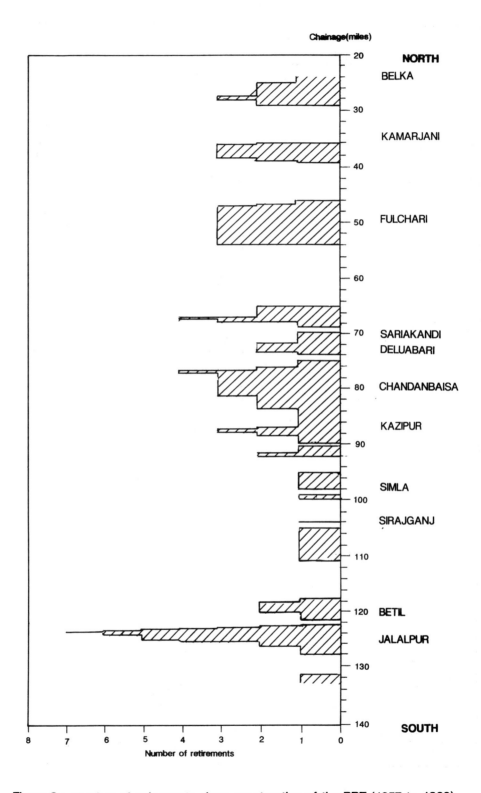

Figure 2 : Number of retirements since construction of the BRE (1957 to 1960)

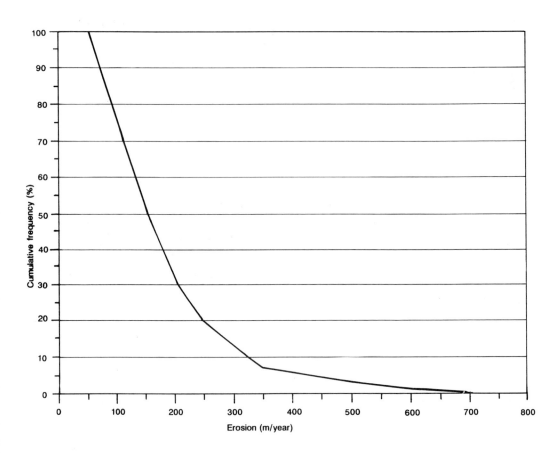

Figure 3 : Cumulative frequency distribution of annual erosion rates, Reach 3, 1973 - 1992

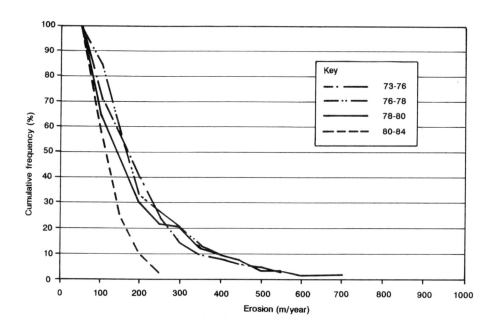

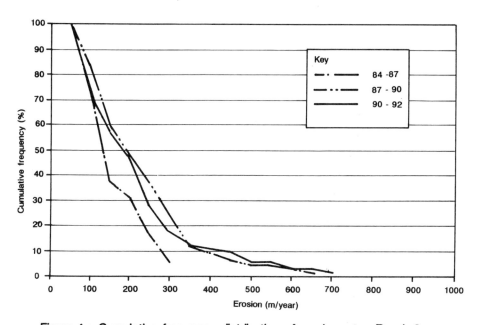

Figure 4 : Cumulative frequency distribution of erosion rates, Reach 3

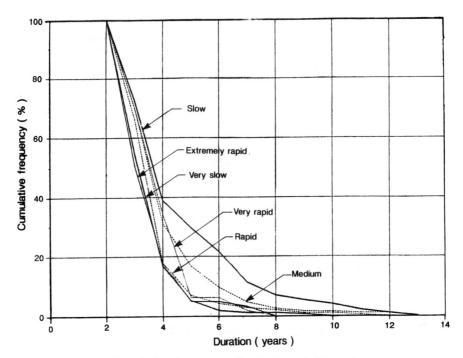

Figure 5: Cumulative frequency distribution of different
levels of erosion , Reaches 1 to 4, 1973-1992

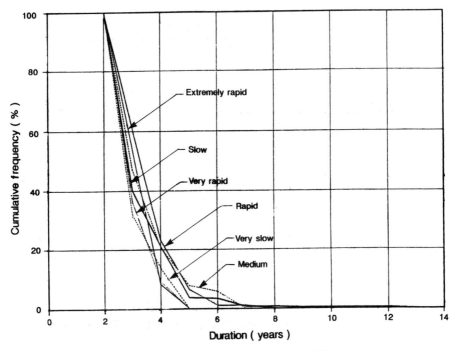

Figure 6 Cumulative frequency distribution of different
levels of accretion , Reaches 1 to 4, 1973-1992

576

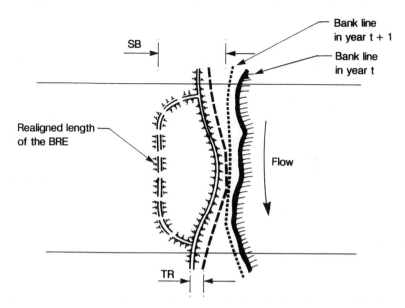

Figure 7A: Planform definition sketch for SB and TR

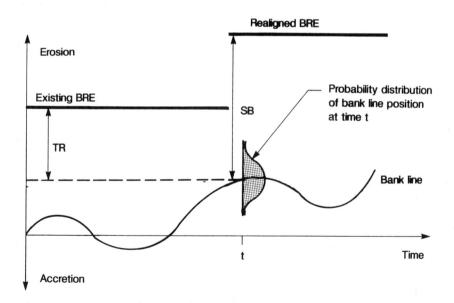

Figure 7B: Time related definition sketch for SB and TR

577

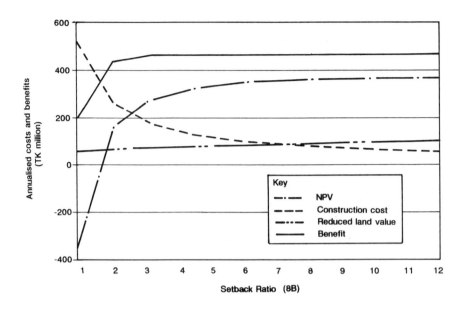

Figure 8A : Comparison of realignment costs and benefits with
SB for TR = 2 times the mean annual erosion rate

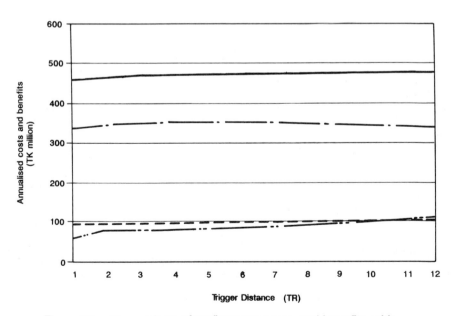

Figure 8B : Comparison of realignment costs and benefits with
TR for SB = 6 times the mean annual erosion rate

FLOOD PROOFING POTENTIALS IN BANGLADESH FLOOD MANAGEMENT

Muhammad F. Bari, MASCE, MASEE, FIEB
Professor & Head of Water Resources Engineering
Faculty of Civil Engineering
Bangladesh University of Engineering & Tech
Dhaka 1000, Bangladesh

ABSTRACT

Floods are part of the natural environment of Bangladesh and
flood control continues to be an issue of increasing importance
due to the vulnerability of occupants of riparian land.   Large
flows, vast flood plains, flat slopes, tidal backwater, shifting
micro topography, and alluvial channels of this country make
flood control and management a major challenge.
     Starting from the mid 1960's embankments and appurtenant
structures have been constructed together with some improvement
of drainage channels as there is no scope for mitigating flood by
provision of storage reservoirs. Flood forecasting and   warning
are also used. The inadequacies of present flood mitigation
measures were apparent in 1987 and 1988 when the magnitude and
extent of the monsoon floods had disastrous consequences over
large areas of the country and caused widespread disruption of
normal social and economic activities. Again in 1991, the
inadequacies of flood mitigation measures in coastal areas was
evident when the coastal areas were hit by one of the most severe
cyclonic surges of this century.
     Consequently emphasis is also being given on the role of
flood proofing as a non-structural flood damage mitigation
measure. Flood proofing holds potential of substantially reducing
the damage and human suffering caused by major flood. This is
especially true in areas that are not covered by the various
structure-based projects, or even in protected areas which still
carry a finite risk of incurring flood damage at any given time.
The development of flood proofing programme under the Flood
Action Plan (FAP) of the country is seen as a key non-structural
measure which is envisaged to make a significant contribution to
flood damage avoidance and hence to the nation and country.

2nd International Conference on River Flood Hydraulics. Edited by W. R. White and J. Watts
© 1994 HR Wallingford Ltd. Published by John Wiley & Sons Ltd

1. INTRODUCTION

Bangladesh is known as the land of six seasons, the most dominant being the rainy season which lasts from May to September. The country is located at the Tropic of Cancer at longitude 90°E and has a land area of 145,000 sq. km. About 80% of the land is comprised of floodplain of the Brahmaputra, Ganges and Meghna and some smaller rivers, while 8% is terraces and 12% is hills. The average land elevation is about 3 m above mean sea level. Gradients on the floodplain are generally low: the average gradient from the north-western part of the country to the coast is less than 20 cm/km; near the coast gradient average about 1.6 cm/km.

The major rivers and their tributaries have their origins outside Bangladesh. Only about 7.5% of their total catchment area of about 1.5 million sq. km lie within Bangladesh. Similarly 90% of their annual flows originates outside the country. Having predominantly a monsoon climate the catchment areas of these rivers receive heavy rainfalls concentrated in 3 to 5 months (May to September). Within the country mean annual rainfall ranges between 1250 mm to more than 5000 mm. There is significant variations in the monthly and annual rainfall occurring in different years, leading to considerable differences in peak flood levels and the extent of flooding each year.

1.1. Flood Problems in Bangladesh

Flooding to a lesser or greater extent is an annual phenomena --- in the more extreme years well over one-third of the country may be affected by floods. The country experiences several different types of floods: rainfall-induced floods, monsoon riverine floods, flash floods, and coastal floods due to tides and cyclones.

Riverine and cyclonic floods cause most of the damage. About 60% of the land in Bangladesh is an active delta which is annually flooded during the monsoon period by major rivers including the the Ganges, the Brahmaputra, and the Meghna. The magnitude of normal annual flood events is emphasized by the fact that the Lower Meghna River, which carries combined flows of the Brahmaputra and the Ganges, achieves annual peak discharges of approximately 141,585 m^3/s (Simon, 1971). The gradient of the Meghna channel as it enters the Bay of Bengal is 0.0189-0.0284 m/km. The lower delta is continuously subjected to the threat of major cyclones and storm surges that can generate huge waves of water that sweep inland up the flat channel causing tremendous damage. The April 1991 cyclone is estimated to have killed 140,000 inhabitants (Simons, 1992). In 1971 another cyclone and storm surge claimed the lives of some 200,000 people (Rogers et al. 1989).

The normal sequence of floods starts with flash floods in the eastern hill streams during the pre-monsoon months of April and May. The onset of the monsoon generally occurs in June. The Meghna and the Brahmaputra rivers normally reach their flood peaks during July and August and the Ganges river during August and September. Severe flooding occurs if the peaks of the Ganges and the Brahmaputra rivers coincide.

During the last 40 years or so the country experienced
several large floods such as in 1954, 1955, 1974, 1987 and 1988.
Two catastrophic floods happened in succession in 1987 and 1988.
Floods in 1987 inundated about 40% of the land area (57,000 km^2,
affected about 30 million people, and caused about 1800 deaths.
In 1988, the floods inundated about 60 percent of the land area
(82,000 km^2), affected 45 million people, and caused about 2330
deaths. Damages from the 1987 and 1988 floods have been estimated
to be about US $ 500 million and US $ 1200 million respectively.
In 1988 flood, about 7.2 million houses were totally or partially
damaged, accounting for 66% of total damages, while
infrastructure accounted for 29%, agriculture 2%, industries 2%
and health and sanitation 1% of damages. Thus, the main
facilities damaged by the flood were housing and infrastructure.
The extent of damage has increased as new development activities
have become established on the floodplain and impacts are greater
because larger populations are adversely affected.

1.2. Flood Mitigation Measures

Little can be done to prevent a major flood, but it may be
possible to minimize damage to crops and property within the
flood plain of the river. Humanity has always tried to avoid
flood damage by one method or another, but the increase in
population and property values in the flood threatened land has
brought the problem into sharper focus in recent years. In
Bangladesh the importance of comprehensive water management in
general and flood control in particular was recognized after the
flood havoc of 1954 and 1955, and most flood mitigation activity
dates from 1964 when a master plan was prepared with emphasis on
reducing flood damage. The master plan has been described as
basically a massive scheme for empoldering large areas of the
country into some 50 projects through construction of earthen
embankments and drainage structures that physically control some
or all flood water from entering a designated area. These
projects were expected to provide flood protection and drainage
facilities to abut 5 million ha and irrigation facilities to 3.2
million ha by 1985. The projects were estimated to cost US $ 2.1
billion over a 21-year period ending in 1985.

Absolute control over floods is rarely feasible either
physically or economically, rather flood damage mitigations the
objective we should pursue. Responsibility of planning and
building flood mitigation projects rests with the Bangladesh
Water Development Board (BWDB). The objective of these projects
is to ensure normal or improved social and economic activity can
continue within the designated area throughout a flood event. The
main purpose of most existing flood protection projects in
Bangladesh is 60 improve agricultural production. Secondary
benefits include flood protection for communities within the
embanked area and utilization of the flood embankment as a refuge
by those people not within the protected area. Flood protection
facilities are designed to protect areas from floods up to a
specific flood event (for example, the 1 in 100 year river flood
or the 1 in 20 year flash flood).

The inadequacies of present flood mitigation measures were apparent in 1987 and 1988 when the magnitude and extent of the monsoon floods had disastrous consequences over large areas of the country and caused widespread disruption of normal social and economic activities. Again in 1991, the inadequacy of flood mitigation measures in coastal areas was apparent when the coastal areas were hit by one of the most severe cyclones of this century.

Large flows, vast flood plains, flat slopes, tidal backwater, shifting micro topography, and alluvial channels in this country make flood control and management a major challenge. Geologically, Bangladesh is a recent formation and is still very active. Much of its land has been formed within the last 10,000 years by river borne sediment. So structural measures leading to extensive confinement of river flood flows are not feasible either economically and physically. Also, this is likely to create adverse impact on river regime, flood plain soil fertility, drainage pattern and the environment. Experience in this country and elsewhere, such as in the U.S., showed that structural measures alone were not sufficient. Effective flood damage mitigation measures have been a combination of structural measures as well as regulatory, incentive and management actions aimed at hazard reductions.

Flood proofing is one approach of flood management that should generally be low cost, nonstructural or minor structural, locally initiated and sustainable. This allows people to do things while living with flooding, and thus add to their incomes and make their investments secure. The objective of this paper is to discuss concepts and issues related to flood proofing, some possible long-term goals, and some preliminary guidelines for the sound planning of a flood-proofing programme. National and international experiences of flood proofing are also reviewed. Efforts are made to assess the needs for, and scope of systematic expansion of flood proofing as a damage avoidance strategy.

2. CONCEPT OF FLOOD PROOFING

According to James and Lee (1971), flood proofing may be defined to include all actions by individuals or small groups within the flood plain to reduce flood damage to their property. This definition could be interpreted to include structural measures, flood fighting, flood-hazard information dissemination, food preparedness and response, flood warning and forecasting, as well as non-structural floodplain management practices that seek to avoid or reduce damages due to floods. These practices can be implemented either by government agencies or non-government organizations (NGOs), as well as by individuals or privately owned organizations.

The objective of flood proofing is to avoid the loss of human life, and reduce the disruption caused by floods by improving the resilience of the society and its economy, agricultural practices and infrastructure to flooding. Flood proofing measures are focused on allowing people to live with floods while improve their lives in an environment that frequently experiences floods.

2.2. Flood Proofing Practices in Bangladesh

Flood proofing activities have been practised by the people of Bangladesh since the time of the first settlers of the region because floods have always been a prominent feature of the natural environment. People have always accommodated floods and have applied the principles of flood proofing within the resources and understanding available. Villages are located on the higher ground, homesteads are raised above normal flood levels and houses near river banks subject erosion are so constructed that these can be easily dismantled and erected elsewhere. Flood proofing measures adopted in rural and urban areas can be grouped together with respect to those that: (a) save human lives and reduce suffering (housing, flood shelters, water supplies and sanitation). (b) affect incomes and livelihood (agriculture, livestock, fisheries, markets); and (c) affect public utilities, infrastructure and government services (roads, railways, public buildings electric supply).

These efforts to protect from floods sometime fail for a number of reasons including the lack of resources to implement effective flood proofing measures and a lack of understanding or information on changes in the larger hydrological processes affecting floods in their locality. There is a definite requirement for more widespread application of flood proofing measures and a flood proofing programme could be designed to have a wide social and economic impact. Measures could be designed to benefit the urban and rural poor by improving their living conditions directly. Women could also be principal beneficiaries of flood proofing by implementing measures related to flood proofing housing, water supplies and income.

2.3. Flood Proofing Experience in Other Countries

2.3.1 United States

Since the late 1960's, floodplain management and other damage avoidance practices have been implemented nationwide with notable results. Numerous large and small scale structural measures (dams, levees, and channel modifications) were implemented during the period from 1930 through the mid 1960's, but flood damages grew at a rate that proved that structural measures alone were not sufficient. Consequently, planners and interest groups with other priorities for public expenditure pressed for alternatives to capital intensive flood control projects (Marshall and Ashton, 1974).

The main result has been a combination of regulatory, incentive and management actions aimed at preventive and hazard reduction measures. Efforts to increase public awareness of hazards and to provide information for individual decisions and action have comprised an important part of the process (Tettemer, 1983).

Included in the programme are federally subsidized insurance coverage for existing property conditional upon enactment and enforcement of local land use regulations that preclude development or rehabilitation of structures in the active floodplain except for limited cases where compensatory measures are included. Insurance is offered by private companies to individuals or private or public bodies in compliance with local control requirements that include zoning and other management practices based on the 100-year flood event. Insurance premiums are based on risk (depth and velocity of flooding at each property).

2.3.2 Australia

Similar floodplain information programmes, adopted and implemented at the federal and state levels, are available in Australia. Historical floods, the 100-year and other floods are routinely computed on a community basis in Australia, using techniques similar to those practiced in the United States. Communities use this information to shape local building codes that ensure new construction be flood-proofed, either structurally or by location away from areas subject to flooding. Flood situation in Australia is similar in many respects to that faced by the United States, and perhaps the similarity of response by the various state and local governments is not surprising.

The trend in many parts of Australia is for local codes to require that individual buildings or entire development areas be raised to some predetermined level to avoid expected floods and for building permits to be issued. Several studies been performed on the economic of relocation, house raising and individual response (Penning-Rowsell and Smith, 1987).

2.3.3 United Kingdom

District Councils regulate urban and rural development activities and they are advised to liaise with the National River Authorities to obtain and incorporate the information in a rational floodplain development programme. There is, however, no legal requirement for the local planning agencies to incorporate the advice from the River Authorities in their planning activities (Penning-Rowsell and Handmer, 1988). Limited land space and development pressures create an atmosphere favoring development of floodplain, which in turn eventually necessitate remedial flood mitigation measures by the River Authorities.

There is some renewed emphasis on the role of flood forecasting and flood warning as a non structural flood damage mitigation measure. The technology of flood warning dissemination, however, is not as advanced as the technology available for forecasting the floods and, hence render this alternative to structural measures relatively unreliable in some parts of the country.

2.3.4 Philippines

Land use planning and land zoning regulations are defined. For example, in town planning, studies should undertaken to assess the adequacy of roads, water works and sewerage systems in areas vulnerable to floods. There is also provision for structures to be a minimum of 10 meters from shorelines, or river banks. However, enforcement of these regulations seems to be weak.

There is a central agency to review and evaluate land use plans and zoning ordinances of local governments. The agency also assists areas in formulating development plans and also enforces guidelines, standards, and regulations for land use development including housing. The administration and enforcement of the related regulations lie with the regions and municipalities, with local zoning administrators deputized for the purpose.

There is also a programme for the construction of cyclone resistant core shelter units. The units are built on a self-help basis, with the beneficiaries themselves pooling their labour resources and contributing indigenous materials under the supervision of locally hired foremen. The modular design of units enables their easy upgrading and expansion as the socio-economic conditions of the owners improve. By 1991, 14,000 units had been constructed. (Brown et al. 1991).

2.3.5 Regional Experience

Flood proofing measures have not been systematically applied in the neighbouring countries or in the region. Most countries have basic disaster legislation and some countries also have building codes, but, as in Bangladesh, the approach to flood proofing has been to leave local people to implement measures on their own initiative and with their own funds. Even where there are provisions for non structural flood proofing measures, governments find them difficult to enforce. Occasionally, governments have taken a more active role in implementing flood proofing measures but their involvement has often been in response to local disasters after they have occurred.

India -- There has been a programme of constructing cyclone and flood shelters in coastal areas (such as Tamil Nadu, Kerala, Andhra Pradesh, Orissa and West Bengal) vulnerable to cyclones and flooding. The number of shelter constructed has not been sufficient for the needs of the local people and the planning and construction process followed have not always ensured the long-term viability of the shelters constructed. In many areas, there is a cyclone warning system to complement the shelters.

Nepal -- Town planning authorities have restricted the expansion of housing in lowlands close to rivers but enforcement is weak.

3. FLOOD PROOFING NEED IN BANGLADESH

Accommodation to flooding is nothing new for Bangladesh; the new element is to make flood proofing a means for promoting diversified development. Accommodation of the past sustained a way of life, the accommodation of the future must sustain a way of growth. There is an increased need for land use controls becuase peoples' activities are encroaching on more vulnerable areas and interfering with natural floodways. Land use controls can be used to regulate settlement and land use in flood-prone areas in order to reduce the vulnerability of people, crops and property to flood damage. There are some legal provisions for

land use planning and controls but they have been rarely used
because of difficulties with their enforcement and lack of
political will. Flood insurance could be another measure for
promoting flood proofing of buildings, but this option would be
suitable for more affluent people.

People and institutions in Bangladesh already use their own
resources to undertake flood proofing measures. The purpose of a
more coordinated flood proofing programme would be to use the
resources and technology available to the government to make
individual, community and institutional actions more effective,
and to oversee their actions to ensure that they do not harm the
physical, social or economic environment.

4. APPROACHES TO A FLOOD PROOFING PROGRAMME

People who experience frequent flooding already use their
personal resources to do many things to protect properties. s
mentiuoned above the purposes of a flood proofing programme are
to use the resources and technology available to government to
make the individual actions more effective, to instill within
their efforts the common long-term goals that will keep people
working together in their common interest,and to oversee their
actions to prevent them from hurting other people or harming the
environment.

By becoming more active in these three roles, the Government
of Bangladesh can do a great deal to reduce flood losses in the
country. Because of the large initial investment to get these
programmes going, help from donors is needed in their initiation.
the ability of these programme to support development of a more
diversified economy will raise income levels and over time make
it possible to generate the revenues necessary to finance the
programme within the country.

Flood proofing measures that may be applicable to
Bangladesh can be classified as local measures that can be
managed by individuals or small groups, community measures that
are more appropriate to implement at the thana level, and
regional programmes that may be implemented over larger areas.
Different people must do different things concurrently at
different levels.

5. COMPONENTS OF A FLOOD PROOFING PROGRAMME

Flood proofing is the provision of long-term non-structural and
minor structural measures to mitigate the effects of floods.
Possible non-structural flood proofing measures can be
grouped together and include the following:

(a) **Legal Measures** comprising of planning controls and
building codes. Land use planning and zoning laws could
be introduced to restrict development activities on
land where the risk of flooding is too high or where
activities interfere with flood flows. Building codes
would be established to specify required standards of
safety and also serve to develop public awareness.

(b) **Provision of Incentives** inducements could be available to encourage people to adopt flood proofing measures. Grants could be paid to private firms or individuals to flood proof their buildings. Tax incentives could be used in a similar way.

    Insurance could also be used to spread risks and providing funds to enable owners to re-build after floods.

(c) **Training and Education** could be used to show people how to inaugurate flood proofing into their daily lives. Training programmes could be developed for public officials, technical students, small builders and craftsmen and school children.

(d) **Public Awareness.** Government could demonstrate sound flood proofing measures by ensuring public buildings, public infrastructure and public services can function throughout floods.

(e) **Institution Building.** Institutions play a vital role in various aspects of flood proofing such as promoting public awareness programmes, training at community levels, linking government resources to individuals, communities and the private sector and implementing flood preparedness programmes including flood forecasting and warning systems.

Non-structural measures yield long-term benefits as they require many years to implement effectively. Many non-structural measures need to be initiated by government as they require regulations and public institutional support for their implementation.

Possible structural flood proofing measures include:
- raising floor levels of houses/homesteads
- improving the quality of housing
- provision of flood or cyclone shelters
- provision of storage areas
- local small scale flood protection and drainage schemes
- protective embankments and drainage flow small urban areas
- protection of commercial premises
- raising ground levels at markets, schools and other communal areas
- ensuring key infrastructure (roads, railways, public buildings etc.) are above specific flood levels.
- ensuring different models of transport can operate effective during floods.

Many structural measures can be implemented in the short term but the main constraints on their more widespread application have been the shortage of resources for their implementation and the lack of information on hydrological changes.

There is no "definitive list" of flood proofing measures because effective flood proofing is based on local needs and the availability of public and private resources to undertake different measures.

6. IMPLEMENTATION ISSUES

Government has the important role in flood proofing of motivating and coordinating private actions. It's available means fall into the categories of education, regulation, technical help, financial help and direct management. Some specific means that may be effective in Bangladesh are:

(i)   Assign a responsibility to oversee and coordinate the total programme.

(ii) Establish a flood risk information center.

(iii) Establish an impartial and objective review process that prevents construction that is not in the public interest and makes field inspections to make sure that construction follows plans.

(iv) Establish a reliable system of flood warnings and support them by helping people with flood flighting evacuation, and relief.

(v)   Develop a plan for economic development so that flood proofing can move effectively towards long-run goals.

(vi) Foster the development of neighborhood and community institutions so that people can establish and manage their local flood proofing activities.

The planning of flood proofing is a combination of determining the best action to take and of getting people to respond in the way determined best. Two important questions need to be answered in planning a programme that combines flood proofing measures.

(a)   What flood proofing measures can be used to sustain growth?
(b)   What incentives can be used to convince people to employ them?

Some of the issues that may be considered as the keys to success in planning and implementing flood proofing measures are highlighted below.

6.1. Integration of Plans into National Policies

The use of flood proofing to promote growth must be part of a programme of economic, social and institutional change and be linked to national policies on land reform, industrialization, and employment diversification. None of these can succeed in Bangladesh without careful consideration of flood risks.

6.2. Integration of Measures and Means into Pilot Programs

Pilot projects are needed to demonstrate 'what works' and 'what does not. Purpose of these pilot projects is to expose people to useful ideas for the diversity of local contexts found in Bangladesh; foster in depth involvements of individuals, businesses, local governments, and NGOs; and demonstrate and strengthen the concepts of continuing monitoring and financial arrangements for timely response to problems. Unless all parties are committed to cooperate from the beginning; the likely scenario is for donors to begin implementation, people to begin getting something without paying; and the disincentive against innovate flood proofing to grow as people await their turn on the gravy train. The opportunity to get people to work together dissipates into grumbling from those who are getting nothing and seeing nothing happen.

6.3. Feasibility and Impact Evaluation

The planning of these pilot programmes and other projects to follow should consider economic, environmental, social financial and political feasibility and impact. For flood proofing in Bangladesh, economic feasibility is achieved if the benefits from less flood damage and faster economic growth exceed the costs. Environmental feasibility, requires that the measures be implementable without harming agricultural fishery or other environmental resources. The test of social feasibility is passed if the people will really sustain flood proofing over time. Financial feasibility can be a major problem in Bangladesh where poor people must pay. Political feasibility of changing a bureaucracy to adopt a new spirit of quality public service.

6.4 Customization of Programmes to Local Conditions

Flood proofing that works one place may not work elsewhere. Programs must match local flood, site and building characteristics vary substantially over Bangladesh among areas that are unprotected or experience bank courting and filling, embankment failures, flash flooding from smaller streams, and poor interior drainage. Different food proofing programmes are needed for each area, and even different flood proofing measures may be best for adjacent properties.

6.5 Peoples' Participation

Flood proofing offers people things to do while living with flooding that add to their incomes and make their investments secure. As people improve their welfare they gain a sense of control over their destiny and are motivated to do more. The same sequence of experiences can also help donor nations build faith that foreign aid works.

6.6 Enhancement of Human Accommodation with the Environment

Flood plains are the natural playgrounds of rivers, and people must learn to play a different land use game on flood prone lands. As waters flow different ways from one flood to the next, people too should adjust as conditions change over time.

6.7 Technology Transfer

A plan should be developed to present flood proofing ideas to land owners, income proofing ideas to displacees, etc. Written manuals can be supplemented by personal contacts from experts in a trained extension service established to promote precautionary and loss reduction measures.

Along these lines flood proofing study was taken up under the currently ongoing Flood Action Plan (FAP) of the country. The FAP was conceived to provide an integrated, coordinated approach to mitigating the effects of flooding in Bangladesh after the great riverine floods of 1987 and 1988 which drew attention of the international community for alleviating flooding problems in Bangladesh. The Flood Proofing Study (FAP-23), was identified as a supporting study concentrating on flood preparedness and floodplain management in the predominantly urban areas, complementing the rural study emphasis of FAP-14 (Flood Response Study). The origin of the FAP and the place of FAP-23 are briefly described below. Then the salient features of the Flood Proofing Study are summarized.

7. The Flood Action Plan

After the exceptionally severe floods in 1987 and 1988, international community offered to assist Bangladesh with its flood problems and diverse programmes were suggested. In mid-1989 Government of Bangladesh requested the World Bank to help coordinate the international donor interest and activities. Accordingly, the Bank in cooperation with Government of Bangladesh prepared a Flood Action Plan (World Bank, 1989), which was endorsed at two meetings of the donors with Government of Bangladesh in December 1989 and January 1990. The Flood Plan Coordination Organization (FPCO), under the Ministry of Irrigation, Water Development and Flood Control was established for coordination with Government of Bangladesh.

The GOB sought an approach which would provide a comprehensive and permanent solution to the recurrent flood problem and so create an environment for sustained economic growth and social improvement. The flood policy that was adopted incorporated a long term plan of major physical works to control flooding, including major embankment and river training works and a set of eleven principles to guide future development.

The principles include a number of so-called "soft" approaches to flood protection and mitigation, including:

0   effective land and water management
0   strengthened flood preparedness and disaster management
0   floodplain zoning
0   coordinated planning of roads and related rural infrastructure to ensure unimpeded drainage
0   increased local and individual participation in all aspects of flood control and drainage works

These soft approaches are intended to apply to all Bangladesh floodplains, which occupy about 60% of the net cultivated area and a total of about 100,000 sq km of the 144,000 sq km territory of Bangladesh. At present, about 30 percent of this area is either partly or fully "protected" against floods. For the remainder:

0   even with full implementation of flood control projects as outlined in the FAP, about 30 percent will remain unprotected;

0   substantial areas that may eventually be provided with protection will remain unprotected for 20 years or more during the implementation period; finally,

0   all protected areas will remain vulnerable to damage during catastrophic failure or overtopping of structures during floods of greater than design protection level (flood recurrence interval).

The FAP comprises eleven major components for identification and planning of structural flood control facilities and fifteen Supporting Studies to be undertaken over a 5-year period (1990-1995). Flood Proofing (FAP 23), is one of the Supporting Studies that has been supported by U.S. Agency for International Development. Flood Proofing includes most of the items on the list of soft flood protection activities, covering floodplain areas listed above. Flood proofing measures should be relatively low cost non structural or minor structural locally initiated and sustainable.

Preliminary accounts concerning the April 1991 cyclone indicate that either the magnitude of loss or the poor performance of some protection works provides sufficient cause for many elements of the FAP to be reconsidered, perhaps most of all FAP-23 Flood Proofing. Hence, this study also addressed measures that would include some level of preparedness and loss avoidance from cyclonic floods and storm surges in addition to riverine floods.

8. THE FLOOD PROOFING STUDY

The overall objective of the Flood Proofing Study (FAP 23) is to identify and implement effective flood proofing measures to avoid or reduce the adverse effects of flooding on the social and economic activities of communities, and on infrastructure, particularly in those areas which are not protected by more comprehensive flood protection measures.

The Flood Proofing Study is being carried out in two phases. During Phase-I, existing flood proofing measures were identified, along with constraints on implementation of more comprehensive flood proofing measures. During Phase II, comprehensive flood proofing measures for individuals, commercial and industrial enterprises, local government and other institutions will be planned and implemented in a number of pilot areas using private, commercial and institutional funds. In addition, the methodology for planning and implementing flood proofing measures nationwide will be developed.

During Phase I of FAP 23, the broader issues of flood proofing have been considered and existing flood proofing measures have been reviewed. The requirements for Phase II is to apply the principles of flood proofing in a number of areas on a pilot basis. The pilot projects would develop flood proofing measures that could be adopted nationwide by individuals, commercial and industrial enterprises and government and no-government institutions, using private, commercial and public funds.

The purpose of Pilot Projects undertaken in Phase II will be to show the benefits of applying flood proofing principles efficiently. The Pilot Projects will involve the comprehensive planning and implementation of flood proofing measures to specific areas. The Pilot Projects will be monitored and evaluated over time to determine the achievements and constraints and the results would be used to develop an flood proofing programme for application nationwide. Training programmes for those involved in flood proofing will also be developed.

As flood proofing measures are being identified and developed under some of the FAP regional studies, a two fold approach to Pilot Proofing Projects has been proposed:

(a) Five pilot projects would be undertaken as part of the development of the priority areas identified by the FAP regional studies; and

(b) Additional pilot projects would be undertaken in a number of other areas to cover a broader range of flood conditions.

To ensure the involvement of local people in flood proofing activities, local people or local institutions should contribute to construction costs and take some responsibility for operation and maintenance of completed measures. Contributions from local communities could be complemented with funds provided by government (in the form of cash or wheat) or by non-government organizations, some of whom are presently implementing flood proofing programme successfully.

9. CONCLUDING REMARKS

Planning for flood proofing needs far more than an ideal, more than a sound technical plan; it needs practical means to institutionalize flood proofing implementation and its continuing maintenance. The maintenance of structural measures has long been a problem when developed countries help developing countries build infrastructure, and the problem is far greater for nonstructural programmes because they are more maintenance intensive. Strong educational and retraining programmes are essential to promote the concept of accommodating to environment and living with floods. Now-a-days people in North America, Western Europe, and Japan are being asked to find ways to live in greater harmony with their environment. They are asked to use less energy, generate less wastes, and avoid degrading natural areas.

Effective institutionalization nee to be built on three E's: education, ethics and evaluation. First flood proofing must be supplemented by building the level of education necessary to train people on what they must do to find better lives. Second, success requires a level of respect for public and private property that lets invest in a better life without fear of theft or vandalism. Third, the evaluation must have the resources needed to evaluate alternatives properly and the power to get people to do what they must and to prevent people from doing what they should not. Accomplishing these three E's is both basic and difficult, these goals must be kept in the foreground each step of the way.

It is hoped that a flood proofing programme, based on comprehensive application of flood proofing principles, would yield substantial benefits in terms of saving human life, reducing suffering, and make local and national economies more resilient to flooding. Investment in flood proofing would allow development of the country to proceed smoothly without catastrophic interruptions from floods.

REFERENCES

James, L.D. and Lee, R.R. 1971. *Economics of Water Resources Planning*, McGraw-Hill Book Co., New York.

Marshall, J.P. and P. Ashton, 1974. Issues in Flood Plan Management, Publication No. 629, Cooperative Extension Service, Virginia, USA.

Rogers, P. Lydon, P. and Seckler, D. 1989. Eastern Water Studies: Strategies to Manage Flood and Drought in the Ganges-Brahmaputra Basin. Prepared for the Office of Technical Resources, Agriculture and Rural Development Division, Bureau for Asia and Near East, U.S. Agency for International Development by the Irrigation Support Project for Asia and the Near East (ISPAN).

Simon, D.B. 1971, The River System. *CER71-72DBS-12*, International Bank for Reconstruction and Development, October.

Simon, D.B. 1992, Future Trends and Needs of Hydraulics, *Jour of Hydraulic Engn, ASCE*, 118(12), 1608-1620, December.

Russell, N., M.R. Acharya and S.R. Pant, 1991. Nepal Country Study, in Disaster Mitigation in Asia and the Pacific, Asian Development Bank, Manila.

Tettemer, J. M. 1983, Impact of Flood on the Economy of Bangladesh, paper presented to ASCE Annual Convention, Houston, Texas.

U.S. Army Corps of Engineers, 1972. Flood Proofing Regulations, Washington, D.C.

World Bank, 1989. Bangladesh Action Plan for Flood Control, Asian Region, Country Department 1, Washington,D.C.

World Bank, 1990. Bangladesh Strategies for Enhancing the Role of Women in Economic Development. A World Bank Country Study. Washington, D.C.

2nd International Conference on
RIVER FLOOD HYDRAULICS
22–25 March 1994: York, England

Floods Management of Large Reservoirs:

A case study of the Operation of Mangla Dam in Pakistan during Floods of 1992

A.S. Shakir[1], B.A. Shahid[2], F.A. Chishti[3]

Abstract

Mangla Dam constructed in early 1965 is the second largest earth and rock fill dam in Pakistan to conserve and control the waters of the River Jhelum, a tributary to River Indus. Recent floods in Pakistan caused an unprecedented loss of life and property. It is estimated that both public and private property damages worth more than 13 billion rupees (0.5 billion US dollars) were occurred in addition to 5000 loss of human lives. The purpose of this investigation is to find out the causes of high magnitude of floods with peak of 28000 m^3/sec(1 Million cfs) and to recommend action for future mitigation of such types of floods.

The analysis suggests that the actions taken by the authority were based on defective operational practice and were followed without any regard to proper flood routing. The inflow and outflow hydrographs of the River Jhelum at Mangla Dam provided an insight to the real problem.

This study concludes that operational practice during floods for Mangla Dam needs to be revised every year after passage of floods. There is very urgent need that highly qualified and competent engineers be made in-charge of these vital installations who can take operational decisions at the spot.

I.   INTRODUCTION

Mangla Dam, the second largest earth and rock fill dam in Pakistan, was primarily designed to supplement the irrigation water supply during low flow season by storing the flood waters of the River Jhelum (see location map-Figure 1). Its secondary functions are to generate hydro power from the irrigation releases and to control floods.

River Jhelum experienced an exceptionally high flood in September 1992, which caused a huge loss of life and property. This flood almost paralysed the infrastructure of the country, that would take sometime to bring it back to the track due to limited financial

1.   Assistant Professor, Civil Engineering Department, University of Engineering & Technology, Lahore, Pakistan.

2.   Executive Engineer, Irrigation & Power Department Punjab, Lahore, Pakistan.

3.   Professor, Civil Engineering Department, University of Engineering & Technology, Lahore, Pakistan.

2nd International Conference on River Flood Hydraulics. Edited by W. R. White and J. Watts
© 1994 HR Wallingford Ltd. Published by John Wiley & Sons Ltd

resources. This situation warrants a thorough study, regarding the flood forecasting system and operation of our major reservoirs during floods, needs to be carried out to avoid any reoccurrence of such events.

Mangla Dam has two spillways: the main spillway and the emergency spillway. The main spillway is designed to;

*   pass floods through the reservoir with minimum rise in water level

*   release water in advance of a flood (flood control), and

*   discharge that portion of the base flow which is in excess of the power requirements, during the time when the reservoir level is at the maximum conservation level of RL 1202 ft (Binnie, 1970).

The emergency spillway is designed to operate when flood inflows are greater than that which can be discharged by the main spillway (Binnie, 1970). The emergency spillway has crest elevation of RL 1202 ft (which is the maximum operating pool elevation) and a 4 ft high erodible bund (crest elevation RL 1206 feet). If the main spillway is out of commission and a flood is anticipated in which the reservoir level is expected to rise above elevation 1206 feet, the erodible bund may be breached manually in advance to gain time and thus provide a greater margin of safety (Binnie, 1970). The principal data of Mangla Dam, is given in table 1.

II. EXISTING OPERATIONAL INSTRUCTIONS FOR MANGLA DAM

According to the Dam Monitoring Organization(1989), Water and Power Development Authority (DMO, WAPDA), the existing operating instructions for Mangla Dam are:

"presently the reservoir is operated according to maximum and minimum rule curve envelope developed by Water Resources Management Directorate(WRMD) of WAPDA, Lahore. These curves are primarily on the basis of record seasonal historic flow and irrigation demand. In extra-ordinary conditions, both the curves are sometimes not followed in consultation with WRMD, keeping in view the actual river inflows, irrigation demand, downstream floods and the safety of the dam." In case of extra-ordinary conditions, the emergency operating procedure is to be followed. As per Dam Operational Manual (Binnie, 1970):

"In the event of a flood forecast, in excess of a given volume (to be determined) the emergency operation procedure would temporarily supersede the normal rule curve.

The emergency operating procedure should be laid down in advance and the operating engineers should be familiar with it. While recognizing that no flood warning system is completely reliable, depending as it does maintenance of communications, nor can it enable a very precise estimate to be made of the volume and the timing of inflow, the procedure should be designed to indicate immediately and without possibility of gross error:

1. the maximum draw down permissible while ensuring that the reservoir will fill before the end of monsoon season, on the assumption that the flood volume is somewhat less than the forecast.

2. the maximum reservoir level would be reached during the flood with any given spillway release on the assumption that the flood volume is somewhat more than forecast.

Using this information a decision could be reached on the preferred programme of gate openings to pass the flood. It is suggested that the emergency operating procedure should be determined on the basis of correlation of historical flood hydrographs with observations at the flood warning stations, together with the reservoir capacity allowing for sediment deposits, and spillway capacity. The procedure should be reviewed from time to time and modified in the light of the experience."

The Resident Engineer O&M (Civil) is responsible for O&M of all civil works, including reservoir operations (DMO,1989).

III.   OPERATION OF MANGLA DAM DURING FLOODS OF 1992

The River Jhelum experienced an exceptionally high flood at Mangla during September 1992. The flow history of the annual maximum flood peaks recorded in the River Jhelum at Mangla dam since the time of record is shown in Figure 2.

The operation of Mangla dam during these floods has been a topic of considerable discussion among the engineers and the public during and after the floods of 1992. It was alleged that the floods occurred as a result of its faulty operation. Only a brief analysis is carried out here to provide an insight into the real situation and a basis for a way forward based on a more detailed analysis.

The inflow and outflow hydrographs of the River Jhelum at Mangla under the actual operation during floods of 1992 with the reservoir levels are shown in Figure 3. The hydrographs show that there were two peaks in the inflow with a time lapse of about 11 hours between them. The important question is to analyse the strategy adopted by the regulating agency to control and regulate these floods.

The outflow hydrograph does not seem apparently to match the forecasts made for the Mangla Reservoir. Lodhi (1992) reported that Pakistan Meteorological Department made a forecast of heavy rains for September 8 to 10th in the catchment areas of the Jhelum and Chenab Rivers. The Flood Warning and Forecasting Centre, Lahore reports that on the morning of September 8, they issued a "special warning of the critical position" of heavy rains and floods and called for precautionary measures to deal with this situation.

The records show that the reservoir had attained its maximum conservation level of 1202 feet sometime before September 8th. However, the outflow hydrograph in Figure 3 shows that the discharge released from the reservoir was about 30,000 cfs till 9 AM of September 9, 1992, where as the inflow at that time had increased to more than 300,000 cfs.

The question now arises with the reservoir level already at the maximum conservation level of RL 1202 feet and forecasts of heavy rains and floods, why no action was taken to empty the reservoir. It was this stage that a better flood management strategy could have alleviated the situation to a great extent.

Another important problem related to the operation of Mangla Dam during the floods of 1992, is the management of outflow from the reservoir. It seems that authorities reacted too late to this critical operation and then over reacted underestimating the impact of very high releases on the areas along the river reaches downstream of the reservoir. This may be due to difficulties in making decisions of such critical operational conditions on the spot by the engineer in-charge. As indicated by the outflow hydrograph in Figure 3, a discharge of more than 930,000 cfs was released for consecutive 7 hours from the reservoir to keep the reservoir level below RL 1208 feet(normal pond level). The Mangla Dam is designed for water levels upto 1228 feet (Harza, 1992). The dam's actual height is 1234 feet with the last 6 feet allowed as free board.

IV.   ALTERNATIVES FOR OPERATION OF RESERVOIR

The critical review of the design parameters of the dam and the operation of the Mangla Dam during the Flood of 1992 suggest that action taken by the authorities to discharge nearly 1 million cfs of water from the reservoir in the early hours of September 10, seems to have been an over reaction to the situation. The analysis reveals that the outflow was allowed without any consideration of its severe effects down stream of the reservoir. The population living within high flood banks were swept away during the night and the close by city of Jhelum with population of over a million was completely inundated. In the early stages the people thought that the Mangla Dam had burst.

When there was good 20 feet reservoir storage available, which could have been utilized without creating any alarming position or acute danger, this action of releasing 930,000 cfs may not in retrospect have been justifiable. As a possible scenario, if release of water at the rate of 450,000 (high bank capacity of river Jhelum downstream of reservoir) in anticipation of the flood waves had been planned and acted as per warning of the Flood Forecasting Centre (FFC), would have increased the reservoir level upto a maximum of 1211.18 feet for few hours (Figure 4). The Figure 4 shows the reservoir levels when the suggested outflow is started from 09 Hours on 9.9.1992. This indicates that the reservoir levels under actual inflow conditions and the suggested outflows would have in no way posing any danger to the safety of dam. With a release of 450,000 cfs the reservoir levels would have been remained well within the safe limits.

Another option was analyzed with the same outflow of 450,000 cfs but released from early hours of 9/9/1992. This, when routed, gives a maximum reservoir level of 1206.12 feet, which is very close to the maximum conservation level of 1202 feet.

This analysis suggests that, with better management of operation of the reservoir, a great deal of loss of life and property could have been averted without any damage to the dam embankment. However, it is emphasized that the operation carried in September, 1992 may have been an error in judgement and was the reaction to the situation to safe guard the dam at all costs.

It is clear that determining an operating procedure for a reservoir during a major flood event is not effective. Adequate procedures must be determined prior to the flood event. These procedures must be based on an analysis of the hydrology of the catchment and flow simulation models.

Safe reservoir operation becomes easier the more data that is available and of great value is the prediction of future inflows into the reservoir. The more accurate and advanced the warning than the better can the dam be operated. There is thus a need for an adequate flood forecasting system to enable future flows into the reservoir to be predicted.

The safe operation of the reservoir ultimately relies upon the engineer in charge of the reservoir. These engineers need to be trained in the operating rules and must be aware of the implications both for the reservoir and the river downstream of different operating strategies. Training cannot be regarded as a on-off event. Major floods occur infrequently and it is important that when a flood occurs, dam operators are familiar with appropriate operating strategies.

In the end, it would be worthwhile to mention that existing operating practice for normal regulation seems reasonable, as the minimum and maximum regulation curves are reviewed by the WRMD regularly. However, the operational practice of Mangla Dam in the event of floods needs to be reviewed critically. Due to the varying nature of floods, it is difficult to suggest any specific operating regulation instructions for all conditions as suggested in the Dam Operating Manual (Binnie, 1970).

The updating of the flood forecasting system for the catchment to provide quantitative forecasts as accurately as possible and the placement of competent engineers equipped with the latest knowledge of flood management in-charge of operation and maintenance of the Mangla Dam, will certainly improve the situation. It would be of great help in the future to take right decisions for the operation of reservoir under extra-ordinary conditions at the site and in time to minimise losses.

V.   CONCLUSIONS & RECOMMENDATIONS

The following conclusions can be drawn from the study:

*   The limit of probable maximum flood for Mangla reservoir needs to be revised using the real data available since the construction of the dam. This will provide for better management of floods in the future.

*   The operation of the Mangla Dam during the floods of 1992 does not appear to have been planned well. Therefore, it can be said that there may have been less loss of life and property if the authorities had managed the outflow differently.

The following recommendations are made for improving the management of floods in the future:

*   It is recommended that research studies relating to the Hydrology and Meteorology should be given due importance. Flow simulation models can help in this regard. The flood warning instruments installed in the catchment require updating.

*   There is an urgent need for the installation of a more advanced flood forecasting system, which can provide the quantitative forecasts rather than the qualitative ones presently available.

*   Only highly qualified and competent engineers should be placed in-charge of the maintenance and operation of large reservoirs. This needs to be done on a top priority basis.

ACKNOWLEDGEMENTS

This study is partly supported by the University of Engineering and Technology Lahore. The efforts made by Mr. Rashad Usmani, Stenographer, Civil Engineering Department,

University of Engineering & Technology Lahore for typing the manuscript are greatly appreciated. The authors also deeply appreciate the help of Mr. Kenneth R. Shams, Secretary/Administrative Assistant of the International Irrigation Management Institute, Lahore for formatting and printing the final manuscript. While preparing the revised version of the paper, the comments of the referees were of great value and are thankfully acknowledged.

REFERENCES

1)   Binnie, Deacon and Gourley, in association with Harza Engineering Company International and Preece, Cardew and Rider "Mangla, Dam Project, the probable Maximum Flood on the Jhelum River at Mangla" prepared for West Pakistan Water and Power Development Authority, Sep. 1959.

2)   Binnie and Partners, in association with Harza Engineering Company International and Preece, Cardew and Rider "Mangla Dam Project, Operation and Maintenance Manual, volume 1, project operation" prepared for West Pakistan Water and Power Development Authority, 1970.

3)   Cudworth, A. G, Jr. "Flood Hydrology Manual, A water Resources Technical Publication, United States Department of the Interior, Bureau of Reclamation surface Water Branch, Earth Science Division, Denver, 1989.

4)   Dam Monitoring Organization, WAPDA, Lahore in association with NESPAK & ACE Lahore "Mangla Dam Project, Fourth Periodic Inspection" March, 1989.

5)   Federal Flood Commission " PC-I Proforma for 1992- Floods/Rains Damage Restoration Project" Lahore, Pakistan, 1992.

6)   Harza Engineering Company International "Mangla Reservoir Study on the possibility of Raising the Maximum Reservoir Operating level" prepared for WAPDA, Pakistan Feb. 1992.

7)   Linsley, R. K. Jr. Max, A. Kohlar and J. L. H. Paulhus "Hydrology for Engineers" Third Edition, McGraw Hill Book Company, New York 1985.

8)   Lodhi, M. A. K "Is WAPDA guilty of criminal negligence?" A special Report in "The Friday Times Lahore", Pakistan, September 24-30, 1992.

9)   Myers, Vance A. Meteorological Consultants, "Meteorological Criteria for the Probable Maximum Flood into Kalabagh Reservoir" A report to Kalabagh consultants Lahore, Pakistan Nov. 1982.

10) Shakir, A.S. and B.A. Shahid   "Flood Management Problems in Pakistan" Proceedings of the International Conference on "Optimum Utilization of Natural Resources in Islamic Countries" Karachi, Pakistan, April 24-29, 1993.

11) World Meteorological Organization, "Manual for Estimation of Probable Maximum Flood Precipitation", Operational Hydrology Report No.1, second Edition, WMO No. 332, Geneva, Switzerland, 1988.

Table 1

PRINCIPAL DATA FOR MANGLA DAM

RESERVOIR

Crest level of embankment	1234(MSL, feet)
Conservation level	1202(feet)
Minimum operating level	1040(feet)
Gross storage at 1202 level	5.88 (MAF)
Type	Earth with clay core

MAIN SPILLWAY

Type	Submerged orifice
Size of orifice, feet	36 x 40
Crest elevation, feet	1086

EMERGENCY SPILLWAY

Type	Weir
Control (located upstream)	Erodible bund
Crest elevation, feet	1202
Erodible bund elevation, feet	1206
Width of weir, feet	500
Width of erodible bund, feet	900

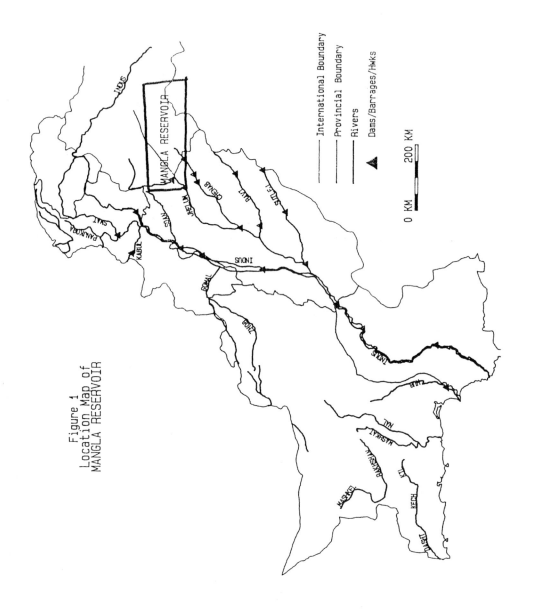

Figure 1
Location Map of
MANGLA RESERVOIR

International Boundary
Provincial Boundary
Rivers
Dams/Barrages/Hwks

0 KM   200 KM

FIG. 2

PEAK FLOWS IN RIVER JHELUM
AT MANGLA

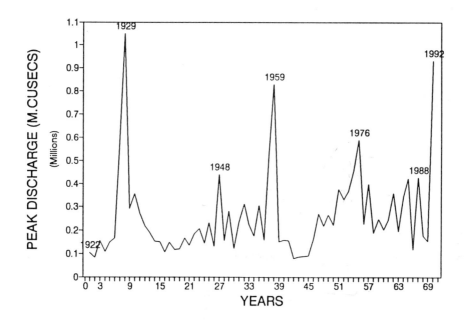

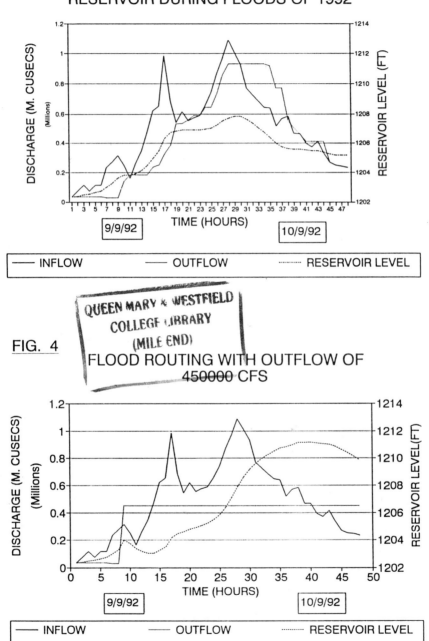

FIG. 3

INFLOW AND OUTFLOW THROUGH MANGLA
RESERVOIR DURING FLOODS OF 1992

9/9/92   TIME (HOURS)   10/9/92

— INFLOW   — OUTFLOW   ······ RESERVOIR LEVEL

FIG. 4

FLOOD ROUTING WITH OUTFLOW OF
450000 CFS

9/9/92   TIME (HOURS)   10/9/92

— INFLOW   — OUTFLOW   ······ RESERVOIR LEVEL

604